McGraw-Hill Electrical and Electronic Engineering Series

FREDERICK EMMONS TERMAN, *Consulting Editor*
W. W. HARMAN and J. G. TRUXAL, *Associate Consulting Editors*

BAILEY AND GAULT · Alternating-current Machinery
BERANEK · Acoustics
BRUNS AND SAUNDERS · Analysis of Feedback Control Systems
CAGE · Theory and Application of Industrial Electronics
CUCCIA · Harmonics, Sidebands, and Transients in Communication
    Engineering
DAVENPORT AND ROOT · Random Signals and Noise
EASTMAN · Fundamentals of Vacuum Tubes
EVANS · Control-system Dynamics
FITZGERALD AND HIGGINBOTHAM · Basic Electrical Engineering
FITZGERALD AND KINGSLEY · Electric Machinery
GEPPERT · Basic Electron Tubes
GLASFORD · Fundamentals of Television Engineering
HAPPELL AND HESSELBERTH · Engineering Electronics
HARMAN · Fundamentals of Electronic Motion
HESSLER AND CAREY · Fundamentals of Electrical Engineering
HILL · Electronics in Engineering
JOHNSON · Transmission Lines and Networks
KRAUS · Antennas
KRAUS · Electromagnetics
LEPAGE · Analysis of Alternating-current Circuits
LEPAGE AND SEELY · General Network Analysis
MILLMAN AND SEELY · Electronics
MILLMAN AND TAUB · Pulse and Digital Circuits
ROGERS · Introduction to Electric Fields
RÜDENBERG · Transient Performance of Electric Power Systems
RYDER · Engineering Electronics
SEELY · Electron-tube Circuits
SEELY · Electronic Engineering
SEELY · Radio Electronics
SISKIND · Direct-current Machinery
SKILLING · Electric Transmission Lines
SKILLING · Transient Electric Currents
SPANGENBERG · Fundamentals of Electron Devices
SPANGENBERG · Vacuum Tubes
STEVENSON · Elements of Power System Analysis
STORER · Passive Network Synthesis
TERMAN · Electronic and Radio Engineering
TERMAN AND PETTIT · Electronic Measurements
THALER · Elements of Servomechanism Theory
THALER AND BROWN · Servomechanism Analysis
THOMPSON · Alternating-current and Transient Circuit Analysis
TRUXAL · Automatic Feedback Control System Synthesis

McGraw-Hill Electrical and Electronic Engineering Series

FREDERICK EMMONS TERMAN, *Consulting Editor*
W. W. HARMAN AND J. G. TRUXAL, *Associate Consulting Editors*

FUNDAMENTALS OF ELECTRON DEVICES

Fundamentals of
ELECTRON DEVICES

KARL R. SPANGENBERG

Professor of Electrical Engineering
Stanford University

McGRAW-HILL BOOK COMPANY, INC.

New York   Toronto   London

1957

FUNDAMENTALS OF ELECTRON DEVICES

Library of Congress Catalog Card Number 56-11056

THE MAPLE PRESS COMPANY, YORK, PA.

To F. E. Terman

PREFACE

This book grew out of the attempt to develop an undergraduate text to serve as an introduction to electronic studies. It attempts to do for the subject of electron devices what Skilling's "Fundamentals of Electric Waves" does for the subject of electromagnetic theory. As the title indicates, it emphasizes the physics of electron devices more than is usually done in such introductory treatments. At one time, it was possible to study electronics after learning a little about the operating characteristics of vacuum tubes and without too much regard for how these operating characteristics came about. With the advent of the transistor, it does not seem possible to be satisfied with a knowledge of operating characteristics because the transistor is a somewhat mysterious device until a study of the physics of its internal operation is made.

This book also attempts to emphasize the similarities between tubes and transistors rather than the differences. This is done in large part through the common denominators of semiconductor and potential theory. In addition, the broader point of view required for transistor studies is given in a way that also embraces tube work. Transistors get the lion's share of attention because they are newer and, in some respects, more complex and therefore require more general treatment.

As much as possible, an attempt is made to show the origin of fundamental relations. To this end, there are included a considerable number of Appendixes giving the derivation of such relations.

The Problems are intended to be suggestive rather than exhaustive. It is hoped that they will suggest to the instructor or reader other questions or problems that will aid in study of the material.

A fairly extensive Bibliography, keyed in throughout the text, is included. These references may prove helpful where more detail is desired than could be given in the text. The older references are mostly books and a few classic articles. The newer references, which are in the majority, are to the periodical literature.

There is authorized a royalty-free translation of this book into Brazilian Portuguese, a version dedicated to the author's Brazilian friends. This book was started in Brazil while the author was head of the electronics division of the Instituto Tecnológico de Aeronáutica in São José dos Campos, São Paulo in 1953.

A special note of appreciation is due to F. E. Terman, Provost and

Dean of Engineering at Stanford University, for his interest and encouragement and for the clarity of his writing, which served as a model for the author.

The author is indebted to many people for direct assistance in the preparation of this book. He is particularly indebted to Chih-Tang Sah and Gregory Loew, who assisted with figures and computations, to Mrs. E. L. S. Rogers and Mrs. H. Kmetovic, who did the typing, and to his wife.

KARL R. SPANGENBERG

CONTENTS

CONTENTS

CHAPTER 1

HISTORY OF ELECTRON DEVICES

1.1. Some Definitions. The field of electronics has some well-defined branches. The first of these is that of *physical electronics*, which is concerned with the physics of electron flow under various conditions. Physical electronics is the basic study that has led to the development of *electron devices*. These are devices in which there is a controlled flow of electrons through vacuum, gas, or crystal lattices. The use of electron devices for various purposes, such as communications, control, or instrumentation, is called *electronic engineering*. *Electronics* is the sum total of all these and may be defined as "the science and technology which deals primarily with the supplementing of man's senses and his brain power by devices which collect and process information, transmit it to the point needed and there either control machines or present the processed information to human beings for their direct use" [EvB].[1] Here the emphasis is properly placed upon the function performed, namely, the handling of information. Thus electronics includes not only communications but also control systems, computers, instrumentation, and, of course, the electron devices that make all this possible.

When we consider an electron device as one in which there is a controlled flow of electrons in a special environment, we deal with the essential component of the field of electronics. Such devices may be *passive* (as, for instance, rectifiers) or *active*, i.e., capable of amplification (as, for instance, control-type tubes and transistors). Generally speaking, the principal forms of electron devices are rectifiers, tubes, transistors, various forms of light-sensitive devices, and indicators, such as cathode-ray tubes. Naturally, interest centers upon devices capable of amplification, though others must not be excluded.

1.2. Background. The history of electronics and electron devices is inextricably bound to the history of physics. Most modern developments in electronics have resulted from fundamental developments in physics. A case clearly in point is the invention of the transistor, which resulted from fundamental studies of semiconductors. On the other

---

[1] Such bracketed letters in the text correspond to the items of the alphabetical Bibliography at the end of the book: The first two letters are the first two letters of the name of the principal author; the remaining letters represent the date, as explained there.

hand, oxide emission has been known and used for half a century; yet only recently has the theory of such emission been reasonably well understood. In a similar way, the history of electronics and electron devices has been closely tied to developments in electricity.

The earliest electron device was probably the Braun tube (1897), the predecessor of the modern cathode-ray and television picture tube. However, the invention of the triode by De Forest in 1906 ushered in the real era of electronics. Since then, numerous other electron devices have been developed and there is no evidence of saturation in sight.

1.3. Chronology of Electron Devices. It would require a large chapter or a small book to tell the history of electron devices completely. Fortunately, this story, though not completely told, is fairly well indicated by a chronological listing of individuals and their contributions. Such a listing is given below. Some related developments in physics and electricity are included.

CHRONOLOGY OF ELECTRON DEVICES

B.C.
600   Thales: observation of electrification
400   Democritus: Speculation on atomic structure of matter
A.D.
1752   Franklin: Observation of positive and negative electricity
1800   Volta: Battery; first steady currents
1800   Coulomb: Inverse-square law of force between charges
1807   Davy: Electrolysis
1819   Oersted: Electromagnetism
1820   Ampère: Law of force between currents
1821   Faraday: Electric motor
1826   Ohm: Linear relation between voltage and current
1831   Faraday: Electromagnetic induction; first dynamo
1857   Maxwell: Kinetic theory of gases
1864   Maxwell: Electromagnetic theory
1869   Mendeleev: Periodic table of the elements
1873   Guthrie: Observation of incandescent electron-emission effects
1876   Wien: Thermal-radiation law
1883   Edison: Edison effect (unidentified electrons)
1887   Hertz: Electromagnetic radiation
1887   Hertz: Photoelectric emission
1889   Thomson: Identification of electron
1892   Lorentz: Electron theory of magnetism
1895   Roentgen: X rays
1897   Thomson: Measurement of ratio of charge to mass of electron
1897   Braun: First cathode-ray tube
1901   Planck: Quantum theory
1903   Wehnelt: Oxide emission
1904   Fleming: Vacuum diode
1904   Einstein: Photoelectric-emission equation
1906   De Forest: Triode
1910   Millikan: Measurement of charge of the electron

1911 Rutherford: Nuclear scattering of α particles
1913 Bohr: Atomic theory
1918 Schottky: Noise in electron streams
1919 Schottky: Tetrode
1921 Hull: Single-anode magnetron
1923 Richardson and Dushman: Thermionic-electron-emission equation
1924 De Broglie: Matter waves
1924 Compton: Compton effect (quantum energy exchange between X rays and atoms)
1925 Pauli: Exclusion principle
1925 Uhlenbeck and Goudsmit: Electron spin
1926 Schrödinger: Quantum mechanics
1926 Fermi and Dirac: Statistics of electrons in solids
1926 Jobst and Tellegen: Pentode
1926 Busch: Electron optics
1927 Davisson and Germer: Wave aspect of the electron
1927 Heisenberg: Uncertainty principle
1928 Farnsworth: First all-electronic television
1928 Johnson and Nyquist: Thermal noise in conductors
1929 Hull: Thyratron
1933 Cleeton and Williams: Microwave spectroscopy
1934 Zworykin: Iconoscope
1934 Ruska: Electron microscope
1935 Heil: Velocity-modulation principle
1936 Zworykin, Morton, and Malter: Secondary-emission multiplier
1938 Schade: Beam power tube
1938 Hansen: Cavity resonator
1938 Varian and Varian: Klystron
1939 Randal, Boot, and Ludi: Cavity magnetron
1946 Kompfner: Traveling-wave tube
1946 Rose, Weimer, and Law: Image orthicon
1947 Haeff: Electron-wave tube
1948 Haeff: Storage tube
1948 Bardeen and Brattain: Contact transistor
1949 Shockley: Junction transistor
1950 Bloch and Purcell: Nuclear induction
1950 Weimer, Forgue, and Goodrich: Vidicon
1952 Wallace: Junction-transistor tetrode
1952 Kompfner: Backward-wave oscillator
1953 Early: p-n-i-p and n-p-i-n junction-transistor triodes
1954 Dacey, Lee, and Shockley: Diffused-base-transistor triode

Many of the items listed in this chronology will be discussed or at least referred to somewhere in the book. It is interesting to make a few speculations relative to the table. In the first place, there appears to be no diminution of developments yet in sight. In other words, the development of electron devices is still in the lower region of a normal growth curve, and many more new developments and devices may be expected in the future. It may also be noticed that there were fewer than normal fundamental developments during wartime and more than normal number of developments after a war. Also, although initially the basic physical developments preceded the electronic developments, electronic devices are now assisting the progress of physics. Thus microwave spectroscopy and nuclear induction were undoubtedly made possible by electron devices and circuits. It is further unlikely that an atomic clock or an atomic bomb could have been produced without the aid of electron devices.

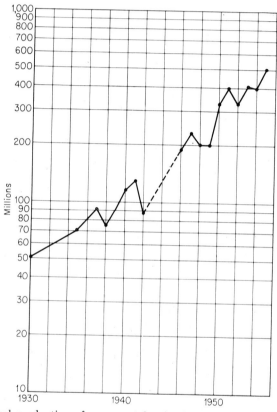

Fig. 1.1. Annual production of vacuum tubes in the United States during the last quarter century.

1.4. Growth of the Prodigy. The electronic industry in the United States has had an extremely rapid growth, one that is little short of phenomenal. Originally the principal activity was radio, which grew rapidly in the twenties and tended to saturate somewhat in the late thirties. However, the electronic industry was stimulated by progressively increasing use of electronics in industry. In the period after World War II, the development of television continued the upward surge, aided by defense activities. The recent development of the transistor promises to continue the development of the industry since the high reliability of

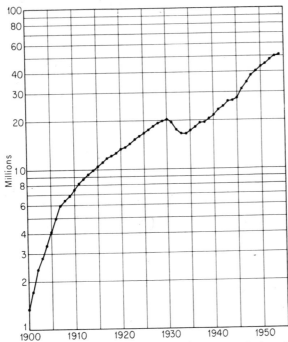

FIG. 1.2. Number of telephones in use in the United States during the last quarter century.

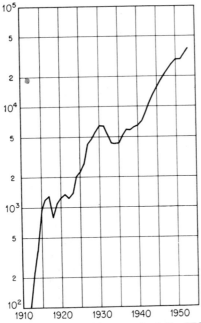

FIG. 1.3. Membership growth of the IRE.

the component will make possible many new applications of electronic systems.

Some idea of the growth of the industry may be gained from the curves of several factors serving as indices: Figure 1.1 is a curve showing the number of vacuum tubes manufactured annually in the United States in the past 25 years; Fig. 1.2 shows the number of telephones in use in the United States in recent times; Fig. 1.3 shows the growth of the membership of the Institute of Radio Engineers (IRE), a professional society concerned with electronics. All these curves show an extremely rapid growth with the rate of increase still positive. It is of interest to comment that the number of radio sets in use in the United States is over one per person and that the number of telephones per 100 persons is about 26. It is also noteworthy that the size of the IRE is now nearly equal to that of the oldest and largest engineering societies.

CHAPTER 2

ELECTRONS AND IONS

2.1. Introduction. All electron devices depend upon charge carriers for their operation. Such charge carriers are called "ions." An ion is a fundamental physical particle with an electric charge. The simplest and commonest ion is the electron, which is the lightest particle of matter and carries the smallest finite amount of negative charge Although the electron is an ion, it is usually referred to as the electron because of its special nature. The majority of ions are atoms that have lost or gained one or more electrons. They may have either negative or positive charge, always an integral multiple of the electron charge. Ions are identified by the atom from which they are derived. Thus a mercury atom that has lost one electron is referred to as the singly charged positive mercury ion.

Another carrier, also classified as an ion, is encountered in certain crystals, notably semiconductors, and is described as a *hole*. A hole is a place in a crystal structure where an electron is missing from the position where it is normally found. (In the vernacular, "A hole is where an electron ought to be, but it ain't.") Charge in this case is actually carried by electrons, which may move in and out of holes in such a way as to give a progressive displacement of the hole. The effect of electrons moving in one direction is to cause the holes to move in the other direction. Thus the holes act like carriers of positive charge moving in a direction opposite to that of the electrons. This action is analogous to that of a bubble rising in a liquid. Here there is a downward motion of the liquid corresponding to the upward movement of the bubble. Holes move in the direction of decreasing potential in the same manner as positive ions.

The effective charge of a hole is equal in magnitude to that of the electron but positive in sign. The effective mass of the hole is about the same as for the electron. However, the mobility of holes is only about one-half that of electrons in the same material.

Charge in motion creates current. The sign convention for electric current is that electric current flows in the same direction as positive charge carriers, i.e., from positive to negative potential and in the opposite direction to negative charge carriers (Fig. 2.1). A flow of 1 coulomb sec^{-1} past a point on a conductor constitutes a current of 1 amp. It takes about 6 million electrons flowing past a point in 10^{-6} sec to produce 10^{-6} amp of current in the opposite direction.

In general, current flow is calculated from the following equation:

$$I = N_- n_- e + N_+ n_+ e \qquad (2.1)$$

where I = current, amp

N_-, N_+ = no. of negative and positive ions, respectively, passing a point, $\sec^{-1}$

n_-, n_+ = no. of electrons in excess and in deficit of a neutral particle on each carrier

e = magnitude of the electron charge

Both terms in the equation are positive though the negative and positive ions flow in opposite directions. For the electron, n_- is considered as unity.

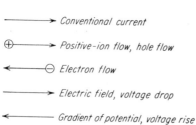

Fig. 2.1. Relative direction of current carriers, field, and gradient.

Current density may also be expressed in terms of charge density and velocity, in which case

$$\mathbf{J} = \rho_- \mathbf{v}_- + \rho_+ \mathbf{v}_+ \qquad (2.2)$$

where $\mathbf{J}$ = current density

ρ = charge per unit volume

$\mathbf{v}$ = velocity

The use of boldface letters indicates space vectors. Current, of course, is given by the product of current density and cross-sectional area. A positive charge density and a positive velocity give a positive current as do a negative charge density and a negative velocity.

2.2. The Fundamental Particles. All matter is made of *molecules*. The molecule is the smallest unit of a given material that has all the physical and chemical properties of the given material. There are millions of different kinds of molecules. Molecules themselves are made up of combinations of other units known as *atoms*. There are 92 stable atoms, and of a material known as an *element* each is the smallest portion that has the principal properties of that element. Molecules of the 92 stable elements are not always single atoms: Thus the molecule of hydrogen consists of two hydrogen atoms. The 92 stable atoms of the elements, in turn, are made up of *three fundamental particles:* the *electron*, the *proton*, and the *neutron*. A single exception is the atom of hydrogen, which in its common form has no neutron.

For most purposes the electron may be described as a particle having a small but definite mass and a small but definite negative charge. The electron at times also acts like a small packet of electromagnetic waves and thus exhibits a dual matter-wave aspect. The proton is a small particle about the same size as the electron (but much heavier) and carries a positive charge equal in magnitude to the electron charge. It also exhibits the dual matter-wave aspect, though this is less conspicuous than in the case of the electron. The neutron is essentially a proton with no electric charge. It is now known that atoms are composed of a nucleus of protons and neutrons with planetary electrons equal in number to the number of nuclear protons so that the atom is normally electrically neutral. The basic properties of the fundamental particles are listed in Table 2.1. Values given there are relative to those for the electron.

TABLE 2.1

Particle	Relative mass	Relative charge	Relative radius
Electron.............	1	−1	1
Proton..............	1,836.1	+1	ca. 1.05
Neutron............	1,837.5	0	ca. 1.05

The absolute values for the electron are given below [DuC]:

Charge $-e = 1.6021 \times 10^{-19}$ coulomb
Mass $m = 9.1085 \times 10^{-31}$ kg
Ratio of charge to mass $-e/m = 1.7589 \times 10^{11}$ coulombs kg^{-1}
Radius $r = 2.8178 \times 10^{-13}$ cm

The electron also exhibits a wave aspect with a wavelength dependent upon its energy. If an electron has been accelerated through V volts, then for V below 50,000 volts it has an equivalent wavelength

$$\lambda = \frac{12.264}{\sqrt{V}} \quad A \tag{2.3}$$

where 1 A (angstrom) is 10^{-10} m. Thus a 50-kv beam carries electrons with equivalent wavelengths of 0.05 A, this property being used in the electron microscope.

Although electron effects had been observed earlier, the identification of the electron came only with observations on cathode rays. These were observed as rays originating on the cathode, or negative electrode, in evacuated tubes. The rays were visible at low pressures, could be deflected by electric and magnetic fields, caused certain minerals to fluoresce, heated thin metal foils to incandescence, actually imparted motion to small wheels, and in general behaved like charged particles with a small but definite mass. Sensitive chemical tests showed that the particles were not atoms of the cathode material. They were named electrons, and Thomson measured the ratio of their charge to their mass by observing the deflecting effect of electric and magnetic fields on them.

It was only in 1910 that Millikan measured the charge of the electron with his celebrated oil-drop experiment [Mid1]. In this experiment a closed chamber was used into which a fine spray of oil drops was introduced. The mass of any drop could be measured by noting its asymptotic velocity when falling freely and by calculating from a viscosity dependence given by Stokes. The gas in the chamber was ionized by X rays, producing free electrons, some of which attached themselves to oil drops. Such oil drops could be held stationary by a properly applied vertical electric field, which balanced the gravitational attraction. From the knowledge of the field and the mass of the oil drop, the charge could be calculated. The charges determined in a number of cases were integral multiples of a given charge, which was then known to be the charge of the electron.

Electrons and protons are extremely small and dense. Further, they are so widely separated in atoms that the latter are mostly made of empty space. For example, if an atom of hydrogen, consisting of a single nuclear proton and a single planetary electron, were enlarged so that with the electron in its smallest possible orbit the atomic radius were 1 km, then the proton and the electron would each be about 3.8 cm in radius; but the mass of the proton, assuming density unchanged, would be about 1 million tons.

The structure of an atom is usually designated by its nuclear charge Ze, a mass number A, and its mass M. Z is the number of protons in the nucleus; A is equal to the sum of the number of protons and neutrons in the nucleus; M is very close to an integral multiple of the mass number A.

The chemical properties of the atom are determined by the number of electrons, equal to Z. An atom of a given element may have various mass numbers, i.e., the number of neutrons is not always the same; but the number of protons and electrons for a given element is always the same. Thus there are three types of hydrogen having zero, one, and two nuclear neutrons, respectively, but always one proton and one electron. Hydrogen with mass number 2 is called heavy hydrogen, or deuterium. Hydrogen with mass number 3 is called tritium. Such different forms of the same element are known as *isotopes*.

In nuclear physics the notation for describing the various isotopes uses the chemical symbol with the nuclear charge as a subscript on the left and the mass number as a superscript on the right. The three isotopes of hydrogen listed above are represented by $_1H^1$, $_1H^2$, and $_1H^3$. In this case 99.98 per cent of all hydrogen atoms are of the first type. Lithium is composed of 92.5 per cent of $_3Li^7$ and 7.5 per cent of $_3Li^6$ with traces of $_3Li^5$ and $_3Li^8$. The structure of some simple atoms is shown in Fig. 2.2.

In addition to the three fundamental particles, a number of others have been found. Most of these exist only for fractions of a microsecond and are so rare that they are not of concern to electronic engineers, but they are worthy of mention [AnA, DyC, MaB, ThD]. In addition to the electron, proton, and neutron, there has been discovered a *positron*. This is essentially an electron with a positive charge. A number of particles with masses intermediate between those of the electron and proton are known as *mesons*. The μ mesons have 216 times the mass of the electron and are found with both positive and negative charges. The π meson has about 273 times the mass of an electron and is found with positive, negative, and no charge. All are observed in cosmic-ray phenomena. In addition the existence of the τ meson, of mass 967 times the electron, of both positive and negative charge is well established. Mesons with three other masses below proton mass are likewise believed possible.

In a class by itself is the *photon*, which is the basic unit of light. Just as the electron sometimes exhibits a wave aspect, so radiant energy sometimes exhibits a corpuscular aspect. The photon is basically a

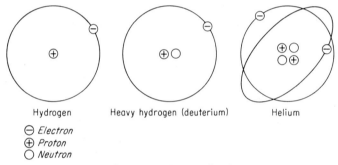

Hydrogen   Heavy hydrogen (deuterium)   Helium

⊖ *Electron*
⊕ *Proton*
○ *Neutron*

Fig. 2.2. Structure of some simple atoms.

quantized packet of electromagnetic energy, of energy $h\nu$, where h is Planck's constant and ν is frequency. As such, it has zero mass and no charge, but it explains photoelectric emission perfectly. It is a direct outcome of the quantum theory, which states that energy is not infinitely divisible but is transmitted in small units known as quanta, which are, however, proportional in size to the frequency of the radiation.

2.3. Sources of Electrons and Ions. Since all matter is made of atoms, which in turn contain electrons, it might be thought an easy matter to produce free electrons and ions. Actually, the possibilities are somewhat limited. It is only in conductors and semiconductors that some electrons are free to move from one atom to another. Such electrons are called *free* electrons in contrast to the electrons of the atoms of an insulator, which are *bound* electrons strongly attached to their atoms. It is not easy to liberate the free electrons from a conductor in order to produce an electron flow in a vacuum or gas. In general, there is a restraining surface potential barrier that the electrons must overcome before they are free from the conductor. The magnitude of the surface potential barrier in volts is known as the work function. The electrons in the conductor must have an energy equal to this multiplied by the electron charge before they can climb the "potential hill" at the surface and escape from the conductor. Ordinarily, they will not have sufficient escape energy, which means that additional energy must be supplied to the free electrons before the conductor can *emit* electrons. Different ways of supplying the escape energy give rise to different forms of electron emission.

If energy is supplied to the free electrons by heating the conductor, there results what is known as *thermionic emission*. Only a small fraction of the free electrons will acquire enough energy to surmount the potential barrier, but thermionic-emission currents can be quite large. It is also possible to illuminate surfaces having small potential barriers and thus to supply enough energy to the free electrons to give rise to *photoemission*. Energy may likewise be supplied by bombarding a surface with other electrons or ions, in which case the resulting electron emission is referred to as *secondary emission*. Finally, if strong electric gradients are applied to a surface, the magnitude of the potential barriers may be reduced enough to permit what is known as *field emission*.

Ions may also be produced in a number of ways. Ions may be produced in electrolytes and solids by dissociation or by the application of electric gradients. Ions are most readily produced in a gas by addition of sufficient energy to the outer electrons of the atoms to enable them to escape from the atoms. Thus ionization may be produced by *thermal* means. It may also be produced by *electron bombardment*. Kinetic energy may also be supplied by *ion bombardment*. Lastly ionization may result from energy supplied by *electromagnetic radiation* and is known as photoionization.

The principal interest in electron devices lies not so much in producing electron or ion currents as in controlling them easily by electrical means. This is done in electron tubes by altering the fields that govern the electron flow. It is done in transistors by changing the carrier densities and junction potentials. This makes possible in each case an electrical valve action, which gives an apparent amplification by allowing a small amount of electrical power to control the flow of a larger amount of power.

2.4. Units. In this book the *rationalized system of mks (meter-kilogram-second) units* is used for the most part. This system of units has been recommended for universal adoption by several international congresses and is now extensively used in engineering work. The units of mass, length, and time in this system are the meter, kilogram, and second, respectively—thus giving rise to the name [Eso]. In many systems of units there appears a factor 4π in electromagnetic relations involving *rectangular* coordinates. Such systems are called "unrationalized." In a "rationalized" system of units this factor is suppressed by absorption into the dielectric constant and permeability of free space. However, the factor 4π can never be suppressed entirely; in rationalized systems it appears in electromagnetic equations involving *spherical* geometry, which is, however, considered more convenient.

The rationalized mks system of units is particularly convenient for electrical quantities because potential, current, resistance, and power are expressed in the practical units of volts, amperes, ohms, and watts, respectively. However, some of the other units are less familiar and deserve comment. The unit of force appears in newtons, 1 newton being equal to 10^5 dynes, 102 g, or a little over $3\frac{1}{2}$ oz. An acceleration of 1 m $\sec^{-2}$ is imparted by 1 newton to a mass of 1 kg. Magnetic flux density appears in webers per square meter, 1 weber m^{-2} being equal to 10^4 gauss. Mmf comes out conveniently in units of ampere-turns per meter and is the value that would occur in an infinitely long solenoid. The permeability and dielectric constant of free space are *not* unity but are special numbers that must be kept available for use. However, electrical problems using these numbers give practical results directly without conversion. The dielectric constant of free space is taken as

$$\varepsilon_0 = \frac{1}{36\pi} \times 10^{-9} = 8.854 \times 10^{-12} \text{ farad m}^{-1} \qquad (2.4)$$

Likewise, the permeability of free space is given by

$$\mu_0 = 4\pi \times 10^{-7} = 1.257 \times 10^{-6} \text{ henry m}^{-1} \qquad (2.5)$$

The dimensions of these units become apparent if one works out the expressions for the capacity of a parallel-plate capacitor and the inductance of a long solenoid in these units. Although the numerical values of the two fundamental constants given above look awkward, they may be remembered or quickly derived by virtue of their relation to two other well-known physical constants. One of these is the velocity of light, which has the value

$$c = \frac{1}{\sqrt{\mu_0 \varepsilon_0}} = 3 \times 10^8 \text{ m sec}^{-1} \qquad (2.6)$$

The other is the so-called intrinsic impedance of free space, which is the ratio of the electric- to the magnetic-field strength in a plane-polarized wave:

$$\eta = \frac{E}{H} = \sqrt{\frac{\mu_0}{\varepsilon_0}} = 120\pi = 377 \text{ ohms} \qquad (2.7)$$

which by coincidence is the same as the angular frequency of a 60-cycle $\sec^{-1}$ wave. From the above it is seen that

$$\mu_0 = \frac{\eta}{c} \qquad (2.8)$$

and

$$\varepsilon_0 = \frac{1}{\eta c} \qquad (2.9)$$

These values are numerically equal to those given above and are given by relations easily remembered.

Dielectric constants of materials other than free space are given by the products of the *relative* dielectric constant and the dielectric constant of free space.   Thus

$$\varepsilon = \varepsilon_r \varepsilon_0 \tag{2.10}$$

Likewise, for permeability,

$$\mu = \mu_r \mu_0 \tag{2.11}$$

where the subscript r denotes the relative value.

CHAPTER 3

ELECTRIC AND MAGNETIC FIELDS

3.1. Electric-field Fundamentals. Electron devices depend for their operation upon the controlled flow of current carriers. Since the flow is controlled by electric and magnetic fields, it is appropriate to study electric and magnetic fields in this chapter. Because most readers will know something of this subject, this chapter will present only a review, with emphasis on special methods useful in device studies.

The reader will be familiar with the concept of *potential difference* as it is used in circuit theory. Here potential difference is associated with a tendency for currents to flow. It will occur even in insulators where no current can flow. Potential difference is defined in all cases as the *work* done in moving a hypothetical positive test charge from one point to another.

In circuit theory the variation of potential is usually one-dimensional, i.e., around the circuit. Current is usually confined to a channel of small cross section. In more general problems potential may vary from point to point in two or three dimensions with an associated variation of *gradient of potential or electric field*. In a given distribution of potential and gradient due to a current flow, the potential and gradient are unchanged by a uniform increase in resistivity out to an infinite resistivity, at which no current can flow.

Gradient of potential, which is the rate of change of potential with distance, has the character of electrical pressure and has the dimensions of force per unit charge. Gradient of potential or electric field is analogous to magnetic field. Electric field is a field of *force*, which is measured on electric charges. Specifically, electric field is the force per unit positive charge on a small positive test charge placed in the field. This is the same as gradient of potential.

The force between two individual charges is given by *Coulomb's law*. The force F between two charges q_1 and q_2 is given by

$$F = \frac{q_1 q_2}{4\pi \varepsilon r^2} \qquad \text{newtons} \tag{3.1}$$

The charges are expressed in coulombs, and the distance r in meters. Here ε is the dielectric constant. The factor 4π appears because of the rationalized units employed. This relation states that the force between

15

two charges is proportional to the product of the two charges and inversely proportional to the dielectric constant and to the square of the distance between the charges. Coulomb's law will be recognized as analogous to the gravitational law. The direction of the force is along a line joining the two charges; it is repulsive when the charges are of the same sign and attractive when they are of opposite sign. This is shown graphically in Fig. 3.1.

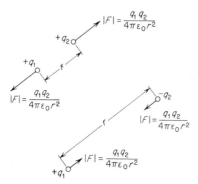

FIG. 3.1. Graphical representation of Coulomb's law (3.1).

The hypothetical positive test charge, the force of which gives the electric field, is assumed to be small enough so that the field is not disturbed by its presence. Electric field is a vector quantity since it has both magnitude and direction. The force on a charge of any size q is given by

$$\mathbf{F} = q\mathbf{E} \tag{3.2}$$

provided that q is small enough so that it does not disturb the field. Electric field is expressed in units of newtons per coulomb, which is the same as volts per meter.

The *difference of potential* between two points is defined as the work, per unit positive charge, done in moving a hypothetical small positive test charge from one point to the other. Potential is a scalar quantity, symbol V, expressed in units of volts or newton-meters per coulomb. Accordingly,

$$-qV_{ba} = -q(V_b - V_a) = q \int_a^b E \cos \alpha \, ds \tag{3.3}$$

where the subscripts a and b refer to terminal points and α is the angle between the field E and the element of path length ds. The test charge is assumed to move without collisions. The negative sign in (3.3) appears because potential difference is defined as the work done *on* the charge rather than *by* the charge. The above expression will hold within dielectrics and conductors as well as in free space.

The work done in moving a charge from a point a to a point b may be shown to be independent of the path by the application of Coulomb's law to the individual charges producing the field. The work done in moving from a to b is the negative of that done in moving from b to a. The work done in moving a charge around any closed path is *always zero* for static fields.

For a positive charge in a field whose potential increases from left to right, the force on the charge is negative, i.e., in the direction of decreasing potential. This is to say that the electric field is in the direction opposite to that of increasing potential. From the definition of potential and (3.3), electric field is seen to be the negative gradient of potential. Thus if we consider the point a to be fixed and the point b variable,

$$E_x = -\frac{\partial V}{\partial x}$$

$$E_y = -\frac{\partial V}{\partial y} \qquad (3.4)$$

$$E_z = -\frac{\partial V}{\partial z}$$

Physically, gradient of a scalar quantity is the rate of change, with distance, of the quantity in the direction of maximum change and, as such, is a vector quantity. It has units of volts per meter in this case.

Electrons experience a force in the direction of increasing potential. This is the direction of positive gradient of potential, or negative field. In contrast, positive charges experience a force in the direction of decreasing potential. This is the direction of positive field, or negative gradient of potential.

3.2. Determination of Electric Fields. Since much of the study of electron devices is concerned with the motion of current carriers in electric fields, it is important to say something about the determination of the form of electric fields. This subject is sometimes referred to as electrostatics or potential theory. As such it is a large subject to which many books have been devoted [Jez, Wea]. Therefore only the basic elements of this subject can be presented in this section.

The electric field due to a distribution of charges is a *vector* field since, by definition, it represents in direction and magnitude the resultant force per unit charge on a small positive test charge in the field. As such, it can be determined by a vector summation of the effects of all charges.

The field due to a *single* point charge is

$$|\mathbf{E}| = E = \frac{q}{4\pi\varepsilon r^2} \qquad (3.5)$$

which is obtained from (3.1) by setting $q_1 = q$ and $q_2 = +1$, the latter corresponding to the test charge. The expression above gives only the magnitude of the force; the direction is along the line between q and the test charge. If q is fixed in position and the test charge moved around, it is seen that E is a function of position.

Where the field is produced by more than one charge, as is usually the case, the resultant force must be obtained by a vector summation of the forces due to the individual charges. This is most readily done in component form:

$$E_x = \frac{\sum\limits_{n} q_n \cos (x,r_n)}{4\pi\varepsilon r_n^2} \tag{3.6}$$

where (x,r_n) is the angle between a vector in the x direction and a vector from the charge q_n to the point at which the field is being determined. Similar expressions can be written for the y and z components of the electric field. These components then determine the resultant field, in magnitude and direction, as a function of position of the hypothetical test charge. Calculating the vector field in this manner is generally a laborious procedure.

It is also possible to determine the field by first calculating the potential and then taking the negative gradient of it according to (3.5). The *absolute* potential at a distance r from a single point charge q is

$$V = \frac{q}{4\pi\varepsilon r} \tag{3.7}$$

This is obtained from (3.5) by integrating E with respect to r from infinity to radius r, potential at infinity being assumed to have the reference value of zero.

The potential due to a group of charges is equal to the sum of the potentials of the individual charges according to (3.6), each calculated for its particular radial distance to the point in question.

$$V = \sum\limits_{n} \frac{q_n}{4\pi\varepsilon r_n} \tag{3.8}$$

For a continuous distribution of charge over a surface, this takes the integral form

$$V = \frac{1}{4\pi\varepsilon} \int \frac{\sigma}{r} \, da \tag{3.9}$$

where σ = charge per unit area
  da = element of area
The integration is taken over the entire area of the surface. For a continuous distribution of charge throughout a volume,

$$V = \frac{1}{4\pi\varepsilon} \int \frac{\rho}{r} \, dv \tag{3.10}$$

where ρ = charge per unit volume
  dv = element of volume
The integration is taken over the volume.

Potential is generally easier to find directly than field because the summation of (3.8) is scalar rather than vectorial as in (3.6). The corresponding integral expressions of (3.9) and (3.10) require only a single integral to give potential, whereas three integral expressions corresponding to (3.6) would be required to give the field.   If one knows potential as a function of position, it is an easy matter to take derivatives as shown in (3.4) to get the negative gradient of potential, which is the electric field. However, even this process has its limitations because the distribution of charges is frequently not given; rather, the potentials, locations, and shapes of a number of electrodes are given.   Before we can treat such problems we need to review some other ideas.

The concept of electrostatic flux is a useful one.   It is strictly analogous to that of magnetic flux.   Lines of flux may be imagined as emanating from positive charges, having everywhere the direction of the electric field, and terminating on negative charges.   Likewise, the electrostatic flux density will be proportional to the product of electric field and dielectric constant

$$\mathbf{D} = \varepsilon\mathbf{E} \tag{3.11}$$

where $\mathbf{D}$ = electrostatic flux density
    ε = dielectric constant
    $\mathbf{E}$ = electric field

just as magnetic flux density is equal to the product of mmf and permeability

$$\mathbf{B} = \mu\mathbf{H} \tag{3.12}$$

where $\mathbf{B}$ = magnetic flux density
    μ = permeability
    $\mathbf{H}$ = magnetic field

Both $\mathbf{D}$ and $\mathbf{B}$ are vectors having in most (isotropic) materials the same direction as $\mathbf{E}$ and $\mathbf{H}$, respectively, crystalline substances occasionally excepted (anisotropic).   The flux density normal to a surface multiplied by the area S gives electric flux.   For a unit positive charge, the flux emanating can be calculated over a sphere of radius r surrounding the charge.

$$\text{Flux} = DS = \varepsilon ES = \varepsilon\,\frac{1}{4\pi\varepsilon r^2}\,4\pi r^2 = 1 \tag{3.13}$$

This is to say that in the rationalized mks system, one line of flux emanates from every unit positive charge.

A more general statement of the above is known as Gauss's law, which states that *the net outward flux through any closed surface is equal to the charge enclosed.*

From Gauss's law the variation of electric field and potential for simple geometries such as plane, cylindrical, or spherical are readily determined. Thus in the case of a cylindrical geometry, such as the field about an infinitely long wire with a uniform distribution of charge on the wire, it is evident that the flux D dilutes itself radially as $1/r$.   Accordingly, electric field E also varies as $1/r$ since $E = D/\varepsilon$.   Since potential is the negative integral of field with radius, potential will vary as $-\ln r$, where ln is the symbol for the natural logarithm to the base $\epsilon = 2.718$. Attention must, of course, be given to the algebraic signs and the numerical coefficients. The results for the three geometries mentioned are summarized in Table 3.1. These relations are important ones, that should

TABLE 3.1

	Plane	Cylindrical	Spherical
Total positive charge..............	σ(area)	λ(length)	q
Charge density..................	σ	λ	q/area
Intensity E....................	σ/ε	$\lambda/2\pi\varepsilon r$	$q/4\pi\varepsilon r^2$
Potential V....................	$-\sigma x/\varepsilon + C$	$-\lambda/2\pi\varepsilon \ln r + C$	$q/4\pi\varepsilon r$

be kept in mind because they may frequently be applied in more complex problems as approximations in certain regions such as close to a plane, close to a cylinder, etc.

3.3. Potential as Determined by Boundary Conditions. The relations in the previous section may be applied when the charge distribution in a given situation is known. More frequently, the potential of certain electrodes or the potential around a closed boundary is known. This gives rise to what is known as a "boundary-value problem," for which other methods than those above are most suitable. A complete discussion of the subject is beyond the scope of this book, but enough can be said here about each of a number of approaches to assist the reader in the visualization and determination of such potential fields [Lia].

The properties of electrostatic fields are such that, with a little practice, it is possible to sketch fields with considerable accuracy and without any computation [Atb]. Field plots should include flux lines whose density at electrodes corresponds to charge densities. There should also be drawn equipotential contours, which, by definition, are equal-work contours and so must be perpendicular to the flux lines. If they were not perpendicular, work would be done in moving a charge along such a line. From the same consideration, flux lines must enter conducting electrodes at right angles. These and other useful properties may be summarized as follows:

PROPERTIES USEFUL IN SKETCHING FIELDS

1. Flux and equipotential lines intersect at right angles.
2. Flux lines are perpendicular to conductors and always terminate on charges.

3. Equipotential contours close to conductors tend to have the same form as the conductors.

4. Equipotential contours are either parallel or perpendicular to lines of symmetry.

5. Flux-potential patterns should be drawn with curvilinear squares, i.e., four-sided figures with right angles at the corners and with equal average lengths of opposite pairs of sides, which maintain these properties upon infinite subdivision. Sides may be curved. With this construction it follows that:

(a) The same potential difference exists across each square.

(b) The same flux passes through each square.

(c) Each square represents the same increment of capacity between electrodes.

In applying the properties of fields given above, the electrodes given should first be drawn and then a few flux and equipotential lines sketched

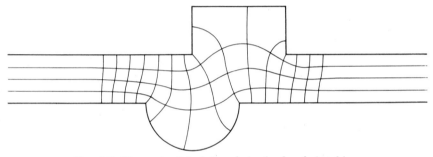

Fig. 3.2. Flux-potential plot made by freehand sketching.

in. The intervals thus given should be subdivided to get a plot with fairly fine subdivisions. As the work proceeds, it usually becomes evident where errors have been made, indicating how lines should be reshaped. This is best done by starting a new plot on tracing paper over the first plot and proceeding until its deficiencies show up. The ultimate test of a good plot is that all the areas between lines are curvilinear squares, not rectangles. From such a plot, capacity between two electrodes, for instance, is equal to the dielectric constant in mks units multiplied by the number of flux tubes and divided by the number of potential intervals. Shown in Fig. 3.2 is a flux-potential plot sketched by the method given above.

Where a more exact determination of flux and equipotential lines is desired without computation, use may be made of a *current-flow model* of potential in which the shape of the field may be measured with high accuracy with simple equipment in a short time. The current-flow model is one in which there are set up, to suitable scale, electrodes corresponding to the electrodes of the problem and in which these electrodes are immersed in a material of uniform conductivity. Usually this is done by immersing metal electrodes in a liquid electrolyte, which must be chosen for the metal of the electrodes so that no electrochemical effects are developed. Potentials of a low frequency are then applied to the electrodes, and the equipotentials in the liquid between the electrodes are measured with a high-impedance detector. These equipotentials correspond to the equipotentials in the electrostatic field. This model works because the law of current flow in a medium of uniform conductivity, namely,

$$\mathbf{J} = g\mathbf{E} \tag{3.14}$$

where $\mathbf{J}$ = current density
  g = conductivity
  $\mathbf{E}$ = electric field, or negative gradient of potential
(basically Ohm's law) is strictly analogous to

$$\mathbf{D} = \varepsilon\mathbf{E} \tag{3.15}$$

which gives the relation between electrostatic flux density $\mathbf{D}$, dielectric constant ε, and electric field $\mathbf{E}$.

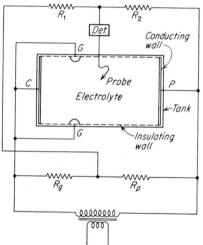

In Fig. 3.3 is shown an arrangement for measuring equipotential contours in a plane-electrode-triode section. This setup uses a special tank with conducting ends and insulating sides. The former represent the cathode and plate electrodes, and the latter establish the conditions of symmetry between sections. The resistances R_g and R_p establish the ratio between positive plate potential and negative grid potential. The ratio

$$R_1/(R_1 + R_2)$$

Fig. 3.3. Current-flow model (electrolytic tank) for the study of plane-electrode-triode fields.

establishes the fraction of the cathode-plate potential that is the equipotential for which zero indication will be given. Headphones, an oscilloscope, or a vacuum-tube voltmeter may be used as a balance detector.

The current-flow model described gives only equipotential contours. However, since these are given quite accurately, it is a simple matter to sketch flux lines by using the principles indicated earlier. In two-dimensional problems conducting paper may be used instead of a wet electrolyte. For problems with cylindrical symmetry, where potential varies with radius and axial coordinate but not with angle, a tilted tank must be used in which the depth of the electrolyte increases linearly with radius. The general method is not restricted to two-dimensional problems, and if necessary, three-dimensional models may be constructed.

Analytically, boundary-value problems for potentials are handled as solutions of a partial differential equation that tells how potential varies from point to point. This equation is known as Laplace's equation, and for three-dimensional rectangular coordinates it has the form

$$\frac{\partial^2 V}{\partial x^2} + \frac{\partial^2 V}{\partial y^2} + \frac{\partial^2 V}{\partial z^2} = 0 \qquad (3.16)$$

This is simply the sum of the second derivatives of potential with respect to the three coordinate directions. A detailed study of methods of solutions of this equation is beyond the scope of this book, although an approximate method of solution will be indicated later. Mathematically, this equation asks the question "How does the potential vary from point to point *in a region free of charge?*" The answer is found in the solution. Some insight as to the significance of this equation is given by outlining briefly its derivation.

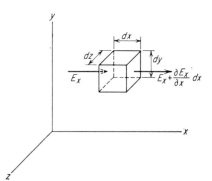

Consider an element of volume in three-dimensional coordinates $dx\ dy\ dz$, as shown in Fig. 3.4. Consider now the net outward electric flux through this little cube. If the flux *into* the left face is $E_x\ dy\ dz$ and the rate of change of E_x with x is $\partial E_x/\partial x$, then the flux *out* of the right-hand face will be equal to the sum of that into the left-hand face plus an increase $(\partial E_x/\partial x)dx\ dy\ dz$,

FIG. 3.4. Element of volume used in deriving Laplace's equation, (3.16).

since dx is the distance over which the variation is considered. Accordingly, the net outward flux for the pair of faces will be simply the increase last quoted. Combining similar terms for all three pairs of faces and recognizing that, *by Gauss's law*, the net outward flux must be equal to the charge enclosed, we get

$$\varepsilon\left(\frac{\partial E_x}{\partial x} + \frac{\partial E_y}{\partial y} + \frac{\partial E_z}{\partial z}\right) dx\ dy\ dz = \rho\ dv \qquad (3.17)$$

where ρ is the volume charge density in the element of volume dv. Since electric field is the negative gradient of potential, this last equation may be written

$$\frac{\partial^2 V}{\partial x^2} + \frac{\partial^2 V}{\partial y^2} + \frac{\partial^2 V}{\partial z^2} = -\frac{\rho}{\epsilon} \qquad (3.18)$$

which is known as Poisson's equation. Mathematically, this equation asks the question "How does potential vary from point to point *in a region containing distributed charge?"* It is used in the study of the influence of space charge on current flow in both tubes and transistors. When the charge density ρ is zero, Poisson's equation reduces to the Laplace equation previously given.

In certain situations the solution to (3.16) is quite simple. Thus in the one-dimensional problem of determining the potential variation between parallel condenser plates, only the first term of (3.16) would be used:

$$\frac{\partial^2 V}{\partial x^2} = 0 \tag{3.19}$$

This integrates readily to give

$$V = a + bx \tag{3.20}$$

where a and b are the first and second constants of integration. If the boundary values are $V = 0$ when $x = 0$ and $V = V_1$ when $x = d$, then the final solution is simply

$$V(x) = \frac{x}{d} V_1 \tag{3.21}$$

It is seen that boundary values, in the one-dimensional case, have the same significance as "initial conditions." Likewise it is seen that this approach yields the same answer as that obtained in Table 3.1 by the application of Gauss's law. Similarly, the other values for geometries in Table 3.1 may be obtained by using the single second-partial-derivative term giving the variation of potential with radius for cylindrical and spherical geometries.

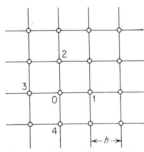

A further insight into the significance of Laplace's equation is found by writing the *difference equation* corresponding to this *differential* equation. This amounts to writing for the derivative dV/dx the ratio of increments $\Delta V/\Delta x$ before Δx goes to a limit zero. Consider that potential is known at the intersections of a rectangular lattice whose spacing h is small, as shown in Fig. 3.5. Then the difference operators corresponding to the partial derivatives about the point 0 are

FIG. 3.5. Net-point notation for computation of potential fields.   See (3.26).

$$\frac{1}{h}(V_0 - V_3) \doteq \frac{\partial V}{\partial x} \doteq \frac{1}{h}(V_1 - V_0) \tag{3.22}$$

$$\frac{1}{h}(V_0 - V_4) \doteq \frac{\partial V}{\partial y} \doteq \frac{1}{h}(V_2 - V_0) \tag{3.23}$$

Similarly, the difference operators corresponding to the second derivatives are

$$\frac{\partial^2 V}{\partial x^2} \doteq \frac{1}{h}[V_1 - V_0 - (V_0 - V_3)] \tag{3.24}$$

$$\frac{\partial^2 V}{\partial y^2} \doteq \frac{1}{h}[V_2 - V_0 - (V_0 - V_4)] \tag{3.25}$$

By adding these two operators and setting equal to zero, as is required to give Laplace's equation in two dimensions, there results

$$V_0 = \tfrac{1}{4}(V_1 + V_2 + V_3 + V_4) \tag{3.26}$$

which states that the potential at any given lattice point is the average of the potentials of the four surrounding lattice points.

The simple relation of (3.26) makes possible the rapid approximate determination of potential in relatively complex problems. The procedure to be used is this:

1. Mark off the region of potential variation with numbered lattice points. These should include points on the electrodes at which the potential is known and fixed.

2. *Assume* values of potential at *all* points.

3. Correct progressively the potential at each point by means of (3.26), using always the most recently corrected values. Do this until corrections bring small changes in previous values.

Application of the above procedure will be found to give successive values at a given point that converge rapidly to a fixed value. Corrections can be imagined to flow from the fixed electrode potentials into the interior points of the network [Shm, Sok]. In Fig. 3.6 is shown the approximate potential configuration in a section of a plane-electrode triode, which was determined by numerical calculation. An important feature of this method is that it shows clearly that if the potential is prescribed completely over a boundary enclosing a region, then there is a unique set of potential values that gives the potential variation within the region.

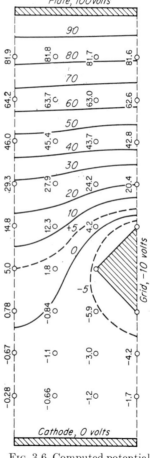

FIG. 3.6. Computed potential field of a triode section.

3.4. Determination of Magnetic Fields.   Electrons and ions in electron devices are frequently controlled or at least influenced by magnetic fields. Before studying the interaction of ions and magnetic fields, it is appropriate to review the laws that determine the shape and strength of magnetic fields.

It was found by Ampère that a wire carrying a current produces a magnetic field. Basically, all magnetic fields are produced by currents. Even permanent magnetism can be considered to be caused by tiny current loops corresponding to electrons circulating about their atoms. The magnetic flux produced by a straight wire carrying current is considered to form closed circular loops about the wire. However, a more basic relation expresses the magnetic field produced by an elementary length of wire carrying current. The relation describing this effect is given with reference to Fig. 3.7. The property involved is that a wire of elemental length dl carrying a current I produces a magnetic field whose strength is proportional to both the current strength and to the length of the wire. In addition the field strength is inversely proportional to the square of the distance to the point where the field is measured and is also proportional to the sine of the angle between the wire and the line joining the elementary length and the point in question. Furthermore, the direction of the field is such that it lies in a plane perpendicular to the direction of the current and is also perpendicular to the plane through the wire and the line joining the element of current and the point where the field is measured. Finally, the direction of magnetic field is that given by the well-known right-hand rule, which says that if the wire carrying current is grasped by the right hand with the thumb in the direction of current, then the fingers will indicate the direction of the magnetic flux lines surrounding the wire. Such lines will be circles, and flux and field have the same direction. All this is shown in Fig. 3.7. Mathematically, the relation is stated as

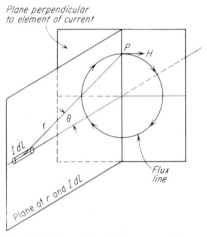

FIG. 3.7. Magnetic field produced by an element of current.   See (3.27).

$$dH = \frac{1}{4\pi} \frac{I \, dl \sin \theta}{r^2} \qquad \text{amp-turns m}^{-1} \qquad (3.27)$$

Here dH is the magnetic field, defined as the force per unit test north magnetic pole, and $1/4\pi$ is the coefficient of proportionality required by rationalized mks units.   The magnetic flux density is simply related to this by the factor μ_0, the permeability of free space:

$$dB = \frac{\mu_0}{4\pi} \frac{I\,dl\sin\theta}{r^2} \qquad \text{webers m}^{-2} \qquad (3.28)$$

This is seen to be similar to the expression for electric field due to a point charge as given in Table 3.1 and is known as the law of Biot and Savart.

Biot and Savart's law is easily applied to give magnetic flux densities for simple current configurations.   For a long straight wire carrying current, this involves an integration of the effects of all the elementary portions of the configuration to get the effect of the whole.   This integration yields

$$B = \frac{\mu_0}{2\pi}\frac{I}{r} \qquad (3.29)$$

where I = current in wire

r = radial distance from wire to point where flux density B is measured

B is perpendicular to the radial line, and the flux lines are circles surrounding the wire as shown in Fig. 3.8.   The principal features here are the direct proportionality to current and the inverse-distance relationship.   It is seen to be similar to the expression for electric field about a linear distribution of charge (cylindrical geometry), as given in Table 3.1.   The magnetic field is, of course, $1/\mu_0$ times this.

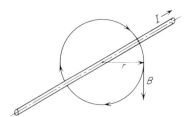

Fig. 3.8. Magnetic field about a long wire carrying current.   See (3.29).

The work done in carrying a unit north magnetic pole about a flux line surrounding the wire is

$$W = \int H\,dl = 2\pi r H = 2\pi r \frac{I}{2\pi r} = I \qquad (3.30)$$

This indicates that the work done in carrying a unit magnetic pole around a closed path is equal to the current enclosed.   This is a particular demonstration of a more general relation, which has the form

$$\oint H\cos\theta\,dl = I \qquad (3.31)$$

Here the small circle on the integral sign indicates that the integration is taken once over a closed path.   This is known as a line integral.   The angle θ is the angle between the magnetic field and the tangent to the path or to the element of length dl.   This relation is often referred to as *Ampère's law*.   It is one of the most useful of the magnetic relations.

It may be used to determine the strength of magnetic field for cases of simple geometries.

Another simple problem for which it is useful to have the answer available is that of the magnetic flux density on the axis of a circular loop of wire, as shown in Fig. 3.9. This is readily found, by application of (3.28), to have the value

$$B = \frac{\mu_0}{2} \frac{Ir^2}{(r^2 + b^2)^{\frac{3}{2}}} \tag{3.32}$$

Here B is in the positive z direction if the current loop lies in xy plane as shown. At the center of the loop, the magnetic flux density reduces to

$$B_0 = \frac{\mu_0}{2} \frac{I}{r} \tag{3.33}$$

Another case frequently referred to and one which may be solved by the application of Ampère's law is the field on the axis of a long solenoid

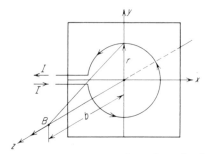

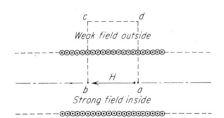

FIG. 3.9. Magnetic field on the axis of a circular conductor carrying current. See (3.32).

FIG. 3.10. Magnetic field on the axis of a long solenoid. See (3.35).

as shown in Fig. 3.10. Here the field inside the solenoid is expected to be very strong and parallel to the axis. At the end of the solenoid the flux will diverge and return by long paths to the other end. Accordingly the field outside will be very weak and in the opposite direction. Let the closed path for the application of (3.31) be that indicated by $abcd$. Let the distance ab and also cd be unity, and let the radial distances bc and ad be r. For the segment ab, cos θ will have a value of unity. The same will be true for the segment cd. For the segments bc and da, cos θ will be 0 because the direction of the path and the direction of the flux are at right angles to each other. Further, let the magnetic field outside the solenoid be considered so weak as to be substantially zero. Then the line integral around the path $abcd$ will be

$$\oint H \cos \theta \, dl = H_0(1)(1) + H(0)r + 0(-1)(1) + H_0(0)r = NI \tag{3.34}$$

or

$$H_0 = NI \quad \text{amp-turns m}^{-1} \tag{3.35}$$

where H_0 = magnetic field on the axis

N = no. of turns *per unit length*

I = current

This serves to demonstrate the reason for the units of H in the rationalized mks units.

For more complex magnetic fields, no simple methods are available. Recourse to the law of Biot and Savart [(3.28)] is frequently required where the field results from a current coil. A useful observation is that flux lines always form closed loops surrounding current. Also, *in regions free of current*, magnetic fields will obey Laplace's equation. This follows from the fact that under these conditions the work done in carrying a unit north magnetic pole around a closed path is zero, analogous to the situation with electrostatic fields, where the work done in carrying a unit positive charge around any closed path is *always* zero, consideration here being restricted to non-time-varying fields. Many times, magnetic fields will be found to resemble electrostatic fields, though sometimes the flux lines and lines of constant work are reversed. Thus in the case of the magnetic field about a long wire carrying current, the magnetic flux lines are circles and lines of constant work are radial lines. In the case of the electrostatic field about a linear distribution of charge, electric flux lines are radial lines while lines of constant work (equipotential lines in this case) are circles about the line charge.

Problems involving iron pole pieces can be solved approximately in a current-flow model or an electrolytic tank. Here the pole pieces are simulated by the electrodes and the current-flow lines correspond to the magnetic flux lines. The equipotential lines in the tank, the measured curves, correspond to lines of constant work. The flux lines may be sketched perpendicular to these. The solution is only approximate here because the permeability of the iron is not infinite (analogous to a conductivity of zero for conductors in the current-flow model). For ordinary cases, the error is negligible. However, in cases where the pole tips are saturated, the permeability may be reduced sufficiently to cause serious error.

3.5. Vector Form of Basic Relations. In the main body of the text, vector notation is used only where necessary because many readers will not have studied vector analysis. However, for the benefit of those readers who are familiar with vector notation, the most important relations of this chapter will be restated in vector form. The boldface quantities represent vectors.

Coulomb's law:

$$\mathbf{F} = \frac{q_1 q_2}{4\pi\varepsilon r^2}\, \mathbf{a}_{12} \tag{3.1}$$

where $\mathbf{a}_{12}$ is a unit vector in the direction 1 to 2.

Relation between force on a charge and electric field:

$$\mathbf{F} = q\mathbf{E} \tag{3.2}$$

Relation between electric field and potential:

$$\mathbf{E} = -\boldsymbol{\nabla} V \tag{3.4}$$

Field due to a point charge:

$$\mathbf{E} = \frac{q}{4\pi\varepsilon r^2}\, \mathbf{a}_{12} \tag{3.5}$$

Relation between electric flux density and field:

$$\mathbf{D} = \varepsilon\mathbf{E} \tag{3.11}$$

Relation between magnetic flux density and mmf:

$$\mathbf{B} = \mu\mathbf{H} \tag{3.12}$$

Gauss's law:

$$\int \mathbf{D} \cdot d\mathbf{A} = \int \boldsymbol{\nabla} \cdot \mathbf{D}\, dv = \int \rho\, dv = q \tag{3.13a}$$

Relation between current density and electric field:

$$\mathbf{J} = g\mathbf{E} \tag{3.14}$$

Law of Biot and Savart:

$$dH = \frac{1}{4\pi} \frac{I\, d\mathbf{l} \times \mathbf{a}_{12}}{r^2} \tag{3.27}$$

where $\mathbf{a}_{12}$ is a unit vector from $d\mathbf{l}$ in the direction of P (Fig. 3.7).

Ampère's law:

$$\int \mathbf{H} \cdot d\mathbf{l} = I \tag{3.30}$$

CHAPTER 4

ION MOTION IN A VACUUM

4.1. Introduction. In this chapter there will be discussed the motion of ions in a vacuum due to simple non-time-varying fields. Since the ion most frequently encountered is the electron, discussion in each section will be centered around the electron, but the behavior of other ions will also be given. In general, the differential equations of motion of an ion are easily written but are easily solved only in simple cases. However, if recourse is had to numerical computation, approximate answers can always be had. Nevertheless, by studying some of the simple cases, one can learn enough to assist in estimating the result for more complicated cases.

The motion of electrons and ions in free space follows classical laws at low velocities. This is to say that everything can be explained starting from Newton's second law of motion. As a result, this subject is relatively simple and understandable since it ties in well with everyday experience. Free space (vacuum) is a relative term, because even in a good man-made vacuum (10^{-7} mm Hg, or 1.3×10^{-10} atm), there are of the order of 3 billion molecules per cubic centimeter. However, even at pressures a thousand times higher, such as are used in gas tubes, the molecules are relatively far apart compared to the dimensions of the electrons and atoms involved. Later, when currents in solids are discussed, it will be found that the distance between electrons may be so small that newtonian mechanics do not hold and that an entirely different set of relations will have to be used. Likewise, at high velocities ($v > c/10$) relativity corrections must be applied.

A knowledge of ion motion in a vacuum is chiefly useful in tube studies. Even here it needs to be supplemented with a knowledge of the effect of other electrons in the electron streams. Such "space-charge effects," as they are called, will be treated in Chaps. 9 and 10. The motion of ions in solids will be discussed in Chaps. 6 and 7.

4.2. Electrons Starting from Rest in a Uniform Field. An electron starting from rest in a uniform field obeys the simple laws of a freely falling body under the influence of gravity in the absence of friction. Here the acceleration is given by

$$F_e = m\frac{d^2x}{dt^2} = +e\frac{dV}{dx} = -eE_x \qquad \text{newtons} \qquad (4.1)$$

where F_e = force of electric origin on an electron

m = electron mass, kg

e = *magnitude* of electron charge, coulombs

V = potential, volts

x = distance, m

E_x = electric intensity, volts m^{-1}

It is important to note that the charge of the electron is $-e$ and that it experiences a force and acceleration in the direction of increasing potential, which is the opposite direction to the electric field since the latter is defined as the force per unit *positive* charge. Equation (4.1) is seen to be the counterpart of the equation for a freely falling body, for which

$$\frac{md^2x}{dt^2} = -mg \qquad (4.2)$$

where the positive x direction is taken as up and g is the gravitational constant. It is seen that the analogue of the gravitational constant is $(e/m)(dV/dx)$.

A first integration of (4.1) gives

$$v = \frac{dx}{dt} = \frac{e}{m}\frac{dV}{dx}t \qquad \text{m sec}^{-1} \qquad (4.3)$$

or a velocity increasing linearly with time, since initial velocity here is assumed zero.

A second integration gives

$$x = \frac{e}{m}\frac{dV}{dx}\frac{t^2}{2} \qquad \text{m} \qquad (4.4)$$

The variation of x and v with time is shown in Fig. 4.1. If time is eliminated between (4.3) and (4.4), there results

$$\frac{mv^2}{2} = \frac{ex\,dV}{dx} = eV \qquad \text{watt-sec} \qquad (4.5)$$

if V is zero when x is zero and increases linearly in the positive x direction. This relates the kinetic energy $mv^2/2$ gained to the potential energy $-eV$ lost. From this,

$$v = 5.93 \times 10^5 \sqrt{V} \qquad \text{m sec}^{-1} \qquad (4.6)$$

which, it must be emphasized, applies only to electrons starting from rest at a point of zero potential. This is analogous to

$$v = \sqrt{2gh} \qquad \text{m sec}^{-1} \qquad (4.7)$$

for the freely falling body. Note that (4.6) applies to *any type* of potential variation, not just to the linear variation with distance.

An alternative convenient form of (4.6) is

$$\frac{v}{c} = \frac{\sqrt{V}}{506} \tag{4.8}$$

where c is the velocity of light. This gives the ratio of the electron velocity to the velocity of light as acquired in falling through a potential V. This expression is accurate to within 1 per cent up to potentials of 20,000 volts. Beyond this value the velocity is reduced by relativity effects, which will be discussed at the end of this chapter.

The behavior of negative ions is the same as that of the electrons except that the velocity acquired and the distance traversed in a given time is reduced by the mass ratio. Likewise the velocity acquired in falling

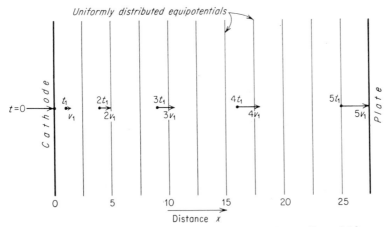

FIG. 4.1. Motion of an electron starting from rest in a uniform field.

through a given potential is reduced by the square root of the mass ratio and increased by the square root of the number of excess electrons, giving

$$v = 5.93 \times 10^5 V^{\frac{1}{2}} \left(\frac{mn}{m_i}\right)^{\frac{1}{2}} \quad \text{m sec}^{-1} \tag{4.9}$$

where m_i = mass of ion
   m = mass of electron
   n = no. of excess electrons on ion
The same formula applies for positive ions, except that the motion is in the opposite direction and n in this case is the integral measure of the electron deficiency. Because of the greater mass of the ions, this formula is valid up to voltages of the order of 1 million volts before relativity effects are detectable.

4.3. Effect of Initial Velocity in a Uniform Electric Field. Injecting an electron at various angles into a uniform electric field gives rise to a parabolic path because there is constant acceleration along the component parallel to the electric field and a constant velocity perpendicular to the field.

A representative problem in this case is that of determining the deflection produced by parallel electrostatic deflecting plates such as are used

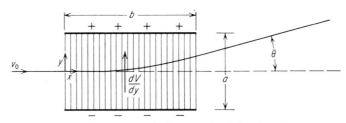

FIG. 4.2. Action of cathode-ray-tube deflecting plates.

in a cathode-ray tube, as shown in Fig. 4.2. The differential equations of motion in this case are

$$m \frac{d^2x}{dt^2} = 0$$
$$m \frac{d^2y}{dt^2} = e \frac{dV}{dy}$$

(4.10)

Initial conditions are conveniently taken as (when $t = 0$)

$$x = 0 \qquad \frac{dx}{dt} = v_0$$
$$y = 0 \qquad \frac{dy}{dt} = 0$$

(4.11)

with the origin of coordinates located on a mid-plane between the deflection plates at the point where the electrons enter the field between the plates. It is also assumed for convenience that the electric field between the plates is free of "fringing" effects; i.e., there is no field outside the plates, and in the region between them, it is uniform and perpendicular to the plates. A first integration of (4.10) and application of (4.11) give

$$\frac{dx}{dt} = v_0$$
$$\frac{dy}{dt} = \frac{e}{m} \frac{dV}{dy} t$$

(4.12)

Thus a constant x component of velocity remains at the initial value because of zero acceleration in this direction. The y component of velocity increases linearly with time because of the constant of acceleration in this direction.

A second integration gives

$$x = v_0 t \qquad y = \frac{1}{2} \frac{e}{m} \frac{dV}{dy} t^2 \qquad (4.13)$$

This action is shown in Fig. 4.3.

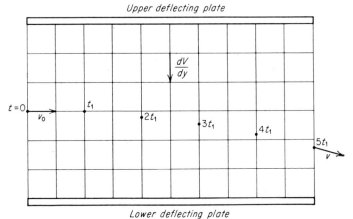

FIG. 4.3. Electron motion between parallel deflecting plates.

At the exit plane of the deflecting plates

$$t_e \cong \frac{b}{v_0} \qquad (4.14)$$

and since

$$\frac{dV}{dy} = \frac{V_d}{a} \qquad (4.15)$$

where V_d is the deflecting potential, the angle of deflection resulting in the exit plane is

$$\tan \theta = \frac{dy/dt}{dx/dt} = \frac{e}{m} \frac{V_d}{a} \frac{b}{v_0} \frac{1}{v_0} \qquad (4.16)$$

from (4.12); and since

$$v_0^2 = 2 \frac{e}{m} V_0 \qquad (4.17)$$

where V_0 is the electron-beam potential relative to the cathode of the cathode-ray tube,

$$\tan \theta = \frac{b}{2a} \frac{V_d}{V_0} \qquad (4.18)$$

The deflection y_s at a screen a distance x_s from the center of the deflecting plates will accordingly be given by

$$y_s = \frac{b}{2a} \frac{V_d}{V_0} x_s \qquad (4.19)$$

The above equations show deflection to be linear with the ratio of deflecting voltage to beam voltage and sensitivity to be proportional to the ratio of plate length to plate spacing.

Examination of the initial differential equations of motion (4.10), which are typical of injection with initial velocity, shows that the motions in the component directions are independent in this case. Accordingly, they may be treated separately and interpreted according to the falling-body action, with final results obtained by parametric combination of component motion.

4.4. Behavior of Electrons in a Uniform Magnetic Field. The behavior of an electron in motion in a magnetic field may be found from a modification of the "motor law" giving the force on a wire carrying a current. An electron in motion with a velocity v behaves like a current of magnitude ev moving in the opposite direction. As such it experiences a force at right angles to the plane of velocity and the magnetic field of magnitude

$$F_m = evB \sin \theta \qquad \text{newtons} \qquad (4.20)$$

where F_m = force of magnetic origin on electron
   e = magnitude of electron charge
   v = velocity
   B = magnetic flux density, webers m^{-2}
   θ = angle between direction of motion and magnetic field

Thus the force is always at right angles to *both* the velocity and to the magnetic field. The sense of the force on *electrons* is given by a *right-hand* rule. Thus if the index finger points in the direction of the magnetic field and the middle finger points in the direction of the electron velocity, then the thumb, held at right angles to the fingers, points in the direction of the force. For a particle with a *positive* charge, a corresponding *left-hand* rule must be used.

The effect of the magnetic force is seen to depend upon the relative magnitude and direction of the velocity and of the magnetic field. Let it first be assumed that the magnetic field is uniform, that the electric potential is uniform, and that an electron is injected at right angles to the magnetic field. Under these conditions the electron will experience a constant sidewise force of magnitude evB since θ in this case is 90°. Such a force causes a progressive change in the direction, but not the magnitude, of velocity, resulting in a curved path. Even though the direction changes, the magnetic force continues to be constant in magnitude and perpendicular to the instantaneous velocity. The curvature of the path adjusts itself until the centrifugal force developed just balances the magnetic force. The only curve that has a constant centrifugal force at a constant velocity is a *circle*. Accordingly a circular path results. For this, equating the centrifugal force and the magnetic force,

$$\frac{mv^2}{r} = evB \qquad (4.21)$$

where r is the radius of the circular path.   Solving for r,

$$r = \frac{mv}{eB} \qquad \text{m (mks units)} \qquad (4.22)$$

Putting this into more convenient units for visualization and expressing the velocity as an equivalent potential, assuming the electron started from rest at a point of zero potential,

$$r_1 = \frac{3.37 V^{\frac{1}{2}}}{B_1} \qquad \text{cm (mixed units)} \qquad (4.23)$$

where V = potential, volts
$\quad B_1$ = magnetic flux density, gauss
Thus a 100-volt electron in a field of only 10 gauss moves with a radius of curvature of 3.37 cm.

Also of interest is the *angular velocity* in this case; from (4.21),

$$\omega_0 = \frac{v}{r} = \frac{eB}{m} \qquad \text{radians sec}^{-1} \text{ (mks units)} \qquad (4.24)$$

This is sometimes known as the *cyclotron* angular frequency, given by

$$f_0 = \frac{\omega_0}{2\pi} = 2.800 B_1 \qquad \text{M (mixed units)} \qquad (4.25)$$

where B_1 is again in gauss for convenience in visualization.   Thus a magnetic field of 1,000 gauss produces a cyclotron frequency of 2,800 Mc, indicating why the magnetron that makes use of this property is such a good generator of microwaves.

It should be noted that the angular frequency of (4.24) is independent of both the velocity and resultant radius but depends only on the magnetic field.   This comes about because by (4.21) radius is directly proportional to velocity.   Thus a high-velocity electron traces out a large-radius circle; and since the time required for this is proportional to velocity divided by circumference, perfect compensation results in constant angular frequency or angular velocity in all cases.   A high-velocity electron traces out a large-radius circle in the same time that a low-velocity electron traces out a small circle.

For ions with n times the charge of an electron, the radius of motion and the cyclotron frequency are

$$r_1 = \frac{3.37}{B_1} \frac{m_i V^{\frac{1}{2}}}{mn} \qquad \text{cm (mixed units)} \qquad (4.26)$$

and

$$f_0 = 2.800 B_1 \frac{nm}{m_i} \qquad \text{Mc (mixed units)} \qquad (4.27)$$

where m = mass of electron

m_i = mass of ion

B_1 = magnetic flux density, gauss

V = potential equivalent of velocity, volts

There are several applications of the circular paths of electrons in uniform magnetic fields. A first application is that of magnetic deflection of cathode-ray beams. In Fig. 4.4 is shown the effect of passing an electron through a region of constant magnetic field such as may be produced by connecting in series two coils in parallel planes on opposite sides of a tube neck. The angle of deflection is given approximately by

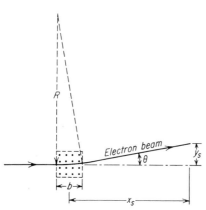

Fig. 4.4. Action of a cathode-ray-tube magnetic deflecting coil.

$$\tan \theta = \frac{b}{R} = \frac{y_s}{x_s} \qquad (4.28)$$

where θ = angle through which beam is rotated

R = radius of curved portion of path

b = axial length of region of uniform magnetic field

y_s = linear beam displacement at a fluorescent screen a distance x_s from deflecting coil

By use of (4.23), the beam deflection is

$$y_s = \frac{x_s b B_1}{3.37 V^{1/2}} \qquad \text{cm} \qquad (4.29)$$

where B_1 = magnetic flux density, gauss

V = beam potential, volts

The deflection is seen to be approximately linear with magnetic flux density.

Another application of this type of motion is found in the Bainbridge mass spectrograph [Inc]. One form of this injects a parallel beam of ions into a region of uniform magnetic field through a velocity selector, as shown in Fig. 4.5. From a source, not shown, ions pass through slits S_1 and S_2 for collimation. They then pass between plates P_1 and P_2 where they are subjected to a constant transverse electric field in the plane of the figure. In this same region there is a uniform magnetic field perpendicular to the plane of the figure into the paper. The polarity of the electric and magnetic fields is such as to produce opposing electric and magnetic deflecting forces to the left and to the right, respectively.

These opposing forces are

$$F_e = Ee \qquad F_m = Bev \qquad (4.30)$$

For ions of a given velocity, namely,

$$v_b = \frac{E}{B} \qquad \text{m sec}^{-1} \qquad (4.31)$$

with electric field E in volts per meter and magnetic flux density in webers per square meter, the electric force F_e and the magnetic force F_m are in balance. This ratio of fields is known as the balance ratio. By virtue of this relation, the plates P_1 and P_2 together with the slits S_2 and S_3 act as a *velocity sorter*, permitting only ions in a small range of velocities to pass, *regardless of their mass.* Ions with velocities higher than that determined by the balance ratio [(4.31)] will experience a magnetic deflecting force greater than the electric force and be deflected to the right. The ions that pass the slits move into a region of uniform magnetic field perpendicular to the paper, where they are deflected to describe semi-

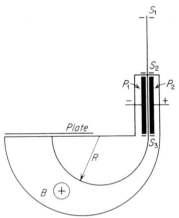

FIG. 4.5. Schematic diagram of a mass spectrograph (Bainbridge).

circular paths with radius proportional to mass in accordance with (4.26). The radius is proportional to mass, and hence markings on a photographic plate have a linear mass scale. Figure 4.6 shows a mass

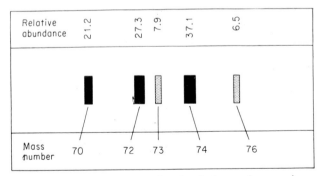

FIG. 4.6. Mass spectrogram, showing isotopes of germanium.

spectrogram of germanium, revealing the relative amounts of the isotopes of mass numbers 70, 72, 73, 74, and 76. Such devices can separate mass numbers differing by a few tenths of a per cent and are extensively used in chemical analysis.

The same device usually has provision for electrical observation of mass components.   For this, the photographic plate is replaced by a slit with a collector electrode behind it.   Amplified collector current may then be observed as a function of magnetic field to get a rapid indication of relative numbers of ions of different masses.   The part of the mass spectrograph after the velocity sorter thus acts as a *mass sorter*.

4.5. Electrons in Combined Electric and Magnetic Fields.   When an electron is subjected to the combined action of both electric and magnetic fields, the path may become quite complex.   Some cases are, however, quite simple and give a clue to the understanding of the more complex instances.   There has already been mentioned in the last section the most simple case, namely, that of an electron injected into a region of transverse electric and magnetic fields at right angles to each other and to

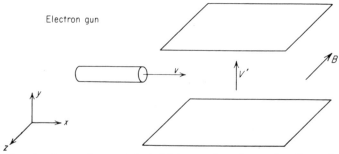

Fig. 4.7. Notation for an electron injected into a region of crossed uniform electric and magnetic fields.

the initial velocity, as encountered in the velocity sorter of the mass spectrograph.   Here the net deflection can be made zero, positive, or negative.   Actually, a modified form of this balanced-deflection scheme was originally used by Thomson to measure the ratio of charge to mass of the electron [Thz].

A better illustration of the behavior of an electron in combined electric and magnetic fields is found by studying the effect of variations of injected velocity for the same case, namely, an electron shot into a region where it encounters crossed uniform electric and magnetic fields, as shown in Fig. 4.7.   Here the electron encounters a fixed force upward due to electric field and a force downward dependent upon its velocity and the magnetic field.   It may also experience force forward due to a downward-component velocity and the magnetic field.   The differential equations for the subsequent motion may be written simply as

$$\frac{d^2x}{dt^2} = \omega_0 \frac{dy}{dt} \tag{4.32}$$

$$\frac{d^2y}{dt^2} = \zeta V' - \omega_0 \frac{dx}{dt} \tag{4.33}$$

where ω_0 = cyclotron angular frequency eB/m
$\qquad V'$ = gradient of potential
$\qquad \zeta$ = ratio of charge to mass of electron e/m

The first of these equations indicates forward acceleration dependent upon the transverse magnetic field and any upward velocity acquired. The second of these gives upward force due to the electric field and downward force due to the reaction of the forward velocity and the transverse magnetic field.

Simple physical reasoning indicates that as the electron enters the field it acquires a downward component of velocity due to the forward component of velocity and the transverse magnetic field. Actually, this force will be downward only if the initial velocity is greater than that at which the electric and magnetic forces balance. The result of the downward component of velocity and the transverse magnetic field produces a backward component of force that may be sufficient to cause the electron to turn a loop. If the initial velocity is less than that for which the electric and magnetic forces are in balance, the electron will experience an upward force, which, in turn, gives a forward acceleration. The result here is an undulating forward progression. If it is assumed that the initial conditions are (when $t = 0$)

$$x = 0 \qquad y = 0$$
$$\frac{dx}{dt} = av_b \qquad \frac{dy}{dt} = 0 \qquad\qquad (4.34)$$

where v_b = balance velocity of (4.31) equal to $-V'/B$
$\qquad a$ = fraction that dx/dt is of this value

then the solution for any value of a may be expressed simply as

$$x = v_b t - R \sin \omega_0 t$$
$$y = R(1 - \cos \omega_0 t)$$
$$R = \frac{v_b}{\omega_0}(1 - a) \qquad\qquad (4.35)$$

These equations show a forward motion at the balance velocity with a superimposed circular motion at an angular frequency ω_0 and a radius dependent upon the initial velocity relative to the balance velocity. Some representative resultant motions are shown in Fig. 4.8. The motion is in all cases that of a point on the spoke of a rolling wheel whose hub is moving forward at the balance velocity. The lowest curve is for zero injected velocity, $a = 0$. The resultant curve is a cycloid corresponding to a generating point on the rim of the rolling wheel. The second curve is for $a = \frac{1}{2}$ and yields a nearly sinusoidal path for the generating point at the mid-point of the spoke of the generating wheel. The third curve, for $a = 1$, is for an electron injected at the balance velocity and yields a straight line corresponding to a generating point at the hub of the rolling wheel.

For larger values of a, R becomes negative, corresponding to a generating point on an upper spoke. The radial distance to the generating point may now become greater than the radius of the rolling wheel. Such a case is shown in the fourth curve for a value of $a = 2.5$, for which the electron turns a loop giving rise to what is called a trochoidal path. Such gyrations are fairly typical of the motions encountered with combined electric and magnetic field.

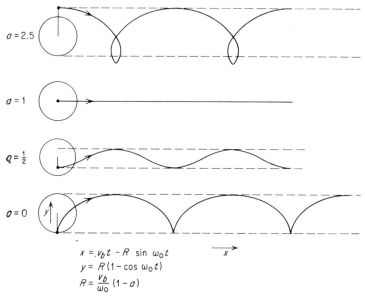

$$x = v_b t - R \sin \omega_0 t$$
$$y = R(1 - \cos \omega_0 t)$$
$$R = \frac{v_b}{\omega_0}(1 - a)$$

Fig. 4.8. Representative possible paths of an electron injected into crossed uniform electric and magnetic fields.

An important observation in connection with combined electric and magnetic fields arises from the fact that the magnetic force is always perpendicular to the instantaneous direction of motion. Accordingly, magnetic forces can do no work on the electron, and there is no energy gained or lost through such forces. As a result, the same energy equation which applied for electric fields alone [(4.5)] also applies to combined fields. In the example just discussed, the velocity of the electron varies from point to point, but it is always related to the electric potential at that point by (4.6) if the electron started from rest at a point of zero potential. Such a relation gives only the magnitude of the velocity but *cannot* give the direction.

4.6. Electrons in Nonuniform Electric Fields. Electrons in nonuniform electric fields may trace out rather complex paths. The differential equations for this case are easy to state but not easy to solve. They are

$$\frac{d^2x}{dt^2} = \frac{e}{m}\frac{\partial V}{\partial x} \qquad \frac{d^2y}{dt^2} = \frac{e}{m}\frac{\partial V}{\partial y} \qquad (4.36)$$

These equations look deceptively simple, but there are only a few nonuniform problems that can be solved with them.

One of the few problems of this kind that can be solved is that of an electron starting from rest at a point near an inside right-angled corner that has an outward gradient of potential due to a remote, more positive

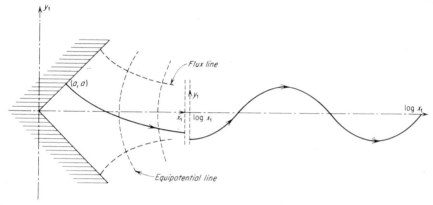

FIG. 4.9. Path of an electron emitted from a right-angled corner.

electrode, as shown in Fig. 4.9. The equations for the field in this case are simply

$$\frac{\partial V}{\partial x} = bx \qquad \frac{\partial V}{\partial x} = -by \qquad (4.37)$$

For an electron released at the point (a,a) the resultant motion is given by

$$x = a \cosh \frac{e}{m} bt$$

$$y = a \cos \frac{e}{m} bt \qquad (4.38)$$

This is a parametric representation of a path which moves to the right with increasing velocity and oscillates about the line of symmetry. An important observation here is that the electron does *not* follow a flux line but overshoots because of its finite mass. A mechanical analogue of this problem would be that of a ball rolling down a curved trough.

In most cases of nonuniform fields, the equations of motion are too difficult to solve because potential varies from point to point. However, some general observations can be made that are very helpful. At any instant, the centrifugal force due to the curvature of the trajectory at that point is in balance with a sidewise component of electric force, as shown in Fig. 4.10.   This may be written

$$\frac{mv^2}{R} = \frac{2eV}{R} = eV'_n \tag{4.39}$$

where R is the instantaneous radius of curvature.   The equivalence of the first two terms results from the energy equation, assuming the electron starts from rest at point of zero potential. V'_n is the component of

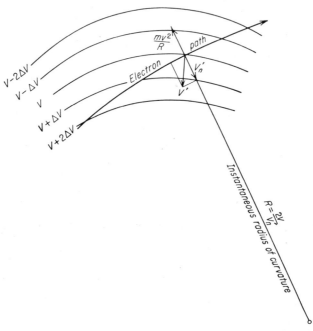

Fig. 4.10. Determination of the instantaneous radius of curvature of an electron path.

gradient normal to the path.   Solving for the instantaneous radius of curvature gives

$$R = \frac{2V}{V'_n} \tag{4.40}$$

This equation may be used for point-by-point numerical computation of electron paths [San].   More important, however, are some general observations that can be made about electron paths from this equation.   The observations are:

1. The shape of the path is independent of the charge and mass of the particle.   A negative ion would trace out the same path as an electron; however, it would take more time to do it because of its greater mass.

2. The shape of the path is independent of the magnitude of potential. Uniformly increasing the potential of a set of electrodes raises the potential and the gradient at any point in the same proportion and so does not affect the radius of curvature. This important property gives current ratios and focusing properties dependent only on voltage ratios.

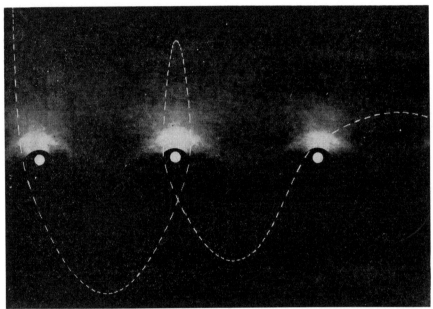

FIG. 4.11. Photograph of an electron path made with an elastic-membrane model. (*Courtesy of J. H. L. Jonker.*)

3. If the structure is enlarged by a given factor, the electron path is enlarged by the same factor. This is the basis of scaling used in designing similar tubes of different sizes and also the basis for certain kinds of model studies.

Reference to the example of the electron emitted from a point near an inside corner, as shown in Fig. 4.9, and examination of (4.38) show that all the properties enumerated above are observed, as indeed they must. Transit time must be determined from other considerations. Reference to Newton's second law of motion shows transit time squared to be proportional to particle mass and distance traveled and inversely proportional to charge and gradient of potential.

Another means of estimating electron paths in complex electric fields is by means of a mechanical model. It has been found that if an elastic membrane, such as a rubber sheet, is stretched over blocks shaped like electrodes with their height above a reference plane proportional to relative negative potential, then the sheet assumes a shape such that the elevation at every point above the reference plane is proportional to the negative potential at the point. This is to say that the sheet solves approximately Laplace's equation [Kln, Spc]. This works only for two-dimensional problems which can be expressed in rectangular coordinates and in which the charge density of the electrons is small. Thus the membrane model of a negative-grid triode would consist of a cathode block, cylinders pushed up into the membrane from below to represent negative grids, and a plate block pushed down from above to represent a

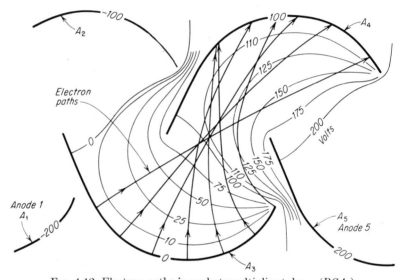

FIG. 4.12. Electron paths in a photomultiplier tube.   (RCA.)

positive plate. Electrons that normally move in the direction of positive potential would roll downhill on such a model of negative potential. The electrons are simulated by little spheres—commonly ball bearings. These are found to trace out paths that correspond closely to electron paths in the actual problem. Shown in Fig. 4.11 is an electron path obtained by photographing with a stroboscopic light source a small sphere in motion on a rubber sheet stretched to represent a positive-grid triode [Jof]. It is seen that the method is capable of giving considerable detail. This model has also been extensively used to obtain optimum electrode shapes in the secondary-electron multiplier, shown in Fig. 4.12 [Joj].

4.7. Electrons in Nonuniform Magnetic Fields. Such electron paths tend to become quite complex so that it is possible to make only general observations. A first observation relates to the direction of the forces developed. Because of the basic force law of (4.20), an x component of magnetic field and a y component of velocity will develop a z component of force.   Similarly a y component of magnetic field and an x component of velocity will develop a $-z$ component of force.   The second observation is that since the force and the motion are at right angles to each other, no energy is gained or lost as a result of the action of the magnetic forces alone.   A third observation relates to the fact that an electron in a uniform magnetic field moves in a circular path; or if it has an initial component of velocity parallel to the magnetic field, it will move in a helical path spiraling around a flux line.   Now if the radius of the helix is relatively small, the electron will move in a tightly wound spiral about a flux line [Spc].   This is most frequently encountered with low-velocity electrons in relatively strong fields.   This property is used in electron focusing, as, for instance, in the traveling-wave tube.   It is also used in a type of orthicon television-camera tube.

In cases where both the magnetic and electric field are nonuniform, it is again true that no energy is gained or lost as a result of the action of the magnetic field.   Accordingly, the energy equation is the same as for electric fields alone, namely, (4.5).

4.8. Relativity Effects in Electron Motion.   It has been shown previously that electron velocity increases as the square root of potential. This is true up to velocities of about one-tenth the velocity of light, which is attained at about 2,600 volts.   Beyond this value of potential the velocity increases less rapidly.   This comes about because one of the fundamental postulates of the theory of relativity is that no object can acquire speeds greater than the velocity of light.   If this is to be true, then the mass of a particle must increase as it is accelerated, for otherwise a constant accelerating force would in time bring it to velocities greater than that of light.   This is consistent with another postulate of relativity, namely, that mass is a manifestation of energy.   When a particle is accelerated, it acquires kinetic energy, which manifests itself as an increase in mass.

If the velocity law of an electron is worked out in accordance with the assumptions given above, it is found to be

$$\frac{v}{c} = \sqrt{1 - \frac{1}{[1 + 1.965(MV)]^2}} \tag{4.41}$$

where (MV) = potential through which electron has been accelerated, megavolts

   c = velocity of light

Like (4.8) this ratio increases for low values of potential, i.e., follows the square-root law, but becomes asymptotic to unity at high values of potential.   A curve of velocity as a function of potential is shown in Fig. 4.13.   If the mass of the electron did not increase with potential the electron would reach the velocity of light at a potential of about 255,000 volts.   Actually, the value of v/c will be 0.745 at this potential.

The corresponding increase in the mass of the electron is given by

$$\frac{m}{m_0} = \left(1 - \frac{v^2}{c^2}\right)^{-\frac{1}{2}} \tag{4.42}$$

where m = actual mass of electron as a function of velocity

m_0 = mass at zero velocity, or so-called rest mass

This relation is more clearly understood if the mass ratio is expressed in terms of the potential through which the electron has been accelerated,

$$m = m_0[1 + 1.965(\text{MV})] \tag{4.43}$$

(A derivation of the above relations is given in Appendix 1.)   Here it is seen that the mass of an electron is doubled at about 500,000 volts and

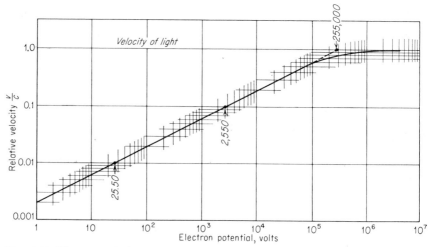

Fig. 4.13. Electron velocity as a function of accelerating potential, showing relativity effect.

tripled at 1 million volts.   A billion-volt electron has roughly the mass of a proton.   It has been suggested that some of the modern electron accelerators be called "imponderators" instead of "accelerators" because after the first million volts the velocity is increased very little and the principal change is an increase in mass.

In most electron-tube applications the relativity effects are small enough to be neglected.   Thus at 5,000 volts the mass of an electron has increased only 1 per cent.   However, some modern high-power tubes are now operating with voltages as high as several hundred thousand volts. For such tubes the departures from the low-velocity relations must be considered.

4.9. Vector Form of Basic Relations.   In this section there will be given in vector form the principal relations of this chapter for the benefit of those readers who have studied vector analysis.   In addition, there are given some equations in coordinate form for the commonest coordinate systems.

Force on an electron in an electric field:

$$\mathbf{F}_e = m\mathbf{a} = -e\mathbf{E} \tag{4.1}$$

Force on an electron in a magnetic field:

$$\mathbf{F}_m = m\mathbf{a} = e\mathbf{B} \times \mathbf{v} \tag{4.20}$$

Force due to combined electric and magnetic fields:

$$\mathbf{F} = m\mathbf{a} = e\mathbf{E} + e\mathbf{B} \times \mathbf{v} \tag{4.44}$$

Force due to combined electric and magnetic fields in rectangular coordinates:

$$
\begin{aligned}
m\ddot{x} &= e(-E_x + B_y \dot{z} - B_z \dot{y}) \\
m\ddot{y} &= e(-E_y + B_z \dot{x} - B_x \dot{z}) \\
m\ddot{z} &= e(-E_z + B_x \dot{y} - B_y \dot{x})
\end{aligned}
\tag{4.45}
$$

Force due to combined electric and magnetic fields in cylindrical coordinates:

$$
\begin{aligned}
m(\ddot{r} - r\dot{\theta}^2) &= e(-E_r + B_\theta \dot{z} - B_z r\dot{\theta}) \\
m\frac{1}{r}\frac{d}{dt}(r^2\dot{\theta}) &= e(-E_\theta + B_z \dot{r} - B_r \dot{z}) \\
m\ddot{z} &= e(-E_z + B_r r\dot{\theta} - B_\theta \dot{r})
\end{aligned}
\tag{4.46}
$$

where

$$
\begin{aligned}
E_r &= -\frac{\partial V}{\partial r} \\
E_\theta &= -\frac{1}{r}\frac{\partial V}{\partial \theta} \\
E_z &= -\frac{\partial V}{\partial z}
\end{aligned}
\tag{4.47}
$$

CHAPTER 5

THE ATOM

5.1. The Evidence for Atoms. The first ideas about atoms were given by Democritus in the fourth century B.C. Reasoning correctly from observations on the wearing of rocks and the evaporation of liquids, he stated that all materials were composed of small particles, each having the same physical characteristics as the parent material. He originated the word "atom," which comes from the Greek word meaning "indivisible." He did not, however, distinguish properly between atoms and molecules. It remained for chemical developments in the nineteenth century to show that there were certain materials called "elements" which could not be further decomposed. The elements, in turn, could be combined in various ways to give different "compounds." The smallest particles of the compounds preserving the characteristics of the compounds are called "molecules," and the smallest particles of the elements preserving the characteristics of the elements are called "atoms."[1]

Most molecules and atoms are too small to see by any means, including the most powerful microscopes. However, evidence of their existence is indirectly visible. It is possible with a high-power microscope to observe a continuous irregular motion of small particles. Such motion is called "Brownian motion." It is now known to be caused by the impact of invisible molecules upon visible aggregates of molecules. The energy of the agitation comes from thermal energy, which is known to give molecules a random motion in all directions.

A second evidence of atomic structure is observed in the behavior of oil films on water. A drop of oil will spread over a considerable area of water. In doing so, it will produce a film so thin that colors may be seen because of selective reinforcement of light of certain wavelengths from the two sides of the film. This indicates that the film is an integral number of half wavelengths thick for the color observed. If the effort is made to cause the film to cover a large area it will break up into patches. The interpretation of this is that the film spreads out until it is a layer just one molecule thick and that the thickness then gives the average diameter of the molecules.

Recent work with electron microscopes has produced pictures of some

[1] General references: [Hud, RiE, SlA].

large molecules. Figure 5.1 shows such a picture of the ball molecules of the poliomyelitis virus. It is also possible to superimpose X-ray diffraction patterns in such a way as to obtain pictures showing the arrangement of atoms in a crystal; such pictures may be considered as pictures of the atoms themselves!

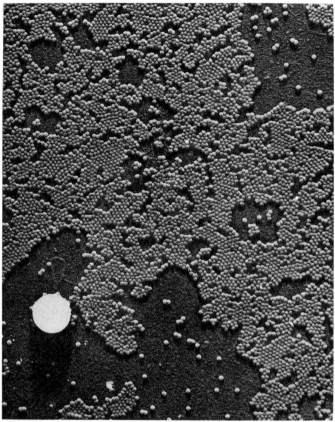

FIG. 5.1. Electron-microscope picture of the ball molecules of the poliomyelitis virus. The large sphere is a particle of polystyrene latex 0.25 μ in diameter for reference size. (*University of California, Virus Laboratory.*)

However, the development of a complete theory explaining the structure and physical properties of atoms has taken a long time. By now, the picture is fairly complete. It is the purpose of this chapter to summarize this development for the benefit of readers who are not familiar with it.

5.2. Early Theories of the Atom. Early investigators knew from chemical experiments that there are atoms and molecules. Electrons were first observed in low-pressure electric discharges. It was surmised that atoms contained electrons because the electrons came from atoms and recombined with atoms to give electrically neutral materials. J. J. Thomson identified and measured the ratio of charge to mass of electrons in cathode rays. He did the same for hydrogen ions and found that their mass was roughly 2,000 times the mass of the electron. Also early in the century the number of electrons in the atoms of the various elements was estimated by Moseley from X-ray scattering [RiE]. Here it was assumed that X rays set the electrons into motion, which motion gave rise to a secondary radiation whose characteristics depended upon the number of nuclear protons. The generation of X rays in turn was explained by saying that high-energy electrons had been rapidly decelerated and in doing so gave rise to radiation. Thus it was known that atoms contained electrons and, since atoms are usually electrically neutral, also contained positive charge. Furthermore, the mass of the positively charged material was apparently much greater than that of the electrons.

Thomson proposed the idea of an atom consisting of a large mass of positively charged material having smaller negative electrons embedded in it, assuming quite naturally that since the positively charged material had the greater mass, it also had the greater volume.

In 1911 Rutherford observed the scattering of α particles on passing through a thin foil of metal. The α particles were obtained as continuous spontaneous emission from radioactive materials. They were known to have a positive charge twice that of the electron and a mass nearly equal to that of helium. They were, therefore, correctly assumed to be helium atoms that had lost two electrons. Rutherford's experiment showed diffraction patterns with many more α particles being deflected through large angles than could be explained on the basis of the atom model proposed by Thomson. Accordingly, Rutherford was led to conclude that the positively charged material was concentrated in a much smaller volume than had been previously supposed. This volume was so small that it was referred to as the nucleus and the electrons were supposed to exist outside it. The charge of the nucleus was taken to be the same as the total electron charge but positive. However, the mass of the nucleus —virtually the entire mass of the atom—was found to be greater than could be accounted for by assuming one hydrogen nucleus for each electron. It was not until considerably later that the composition of the nucleus in terms of protons and neutrons was established. Nevertheless, the scattering theory based on the Rutherford model was so successful that it was adopted in spite of serious objections. In Fig. 5.2 are shown schematically the Thomson and Rutherford atom models. Also shown is the Bohr atom model, to be discussed later.

The Rutherford theory could say nothing about the location or movement of the electrons about the nucleus. In fact, there was no good way to explain how an electron could remain in equilibrium about a nucleus. If it were assumed to be in rotation in some orbit, as a planet about the sun, then classical theory would lead to an expected loss of energy through radiation, which would cause it to slow down and finally fall into the nucleus as a result of the Coulomb attraction between the negatively charged electron and the positively charged nucleus.

Another limitation of the Rutherford theory was that it gave no explanation of observed spectrographic effects: It has long been observed that when the light given off by the ionized vapor of an element was spread out with a prism or, better yet, with a grating of fine, closely spaced parallel lines, there was obtained not a continuous spectrum but a discontinuous one that could be resolved into one or more series of lines.

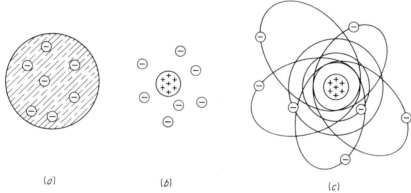

(a)   (b)   (c)

FIG. 5.2. The atom models of (a) Thomson, (b) Rutherford, and (c) Bohr.

Such spectra were different from element to element but always the same for a given element. As early as 1885, Balmer found an empirical formula which gave a relation between the then known lines of the hydrogen spectrum. His formula was of the form

$$\lambda = 3{,}645.6 \, \frac{n^2}{n^2 - 4} \qquad A \qquad (5.1)$$

where n is an integer that assumes values of 3, 4, 5, 6, . . . to give the wavelength λ of the different lines of the spectrum in a unit of length called the "angstrom," where $1 \, A = 10^{-10}$ m.[1] Rydberg carried experimental work further and found a universal formula for line wavelengths of all spectra, of the form

$$\frac{1}{\lambda} = \frac{1}{\lambda_1} - \frac{R}{m^2} \qquad m^{-1} \qquad (5.2)$$

[1] Other units of length commonly used in spectrography are the micron ($1 \, \mu = 10^{-6}$ m), the millimicron ($1 \, m\mu = 10^{-9}$ m), and for X rays the X unit ($1 \, X.U. = 10^{-13}$ m).

where λ_1 = long limit of wavelength of the series
R = a universal constant, later known as the "Rydberg constant," 1.0974×10^7 m^{-1}

m assumes integral values.

With such obvious order in the line spectra, it seemed that any theory of atomic structure should be capable of being correlated with formulas such as the above. No such correlation was, however, forthcoming.

This is where matters stood until Bohr proposed the application of quantum theory to give a new atom model. This model explained almost perfectly the behavior of the hydrogen atom. This involved a sharp break with classical ideas. Before we can discuss the Bohr model of the atom it is desirable to review the basic elements of the quantum theory, whose application made the model possible.

5.3. The Quantum Theory. The quantum theory came into being at the beginning of the present century as a result of efforts to explain the thermal-radiation laws of hot bodies. In order to make the theory fit the observed facts, it was necessary to assume that energy is not transmitted continuously but rather in small packets known as quanta. Novel as this idea may seem on first contact, it is quite consistent with our other ideas of the physical world. To the human observer, large-scale phenomena seem continuous. However, it was realized early that matter was not continuous but was made of atoms. Likewise, electric charge was apparently not continuous but carried in small units on small particles called electrons. The idea of the discontinuity of energy proved to be the key that led to the solution of the problem of atomic structure.

Experiments with thermal radiation are conveniently referred to ideal radiators known as "black bodies." A black body is a perfect radiator, i.e., its emissive power measured in watts per unit area at a given temperature or wavelength is the maximum possible. By the same token, its absorption coefficient or ratio of absorbed to incident radiation is unity. No such body occurs naturally in nature, although black velvet and lamp black are almost perfect absorbers and radiators. Experimentally, a nearly perfect approximation to a black body can be made by viewing through an aperture an enclosure heated to a uniform temperature. Such an enclosure will absorb practically all incident radiation by virtue of multiple internal reflections. In the same manner, the enclosure will radiate a maximum value through the aperture.

Reference has already been made to thermal and electromagnetic radiation. At this point it is important to be sure that the concept of radiation and its basic characteristics are well understood. When Hertz verified Maxwell's theoretical deduction that the velocity of radio waves was the velocity of light, it was shown that visible and electromagnetic radiation were the same phenomena. The electromagnetic spectrum runs from very-low-frequency radio waves through ultrahigh-frequency

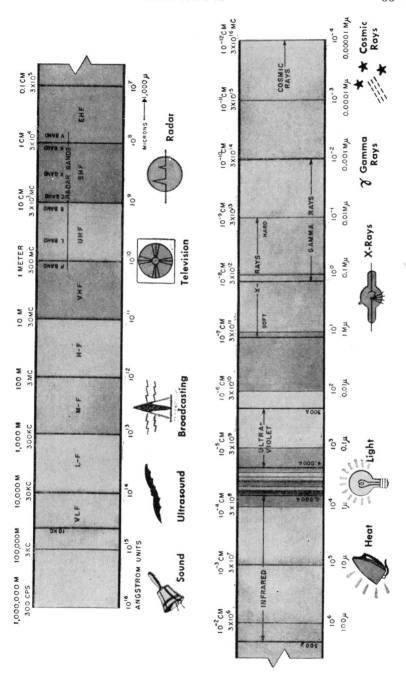

Fig. 5.3. The electromagnetic spectrum.

waves. It does not stop there. Raising the frequency still further leads to the region of heat waves, after which the visible spectrum occurs, to be followed by X rays. The visible spectrum, sandwiched between invisible low-frequency infrared heat waves and equally invisible high-frequency ultraviolet waves, is but a small part of the entire spectrum. In Fig. 5.3 is shown a pictorial representation of the electromagnetic spectrum.

The physical evidence of electromagnetic waves, whether they be radio, thermal, or visible, is different for each part of the spectrum. All, however, have in common a constant velocity, in free space equal to the velocity of light. Likewise, all may be described in terms of either a frequency f or a wavelength λ. The frequency is the number of times per second that the intensity of the wave reaches a maximum of a given polarity. This is given as a certain number of *cycles* per second. The wavelength is the distance in space that the wave advances in 1 cycle. The frequency may also be taken as the number of wavelengths that the wave advances in 1 sec. As a result of these relations, the product of frequency and wavelength is equal to the wave velocity in appropriate units. Thus

$$c = \lambda f = 3 \times 10^8 \text{ m sec}^{-1} \tag{5.3}$$

where c = velocity of light in free space
λ = wavelength, m
f = frequency, cycles sec^{-1}
The velocity of light c in rationalized mks units is given by [as previously given in (2.6)]

$$c = \frac{1}{\sqrt{\mu_0 \varepsilon_0}} \tag{5.4}$$

where μ_0 = permeability of free space, 1.257×10^{-6} henry m^{-1}
ε_0 = dielectric constant of free space, 8.854×10^{-12} farad m^{-1}
One of the first observations made on the radiation of black bodies was that the total energy radiated per second was proportional to the absolute temperature to the fourth power. Thus

$$w = \sigma T^4 \qquad \text{watts cm}^{-2} \tag{5.5}$$

where σ is the Stefan-Boltzmann constant of value 5.673×10^{-12} watt cm^{-2} °K^{-4} (273 + °C). This relation is known as the Stefan-Boltzmann law [RiE]. It was possible to derive this law without recourse to quantum ideas by classical thermodynamics. A curve showing the power radiated per square centimeter by a black body as a function of temperature is given in Fig. 5.4. The radiation of bodies other than a black body is given by (5.5) multiplied by a coefficient of thermal emissivity, which is always less than unity and commonly is of the order of one-tenth to one-half.   Reference to Fig. 5.4 shows that the total power radiation varies rapidly with temperature.   Usually bodies must be heated to near incandescence before energy loss by radiation is greater than by other means, such as conduction.

The energy radiated by a black body at a given temperature is not uniformly distributed over the frequency spectrum.   There is a peak in

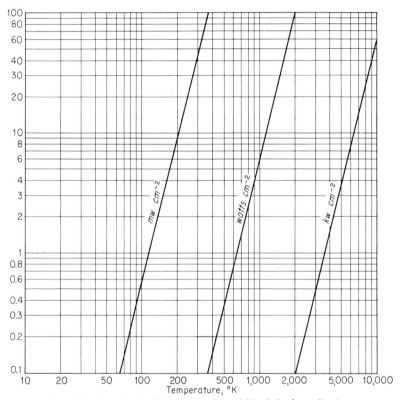

Fig. 5.4. The Stefan-Boltzmann law of black-body radiation.

the energy distribution that moves to higher frequencies or shorter wavelengths as the temperature increases.   Thus bodies just barely incandescent glow a dull red, but as the temperature increases, the color becomes yellow.   A family of curves showing the energy radiated by a black body as a function of wavelength for various temperatures is shown in Fig. 5.5.   Wien found that this action was partially described by the fact that the product of the wavelength for maximum radiation and the corresponding temperature is a constant:

$$\lambda_m T = A = \text{const} \tag{5.6}$$

This is a deduction from a more general law, which stated that the energy radiated at any wavelength was inversely proportional to the fifth power of wavelength multiplied by a function of the product of wavelength and temperature

$$\mathcal{E}_\lambda = \frac{1}{\lambda^5} F(\lambda T) \qquad \text{watts cm}^{-2} \text{ sec}^{-1} \text{ (unit wavelength)}^{-1} \qquad (5.7)$$

which is known as the *Wien displacement law*. Here $\mathcal{E}_\lambda$ is the energy radiated per square centimeter per second in a constant band of wavelength $d\lambda$, and T is the absolute temperature. Various attempts were

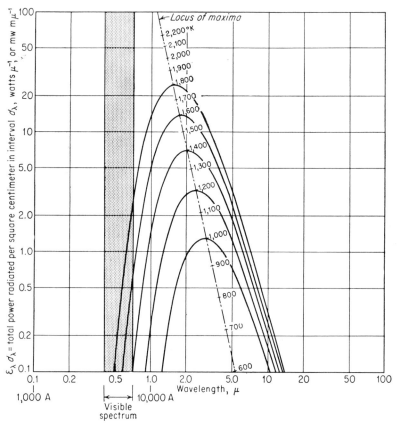

FIG. 5.5. Spectral distribution of energy in black-body radiation: $\lambda_m T = 0.2884$ cm-°K; $\mathcal{E}_\lambda = (1/\lambda^5)F(\lambda T) = a\lambda^{-5}/(e^{b/\lambda T} - 1)$, where $a = 3.703 \times 10^{-12}$ watt cm^{-2}, $b = 1.433$ cm-°K, $\lambda = $ wavelength, cm.

made to find the function $F(\lambda T)$ reasoning from classical thermodynamics. One such effort, known as the Raleigh-Jeans formula, led to the expectation that $F(\lambda T)$ was a constant times temperature or that the radiation was proportional to temperature and inversely proportional to wavelength to the fifth power. This fitted observations at long wavelengths but obviously failed at short wavelengths, where it predicted radiation increasing as the fifth power of frequency, an effect sometimes referred to as "ultraviolet catastrophe." As a result, the Wien displacement law represented the limit of success of classical thermodynamics.

Planck found an empirical formula fitting the facts of thermal radiation, of the form

$$\mathcal{E}_\lambda = \frac{a\lambda^{-5}}{\epsilon^{b/\lambda T} - 1} \tag{5.8}$$

where a and b are constants. The constant $a = 3.703 \times 10^{-12}$ watt cm^{-2} and $b = 1.433$ cm-°K [Foq]. This is consistent with the Wien displacement law. Later, in an effort to develop a theory which would fit this formula, Planck considered the radiation to be due to an ensemble of electric oscillators. However, to make the theory fit the facts, he had to postulate that the different oscillators had energy levels that were integral multiples of a fundamental unit of energy. Furthermore, the fundamental unit of energy had to be proportional to frequency. Thus

$$\mathcal{E} = nh\nu \tag{5.9}$$

where n = a positive integer

h = Planck's constant, 6.610×10^{-27} erg-sec, or 6.610×10^{-34} watt-sec^2

ν = frequency, cycles sec^{-1}

The symbol ν is used here instead of the symbol f because it is universally used in connection with this subject by physicists. Thus each little oscillator could have energy levels of 0, $h\nu$, $2h\nu$, $3h\nu$, . . . , but it could not have intermediate values, such as $0.333h\nu$. Furthermore, radiation and absorption were assumed to take place as a result of transitions, or jumps, between these energy levels, the energy gained or lost being an integral multiple of $h\nu$.

The assumptions of Planck involved quite a departure from classical ideas. Up to this time it had always been considered that energy was continuous. It should be pointed out that Planck did not present any logical demonstration that this was not the case but simply that the observed facts indicated that energy was discontinuous.

At first the evidence in support of Planck's theory was meager. The principal evidence was that his theory gave a formula that fitted observations on thermal radiation better than any other. However, as time went on, more supporting evidence for the validity of his theory was developed. A few years later, Einstein was able to explain an important and baffling aspect of the photoelectric effect by applying Planck's theory. This will be discussed in some detail in Chap. 17, Photoelectric Devices, but only qualitatively here.

Experiments with photoelectric emission showed that light falling upon certain specially prepared surfaces in vacuum gave rise to electron emission. It was presumed that the electromagnetic energy was somehow transferred to electrons in the metal in a way that gave them enough extra energy to escape from the surface. The baffling aspect of the effect was that for each surface the maximum energy of the electrons emitted decreased linearly with the frequency of the incident exciting light, down to an "extinction frequency" beyond which no amount of light, however large, would produce emission. Further, the slope of the linear relation between maximum energy and frequency was the same for all materials. Einstein proposed a theory that made use of Planck's theory and explained this effect: He considered that the light consisted of little packets of energy of size $h\nu$. Not only was the energy quantized in amount but also apparently localized in space. He thus proposed what was actually a corpuscular theory of light. Each little package of light was called a "photon," and each was considered capable of reacting individually with an electron in the metal. Thus each photon could impart an energy $h\nu$ to an electron in the metal. A fixed minimum amount of this energy would be used up in escaping from the metal, leaving an amount linear with frequency. Thus the quantum theory, applied to electromagnetic radiation, explained the photoelectric effect. It should be pointed out that this same theory could not explain all optical phenomena, such as, for instance, interference of light rays, which was easily explained on a wave-theory basis. It was not until later that the duality of the wave and mechanical aspects of all energy was demonstrated.

The Einstein theory of photoemission served to confirm the quantum theory of Planck. However, the most striking confirmation was given by Bohr, who applied it to produce an atom model that explained the line structure of atomic spectra.

5.4. The Bohr Atom. In 1913 Niels Bohr proposed a model of the atom, using a combination of quantum and classical ideas that was the first to account successfully for the basic features of line spectra. In particular, the Bohr model of the atom explained almost perfectly the spectrum of hydrogen. Bohr's original model was based upon two assumptions:

1. Electrons moved in circular orbits about a nucleus just as planets move around the sun. However, only certain values of radius were permitted, these being those for which the angular momentum multiplied by 2π was equal to an integral multiple of Planck's constant. Such orbits are stable and the electron does not radiate while remaining within such an orbit.

2. Radiation will take place only when electrons jump from one allowed orbit to another, in which case the frequency of the radiation is determined by the relation that the difference in the energies of the two orbits shall be equal to the product of Planck's constant and the frequency.

These assumptions appear a bit arbitrary and indeed were postulates made to produce a theory in accord with the observed results. The first

condition assumed is known as the *Bohr-Sommerfeld quantum condition.*
It was later shown that, when one considered the wave aspect of such
rotating electrons, *the condition corresponded to having an integral number
of wavelengths around each orbit.* The second condition is known as the
Einstein frequency condition. It is basically the same assumption that
was originally suggested by Planck and used by Einstein to explain
photoemission. Physically it may be considered that the electron acts
like a quantized energy-storage device. As a result, radiation can occur
only when there is a transition from a higher- to a lower-energy state. In
an actual body there will be many atoms contributing to the over-all
effect. Electrons will be jumping back and forth between allowed orbits
in large numbers and in a random fashion. Accordingly, radiation of a
given frequency will appear to be continuous.

A better idea of this process is obtained if there are considered the
relations for circular orbits. Here, considering Coulomb's law, in mks
units, for one proton and one electron of hydrogen and assuming that the
proton does not move,

$$\text{Kinetic energy} = T = \frac{1}{2} mv^2 = \frac{k_1}{r} \tag{5.10}$$

where $k_1 = e^2/8\pi\varepsilon_0$. This is obtained by equating outward centrifugal
force mv^2/r to inward Coulomb attraction force $e^2/4\pi\varepsilon_0 r^2$, where e and
m are the charge and the mass of the electron, ε_0 is the dielectric constant
of free space, and r is the radial distance between electron and proton.
Similarly, integrating Coulomb force from infinity to r,

$$\text{Potential energy} = U = -\frac{2k_1}{r} \tag{5.11}$$

As a result,

$$\text{Total energy} = \mathcal{E} = T + U = -\frac{k_1}{r} \tag{5.12}$$

These energies are in joules or watt-seconds (1 joule = 10^7 ergs). A curve
showing the relative energy components vs. radius is shown in Fig. 5.6.

Applying the Bohr-Sommerfeld quantum condition for orbits,

$$2\pi \text{ (angular momentum)} = 2\pi mvr = 2\pi(2mk_1 r)^{\frac{1}{2}} = nh \tag{5.13}$$

Eliminating r between (5.12) and (5.13),

$$\text{Total energy} = \mathcal{E} = -\frac{Rch}{n^2} \quad \text{joules} \tag{5.14}$$

Here c is again the velocity of light, and R is the Rydberg constant, of
value

$$R = \frac{me^4}{8\varepsilon_0^2 h^3 c} = 1.0974 \times 10^7 \text{ m}^{-1} \tag{5.15}$$

The value of the total energy for n at its lowest value, namely, unity, is
known as the *Rydberg energy* and is equal to -13.58 ev. The electron-

volt is a convenient unit of energy equal to the energy acquired by an electron starting from rest on being accelerated through a potential of 1 volt.   Energies of other orbits are $1/n^2$ times as great.

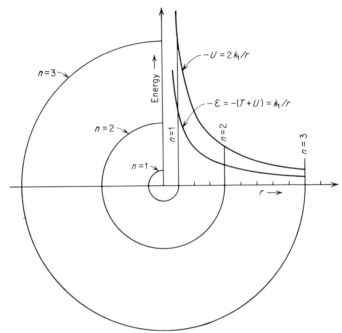

FIG. 5.6. Energy components of the hydrogen electron.

Of interest also is the radius of the smallest allowed orbit.   From (5.13), for $n = 1$, this is

$$r_1 = 5.27 \times 10^{-11} \text{ m} = 0.527 \text{ A} \qquad (5.16)$$

which agrees with other estimates of the size of the hydrogen atom.

If we introduce the Einstein frequency condition, the difference in energies between two orbits gives the product of frequency and Planck's constant:

$$h\nu = \mathcal{E}_2 - \mathcal{E}_1 \qquad (5.17)$$

Using now (5.14) for two values of n and expressing the reciprocal wavelength as the frequency divided by c,

$$\frac{1}{\lambda} = R\left(\frac{1}{n_1^2} - \frac{1}{n_2^2}\right) \qquad \text{m}^{-1} \qquad (5.18)$$

where λ is the wavelength of the emitted radiation if n_2 is greater than n_1.   A somewhat more convenient form giving wavelength directly is

$$\lambda = 911.3 \, \frac{n_1^2 n_2^2}{n_2^2 - n_1^2} \qquad \text{A} \qquad (5.19)$$

This is seen to confirm (5.1) directly for $n_1 = 2$.   Likewise, (5.18) is of
the same form as (5.2).   The initial agreement between the experimental
and theoretical values of R was only fair but it became almost perfect as
various refinements were introduced into the theory.   Such refinements
included allowance for the fact that the nucleus did not remain fixed in
position but rotated about the center of gravity of the system and also

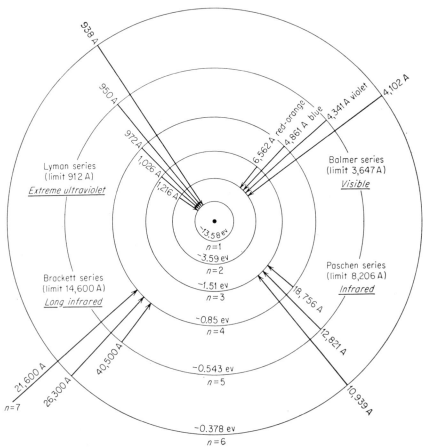

Fig. 5.7. Energy-level diagram of the hydrogen atom.

that the high-speed electrons would have their mass increased by relativity effects.

Thus the original Bohr theory immediately gave a good prediction of
most of the lines of the hydrogen spectrum.   It also gave a new physical
picture of the mechanism of radiation.   Shown in Fig. 5.7 is a diagram
showing the energy levels in the hydrogen atom according to the ideas so
far presented.   Transitions between the various levels give rise to radiation of wavelengths indicated.   This picture explains the origin of the

principal series in the hydrogen spectrum.   Energy is lost if an electron goes from a given value of n to a lower value.   This is always accompanied by radiation.   Energy is absorbed if an electron goes from a given value of n to a higher value.   This may be caused by absorption of radiant energy of the corresponding wavelength, but it may be caused by absorption of energy in other forms, such as by electron bombardment or thermal excitation.   Electrons in the lowest orbit can accept a maximum energy of 13.58 ev and still remain attached to the nucleus.   If they accept more energy they are freed from the nucleus and the atoms are said to be "ionized."   A positive hydrogen ion, or free proton, can accept a free electron to become a neutral atom.   In doing so, there is emitted radiation of frequency equal to the energy difference of the electron, before and after recombination, divided by Planck's constant.   Since the positive ion can accept electrons with energies greater than zero there will be caused radiations with frequencies greater than those caused by transitions of a bound electron.   This gives rise to a continuous spectrum beyond the group of lines in each series, as shown in Fig. 5.8.

FIG. 5.8. Spectrogram of Balmer series for hydrogen, showing continuum.

As instruments became more precise and measurements more accurate, it became evident that specification of all spectroscopic lines by a single quantum number was not adequate.   There was then introduced a second quantum number, k, by allowing for elliptical as well as circular orbits.   Now the first, or principal, quantum number, n, was associated with the orbit energy, as in (5.14).   This quantum number also gives the major axis of the ellipse as twice the radius specified in the right-hand part of (5.13).   The second quantum number, k, specifies the angular momentum as $k/2\pi$ instead of $n/2\pi$, as in circular orbits. k also determines the ratio of the minor to the major axis of the ellipse as k/n and can take on only integral values from 1 to n.   For $k = 1$, the orbit is most elongated; for $k = n$ it is circular.

However, even the first two quantum numbers were not able to explain all observations.   It was observed that when radiation occurred in the presence of a magnetic field, some of the lines split up and became groups of lines.   This effect is known as the Zeeman effect.   To account for this, it was considered that the electron in rotation produced an equivalent current loop whose magnetic field reacted with the external magnetic field.   The angular momentum of the orbit, $k/2\pi$, was considered as a vector normal to the plane of the orbit.   The projection of this vector on the vector of the external magnetic field was considered as quantized with a third quantum number, m, so that the component of $k/2\pi$ in the direction of magnetic field was taken as $m/2\pi$.   This amounted to quantizing the orientation of the plane of the orbit and gave rise to allowed integral values of m between $-k$ and $+k$. Further attempts to explain the fine structure called for the use of a fourth quantum number of value $\pm\frac{1}{2}$ with momentum value $\pm\frac{1}{2}(h/2\pi)$ attributed to "electron spin" around its own axis.

In spite of all this patching up, the Bohr theory was unable to go beyond certain limits in explaining complex spectra. It did fairly well on certain atoms presumed to have a single remote planetary electron, like sodium and lithium, but it failed to explain the spectrum of a simple atom like helium. This was more or less inevitable because the Bohr theory had an inherent logical inconsistency in that it combined orbits explained in terms of classical mechanics with transitions of a quantum nature. The various bits of patching up introduced to cope with more complex situations became more and more arbitrary and artificial. It was necessary at this point to have a new point of view. Such was provided by the development of the ideas of the duality of waves and corpuscles, of the uncertainty principle, and finally of wave mechanics. These ideas will now be briefly presented.

5.5. The Wave Aspect of Matter. It has been seen that radiant energy in the form of light exhibits a dual aspect, namely, wave and corpuscular. The wave aspect is most prominent in such phenomena as diffraction and interference, whereas the corpuscular aspect is most prominent in photoelectric emission. Reasoning from the fact that the two great entities in the physical world were matter and energy, de Broglie proposed (1924) that since the latter exhibits a dual aspect, so should the former. Many bits of evidence contributed toward this relation. Matter and energy were both known to be conserved. Further, the theory of relativity showed them to be equivalent. Close analogies were known to exist between certain laws of optics and mechanics. These relations were later developed into the science of electron optics. Specifically, de Broglie proposed that an electron in motion should exhibit the properties of a packet of energy with wave properties.

De Broglie's suggestions were confirmed by Davisson and Germer (1927) and G. P. Thompson (1927), who showed that a stream of electrons was reflected from crystals in much the same way as were X rays. That is, the reflection, instead of being diffuse like that of light from a rough surface, was selective with angle, indicating that there was reinforcement of a wavelike property in certain preferred directions depending upon the spacing of the atoms in the crystal. This work verified experimentally an *equivalent wavelength* of the electrons, of value, as proposed by de Broglie,

$$\lambda = \frac{h}{mv} = \frac{h}{p} \tag{5.20}$$

where λ = wavelength
  h = Planck's constant
  m = mass
  v = velocity
  p = momentum

For electrons starting from rest at a point of zero potential, this takes the more specific form

$$\lambda = \frac{12.26}{\sqrt{V}} \quad \text{A} \qquad (5.21)$$

where V is potential in volts, which holds for nonrelativistic velocities. Note that the wavelength of a 150-volt electron is about 1 A.

The picture of the electron as a "wave packet" may be considered to be something like that shown in Fig. 5.9. Here is shown a wave train whose envelope moves along with a velocity v corresponding to that of the electron. However, the waves within the envelope are moving faster at a velocity u and thus appear to originate at the tail, move through the packet, and pass out the nose. The shape of the envelope and the components of velocity may change with time. This is similar to an effect encountered with water waves, where individual ripples in a group of waves move about twice as fast as the group itself. The two velocities here are so-called *phase velocity*, corresponding to u, and a so-called *group velocity*, corresponding to v. Phase velocity is the velocity with which the zeros or, more generally, the equiphase surfaces move. It is the velocity associated with the equivalent wavelength.

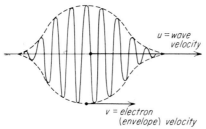

FIG. 5.9. Representation of an electron wave packet.

Group velocity is the velocity with which the energy or the center of gravity of a pulse moves (it is the velocity of the electron in this case). It is the velocity with which energy is transmitted. Actually, the de Broglie relation (5.20) may be explained by reference to these components of velocity and the relation $\mathcal{E} = h\nu$ [RiE]. It may also be demonstrated by reference to relativity theory [SlA].

In this manner the dual aspect of both radiant energy and matter is established. To harmonize these ideas entirely, however, it is necessary to say that the intensity of radiation in the wave interpretation corresponds to the probability of encountering particles in the corpuscular interpretation. An extension of this idea of probability, when applied in connection with the wave-matter equivalence, leads to a fairly complete and satisfactory picture of electron behavior and atomic structure.

5.6. The Uncertainty Principle. When we deal with phenomena having a dual aspect, it is found that the more closely we specify one aspect, the less closely we can specify the other. This is a matter familiar to radio engineers in other terms. Thus, in dealing with pulses of electrical energy, we can describe such pulses either as a function of time or by their distribution of energy over the frequency spectrum. A pulse of energy therefore displays a dual frequency-time aspect. With radar pulses, for instance, the more we make the pulse very short in time, i.e., the more accurately we specify its location in time, the more the energy spreads out in frequency, i.e., the less accurately we specify its frequency. If we call the length of the pulse δt and the portion of its frequency spectrum containing a certain fraction of its total energy $\delta\nu$, then it is found that

$$\delta t \ \delta\nu \cong 1 \tag{5.22}$$

which means that the product of the spread in time and the spread in frequency is of the order of unity. This also says that the product of the uncertainties of time and frequency is of the order of unity. This follows because we can specify the location in time and frequency only within limits δt and $\delta\nu$.

The above wave relation can be carried over into a particle relation by multiplying the first factor in (5.22) by c, the velocity of light, and dividing the second by the same factor. This yields

$$\delta x \ \delta\left(\frac{1}{\lambda}\right) \cong 1 \tag{5.23}$$

If we now multiply both sides by h, Planck's constant, and recognize $h \ \delta(1/\lambda)$ as δp from the de Broglie relation (5.20), then

$$\delta x \ \delta p \cong h \tag{5.24}$$

which says that the product of the uncertainty of the position and the momentum of a particle is of the order of Planck's constant. A similar relation holds between energy and time:

$$\delta\varepsilon \ \delta t \cong h \tag{5.25}$$

This results from (5.22) by multiplying $\delta\nu$ by h and dividing δt by h. The factor $h \ \delta\nu$ is then identified as $\delta\varepsilon$ by Planck's relation (5.9). These are equivalent statements of the so-called *uncertainty principle* proposed by Heisenberg in 1927. Stated in other terms, the more accurately we determine the location (or energy) of a particle, the less accurately will we know its momentum (or time). A graphical representation of the uncertainty principle is shown in Fig. 5.10. Here are shown three areas against axes of momentum p and location x. Each has an area equal to Planck's constant h. The figure indicates that narrowing the spread in one dimension increases it in the other.

Heisenberg arrived at the above principle by considering what would happen if one tried to determine the location of an electron in motion in a hypothetical experiment using two microscopes to observe the electron at successive instants in time. To locate the electron accurately, we use light of a very short wavelength, which increases the resolving power of the microscope. The least amount of light that can be used is one photon with an energy $h\nu$, which becomes greater as the wavelength becomes shorter. However, as demonstrated by photoelectric emission, one photon can impart all its energy to an electron in a metal; and as demonstrated by the *Compton effect* (1924), a photon can impart part of its energy to a free electron, with the remaining energy appearing as scattered light of a lower frequency. In any event, observation of an electron with a photon can impart a definite change in momentum to the former; and the very act that increases accuracy of observation, namely, higher frequency, increases the probable change in momentum.

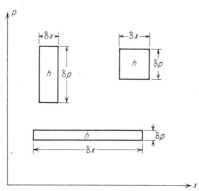

FIG. 5.10. Graphical representation of the Heisenberg uncertainty principle.

Because of the small size of Planck's constant, this effect is important only when the dimensions of the phenomenon involved are of the order of the de Broglie wavelength or smaller. This criterion may be taken as a limit of the validity of classical mechanics and classical wave theory. The uncertainty principle, we shall see, plays an important role in the interpretation of atomic theory as developed by the concepts of quantum mechanics.

5.7. Quantum Mechanics. When it was realized that electrons have a wave as well as a particle aspect, the application of wave theory to atomic structure was a natural consequence. Waves of various kinds had been studied for some time and their characteristics were well known. A general differential equation describing wave motion in one dimension is of the form

$$\frac{\partial^2 \Psi}{\partial x^2} = \frac{1}{v^2} \frac{\partial^2 \Psi}{\partial t^2} \tag{5.26}$$

where Ψ = amplitude of some aspect of wave
x = distance in allowed direction of movement
v = velocity
t = time

This equation serves for waves on a stretched string, electric waves on a transmission line, or radio waves in free space, with proper interpretation.   For waves on a stretched string, Ψ will be the displacement from a rest position.   For electric waves on a transmission line, Ψ will be voltage or current.   For radio waves, Ψ will be electric or magnetic field.   Such factors will depend upon both location and time and, in general, will be products of separate time and location functions, that is,

$$\Psi(x,t) = \psi(x)T(t) \tag{5.27}$$

where $\psi(x)$ = function of x alone, and thus a *space function*
$\quad\quad T(t)$ = function of t alone, and thus a *time function*
Let us assume the time variation to be cosinusoidal, which is conveniently done by letting $T(t)$ be the real part of an exponential term of the form

$$T(t) = \mathrm{Re}\ \epsilon^{j\omega t} \tag{5.28}$$

where ϵ = 2.718 (the naperian base)
$\quad\quad j = \sqrt{-1}$
$\quad\quad \omega = 2\pi$ (frequency)
$\quad\quad t$ = time
If this substitution is made in the differential equation (5.26), time is eliminated and there results a simpler differential equation, in amplitude and distance alone, whose solutions give the form of standing waves in the system under discussion.   Standing waves are configurations produced by the summation of incident and reflected traveling waves.   This equation is of the form

$$\frac{\partial^2\psi}{\partial x^2} + \frac{\omega^2\psi}{v^2} = 0 \tag{5.29}$$

which may also be written

$$\frac{\partial^2\psi}{\partial x^2} + \left(\frac{2\pi}{\lambda}\right)^2 \psi = 0 \tag{5.30}$$

since $v = \lambda f$, where λ is wavelength, f is frequency, and, of course, $\omega = 2\pi f$. This differential equation gives the variation of maximum amplitude from point to point, it being remembered that a cosinusoidal variation with time is also involved.   A solution of (5.30) that may be easily verified by substitution is

$$x = A \sin\frac{2\pi x}{\lambda} + B \cos\frac{2\pi x}{\lambda} \tag{5.31}$$

where A and B are constants, real numbers, determined by end (boundary) conditions and the choice of reference origin.   With a stretched string, e.g., with fixed ends and an origin of x at one end, only sine waves will be permitted since the displacement must be zero when x is zero.   If the string has a length a, then only values of λ are allowed, for which

$$\lambda = \frac{2a}{n} \tag{5.32}$$

where n assumes integral values of 1, 2, 3, . . . , since the amplitude must always be zero at the other end of the string for which $x = a$. These values of n are known as characteristic values and determine the natural resonant frequencies of the string. In Fig. 5.11 are shown various possible oscillations of a stretched string. For $n = 1$, the string is half a wavelength long, giving rise to the fundamental frequency of oscillation. For $n = 2$, the string is one wavelength long, giving rise to a frequency equal to twice the fundamental frequency and called the second harmonic, or first overtone. For $n = 3$, the string is three half wavelengths long, and the frequency of the third harmonic, or second overtone, is three times the fundamental frequency.

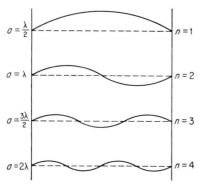

Fig. 5.11. Natural resonance modes of an elastic string.

If we refer to the wave equation of (5.30) and consider now how this may be used to describe electron wave effects, it appears logical to substitute for wavelength in terms of momentum, as determined by the de Broglie relation of (5.20). If in addition we recall that total energy is the sum of kinetic and potential energy,

$$\varepsilon = \tfrac{1}{2}mv^2 + U(x) = \frac{p^2}{2m} + U(x) \tag{5.33}$$

so that
$$p^2 = 2m[\varepsilon - U(x)] \tag{5.34}$$

where p = momentum
    m = particle mass
    ε = total energy
    $U(x)$ = potential energy

It is important to remember that potential is a function of position. Using this and the substitution $1/\lambda = p/h$ in (5.30), we obtain the result

$$\frac{\partial^2 \psi}{\partial x^2} + \frac{8\pi^2 m}{h^2}(\varepsilon - U)\psi = 0 \tag{5.35}$$

This is Schrödinger's wave equation (1926) in its simplest form. It gives rise to a new approach on quantum theory known as *quantum mechanics*. Its solutions properly interpreted have cleared up most of the inadequacies of previous atomic theory and have given answers to a host of new questions as well. It has given an entirely new insight into the problems of modern physics.

Schrödinger's equation has an analogy with certain electric-circuit and transmission-line problems. Suffice it to say that if $\varepsilon - U$ is positive (kinetic energy positive), the solutions will correspond to the solutions for a transmission line or a filter in its pass band and be expressed in sines and cosines of distance representing standing waves (actually combinations of traveling waves). If, however, $\mathcal{E} - U$ is negative (kinetic energy negative), the solutions will correspond to the solutions for a filter in its rejection band and be expressed in terms of negative and positive exponential functions of distance representing fields attenuating with distance but not traveling. In classical mechanics a negative kinetic energy is not permitted, but in quantum theory it is.

This brings up the question as to just what amplitude or aspect of the electron is represented by ψ. *The best interpretation is that the amplitude of ψ squared, when properly normalized, is a so-called probability amplitude that indicates the probability of finding an electron at the point in question.* According to classical mechanics, an electron is like a hard little sphere; but according to quantum mechanics, bearing in mind that the uncertainty principle says that the location and velocity of an electron cannot both be known accurately, an electron presents a very diffuse aspect, looking somewhat like a light seen in a heavy fog. Schrödinger's wave equation and the uncertainty principle admit of electrons being distributed in space. They also admit of electrons diffusing into regions where the kinetic energy is computed to be negative. This interpretation explains how a certain number of electrons can pass over potential barriers that they could not pass over from classical considerations.

When Schrödinger's equation is applied to a simple atom, such as that of hydrogen, a complete set of solutions is found that is at first somewhat surprising but in complete agreement with experimental findings and an improvement on the orbital model of Bohr. Here solutions come out in terms of three dimensions instead of one, as for the string problem. It is found that the solutions are described by three characteristic numbers, which may be identified with the quantum numbers.

A similar situation is encountered in other, more familiar, three-dimensional wave problems, such as, for instance, acoustical or electromagnetic vibrations inside a rectangular box. Here there are numerous possible resonance modes, each with a different frequency and each with a different standing-wave pattern. In the case of the acoustical resonator, the standing wave can be observed as either pressure (scalar quantity) or velocity (vector quantity), the patterns being complimentary. In the case of the electromagnetic resonator, the standing wave can be observed in terms of electric or magnetic field (both vector quantities). For the rectangular-box resonator, there will be standing waves within the box for which there will be nodal planes, i.e., planes where the wave amplitude is zero, parallel to the sides of the box. The three characteristic numbers in this case can be taken as the number of nodal planes l, m, and n perpendicular to each axis (more often taken as $l + 1$, $m + 1$, and $n + 1$). The nodal planes break up the waves into a number of rectangular nodal cells within the larger box. These effects are illustrated in Fig. 5.12. This shows the nodal cells in a rectangular acoustical resonator. Along the nodal planes, velocity will be zero at the frequency of resonance. Also shown is the distribution of kinetic energy within a typical nodal cell.

For the hydrogen atom, *the solutions of Schrödinger's equation bear a striking similarity to the standing waves within a spherical resonator,* the counterpart of the rectangular one just described. In this case the characteristic numbers are associated with the radial-distance, polar-angle (latitude), and azimuthal-angle (longitude) coordinates. Again there may be nodal surfaces. For this case, however, the nodal surfaces associated with the radius are spheres, those associated with the polar angle are cones

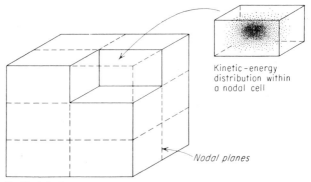

Kinetic-energy
distribution within
a nodal cell

Nodal planes

FIG. 5.12. Nodal planes and energy distribution in a rectangular resonator.

about the same axis and with apex at the nucleus, and those associated with the azimuthal angle are planes through an arbitrary axis passing through the nucleus. The direction of the arbitrary axis is taken as that of an external magnetic field because of the tendency of the "orbits" to line up and react with such magnetic fields. In the absence of any man-made fields, this direction can be taken as that of the earth's magnetic fields.

The quantity in quantum mechanics that corresponds to *frequency* in the resonator case is *energy*. Just as a cavity resonator may have many distinct resonant frequencies, each with a distinctive field distribution, so may an atom have many different energy levels, each with a distinctive electron probability distribution.

The three characteristic, or quantum, numbers come out of the Schrödinger equation without any assumption about orbits. In fact, the distribution of probability amplitudes is such that the concept of orbits is almost lost or at least strained. The three characteristic numbers are practically the same as those encountered in the Bohr theory and the same interpretation is often employed, although recognized as a little arbitrary. It is still necessary to assume a fourth quantum number associated with electron spin to give the complete picture. The characteristics of, and relations between, the four quantum numbers are as follows:

1. The principal quantum number, n, assumes values of 1, 2, 3, 4, 5, 6, 7, fixes energy of state, and is associated with radial variation of amplitude probability.

2. The angular-momentum quantum number, l, assumes values $0 \leqq l \leqq n - 1$, has a second-order influence on energy of state, and is associated with polar-angle variation of amplitude probability.

3. The magnetic quantum number, m, assumes values $-l \leqq m \leqq + l$, has a slight influence on energy, and is associated with azimuthal variation of amplitude probability.

4. The spin quantum number, m_s, assumes values of $+\frac{1}{2}$ and $-\frac{1}{2}$.

The relation between the first three quantum integers is expressed by the single relation

$$|m| \leqq l < n \tag{5.36}$$

A notation borrowed from spectroscopy is commonly used for the second quantum number. This is as follows:

Value of l...............	0	1	2	3	4	5	6
Letter symbol...........	s	p	d	f	g	h	i

The first four letters stand for *sharp, principal, diffuse,* and *fundamental.* The relations between the quantum numbers determine the groupings

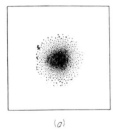

(a)   (b)   (c)

Fig. 5.13. Radial variation of electron probability amplitudes in a hydrogen atom: (a) 1s, (b) 2s, (c) 3s states.

that they may form. Thus for $n = 1$, l and m must be zero, but m_s assumes values of $\pm\frac{1}{2}$. For $n = 2$, l may assume values of 0 or 1. For $l = 1$, m may assume values of -1, 0, 1. For each combination of the first three quantum numbers, m_s may assume values of $\pm\frac{1}{2}$.

Shown in Fig. 5.13 is one representation of the electron probability amplitude for cases in which there is only radial variation. These show the diffuse aspect of the electron. The darker the area, the more probable it is that an electron will be found there. The nodal rings (spherical shells) are clearly evident for n greater than 1. Each diagram corresponds to one orbit. These diagrams look like standing waves in a circular tank. The interpretation is that for each state the electron moves around in such a way that its probable location is given by the darkness of the area. No radiation occurs in any given state, and the electron traverses nodes at will. Radiation occurs only with a change from one state to another.

In Fig. 5.14 is another representation showing the variation of the electron probability amplitude with azimuthal and polar angle for several combinations of the second and third quantum numbers. These are a type of polar diagram which look like certain antenna array patterns though they represent nonradiating states of the electron. These must be multiplied by the radial distribution diagrams of Fig. 5.13 to give the

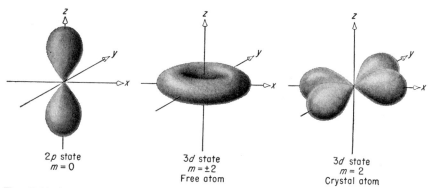

2p state
m = 0

3d state
m = ±2
Free atom

3d state
m = 2
Crystal atom

FIG. 5.14. Angular variation of electron probability amplitude in a hydrogen atom.

complete picture. Here the orbit concept is even more difficult to support. The lobes shown are intended to have diffuse rather than sharp boundaries. The lobes also have significance in the determination of the chemical properties of atoms and enter into the determination of valence. Atoms with outer electrons in states with such lobes may share electrons in a joined lobe.

In spite of some great differences in interpretation introduced by quantum mechanics, it is important to remember that the following features of the Bohr atom are preserved:

1. The energy levels of the various electron states are quantized.

2. Radiation occurs only when there is a change of state. The frequency of the radiation is determined by the energy difference of the states divided by Planck's constant.

3. There remains a general concept of orbit, or preferred location, going with the amplitude-probability distributions.

5.8. The Electron Structure of Atoms. When the ideas of quantum mechanics are applied to atoms with more than one electron, it is found that the same amplitude-probability distributions, or quantum states, exist for the separate electrons. However, the energy levels associated with these states are changed by the difference in nuclear mass and the interactions of the electrons. A general question arises as to the distribution of the electrons in various states. In general, it is expected that in an atom at rest the electrons will occupy states with the lowest possible energy. Shown in Fig. 5.15 is an energy diagram of the electron energy states of hydrogen. Each state is shown as a line segment and is

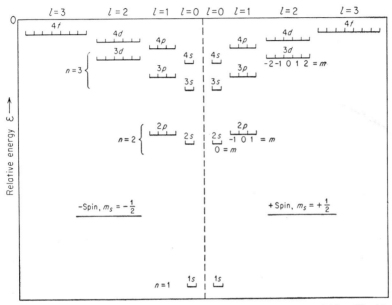

FIG. 5.15. General energy levels of the various quantum states. (*After Shockley.*)

identified by four quantum numbers. Differences in the values of the principal quantum number n are responsible for the principal differences in energy, although there are smaller differences due to the second quantum number l. Differences in energy due to the other quantum numbers are neglected. This same general scheme applied to atoms with more than one electron, with modifications as indicated above.

To bring the observed spectroscopic results into harmony with the theory, it was necessary to make the additional assumption that *no two electrons may occupy the same quantum state*. This is known as the *Pauli exclusion principle* (1925). This means that in an atom at rest, i.e., when electrons are at the lowest possible energy levels, no two electrons can have all four quantum numbers the same. The Pauli exclusion principle was originally an empirical assumption. It was later found to be a consequence of a more general form of Schrödinger's equation. We may note that, if the principle did not hold, all the electrons of an atom at rest would be in the lowest energy state, which would give little basis for distinguishing one atom from another.

The Pauli exclusion principle applied to the results of quantum mechanics gives a basis for explaining atomic structure. Thus an atom at rest with one electron may have quantum numbers n, l, m, m_s of 1, 0, 0, $\pm\frac{1}{2}$. This is recognized as hydrogen. The establishment of n as unity determines the zero values of l and m. An atom with two electrons may have electrons in states 1, 0, 0, $\frac{1}{2}$ and 1, 0, 0, $-\frac{1}{2}$. This is recognized as helium. Reference to the relations between the quantum numbers of the last section shows that these are the only two quantum states allowed for $n = 1$. An atom with three electrons must therefore have one electron for which $n = 2$. The lowest energy states here are 1, 0, 0, $\pm\frac{1}{2}$ and 2, 0, 0, $+\frac{1}{2}$. This is lithium. For $n = 2$, if we consider that l ranges from 0 to $n - 1$ and m ranges between $+l$ and $-l$ and that for each combination of the first three quantum numbers two spin states are possible, it is seen that eight states are possible. Groups of electrons in quantum states with the same value of n are known as *shells*. For $n = 1$, there is the so-called K shell, which can hold 2 electrons. For $n = 2$, there is the L shell, which can hold 8 electrons. For $n = 3$, there is the M shell, which can hold 18 electrons, etc.

A convenient way of showing the structure of the elements is to show which of the energy states in Fig. 5.15 are filled. In this diagram are shown the relative energy levels for the different quantum states. Each state is shown as a U-shaped niche. States with a spin number m_s equal to $\frac{1}{2}$ are shown in the right half of the diagram, and those with a spin number equal to $-\frac{1}{2}$ are shown on the left. This gives a diagram symmetrical with respect to the center line. States for the various values of the principal quantum number n are aligned at various levels corresponding to their energy, the energy increasing with the value of n. Values of the second quantum number l are indicated by displacement of groups of states from the center line. For each value of n and l, there will be permitted several values of the third quantum number m. States with the same value of n, l, and m_s but different values of m are grouped. In general, all states with the same value of n have nearly the same energy, but there is a small spread with the different values of l. However, for the same n and l, the change in energy level with different values of m is too small to be shown on a diagram of this sort.

Shown in Fig. 5.16 are the states of some of the elements with low atomic weight. The two lowest states for which $n = 1$ are filled by electrons in all cases and not shown. It is of interest to note that the effect of nuclear mass and electron interaction is to change the energy levels somewhat. In this figure there is used a notation commonly employed to describe the electron structure of the atoms. This employs a series of groups of three symbols giving, respectively, the value of n, the letter symbol of l, and as an exponent, the number of electrons in each nl combination. Thus the lithium notation $1s^2$, $2s$ means that there are two electrons for which $n = 1$ and $l = 0$ and one electron for which $n = 2$ and $l = 0$ (the exponent being omitted if it has a value of unity).

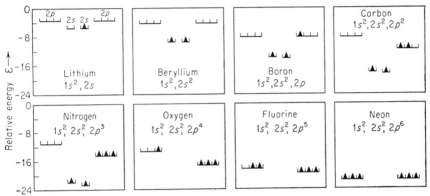

FIG. 5.16. Specific electron energy levels of some of the lighter elements. (*After Shockley.*)

Ultimately, recourse is best had to a tabulation of the quantum numbers associated with the electrons of each atom. Such tabulation is given in Appendix 2. Indicated here are the number of electrons in each atom for various combinations of the quantum numbers. The valence proper-

TABLE 5.1

l designation........	s	p	d	f
Value of l..........	0	1	2	3

Shell designation	Value of n	Composite notation and max no. of electrons			
K	1	$1s$ 2			
L	2	$2s$ 2	$2p$ 6		
M	3	$3s$ 2	$3p$ 6	$3d$ 10	
N	4	$4s$ 2	$4p$ 6	$4d$ 10	$4f$ 14
O	5	$5s$ 2	$5p$ 6	$5d$ 10	
P	6	$6s$ 2	$6p$ 6	$6d$ 10	
Q	7	$7s$ 2			

ties of the atoms are determined by the electron grouping. Also the electron grouping serves as the basis for establishing the periodic table.

Table 5.1 shows the maximum number of electrons that can be associated with each combination of the first two quantum numbers. It must be remembered that (5.36) holds for the relation between the first three quantum numbers and that there are two spin states for each combination of these three.

It is seen from Table 5.1 that for any value of l there are allowed $4l + 2$ states. The $6d$ state has 10 allowed states, but only 4 of them are found in the elements of the periodic table. Reference to Appendix 2 shows the states of the atoms of the elements and the order in which they are filled. Elements with all the states for a given value of n filled, i.e., with all shells filled, are the inert elements. Likewise, elements with all nl combinations filled are also very stable. Atoms with one electron in an nl state are the electropositive metals. Elements with $l - 1$ electrons in the highest state are the halogens.

CHAPTER 6

CONDUCTORS, INSULATORS, AND SEMICONDUCTORS

6.1. Some Ideas about Solids. Materials in the physical world are readily classified as being in the gaseous, liquid, or solid state. In electronics, the state of most interest is the solid state. Solids have many properties—chemical, thermal, and mechanical, as well as magnetic and electrical. Accordingly, various classifications of solids are possible—in general, a different classification for each group of characteristics. Solids may also be classified as to structure.[1]

For the purposes of this chapter, solids are best classified in accordance with their electrical conductivity as conductors, insulators, and semiconductors.

Conductor. A solid exhibiting a low electrical resistivity at room temperature. Resistivity is of the order of 1.6×10^{-6} to 100×10^{-6} ohm-cm, and increases approximately linearly with temperature. In this group are included most of the common metals, such as copper or silver.

Insulator. A solid exhibiting a high electrical resistivity at room temperature. Resistivity is of the order of 10^9 to 10^{18} ohm-cm. Such materials usually have dielectric constants between 1 and 10. Examples include quartz, sulfur, and porcelain.

Semiconductors. A solid exhibiting a value of resistivity intermediate between conductors and insulators. Resistivity is of the order of 0.01 to 50 ohm-cm at room temperature. Resistance variation with temperature is nonlinear and may have either a positive or negative temperature coefficient at room temperature. Resistance characteristics depend strongly on impurities in the material. Examples include both compounds, such as zinc oxide and copper oxide, and elements, such as germanium and silicon.

The resistivity of some well-known materials is shown in Fig. 6.1.

A more general classification can be stated as follows: A conductor is a solid with a relatively large number of current carriers (electrons), a number independent of temperature. An insulator is a solid with few current carriers at ordinary temperatures. A semiconductor is a solid in which the number of current carriers is temperature dependent, there

[1] General references on solids: [Sek, Hud, Sha, Wil, Toc].

being generally a fairly large number at high temperatures and a relatively small number at low temperatures. The above statements were purposely restricted to solids to exclude ionized gases and liquids.

This is all that can be said about the electrical characteristics of solids at this point. To understand *why* some materials are insulators and some conductors and *why* some materials have a resistance that increases with temperature, whereas others have a resistance that decreases with temperature, we must know a bit about the structure of the material and a bit about the laws governing the behavior of electrons in metals. A study of these subjects will be undertaken in subsequent sections.

Another basic idea introduced here is the fact that most of the conductors and semiconductors of interest are crystals. *A crystal is a regular array of atoms.* As such, it has a repetitive geometrical pattern of its atomic structure. This pattern may or may not be visible, depending on the size of the crystal. The structure of quartz, for instance, is usually apparent in large crystals. Ordinary table salt has a cubical structure visible with a low-power magnifying glass. Rock salt has the same basic structure; the pieces are merely larger. Crystals are not to be considered molecules. A molecule has a definite number of atoms assigned to it, whereas a crystal does not. A crystal may have any number of atoms, though where more than one element is involved, the elements will be in constant ratio for a given material. Thus a crystal can be compared to a section of arbitrary length of a roll of wallpaper but so cut that the basic pattern appears an integral number of times. A molecule, on the other hand, is like a single picture which has no repetitive feature.

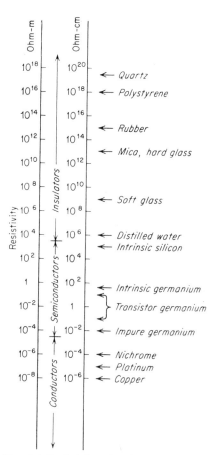

FIG. 6.1. Resistivity of various conductors, insulators, and semiconductors.

Although a large number of crystal structures is possible, the metals generally fall into one of three groups: They are (1) body-centered cubic, (2) face-centered cubic, and (3) close-packed hexagonal. These three geometric arrangements of atoms are shown in Fig. 6.2. These three crystal structures have the most compact structures and hence the largest number of atoms per unit volume. They are probably assumed frequently because they result in the lowest over-all energy of the system of particles

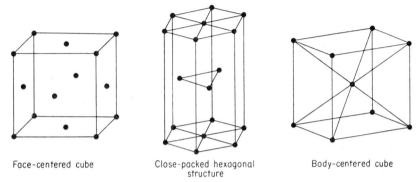

Face-centered cube   Close-packed hexagonal structure   Body-centered cube

FIG. 6.2. Some common crystal structures.

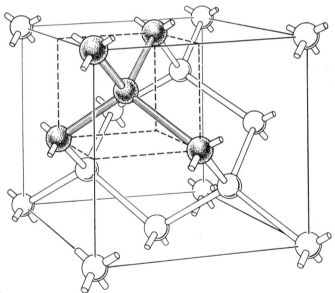

FIG. 6.3. The tetrahedral crystal structure of germanium and silicon. (*The Bell System Technical Journal.*)

and associated charges. The same structures may be encountered in compounds or alloys, as well as in elemental metals.

Interatomic spacings are commonly of the order of an angstrom or two. The details of crystal structure are best studied by X-ray diffraction. The forces holding the atoms together are electrostatic and give rise to what is known as metallic binding.

Another structure frequently encountered is shown in Fig. 6.3, which is the crystal structure of germanium and silicon. The same structure is encountered in carbon in diamond form. Each of these materials has a valence of four. Their electron arrangements are:

Carbon: $1s^2$, $2s^2$, $2p^2$
Silicon: $1s^2$, $2s^2$, $2p^6$, $3s^2$, $3p^2$
Germanium: $1s^2$, $2s^2$, $2p^6$, $3s^2$, $3p^6$, $3d^{10}$, $4s^2$, $4p^2$

Here the exponents indicate the number of electrons associated with each combination of the first two quantum numbers n and l. The number gives the first quantum number n directly; the letter gives the second quantum number l according to the code that s corresponds to $l = 0$, p to $l = 1$, d to $l = 2$, f to $l = 3$, then continuing with letters in alphabetical order. Thus carbon has two electrons for which $n = 1$ and $l = 0$ plus two for which $n = 2$ and $l = 0$ plus two for which $n = 2$ and $l = 1$.

In each case, although the total number of electrons is different, the outer shell (last group) is four electrons short of being full. This gives rise to a structure in which a given atom at the center of a cubical cell is surrounded by four other atoms occupying four of the eight corners of the cube. The cohesive force in this case comes from electrons that are shared between atoms, giving rise to what is known as a homopolar or covalent bond.

Another structure commonly encountered is the ionic crystal, as exemplified by sodium chloride and shown in Fig. 6.4. Here sodium chloride atoms occupy alternate positions in a simple cubical lattice.

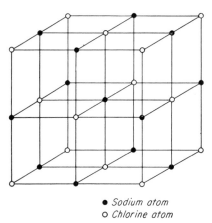

● *Sodium atom*
○ *Chlorine atom*

Fig. 6.4. The cubical-lattice form of sodium chloride.

In the crystal structure diagrams already shown, the connecting lines are symbolic of the cohesive forces. The electrons in crystals have their probability distributions altered by the proximity of other atoms, but the probabilities are still obtained through the use of Schrödinger's equation.

6.2. Energy Bands in Solids. Most of the electrical characteristics of solids can be explained by reference to the energy levels that the electrons of the atoms can assume, just as the spectroscopic behavior of atoms can be explained by reference to electron orbits and the associated electron energies. Briefly, the allowed energy levels of an atom are modified by the proximity of other atoms so that what are discrete energy *levels* in the individual atoms become *bands* in crystals, as will be explained below.

Electrical conduction takes place, as usual, by the movement of electrons. However, in order to move, the electrons must accept energy from the applied electric field in order to go to a larger orbit that includes adjacent atoms. In some materials, the allowable energy levels, so close that they form continuous bands, may be such that the highest-energy electrons have unoccupied adjacent levels above them to which they can move. Such a material is a conductor.

Other materials have all the levels in the highest occupied energy band filled, and a sizable gap exists to the next allowable level. Under this condition, ordinary electric fields will not be able to elevate electrons to the next band; such materials will not conduct electricity readily and are therefore insulators. Other materials have a small gap between a full energy band and the next highest allowed unoccupied band. At high

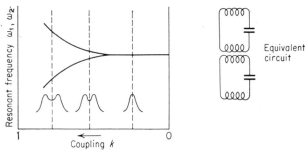

FIG. 6.5. The resonant frequencies of a two-mesh coupled circuit as a function of coupling.

temperatures or with certain impurities present, sufficient electrons can be elevated in energy to give moderate conduction. Such materials are semiconductors.

When two atoms are brought together, their external electrons interact. For spacings less than a certain value, the electrons may have orbits that surround both nuclei. When the atoms are far apart, they each have the same allowed electron energy levels as they do individually. When they get close together, they form a system having a total number of electron energy levels equal to the sum of those of the individual atoms but displaced slightly from the individual values. This is analogous to the behavior of the resonant frequencies of two identical coupled resonant circuits. When the coupling is small, each circuit has the same resonant frequency. As the coupling is increased, a value is reached at which the two resonant frequencies are not the same but differ slightly, one lower and the other higher than the original value. This behavior is shown in Fig. 6.5. The splitting of the resonant frequencies is evidenced by a double-humped response to a variable frequency beyond a so-called critical coupling.

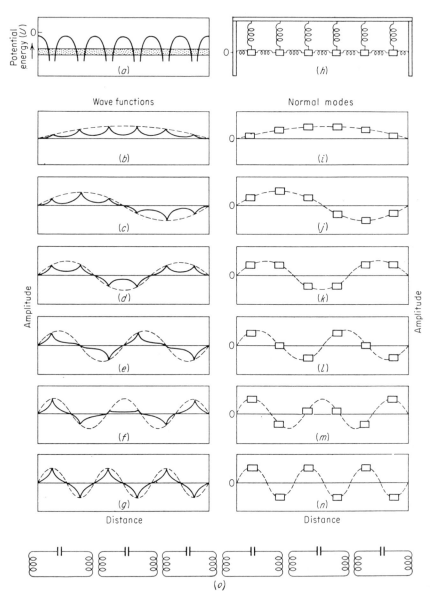

Fig. 6.6. Resonant modes of a one-dimensional crystal: (a) Potential energy of an electron for points on a line through the nuclei. (b–g) Wave functions for points on the same line. (h) Coupled oscillators. (i–n) Their normal modes of vibration. (o) Coupled circuits. (After Shockley.)

The basis of the above analogy is that solutions of the wave equation, as in the case of a resonant cavity, yield resonant or allowed frequencies. Solutions of the Schrödinger equation yield allowed energy levels. Accordingly, frequency for problems in waves and circuits is the analogue of energy for problems in atomic orbits. Coupling in resonant circuits is the analogue of reciprocal spacing for atomic-orbit problems.

For more than two resonant systems or atoms, the same general picture holds. Shown in Fig. 6.6 is a hypothetical one-dimensional crystal with six atoms and both electrical and mechanical analogues. Such a system also approximates a stretched loaded string and is capable of oscillation on a number of modes. The six possible modes of oscillation for this system are shown. In this analogy, the spacing between the atoms corresponds to the coupling between the resonant systems. Shown in Fig. 6.7 are the two lowest groups of energy levels for a crystal with six atoms. Each state exhibits a behavior similar to that of resonant frequencies for the systems of Fig. 6.6. In this case, the individual states split into six levels. This figure illustrates two important prop-

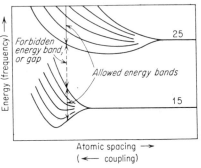

FIG. 6.7. Energy levels of a simple crystal as a function of assumed atomic spacing (theoretical).

erties encountered in crystals: (1) The total number of quantum states will be the sum of the states of the individual atoms; this is known as the theorem of the conservation of quantum states. (2) The width of the band is independent of the number of atoms in the crystal.

The theorem of the conservation of states in crystals has an analogue in circuit problems. If n identical resonant circuits are coupled to form a filter, the resultant filter will have a bandpass action and the curve of insertion loss vs. frequency will have n peaks corresponding to a splitting of the resonant frequency for the individual circuits, one resonant peak for each circuit. This is well known for small n, two coupled resonant circuits having a double-humped response, three having a triple-humped response, and so on. The fact that the width of the energy bands in crystals is independent of the number of atoms in the crystal likewise has an analogue in circuit theory. If a filter is made by coupling n identical resonant circuits, the width of the pass band depends upon the coupling between circuits and the circuit constants but not upon the number of circuits in the filter. The number of circuits will affect the attenuation outside the pass band and the number of ripples in the pass band but will not greatly affect the width of the pass band.

It will also be noted in Fig. 6.7 that the higher-energy band splits before the lower-energy band does. This is because the higher-energy electrons have wave functions with a greater spatial distribution, giving rise to a greater effective radius of orbit than for the lower-energy electrons. The outer electrons naturally interact before the inner ones do. All this information is obtained by finding solutions of Schrödinger's equation for the assumed crystal structure. The spacing between atoms of a material is only theoretically variable and in nature assumes a value corresponding to the minimum energy of the system.

In an actual crystal, there will be billions of atoms per cubic millimeter. Accordingly, there will be billions of allowable energy levels. With such a large number, the difference between levels is so small that the bands can be considered continuous. Their width is limited, however, and the bands may or may not overlap. The specific energy-band characteristics of insulators, conductors, and semiconductors will be considered in the following paragraphs.

6.3. Energy-band Structure of Metals. We have seen in the last section that the electrical properties of solids are related to the energy-band structure of the electrons of the atoms. Shown in Fig. 6.8 is the

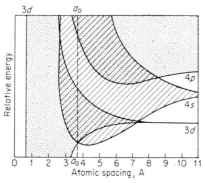

FIG. 6.8. Energy bands in copper as a function of assumed atomic spacing (theoretical).

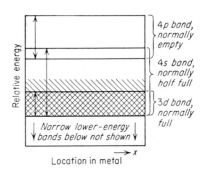

FIG. 6.9. Actual energy bands in copper vs. distance.

theoretical variation of the electron band widths of copper as a function of the atomic spacing [Shl]. The actual atomic spacing is shown by the vertical dashed line for a spacing of a_0. An equivalent representation for the actual spacing is shown in Fig. 6.9, in which there is shown the width of the energy bands approximately independent of location in the material. Copper has an electron structure given by $1s^2$, $2s^2$, $2p^6$, $3s^2$, $3p^6$, $3d^{10}$, $4s$. The $3d$ band ($n = 3$, $l = 2$) is full but the $4s$ band ($n = 4$, $l = 0$), which can hold two electrons, has only one. Accordingly, this band is only half full. Also, it is noticed that the $4s$ band is overlapped by the $4p$ band ($n = 4$, $l = 1$). In addition, $4s$ also overlaps $3d$. This is to say that there are no energy gaps between bands. This makes copper a good conductor because there are no quantum restrictions on the outermost electrons relative to acquiring energy enabling them to migrate with an electric field.

6.4. Electrical Properties of Metal Conductors. The best conductors are the metals. Their most outstanding electrical characteristic is their low electrical resistivity, already indicated as being of the order of 10^{-6} ohm-cm. Thus a copper wire $\frac{1}{16}$ in. in diameter and 250 ft long has a resistance of only 1 ohm at ordinary temperatures. A second observation relative to resistivity is that it increases almost linearly with absolute temperature over the ordinary range of temperatures for most metals. A third observation is that the resistance is constant with current, this being the justification of Ohm's law. Furthermore, metal resistance is bilateral, i.e., independent of the direction of current. These characteristics are readily explained in terms of the behavior of electrons in the metal.

The outer electrons of a metal like copper are loosely bound to their individual atoms. This is to say that their wave functions include more than one atom; and the higher the order (and hence the energy of an orbit), the larger its spatial distribution. In the absence of electric fields at ordinary temperatures, the electrons share the thermal energy of the molecules and have a random movement from atom to atom. Actually, the binding forces under these conditions are so low that the electrons are virtually free and behave much like the molecules in a gas. Under the influence of their thermal energy, the electrons will move over paths long compared to the atomic spacing before experiencing collision with an atom. Such "collisions" tend to be nearly elastic, with the result that the electron starts off again with about the same velocity but in a direction that is quite random. This action is shown in Fig. 6.10a. The action here may be imagined as similar to what would happen on a level pinball machine where the obstacles were regularly spaced posts vibrating with random amplitude and direction. An individual ball may make some large random excursions without getting anywhere on the average.

If now an electric field is applied so that a gradient of potential exists within the metal, there is then a drift component added to the random straight-line-path movements. This action is shown in Fig. 6.10b. The component due to the gradient is shown in Fig. 6.10c. This corresponds to what would occur if the imaginary pinball machine were tilted slightly. The effect of the tilt might be small as far as the path between any two collisions was concerned, but there would be a progressive drift of the ball. The correspondence between the paths in parts (a) and (b) of the figure is soon lost; but since there is no great change in the mean free path, i.e., the average distance between collisions, and the mean free time, i.e., the average time between collisions, the distance drifted in the direction of the gradient of potential is constant in a given time for a given gradient. Furthermore, the distance drifted per unit time is proportional to the gradient, thus giving rise to the linearity of current with voltage. Since there is nothing in the nature of the collisions or the ordinary crystalline structure to permit discrimination between a given direction and its opposite, the equivalent resistance is bilateral. The resistance itself arises from the fact that a limited number of electrons per second will cross an equipotential plane under the influence of a given gradient.

As temperature increases, the amplitude of the vibration of the atoms in the metal increases. This increases the probability of a collision between an electron in motion and an atom and thus decreases the mean free path and the mean free time. This, in turn, decreases the distance

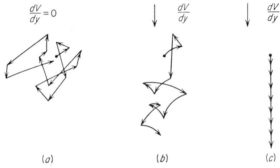

Fig. 6.10. Random motion of an electron in a metal: (a) Motion without electric field. (b) Motion with electric field. (c) Component of motion due to electric field.

that a given electron drifts under the influence of an electric field in a given time and so gives a resultant increase in the resistance of the conductor. The various factors involved are interrelated in such a way that resistance increases very nearly linearly with absolute temperature, except at very low temperature. At very low temperature, the resistance is very low and in some metals actually zero, a condition known as superconductivity.

It should be mentioned that early attempts to explain electrical conduction by assuming that the free electrons moved as molecules in a gas failed in that this approach gave the wrong variation of resistance with temperature. A complete understanding of the difference in the classical and quantum-theoretical points of view must wait until there is discussed the statistical distribution of energy of electrons according to the two theories. This will be discussed in Chap. 7, Junction Effects.

6.5. Structure and Characteristics of Insulators. The same methods that have been applied to the metals have been applied to insulators to explain their characteristics. This involves finding the wave functions of the electrons for the known crystal structure. The atomic spacing is found to be that associated with the minimum energy. Again the energy levels of the individual atoms split to become bands. In the case of insulators, however, the outermost electron shell will be filled, and there will be a gap between the energy band of this shell and the next band of higher energy. This is illustrated in Fig. 6.11 for the diamond crystalline form of carbon [Shl]. This shows the result of calculation on carbon crystals with the diamond structure for various *assumed* atomic spacings. For large spacings, the 2s state ($n = 2, l = 0$) has two electrons in its two allowed states. At the same time, the 2p state ($n = 2, l = 1$) has only two electrons in its six allowed states. As the atomic spacing is decreased, the two energy levels spread into bands that cross. When the crossing occurs, the electrons and states rearrange themselves, resulting in a lower band with four states per atom filled by four electrons per atom and an

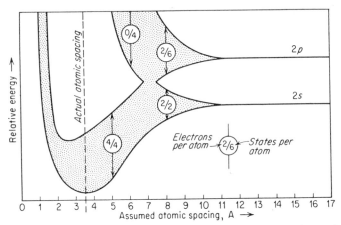

FIG. 6.11. Energy bands in diamond as a function of assumed atomic spacing (theoretical).

upper band with no electrons in its allowed four states per atom. The actual atomic spacing is found to correspond with that for minimum total energy. There is, as a result, a group of outer electrons completely filling a quantum band with a large gap to the next allowed band. In a situation like this, the electrons are immobile in that only an extremely high electrical gradient can supply enough potential energy to elevate an electron to the next allowed band. An equivalent representation of the energy bands for the actual spacing of atoms in a diamond crystal is shown in Fig. 6.12.

With reference to Fig. 6.11 again, it is believed that the atomic spacing in graphite, a conducting form of carbon, is nearly that at the crossover in the diagram. This would make available allowed higher energy states to the outer electrons and account for the conducting property.

Insulators have another important electrical characteristic: They are all dielectrics, i.e., materials with dielectric constants greater than unity.

The basic ideas about dielectrics are probably known to the reader and will be mentioned only briefly here. Also the behavior of dielectrics is adequately explained without recourse to quantum mechanics so that this aspect of the subject will not be developed.

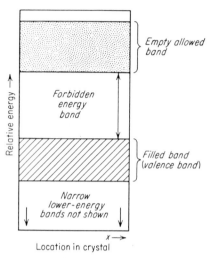

Fig. 6.12. Actual energy bands in diamond vs. distance.

If a block of solid insulating material is placed between the plates of a large parallel-plate capacitor, the capacity of the capacitor will increase by a certain factor. The factor of increase in this case is called the *relative dielectric constant*. The increase in capacity comes about because there is a displacement of the charges in the solid, which produces more charge on the surface of the plates of the capacitor for a given potential difference than would exist without the insulator. Since capacity is the ratio of charge to potential, the capacity is increased, and the increase in capacity is a measure of the so-called dielectric constant of the material.

The displacement of the charges in the dielectric may come about in two ways: (1) The electrons in the atoms will slightly displace themselves relative to the nucleus in the presence of an electric field. (2) In crystals involving more than one kind of atom, the atoms will rearrange themselves relative to each other. The first effect, in terms of quantum theory, results in a deformation of the electron orbits under the influence of an electric field. This change is a gradual one, resulting in an elevation of the energies of all the states but not involving quantum transitions. The energy stored in the dielectric is thus ultimately stored in the atoms themselves. Quantum transitions cannot occur at ordinary temperatures and ordinary electric fields because the allowed energy states are all filled. The second effect mentioned also does not involve quantum effects. These remarks refer only to continuous, or low-frequency, fields. High-frequency fields present different effects. Here, in general, there will be losses associated with the movement of the electrons. Furthermore, the properties of materials may change drastically with frequency, although such changes usually occur between radio and optical frequencies or, at least, at microwave frequencies. Thus certain materials can be transparent to radio waves but opaque to light waves. This difference can be accounted for by a difference in the behavior of the electrons as a function of frequency.

6.6. Energy-band Structure of Semiconductors. Semiconductors are best discussed with reference to their energy-band structure. In general, a semiconductor is one in which the highest energy band is filled at zero temperature but in which the gap to the next allowed band is small. The first property causes a semiconductor to be a dielectric at low temperatures, although the dielectric aspect is important at all temperatures. By a small energy gap is meant one of the order of 1 ev. This is small enough so that at high temperatures a few electrons from the highest normally filled band can "diffuse" over the gap to enter the next highest band, where they become conduction electrons and give the semiconductor its conducting properties. A material with the properties described is called an *intrinsic semiconductor*. The energy-band structure of an intrinsic semiconductor is shown in Fig. 6.13. As we shall see, the characteristics of some semiconductors may be modified by the presence of impurities in amounts as small as parts per million. Accordingly, it is almost impossible to purify some materials to the point where they become intrinsic semiconductors, and instead they remain *extrinsic*, or *impurity-type*, *semiconductors*.

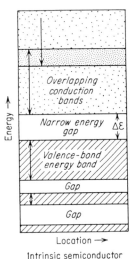

Intrinsic semiconductor

FIG. 6.13. The energy-band structure of an intrinsic semiconductor.

Semiconductors are found among both the elements and the compounds. The semiconductor elements are few and are found in the middle of the periodic table between the electropositive and the electronegative elements. The elements of most interest here are the so-called valence crystals in the fourth column of the periodic table. These have four outer electrons, which form valence bonds with the electrons of adjacent atoms in such a way that each atom is joined to four adjacent atoms. The binding forces between the atoms result from alignment of the electrons to give the structure already shown in Fig. 6.3.

A schematic planar representation of the electron-nucleus arrangement in a crystal of tetravalent atoms is shown in Fig. 6.14. The shaded areas are intended to show the electron probability distribution and have diffuse rather than sharp edges. It is seen that the electron distribution produces a pattern resembling a network connecting the nuclei. The dense spokes between nuclei are often referred to as valence bonds. In the presence of an electric field, the distribution is distorted, with the nuclei tending to move in the direction of the field and the electrons moving in the opposite direction (direction of gradient of potential). This action, referred to in the previous section, is shown in Fig. 6.15.

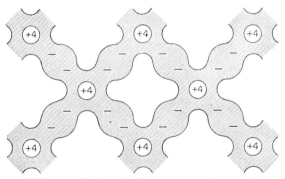

FIG. 6.14. Electron distribution in a crystal of tetravalent atoms.

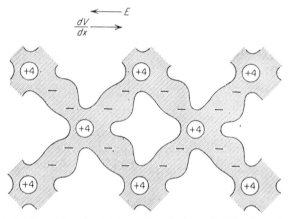

FIG. 6.15. Effect of an electric field on the electron distribution of a tetravalent crystal.

In the tetravalent group of elements are found carbon (atomic number 6), silicon (14), germanium (32), tin (50), lead (82). At the low end of this scale of atomic numbers, we find insulating properties and at the high end, conducting properties. This situation is indicated by the tabulation in Table 6.1 of the energy gap $\Delta\mathcal{E}$ shown in Fig. 6.13.

TABLE 6.1

Element	Energy gap, ev	Comments	Dielectric constant
Carbon (diamond).........	6–7	Insulator	
Silicon...................	1.03	Semiconductor	12
Germanium...............	0.72	Semiconductor	16
Tin (gray)...............	0.1		
Tin (metallic)............	....	Conductor	
Lead....................	....	Conductor	

Some of the other elements also exhibit semiconducting properties. These include boron, valence 3, with an energy gap of 0.9 ev, and tellurium, valence 3, with an energy gap of 0.38 ev.

Various types of imperfections or impurities cause semiconductors to act differently from the intrinsic, or pure and perfect, materials. (Such imperfect, or impure, materials are called extrinsic semiconductors.) In general, these will have extra energy levels in the forbidden band and will, as a result, have much higher conductivities than the intrinsic material. The various defects can be classified as follows:

1. *Substitutional (Chemical)*. Occasional foreign atoms are substituted for normal atoms. Known in impurity-type semiconductors, this defect is deliberately created and controlled for transistor materials.

2. *Vacancies*. An occasional atom is missing from the crystal structure. These lacks are known as *Schottky* effects. They are essential to copper-oxide rectifier and oxide-emitter operation.

3. *Interstitial*. There are extra atoms between the regular atoms of the crystal. These are called *Frenkel* defects.

4. *Dislocations*. These are irregularities in the crystal structure. They are used to make nonrectifying junctions by polishing or sandblasting.

The above classification is somewhat arbitrary. Some writers include electrons, holes, and "phonons" in the list. Other terms such as "excitons," "traps," "color centers," and "recombination centers" will be discussed as the need arises.

It is possible for impurities in the form of occasional atoms with valences of three or five to substitute for tetravalent atoms in the germanium and silicon crystal structure. If the foreign atom has a valence of five, four of its outer electrons will form bonds with the adjacent tetravalent atoms, and the fifth electron will be at liberty to distribute itself about the impurity atom. The behavior of such an excess electron is again expressed as a wave function or probability amplitude in an equivalent orbit. Because of the high dielectric constant of semiconductors, the force binding such an excess electron to its nucleus is much smaller than in free space, and the extent of the orbit will be greater by the relative dielectric constant.

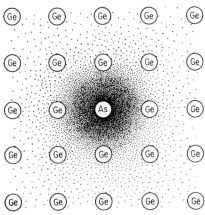

FIG. 6.16. The wave function of an excess electron about an impurity in a semiconductor crystal.

In Fig. 6.16 is shown the wave function of an excess electron in a crystal lattice of the type encountered in semiconductors. It is seen that the excess electron has an orbit which may include many atoms of the crystal. The case shown is that of an arsenic atom of valence 5 in a crystal of germanium atoms of valence 4. Such an impurity semiconductor is known as an *n-type* semiconductor because the excess electron is capable of carrying current and as such is a *negative* carrier.

It should be noted that in the *n*-type semiconductor the electron that does not fit into the normal crystal pattern is in excess only for the bond structure. The crystal is electrically neutral for any number of impurity

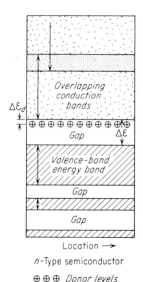

n-Type semiconductor

⊕ ⊕ ⊕ *Donor levels*

Fig. 6.17. Energy bands of an *n*-type semiconductor.

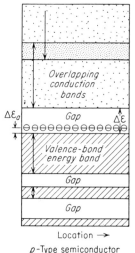

p-Type semiconductor

⊖ ⊖ ⊖ *Acceptor levels*

Fig. 6.18. Energy bands of a *p*-type semiconductor.

centers. It is found that there are extra energy levels associated with impurity atoms having an extra valence electron, which are just a little below the normally empty conduction band in the forbidden energy gap, as shown in Fig. 6.17. These extra energy levels are only a few hundredths of an electron volt below the conducting band. As a result, some of the excess valence electrons are easily given enough extra energy to get into the conduction band, where they give rise to electrical conduction. Because of this action, the impurity centers in this case are called *donors*, since they may give an electron to the conduction band. Those centers which give up their electrons have a residual positive charge that is immobile, although the electrons they give up are free to move through the crystal under the influence of electric fields.

In a similar manner, occasional atoms with valence 3 may fit into the regular crystal structure in place of a tetravalent atom. When this happens, there is a shortage of one electron in the bond structure of the crystal, giving rise to what is called a *hole*. Again there are some extra unfilled energy levels associated with the impurity atoms, which in this case are a few hundredths of an electron volt above the normally filled valence bond band, as shown in Fig. 6.18. In this case, it is easy for some electrons in the valence band to acquire enough energy to be elevated to the extra energy levels. When this is done, a mobile hole is left behind in the valence-bond band that is capable of carrying current and acts like a positive electron. For this reason, such impurity atoms are known as *acceptors*, and the semiconductor is known as a *p type*, indicating that the current carriers are effectively *positive* charges.

The process of *hole conduction* is predominant in *p*-type semiconductors. Actually, the conduction is due to movement of electrons, but the effect is that of a hole moving in the opposite direction. This is analogous to the behavior of a bubble of gas moving up in a liquid. Actually, liquid is moving down around the bubble. Electrically, hole conduction exhibits properties of a positive ion moving with the hole. It must be emphasized that in *p*-type semiconductors the acceptors are immobile, but the holes caused by their acceptance of an electron are mobile.

The characteristics of the two types of impurity semiconductors are seen to be quite similar. In Table 6.2 are summarized the principal characteristics of the *n*- and *p*-type semiconductors, as encountered in silicon and germanium.

TABLE 6.2

	n type	*p* type
Impurities......................	Phosphorus, $_{15}$P; arsenic, $_{33}$As; antimony, $_{51}$Sb; bismuth, $_{83}$Bi; elements in group V	Boron, $_5$B; aluminum, $_{13}$Al; gallium, $_{31}$Ga; indium, $_{49}$In; elements in group III
Name of impurities...............	Donor	Acceptor
Valence of impurities.............	5	3
Nature of carrier.................	Negative (electron)	Positive (hole)
Band in which conduction occurs....	Conduction	Valence
Energy gap[1] (see Figs. 6.17 and 6.18).	$\varepsilon_d = 0.05$ ev (Si) $\varepsilon_d = 0.01$ ev (Ge)	$\varepsilon_a = 0.046$ ev (Si) $\varepsilon_a = 0.01$ ev (Ge)

[1] Energy gaps will be different for different impurities. See [CoD].

Semiconductors often have both types of impurity and both types of carrier. In this case, they are named after the majority carrier.

6.7. Electrical Characteristics of Intrinsic Semiconductors. It was shown in the last section that an intrinsic semiconductor is one with an energy gap of 1 ev or less between a valence band and a conduction band. At zero temperature, the valence band is filled and the conduction band is empty. Accordingly, an intrinsic semiconductor is an insulator at zero temperature. It remains an insulator at low temperatures though the conductivity increases as temperature increases.

The increase of conductivity with temperature is an effect just *opposite* to that encountered in metals. It comes about because the number of carriers available for conduction increases with temperature at a rate greater than the effectiveness of the carriers is reduced by thermal vibration of the molecules. In fact, the former effect is so great relative to the latter that the latter can almost be neglected.

As temperature is raised, some of the electrons in the valence band will acquire enough energy to be elevated into the conduction band. This is a statistical proposition in which it is not possible to speak of the behavior of a particular electron but only of the average behavior of a group of electrons. Under the influence of thermal excitation some electrons will be moving back and forth across the energy gap with a net effect of introducing into the conduction band a number of electrons that increases with temperature. The statistical distribution of electron energies as a function of temperature will be discussed more completely in the next chapter.

It is found that the average number of electrons found in the conduction band above an energy gap $\Delta\mathcal{E}$ in an intrinsic semiconductor, as a result of thermal excitation, is given by

$$n_i = k_e T^{\frac{3}{2}} \epsilon^{-\Delta\mathcal{E}/2kT} \qquad \text{cm}^{-3} \qquad (6.1)$$

where $k_e = 2(2\pi mk/h^2)^{\frac{3}{2}}$ = a universal constant of the order of 5×10^{15} cm^{-3} °K$^{-\frac{3}{2}}$

k = Boltzmann's constant

T = absolute temperature

Both factors in this equation contribute to an increase in the number of electrons available for conduction as temperature increases. At room temperature (300°K) the $k_e T^{\frac{3}{2}}$ product is of the order of 2.41×10^{19} cm^{-3}. For intrinsic germanium with an energy gap of 0.72 ev, the electron density is 2.5×10^{13} cm^{-3} compared with 10^{22} for metals. Conductivities tend to be in the same ratio. It is convenient to remember that at room temperature kT has an energy value equivalent to 25.8 emv. Equation (6.1) is similar to the equation for thermionic emission. The equivalence of the various energy scales used in this and later work is shown in Fig. 6.19.

Actually, the conductivity of an intrinsic semiconductor will depend not only on the number of electrons in the conduction band but also on their mobility. However, the change in mobility with temperature is small compared to the change in the number of electrons available for conduction. It should also be remembered that, for each electron elevated from the valence band to the conduction band, there is made available for conduction a hole in the valence band.

Considering all factors, it is expected that the conductivity of an intrinsic semiconductor will be approximately an exponentially increas-

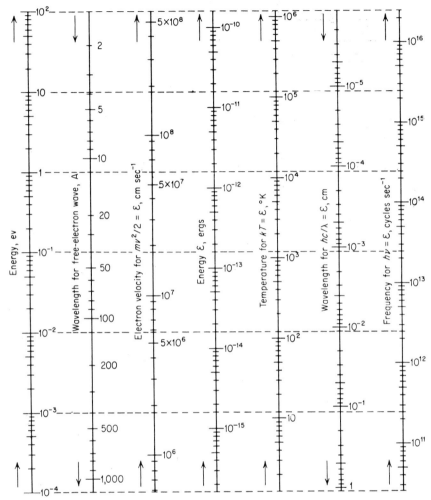

FIG. 6.19. Equivalent energy scales.

ing function of temperature. Accordingly, there will be found the following approximate expression for resistivity:

$$\rho_i \cong A_i \epsilon^{-\Delta\varepsilon/2kT} \qquad \text{ohm-cm} \tag{6.2}$$

where ρ_i = specific resistivity
A_i = a slowly varying function of temperature, practically constant
$\Delta\varepsilon$ = width of forbidden energy gap
k = Boltzmann's constant
T = absolute temperature

In Fig. 6.20 is shown resistivity vs. reciprocal temperature of some semiconducting compounds on a semilogarithmic plot. The straight-line character of these curves confirms the expectations. The curve A is for a mixture of manganese oxide and nickel oxide. The curve B is for a mixture of three oxides, manganese, nickel, and cobalt. From the slope of the curves the energy gap in these materials is estimated to be about 0.6 ev.

The particular combinations of oxides used here are favored because their resistance characteristics are insensitive to impurities, which makes for materials easy to reproduce. This is in striking contrast to the behavior of elements like germanium and silicon, which are so sensitive to impurities that it is practically impossible to purify them to the point where they behave like intrinsic semiconductors at ordinary temperatures.

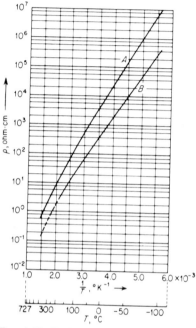

Fig. 6.20. Resistivity of some intrinsic semiconductors as a function of reciprocal temperature.

6.8. Resistance Characteristics of Impurity-type Semiconductors. The variation of conductivity of an impurity-type semiconductor is different from that of an intrinsic semiconductor. In general, there will be a slow increase of conductivity with temperature (less than the intrinsic rate) at low temperature and intrinsic behavior at high temperature. In between these limits, the conductivity may, if sufficient impurities are present, decrease slightly with increasing temperature, as is the case with metals. Shown in Fig. 6.21 is a family of curves of resistivity of a semiconductor vs. temperature for various amounts of impurities.

To understand the reason for the shape of the curves of Fig. 6.21, let us consider the behavior of an n-type impurity semiconductor that has but one type of impurity.

At absolute zero of temperature, the impurity-type semiconductor is also a dielectric. As temperature increases, some electrons from the donor levels shown in Fig. 6.17 may be elevated by thermal excitation across the small energy gap $\Delta \varepsilon_d$, into the conduction band. The number of electrons so elevated *at first* follows a law that is the same as that for intrinsic semiconductors [(6.1)] but determined by the energy gap $\Delta \varepsilon_d$

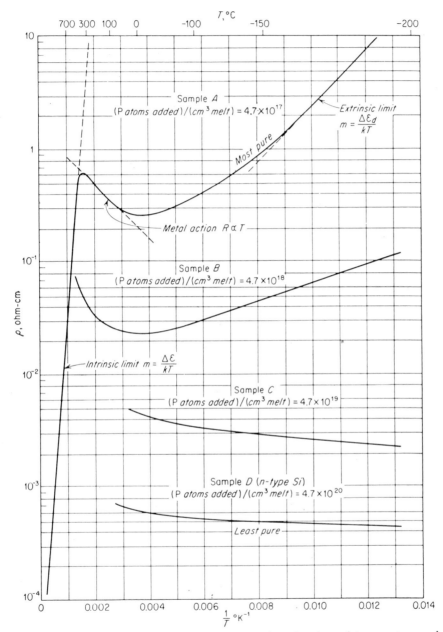

Fig. 6.21. Resistivity of n-type silicon as a function of reciprocal temperature and impurity concentration. (*Bell Telephone Laboratories.*)

between the donor levels and the conduction band:

$$n_d \cong k_e T^{\frac{3}{4}} \epsilon^{-\Delta\mathcal{E}_d/2kT} \tag{6.3}$$

where n_d = no. of donor electrons in conduction band

$k_e = 2(2\pi mk/h^2)^{\frac{3}{2}}$

$\Delta\mathcal{E}_d$ = energy gap between donor levels and conduction band

Since the conductivity is proportional to the product of the number of conduction electrons and their *mobility* and the mobility is a slowly decreasing function of temperature, the conductivity will *at first* increase exponentially with temperature. In Fig. 6.21 is shown a semilogarithmic plot of *resistivity* vs. *reciprocal temperature* for silicon with various amounts of phosphorus constituting an *n*-type impurity. This is like a curve of *conductivity* vs. *temperature* when viewed upside down. Since resistivity is the reciprocal of conductivity, the former is a straight line with a slope proportional to the energy gap $\Delta\mathcal{E}_d$ at low temperature or large $1/T$. This is seen in curve A of the figure. As temperature increases, if the amount of the impurity is small, the donors soon will have given up all their electrons and the decrease in mobility of the conduction electrons with increasing temperature will cause the resistivity to increase with temperature, as in a metal. This gives rise to a region of negative slope in the figure. If temperature is raised still more, some of the electrons in the valence band will acquire enough energy to be elevated into the conduction band, as in an intrinsic semiconductor. This will again give rise to a decrease in resistivity, or increase in conductivity, with temperature so that the slope of the curve in Fig. 6.21 will be proportional to the total energy gap $\Delta\mathcal{E}$ between the valence band and the conduction band at high temperatures.

Curves of resistivity vs. reciprocal temperature for larger amounts of impurity will have the same general form, although as more impurity is added the conductivity will be increased or the resistivity decreased. Also the number of conduction electrons and the mobility will tend to be in balance over a larger range of temperature though generally having a small positive coefficient of temperature (like metals) at room temperature. At sufficiently high temperatures, however, the intrinsic action will dominate and give a decrease in resistivity with temperature independent of the amount of impurity.

The same general action will be encountered in *p*-type semiconductors or in combinations of *n* and *p* type. In the latter case, the conductivity will be the sum of the conductivities due to the holes and to the electrons. It has already been indicated that, for one type of impurity, the conductivity depends upon the product of the number of carriers and their mobility. *Mobility is defined as the magnitude of the average drift velocity of carriers per unit gradient of potential.* Accordingly, it has dimensions of meters per second per volt per meter (or meters squared per second per volt). Drift velocity is linear with potential gradient up to 100 volts cm^{-1} at ordinary temperatures. Conductivity effects of holes and electrons may be added, it being remembered that electron carriers result from n-type impurities and hole carriers from p-type impurities.[1] Thus, for n-type semiconductors,

$$\sigma_n = en\mu_n \qquad \text{mhos cm}^{-1} \qquad\qquad (6.4)$$

where e = magnitude of electron charge
  n = no. of electrons, cm^{-3}
  μ_n = mobility of electrons, cm^2 sec^{-1} volt^{-1}
For p-type semiconductors,

$$\sigma_p = ep\mu_p \qquad \text{mhos cm}^{-1} \qquad\qquad (6.5)$$

where p = no. of holes, cm^{-3}
  μ_p = mobility of holes, cm^2 sec^{-1} volt^{-1}
When there is a combination of carriers, the resultant conductivity is

$$\sigma = e(n\mu_n + p\mu_p) \qquad \text{mhos cm}^{-1} \qquad\qquad (6.6)$$

Even for a single type of impurity, there are two factors contributing to conductivity that cannot be separated by resistance measurements alone. Fortunately, there is an effect associated with application of combined electric and magnetic fields that makes possible the separation of these factors.

It was shown in Chap. 4 that, when a stream of electrons in a vacuum is subjected to a transverse magnetic field, the stream is deflected in a direction perpendicular to the stream and the field. It was further shown that it is possible to apply a compensating force with a transverse electric field so that the net deflection is zero. An action similar to this occurs in a crystal semiconductor. If there is applied a magnetic field transverse to the direction of the current, the carriers will tend to be deflected to one side. This will have the effect of piling up charge and so building up a gradient of potential perpendicular to the magnetic field and to the current, which will finally reach an equilibrium value for which the average electric and magnetic forces on the carriers are in balance. A potential difference across the crystal then exists, which can be measured and which gives a measure of the carrier density. This is known as the Hall effect (1897).

The behavior of carriers exhibited in the case of the Hall effect is a little more complex than the behavior of electrons in a vacuum under the combined influence of electric and magnetic fields, but in principle the

---

[1] Hole and electron densities are, however, *not* directly proportional to acceptor and donor densities when these are nearly equal. This is discussed in connection with Fig. 7.6.

effects are the same. In semiconductors the carriers do not move with uniform velocity but have a random motion upon which is superimposed a drift velocity. Accordingly, one can speak only of average effects. Shown in Fig. 6.22 are the relative directions of current and associated electron flow, transverse magnetic field, and resultant transverse electric field for an n-type semiconductor. As shown here, a current in the positive x direction, corresponding to an electron flow in the negative x direction, is subjected to a transverse magnetic field in the positive z direction. The result of this is to build up a gradient of potential in the positive y direction that can be measured externally.

In (4.31) it was shown that transverse electric and magnetic forces on an electron are in balance for $v_x = E_y/B_z$, in mks units here and for the

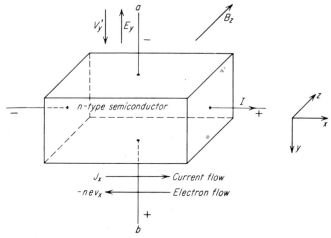

FIG. 6.22. Notation for Hall-effect measurements in an n-type semiconductor.

rest of this section. This is equivalent to the situation in Fig. 6.22 except that the velocity used must be the average drift velocity. The Hall coefficient R is defined as the ratio of the electric field produced per unit current density to the transverse magnetic field. Thus,

$$R_m = \frac{E_y/B_z}{J_x} = \frac{+v_x}{-nev_x} = -\frac{1}{ne} \qquad \text{m}^3 \text{ coulomb}^{-1} \qquad (6.7)$$

Accordingly, the Hall coefficient R_m is inversely proportional to the electron carrier density n. Here R_m is the coefficient that applies to free electrons in *metals*. Because of the fact that the electrons in semiconductors are not entirely free, the Hall coefficient for *semiconductors* is found to be

$$R_n = -\frac{3\pi}{8ne} = -\frac{1.18}{ne} \qquad \text{m}^3 \text{ coulomb}^{-1} \qquad (6.8)$$

for n-type materials. In this case terminal a is negative relative to terminal b, and the Hall coefficient is negative.

For p-type semiconductors, the carriers are holes, or effectively positive ions. Their motion is in the direction of the current, and their reaction to a magnetic field is in the same direction as was the case for the electron carriers since both their charge sign and velocity direction are changed. However, the gradient of potential built up by their slight displacement, which finally gives equilibrium, is of the opposite sign from that for electrons because the charge sign is different. The relations in this case are

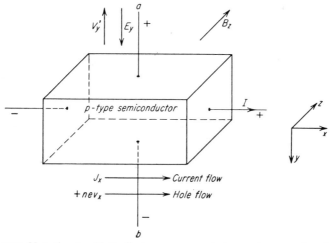

FIG. 6.23. Notation for Hall-effect measurements in a p-type semiconductor.

shown in Fig. 6.23. In this case, the terminal a is positive relative to b, and the Hall coefficient is

$$R_p = \frac{3\pi}{8pe} = \frac{1.18}{pe} \quad \text{m}^3 \text{ coulomb}^{-1} \tag{6.9}$$

It is seen that the Hall coefficient increases as the density of the carriers, and hence the amount of impurities decreases. This makes Hall-coefficient measurements a very sensitive indication of the amount of impurities, much more sensitive than any means of chemical analysis.

After combining the expressions for conductivity [(6.4)] and Hall coefficient [(6.8)], the electron mobility is found to be

$$\mu_n = -\frac{\sigma_n R_n}{1.18} \quad \text{m}^2 \text{ sec}^{-1} \text{ volt}^{-1} \tag{6.10}$$

Similarly,
$$\mu_p = -\frac{\sigma_p R_p}{1.18} \quad \text{m}^2 \text{ sec}^{-1} \text{ volt}^{-1} \tag{6.11}$$

Thus carrier concentrations and mobilities can be determined from measurements of conductivity and Hall coefficient when only one type of carrier is present.   Relations for a combination of carriers are more complicated but follow the same principles.[1]

The Hall coefficient is negative over the entire temperature range for n-type semiconductors.   It is positive for p-type semiconductors at ordinary temperatures but becomes negative for high temperatures when the intrinsic action begins to produce negative carriers with higher mobilities than holes.   Hall coefficients are found to be of the order of 100×10^{-4} m³ coulomb^{-1}, although values larger and smaller by a factor of 100 may be encountered.   Mobilities at room temperature (300°K) for n- and p-type germanium and silicon are found to be [CoB] as listed in Table 6.3.   These values are accurate to about 5 per cent.

TABLE 6.3. MOBILITIES IN CENTIMETERS SQUARED PER SECOND PER VOLT

Carrier	Germanium	Silicon
Electron (n type).............	3,600	· 1,200
Hole (p type)...............	1,700	250

They vary as the inverse three-halves power of temperature.   Further, the mobilities of the semiconductor elements are considerably higher than for the semiconductor compounds.   They are also much higher than for metals, the mobility of electrons in copper being 40×10^{-4} m² sec^{-1} volt^{-1} (40 cm² sec^{-1} volt^{-1}).

6.9. Essential Relations Pertaining to Diffusion.   Even though the mobility of carriers in a semiconductor is greater than that of electrons in metals by a factor of a thousand or so, the conductivity of semiconductors is much less than that of metals because the current carriers are liable to be less numerous by a factor of a million or more.   This conductivity is so much less that the random motion of the carriers is often a more significant effect than the drift due to applied fields.   The random motion of current carriers tends to equalize carrier densities.   If there is a region of high carrier density, the random motion causes carriers to flow from the more to the less dense regions.   This action is known as diffusion, and the accompanying currents are called diffusion currents.

The defining relations for diffusion currents in one dimension are

$$J_n = eD_n \frac{\partial n}{\partial x} \qquad \text{for electrons}$$

$$J_p = -eD_p \frac{\partial p}{\partial x} \qquad \text{for holes}$$

(6.12)

---

[1] The Hall coefficient of a composite semiconductor is given by [ShA]

$$R = -\frac{1.18}{e} \frac{n\mu_n^2 - p\mu_p^2}{(n\mu_n + p\mu_p)^2} \qquad \text{m³ coulomb}^{-1}$$

where J_n = diffusion-current density of electrons

$\quad\quad J_p$ = diffusion-current density of holes

$\quad\quad e$ = magnitude of electron charge

$\quad\quad D_n$ = diffusion constant of electrons

$\quad\quad D_p$ = diffusion constant of holes

$\quad \partial n/\partial x$ = gradient of electron density

The significance of the above equations is that the diffusion current due to random motion of carriers from dense to less dense regions is proportional to the gradient or rate of increase with distance of the carrier density. The coefficient of proportionality is indicated by the letter D, which is called the diffusion constant. In the case of electrons, if the density of electrons increases to the right, the net electron flow is to the left and the conventional current flow is thus to the right. In the case of holes, if the density of holes increases to the right, the net hole flow is to the left and the current is therefore negative. This accounts for the algebraic signs in (6.12). The diffusion constant has the dimensions of meters squared per second in mks units and centimeters squared per second in cgs units. Typical values of D at room temperature are given in Table 6.4.

TABLE 6.4

Material	D_n, cm² sec⁻¹	D_p, cm² sec⁻¹
Germanium............	93.5	44
Silicon...............	31	6.5
Copper...............	1.0	No holes in metal

Conservation of electric charge requires that the time rate of increase of charge density be equal to the rate of generation of charge by any means minus the rate of absorption of charge by any means minus the net outward flow of current per unit volume. Mathematically this is written, for current flow restricted to one dimension,

$$\frac{\partial \rho}{\partial t} = g - r_1 - \frac{\partial J_x}{\partial x} \tag{6.13}$$

where ρ = space-charge density

$\quad\quad g$ = charge generated per unit volume per second by any means (injection, photo-, or thermal action)

$\quad\quad r_1$ = charge lost per volume per unit time by recombination

$\quad \dfrac{\partial J_x}{\partial x}$ = divergence of current or net outward current flow per unit volume with one-dimensional flow

From (6.12),

$$J_d = -D\frac{\partial \rho}{\partial x} \tag{6.14}$$

where J_d = diffusion-current density for either holes or electrons

$\quad\quad D$ = appropriate diffusion constant

$\quad\quad \rho = ep$ or $-en$.

Substituting (6.14) into (6.13), we get

$$\frac{\partial \rho}{\partial t} = g - r_1 + D \frac{\partial^2 \rho}{\partial x^2} \tag{6.15}$$

This is known as the *diffusion equation*.   It is identical to the heat diffusion equation upon substitution of thermal quantities.   This equation is encountered in skin-effect studies.   It also describes chemical diffusion as well as the action of artificial transmission lines with resistance and shunt capacity only or of ideal cables [Pie, chap. 18].   Solutions of this equation tell how space-charge density varies with both distance and time from a given initial distribution.   The diffusion equation may be used for either electrons or holes since ρ is ep or $-en$.

A particular solution of (6.15), for $g = r_1 = 0$ and an initial concentration of charge in a thin layer, is

$$n(x,t) = \frac{n_0}{2 \sqrt{D_n \pi t}} \epsilon^{-x^2/4D_n t} \tag{6.16}$$

where n_0 is the initial electron density.   This shows a probability distribution with x and amplitude decreasing exponentially with time.

For the corresponding three-dimensional problem with initial electron density n_0 in a small sphere, the solution is

$$n(r,t) = n_0(D_n \pi t)^{-\frac{3}{2}} \epsilon^{-r^2/4D_n t} \tag{6.17}$$

This equation shows a probability distribution with radius r decreasing exponentially with time as shown in Fig. 6.24.   If a sphere is drawn with a radius R through a charge density equal to one-tenth of the charge density at the center of the sphere, then

$$R = 9.2 D_n t \quad\quad \text{cm} \tag{6.18}$$

The area of such a sphere grows uniformly with time.

In cases where the generation rate due to injection is constant, the recombination rate will be proportional to the product of the electron and hole densities, $r_1 = knp$.   In this case (6.15) reduces to

$$\frac{\partial (p - p_n)}{\partial t} = -\frac{p - p_n}{\tau_p} + D_p \frac{\partial^2 (p - p_n)}{\partial x^2} \tag{6.19}$$

which applies to holes as minority carriers in an n-type region with holes being injected (see Appendix 3).   Here p_n is the equilibrium value of holes and τ_p is a mean lifetime of holes before recombination.   Solutions of this equation in the steady state, i.e., left member zero, take the form

$$p - p_n = A_1 \epsilon^{x/L_p} + A_2 \epsilon^{-x/L_p} \tag{6.20}$$

where $L_p = (D_p \tau_p)^{\frac{1}{2}}$ is a mean recombination distance of the holes.   This solution says that, with a constant number of holes being injected into a region, the resultant density of holes will be a combination of exponentials

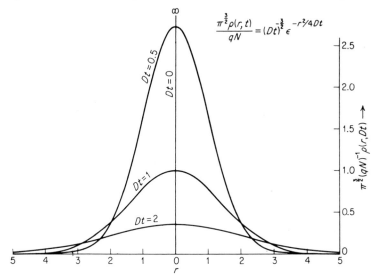

FIG. 6.24. Radial diffusion of charge in a semiconductor as a function of time.

increasing and/or decreasing with distance.   This is the situation commonly encountered in junction diodes and transistors.

Mobility has already been defined as

$$\mu = \frac{v_d}{E} \tag{6.21}$$

where μ = mobility
  v_d = average drift velocity
  E = electric field

Accordingly, conduction current density is given by

$$J_c = e\mu_n n E \tag{6.22}$$

where e = carrier charge
  n = carrier density

Total current will be the sum of conduction and diffusion currents. Thus the total current density, for electrons, is

$$J_n = e\mu_n n E_x + eD_n \frac{\partial n}{\partial x} \tag{6.23}$$

and for holes,

$$J_p = e\mu_p p E_x - eD_p \frac{\partial p}{\partial x} \tag{6.24}$$

There is a simple relation between the mobility and diffusion constants known as the Einstein relation.   It is, at $300°K$,

$$\frac{D}{\mu} = \frac{kT}{e} = 0.026 \text{ volt} \tag{6.25}$$

This may be shown from the fact that the factor n is governed by $\epsilon^{eV/kT}$ and by substituting in (6.20) when total current is zero.[1]

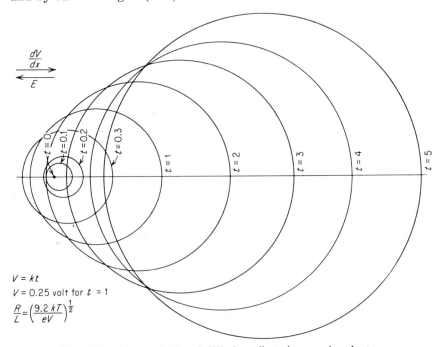

FIG. 6.25. Relative drift and diffusion effects in a semiconductor.

From the Einstein relation above, the diffusion characteristics can be determined from the mobility characteristics.   The mobility characteristics of germanium and silicon have been investigated [PrC, PrD].[2]   In general, mobilities are increasing functions of resistivity and impurity densities.   They are strong inverse functions of temperature, varying experimentally between the -1.5 and -2.3 power of temperature.

Another important relation between drift due to a uniform potential gradient and radial diffusion is

$$\frac{R}{L} = \left(\frac{9.2kT}{eV}\right)^{\frac{1}{2}} \tag{6.26}$$

[1] Since $n = k_1, \epsilon^{eV/kT}$, then $dn/dx = (e/kT)n \, dV/dx = -(e/kT)n \, E_x$.   Substituting into (6.23), $J_n = enE_x[\mu_n - (e/kT)D_n] = 0$, or $D_n/\mu_n = kT/e$, as in (6.25).

[2] Mobility is more readily measured by direct observations on drift than by the Hall effect.

where L = distance drifted over voltage V

R = radial-diffusion distance in the same time

For small voltages, the radial diffusion is greater than the conduction drift. The two distances are equal for about $\frac{1}{4}$ volt. For greater voltages, the drift is greater than the diffusion. This action is shown in Fig. 6.25. Since resistive voltage drops in impurity semiconductors are small in practice, current flow is often largely a diffusion component.

6.10. Vector Form of Diffusion Relations. For those readers who are familiar with vector notation, the important relations of Sec. 6.9 will be rewritten in vector form. An increase in generality and compactness is thereby achieved.

Diffusion current:

$$J_n = eD_n\nabla n \qquad \text{for electrons}$$
$$J_p = -eDp\nabla p \qquad \text{for holes}$$

(6.12)

Continuity of electric charge (diffusion equation):

$$\frac{\partial \rho}{\partial t} = g - r_1 - \nabla \cdot \mathbf{J}$$

(6.13)

Diffusion-current density in terms of space-charge density:

$$J_d = -D\nabla\rho$$

(6.14)

Diffusion equation in terms of space-charge density:

$$\frac{\partial \rho}{\partial t} = g - r_1 - D\nabla^2\rho$$

(6.15)

Diffusion equation in terms of hole density:

$$\frac{\partial (p - p_n)}{\partial t} = -\frac{p - p_n}{\tau_p} + D_p\nabla^2(p - p_n)$$

(6.19)

CHAPTER 7

JUNCTION EFFECTS

7.1. Significance of This Chapter. In previous chapters, the behavior of electrons in free space and within conductors and semiconductors has already been discussed. Actual electron devices include combinations of these various media. It is necessary to know not only how electrons behave in each part but how they behave in passing from one part to another. The latter is the field of junction effects.

This is a large subject. Properly speaking, it includes emission as well as solid junctions of various types. Many aspects of the subject are common to both. However, this chapter will be concerned only with solid junctions since the inclusion of emission as well would make the chapter too large.

7.2. Energy Distribution of Electrons in Conductors and Semiconductors. It has already been shown in previous chapters that electrons in an unfilled conduction band run around pretty much at will. As far as conduction effects go, it is not necessary to know much more than this about these electrons; but when the movement of electrons over barriers (across junctions) is to be considered, it is necessary to know their energy distribution as well.

In speaking of electron energy it is most important to specify what kind of energy one is talking about in order to avoid confusion. It is not always apparent whether the energy is total, kinetic, or potential. In the last chapter, the energy was total unless otherwise specified. In the rest of this book, the effort will be made to distinguish clearly between the different forms of energy. The term energy without a qualifying adjective will always mean total energy. Otherwise, qualifying adjectives will be used.

Our general expectation is that total electron energies will be distributed over a wide range from almost zero upward. We further expect that, at low temperatures, the electrons will have the lowest possible total energies and that, at high temperatures, some of them will have high energies. This is reasonable enough and correct but not quantitative enough to be useful. When we deal with semiconductors, we need the distribution of electrons in the various energy bands. A detailed examination of this subject requires the application of quantum theory to crystal structures [Shl].   The results of such a study can only be summarized here.

The distribution of energy among the electrons in various bands of a solid depends upon two factors: The first factor gives the density of the allowed quantum states as a function of total energy; the second, the distribution of the electrons among these states.   Thus in general,

$$dn = dS(\mathcal{E})f(\mathcal{E},T) \qquad (7.1)$$

where dn is the number of electrons per unit volume in a range of states $dS(\mathcal{E})$, as modified by a distribution function $f(\mathcal{E},T)$ depending upon the relative total energy $\mathcal{E}$ and temperature T.

The first, or state, factor $dS(\mathcal{E})$ is determined by solutions of Schrödinger's equation for the atoms and the crystal structures involved.   The states will form bands, as already indicated, which are overlapping for metals, widely spaced for insulators, and slightly separated for semiconductors. The distribution of energy within the states is indicated by

$$dS(\mathcal{E}) = N(\mathcal{E})\, d\mathcal{E} \qquad (7.2)$$

where $N(\mathcal{E})$ = no. of quantum states per unit energy per unit volume of a crystal

$\mathcal{E}$ = total energy

dS = no. of energy states per unit volume in the energy range $d\mathcal{E}$.

For the *particular case of metals*, the distribution of energy among quantum states in the highest band as a function of energy is nearly the same as for free electrons in an equipotential region.   If the Pauli exclusion principle and the Heisenberg uncertainty principle be applied, it is found that (Appendix 4)

$$dS = k_1 \mathcal{E}^{\frac{1}{2}}\, d\mathcal{E} \qquad (7.3)$$

The constant k_1 is a universal constant of value $(4\pi/h^3)(2m)^{\frac{3}{2}}$, where m is electron mass and h is Planck's constant.   Here the number of states is so great as to give a virtually continuous function.

The second factor of (7.1) is a universal distribution function that tells how the electrons are distributed among the available quantum states. At absolute-zero temperature, it is expected that the electrons will occupy the lowest available energy states but with *not more than one* electron occupying each quantum state in accordance with the Pauli exclusion principle, which still holds for aggregates of atoms.   Accordingly, for zero temperature, the distribution function should be a step function with a value of unity up to the electron in the highest energy state and a value of zero beyond.   For higher temperatures, some of the electrons will acquire thermal energy to send them up to higher energy states.

This is a statistical proposition that leads to a spreading out of the electrons over the step existing at zero temperature.

The statistics describing the above behavior with temperatures are known as the *Fermi-Dirac statistics* after the men who proposed the theory. In accordance with this theory, the distribution function for any temperature has the form (Appendix 5)

$$f(\varepsilon,T) = \frac{1}{1 + \epsilon^{[(\varepsilon - \varepsilon_f)/kT]}} = \frac{1}{2}\left(1 + \tanh\frac{\varepsilon_f - \varepsilon}{2kT}\right) \qquad (7.4)$$

where ε = total energy

ε_f = a reference level, called the Fermi level, for which the distribution function *always has a value of one-half*

k = Boltzmann's constant

T = absolute temperature

This distribution function is seen to be a step function for zero temperature since the exponential term is zero for less than ε_f and infinite for ε

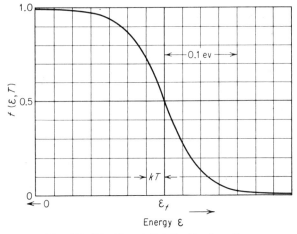

FIG. 7.1. The Fermi distribution function.

greater than ε_f. For finite values of T, the corners of the step are progressively rounded off for increasing values of T. This distribution function plotted with the energy scale horizontal is shown in Fig. 7.1. It is seen to vary from a value of 0.95 to 0.5 over a range of $6kT$. At room temperature (300°K), this is an energy span of about 0.3 ev. At 1000°K, this is an energy span of about 1 ev. It should be remembered that the distribution function is a probability function that indicates the average values expected in a large group of electrons. The Fermi level is virtually independent of temperature in metals, but for semiconductors the Fermi level changes appreciably with temperature.

A combination of the parabolic energy-state law of (7.3) for *metals* with the Fermi distribution function of (7.4) yields an electron-density-energy relation for metals of the form

$$\frac{dn}{d\varepsilon} = k_1 \varepsilon^{\frac{1}{2}} (\epsilon^{(\varepsilon - \varepsilon_f)/kT} + 1)^{-1} \tag{7.5}$$

which holds most exactly for the univalent metals. Here dn is the number of electrons per unit volume in the energy range $d\varepsilon$. The Fermi levels, measured relative to the bottom of the conduction band, range from a few tenths of an electron volt to six or eight electron volts, depending upon the electron density. The Fermi level has a value of

$$\frac{h^2}{8m} \left(\frac{3n}{\pi} \right)^{\frac{2}{3}}$$

where n is the number of free electrons per cubic centimeter. For the representative density of 10^{22} electrons per cubic centimeter, the Fermi

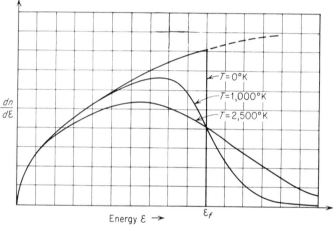

FIG. 7.2. The energy distribution of electrons in a metal at various temperatures.

level has a value of 1.76 ev. The resultant value of $dn/d\varepsilon$ given in (7.5) is shown in Fig. 7.2 for temperature values of 0, 1000, and 2500°K.

An alternative representation of Fig. 7.2 is given in Fig. 7.3. Here in part (a) is shown the energy distribution for zero temperature. In part (b) is a water-tank analogue in which agitation corresponds to the diffusion of energy levels produced by raising the temperature. In part (c) is shown the enlarged portion of (a) at the Fermi level but for room temperature. Part (d) shows the Fermi distribution function in relation to the resulting electron distribution.

It should be pointed out that the state function of (7.3) is only an approximation, which, because of the assumption of constant potential within a metal, is least accurate for low values of energy though quite accurate for high values. Fortunately, the applications of interest

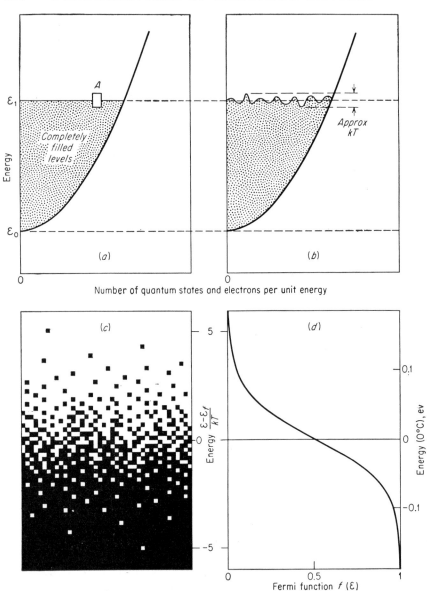

Fig. 7.3. Various representations of the energy distribution of electrons in a metal: (a) Distribution for the absolute zero of temperature. (b) A water-tank analogue. (c) Enlargement of part of (a) but for room temperature, each unit of area representing a quantum state. (d) The Fermi distribution function. (*After Shockley.*)

involve the high energy states so that the relation can be used with assurance.

The above energy distribution for electrons is quite different from what would exist if electrons behaved like molecules of a gas, as was originally believed. The distribution of velocities and energies in a gas was worked out by Maxwell (1857), who thus laid the groundwork for the kinetic theory of gases. Maxwell's work elaborated by Boltzmann gave rise to what is known as Maxwell-Boltzmann, or classical, statistics [Sll]. The energy distribution according to classical statistics is given by

$$dn = \frac{2N}{\sqrt{\pi}} (kT)^{-\frac{3}{2}} \mathcal{E}^{\frac{1}{2}} e^{-\mathcal{E}/kT} \, d\mathcal{E} \tag{7.6}$$

where dn = no. of molecules in interval of energy $d(e\mathcal{E}/kt)$
$\mathcal{E}$ = energy
e = electron-charge magnitude
k = Boltzmann's constant
T = absolute temperature
N = no. of molecules per unit volume

Shown in Fig. 7.4 are curves of the Maxwellian distribution of energies at 1000 and 2500°K. These curves are quite different in both shape and magnitude from the energy-distribution curves for electrons in a metal. The two distributions resemble each other only for high values of energy, for which the tails of the distribution functions have the same exponential form, although the numerical values for the Fermi-Dirac distribution are thousands of times greater than for the Maxwellian distribution.

The same principles indicated above also apply to semiconductors. Shown in Fig. 7.5 is the electron distribution in a typical semiconductor. In part (a) of the figure is shown the state distribution of an n-type semiconductor that, however, also contains p-type impurities. In part (b) of the figure is shown the Fermi distribution function. In part (c) of the figure is shown the product of the curves of parts (a) and (b) for energies above the Fermi level. This serves to give the electron distribution in the conduction band and at the donor level. For energies below the Fermi level, the hole densities are of more interest than the electron densities. These are found by multiplying the state distribution of part (a) by the complement of the Fermi distribution function, namely, $1 - f$, of part (b). The hole distributions in part (c) are shown dotted and give the bound holes at the acceptor level and the conduction holes in the valence band. In a case such as this, the Fermi level, as always, is chosen so that the area under the distribution curve of part (c) is equal to zero. More specifically, the number of electrons in the conduction band and at the donor level plus the number of acceptors must equal the number of holes in the valence band and at the acceptor level plus the number of donors. The Fermi level in germanium as determined by donor den-

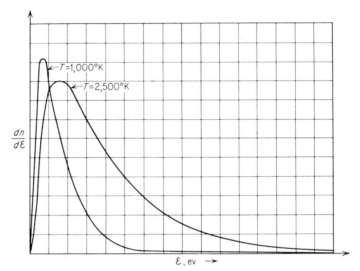

FIG. 7.4. The Maxwell-Boltzmann energy distribution of molecules in a gas at various temperatures.

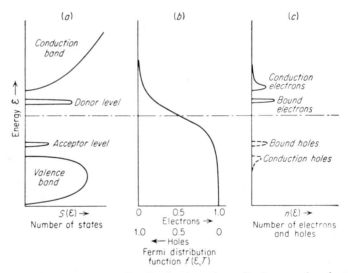

FIG. 7.5. Electron energy distribution in an impurity-type semiconductor.

sity N_d and by acceptor density N_a is shown in Fig. 7.6.   Also shown are the resultant electron and hole densities and the conductivity.

Some important properties are revealed by this figure.   It is seen that for n-type materials the electron density n is nearly equal to the donor density N_d as long as this exceeds the acceptor density N_a by a factor of 50 or more.   A similar statement applies to p-type materials.   *Under* *equilibrium conditions, the product of electron density n and hole density p will be equal to their product for the intrinsic case, that is, $np = n_i p_i = n_i^2$.*

7.3. Work Function of Metals and Semiconductors. It has been shown in the last section that electrons with various energies exist in

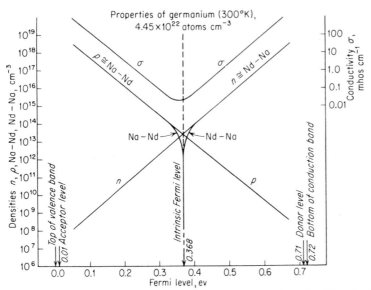

FIG. 7.6. Properties of germanium at room temperature as determined by density of impurities.

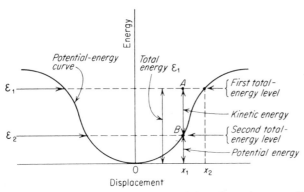

FIG. 7.7. Method of representing kinetic, potential, and total energy illustrated for the case of a simple pendulum.

conductors and semiconductors. Further, the higher the temperature, the greater the range of energies. Accordingly, as temperature increases, a few electrons acquire very high energies and corresponding velocities. They may then have enough energy to surmount potential barriers such as exist at conductor surfaces and junctions. It is now necessary to say something about these potential barriers.

In this and subsequent sections there will be used some diagrams in which there are shown at the same time *levels* of total energy and the *curve* of potential energy.   The nature of these diagrams is illustrated by a similar diagram for a simple pendulum, as shown in Fig. 7.7.   Here there is shown a *curve* of potential energy with an arbitrary reference level of zero potential energy for zero displacement.   The potential energy is a function of position and is *independent* of the total energy of the system. Also shown is a level of total energy $\mathcal{E}_1$.   This is independent of position but bounded by the potential-energy curve.   For a condition of total energy $\mathcal{E}_1$, the pendulum can swing to the right only a distance x_2.   At x_1 with energy $\mathcal{E}_1$ the potential energy is given by the height of B above the zero reference level, and the kinetic energy is given by the height of the

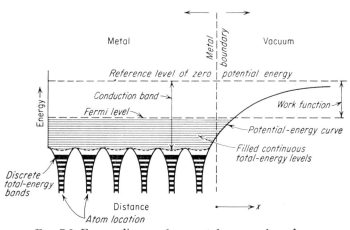

Fig. 7.8. Energy diagram for a metal-vacuum boundary.

total energy line above the potential-energy curve AB.   For a condition of total energy $\mathcal{E}_2$, the pendulum can swing only to x_1, where the kinetic energy will be zero.

The relative energy values of electrons in a metal are shown in Fig. 7.8. Here are shown both the total-energy *levels* and the relative potential-energy *curve*, which applies to all electrons.   The total-energy levels are determined from quantum-mechanical and quantum-statistical considerations, as indicated in previous material.   The potential energy $-eV$ is determined by the work done on an electron by electrostatic forces as it is brought from a point remote from the surface to a point within the metal.   The level of potential energy remote from the metal is arbitrarily taken as zero.   As an electron is brought toward the metal, work is done on it by attractive forces yielding values of potential energy more negative or values of electric potential more positive.

Let us now examine these two energy representations in more detail. The total energy of the electrons in a conductor has a band structure at low levels. The uppermost bands are broad and overlap, forming the conduction band, which is, however, only partly filled. At zero temperature the conduction band is filled up to the Fermi level. For higher temperatures some of the electrons will have energies higher than the Fermi level, and there will be some vacancies in the energy states below, as previously discussed.

The potential-energy curve at points remote from the surface will be determined by work done by an "image" force, which will vary inversely as the square of the distance from the metal. This yields a potential and a negative potential energy which varies inversely as the distance from the metal. This obviously cannot continue right up to the surface of the metal, for it would yield infinite potential energy. Close to the metal the potential energy probably varies linearly down to some finite value, and within the metal it probably varies a little with the distance from the individual atoms. Such expectations, based on classical considerations, are bound to be inaccurate within the metal, where quantum considerations will hold. However, the potential energy is expected to be more or less constant within the metal except in the immediate vicinity of the atoms, as shown by the dotted line in the figure.

The two energy scales are usually matched by considering that the average potential energy between atoms is at the bottom of the conduction band. The difference between the potential energy so adjusted outside the metal and the energy value at the Fermi level is known as the *work function* of the metal. It is the energy that an electron at the Fermi level must acquire to escape from the metal. It is also the work done in removing an electron at the Fermi level from the metal. It is a positive quantity measured in electron volts. Numerically, the work function in electron volts is equal to the height of the potential barrier in volts measured from the voltage equivalent of the Fermi level.

In general, values of the work function are difficult to determine theoretically. It is expected that the work function is higher for small spacing between the atoms, and this has been verified for the halogens. A surface effect must also be considered. There will usually be a change in the atomic spacing at the surface and often an additional component of force due to surface charges as well. Because of these and other factors, the most reliable values of the work function are measured values. We shall see that it is possible to deduce the value of the work function from measured values of thermionic and photoelectric emission. Work functions of practical emitters range in value from about 1 to 5 ev, corresponding to equivalent potential barriers of 1 to 5 volts.

For semiconductors, the picture is a little more complicated. The basic idea is the same, however. It is that there are certain energy requirements that must be met before electrons can escape from the material into an adjacent vacuum. What these are depends upon the type of semiconductor and the distribution of electron energies, which, in turn, depends somewhat upon the temperature.

In this and other parts of the book the following notation will be used in energy diagrams:

- — Electrons
- ⊕ Donors
- ⊖ Acceptors
- + Holes

Holes and electrons are mobile. Donors and acceptors are fixed in position.

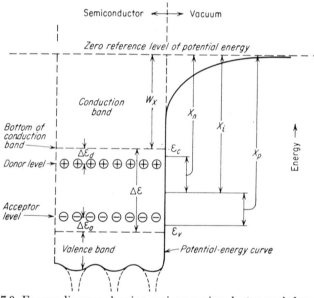

FIG. 7.9. Energy diagram showing various semiconductor work functions.

Several work functions must be defined for semiconductors. This is easily done with reference to Fig. 7.9 by the following tabulation of possible work functions, as designated by the symbol X. The symbols W_X, $\mathcal{E}_c$, and $\mathcal{E}_v$ have the significance shown in the figure.

1. Intrinsic semiconductor:

$$X_i \cong W_X + \tfrac{1}{2}(\mathcal{E}_c - \mathcal{E}_v) \tag{7.7}$$

2. Extrinsic semiconductor, n type:

$$W_X + \tfrac{1}{2}\Delta\mathcal{E}_d \leqq X_n \leqq W_X + \tfrac{1}{2}(\mathcal{E}_c - \mathcal{E}_v) \tag{7.8}$$

3. Extrinsic semiconductor, p type:

$$W_X + \tfrac{1}{2}(\mathcal{E}_c - \mathcal{E}_v) \leqq X_p \leqq W_X + (\mathcal{E}_c - \mathcal{E}_v) - \tfrac{1}{2}\Delta\mathcal{E}_a \tag{7.9}$$

For intrinsic semiconductors, some of the highest-energy electrons will be in the conduction band, and an equal number of holes will exist in the valence band. On the average, the work required to move a sizable number of electrons from the intrinsic semiconductor will require application of energy equal to the difference between the potential energy outside the material and halfway between the conduction and valence bands.

For the n-type semiconductor, most of the electrons will be in the conduction band, a few will be at the donor level, and some will be at the bottom of the conduction band. Statistical considerations show that the average energy required to free an electron from the material is equivalent to removing electrons with energies somewhere between the intrinsic level and a level halfway between the donor level and the bottom of the conduction band. The higher the donor density, the higher the Fermi level. Similar considerations apply to p-type semiconductors.

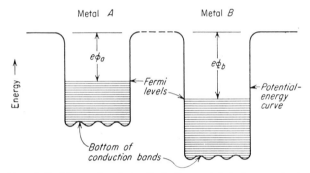

FIG. 7.10. Energy levels in dissimilar metals before contact.

7.4. Contact Difference of Potential between Metals. When two metals are brought together, there will, in general, be developed a difference of potential that depends only on the metals and on the temperature. This is known as the contact difference of potential and is not to be confused with electrochemical potentials as developed in batteries. The difference in potential comes about as a result of the difference of the work functions of the metals.

This may be seen by reference to Fig. 7.10. This shows the situation as two metals are brought into contact. Shown are the conduction bands, Fermi levels, potential-energy curves, and work functions of the two metals $e\phi_a$ and $e\phi_b$. As soon as they are brought into contact, there will be an exchange of electrons between the two metals even though there is a high potential barrier between them. This results from a quantum-mechanical diffusion process allowed by Schrödinger's equation. More electrons will initially pass from the higher energy level in metal A to the lower energy level in metal B than in the reverse direction. Accordingly, metal B will acquire a negative charge, which will cause all its levels to rise in the diagram. There will be established an equilibrium when the Fermi levels of the two metals are at the same height.   The resulting configuration is shown in Fig. 7.11.   Here it is seen that there has developed a potential difference between the two metals of value

$$\phi_d = \phi_b - \phi_a \tag{7.10}$$

This is known as the *contact difference of potential.*

It is a consequence of Poisson's equation (3.18) that a rounded step in potential, as shown in Fig. 7.11, is accompanied by a double layer of charge.   Poisson's equation says that the second derivative of potential is proportional to negative-charge density.   If potential is a step function, the first derivative of it is a single peaked curve.   The second derivative of potential, which is the derivative of the single peak, is a curve with a

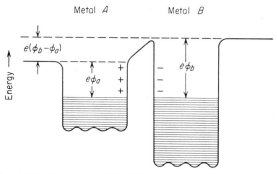

FIG. 7.11. Energy levels in dissimilar metals after contact.

negative peak next to a positive peak.   This corresponds to the double layer of charge shown in Fig. 7.11.

In a closed circuit at constant temperature, the contact differences of potential equalize, yielding a zero net potential difference around the circuit.   If, however, we have two similar junctions at different temperatures, there will be developed a difference of potential that is nearly linear with the temperature difference and with a coefficient dependent upon the metal pair.   This is known as the Seebeck effect and is the basis of operation for the so-called junction thermocouples.   The voltage

TABLE 7.1. PROPERTIES OF THERMOCOUPLES[1]

Junction	Emf $100°C^{-1}$, mv
Copper/Constantan	4.24
Iron/Constantan	5.28
Chromel/Constantan	6.3
Chromel/Almunel	4.1
Platinum/platinum (90)-rhodium (10)	0.643
Carbon/silicon carbide	29.5

[1] From Federal Telephone and Radio Company, "Reference Data for Radio Engineers," 3d ed., New York, 1949.

developed per degree absolute of temperature is known as the *thermo-electric power*. In Table 7.1 are given the characteristics of some practical thermocouples.

7.5. Metal-Semiconductor Junctions. When a metal and a semi-conductor are brought into contact, there will tend to be an exchange of electrons between them, which will have the effect of bringing the Fermi energies to the same level. This action is shown in Figs. 7.12 and 7.13. In the first of these is shown, before being brought into contact, a metal of work function $e\phi_m$ and an n-type semiconductor with a smaller work function $e\phi_s$. In the second figure is shown the situation after the two are brought into intimate contact. Initially, the Fermi level of the semiconductor is higher than that of the metal. Accordingly, electrons,

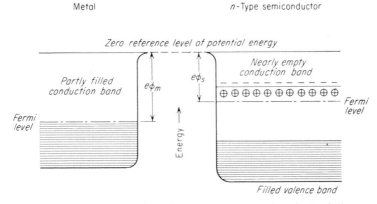

FIG. 7.12. Energy diagram for a metal and an n-type semiconductor before contact.

which tend to roll downhill in this kind of diagram, run out of the con-duction band of the semiconductor near the junction until the semi-conductor develops a net positive charge sufficient to lower the Fermi level of the semiconductor to that of the metal. This results in a curva-ture of the energy levels in the semiconductor near the junction, as shown, with a resultant contact difference of potential. In this case, the differ-ence in potential energies tends to be taken up in the semiconductor rather than in a double layer of charge between the surfaces, as was the case with metals. This comes about mainly because of the relative paucity of electrons in the conduction band of the semiconductor, which is down by a factor of about a million in density compared to that for the metal. Because of the relatively high resistance of the semiconductor, a relatively high potential gradient may develop within it. As noted in the diagram, the electrons in the semiconductor near the surface are detached from their donors, which, however, must remain fixed in position.

If now for the junction of Fig. 7.13 the metal is made positive relative to the semiconductor, the situation shown in Fig. 7.14 results.   Two things happen: (1) The Fermi level of the semiconductor is raised relative to that of the metal.   (2) The so-called space-charge-depletion layer,

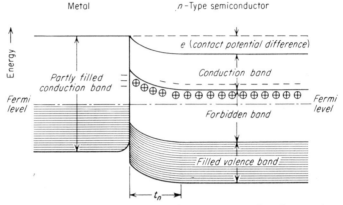

FIG. 7.13. Energy diagram for a metal and an n-type semiconductor after contact.

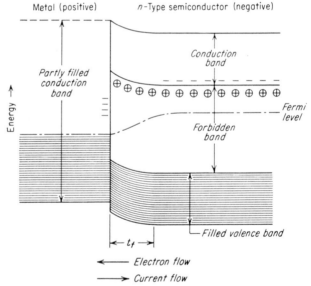

FIG. 7.14. Energy diagram for an n-type semiconductor-metal junction with forward bias.

indicated by t_n in Fig. 7.13, is reduced in size to t_f, where the subscript f indicates forward direction and n means normal.   Electron flow will be from semiconductor to metal and will be relatively large.   Electron flow is large primarily because the thickness of the space-charge-depletion layer is reduced, making it easier for electrons to diffuse through it.

If the semiconductor is made positive relative to the metal, the situation in Fig. 7.15 results. Here the Fermi level of the semiconductor is lowered relative to that of the metal, and the thickness of the space-charge-depletion layer is increased to t_b. Here the subscript b indicates backward direction. Electron flow is now from metal to semiconductor and is relatively small because of the increase in t_b over t_n. This is a rectifying junction whose action depends upon the variation of thickness of the space-charge-depletion layer.

Other types of metal-semiconductor junctions possible are shown in Fig. 7.16 along with the one just discussed. The case discussed is shown

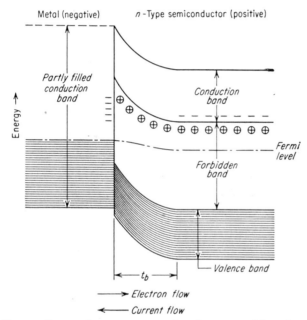

FIG. 7.15. Energy diagram for an n-type semiconductor-metal junction with reverse bias.

in part (a) of the figure. In part (b) is shown a junction of a metal and an n-type semiconductor whose work function is greater than that of the metal. In this case, adjustment of the energy levels is taken up mostly in a surface charge, as was the case for the metal-metal junction of Fig. 7.11. This is a nonrectifying junction. Remembering that electrons tend to roll downhill in such an energy diagram, we see that there is no potential barrier in this case. This makes the junction ohmic.

In Fig. 7.16c is shown a junction of a p-type semiconductor with a metal of a smaller work function. The Fermi level of the semiconductor in this case is near the top of the valence band. Conduction in the semiconductor is by holes. The adjustment of the Fermi levels is made by the repulsion of holes from the junction, giving rise to a space-charge-depletion layer with a net negative charge.   Remembering that holes tend to move upward in an energy diagram, we find there is a potential barrier to the holes.   Current is actually carried by electrons that diffuse across this barrier.   This is a rectifying junction whose action again depends upon the variation of the thickness of the space-charge-depletion layer. In this case, the forward direction, i.e., the direction of greatest current,

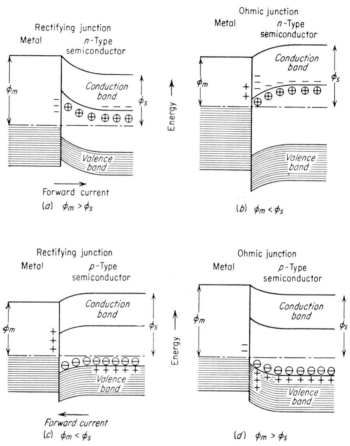

Fig. 7.16. Some possible types of metal-semiconductor junctions.

is with the metal negative in contrast to the case of Fig. 7.16a.   For this polarity, electron flow is from the metal to the semiconductor, corresponding to hole flow and conventional current flow in the opposite direction.   Semiconductors of type n and type p can be distinguished from the above difference.

Figure 7.16d shows a junction of a metal and a p-type semiconductor having a smaller work function.   The energy-level adjustment in this case is taken up mostly in surface charge.   Remembering that holes tend to move uphill in an energy diagram, we see that this is a nonrectifying junction because there is no potential barrier to holes.

There is a capacity effect associated with the rectifying junctions of Fig. 7.16a and c. This is expected in view of the fact that the rectifying action is due largely to a widening and narrowing of the space-charge-depletion layer. This variation in thickness is accompanied by accumulation and loss of charge in the layer, which gives a capacitor action. The equivalent capacity is in shunt with the junction resistance. The capacity is nonlinear and depends upon the bias and the signal strength.

The explanation given above of the action of rectifying metal-semiconductor junctions is a simplification and idealization of the actual circumstances. Two aspects of the actual situation should be mentioned. In the first place, the surface charges on the semiconductor play a more

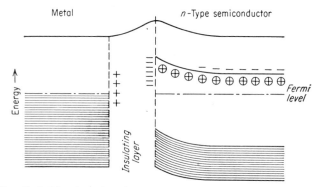

FIG. 7.17. Metal-semiconductor junction showing surface charges.

important role than was indicated above [KiF]. Surface charges are shown in Fig. 7.16a and c. They exist whether the semiconductor is in contact with the metal or not. In many cases this surface-charge effect will be intensified by an insulating layer on the surface. This makes the rectifying properties of the junction almost independent of the work function of the metal. An n-type metal-semiconductor junction is shown in Fig. 7.17. Here is intentionally shown a junction of a metal and a semiconductor with about the same work function. The surface charge and deformation of the energy levels in the semiconductor is seen to be about the same as in Fig. 7.13. This will still be a rectifying junction with about the same properties as that of Fig. 7.13, because of the change in the thickness of the space-charge-depletion layer with variations in potential.

The second departure from the idealized picture given above comes about from the fact that semiconductors have both types of carriers. Even though a semiconductor may be of the n type, it will have an appreciable number of holes, although their number will be smaller than

the number of electrons, as shown in Fig. 7.6.   Such a material in contact
with a metal may have conduction by both electrons and holes.   Further,
the combination of holes and electrons will alter the space-charge conditions near the junction.

   This is shown in Fig. 7.18.   Here a semiconductor of the n type is in
contact with a metal at a slightly more positive potential.   The semiconductor has some acceptors, thus allowing both hole and electron conduction though the majority carriers are electrons.   The Fermi level is
determined principally by the majority impurity.   The space-charge-
depletion layer is smaller in this case; and since conduction is possible by
both holes and electrons, the resistance of the junction is lower.   Shown
are immobile donors, plus signs in circles, and the immobile acceptors,

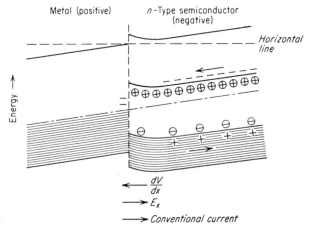

FIG. 7.18. Metal-semiconductor junction showing action of minority carriers.

negative signs in circles.   Mobile electrons in the conduction band and
mobile holes in the valence band are shown by minus and plus signs,
respectively.

   Also shown in Fig. 7.18 is a slight inclination of the energy levels, corresponding to a voltage gradient, to aid in visualizing the behavior of the
junction.   Electrons tend to run downhill and so pass from the conduction band of the semiconductor to the conduction band of the metal.
They also run from the valence band of the semiconductor into the conduction band of the metal.   The latter results in holes rising like bubbles
and running to the right in the valence band of the semiconductor.   This
is the forward direction for such a junction.   The holes cannot all run
out of the valence band, leaving it filled up, because the balance of charge
must be maintained.   New holes are created as electrons run out of the
valence band of the semiconductor into the metal.   Current is thus
increased by the hole conduction.

The above action with combination carriers and, particularly, the so-called hole-injection action encountered is the basis for some types of transistor action and will be dealt with further in later chapters.

Not all metal-semiconductor junctions act like the ones just described. Some junctions that are potentially rectifying are ohmic. In general, junctions will act as described above if the semiconductor surface is chemically etched and the metal is then deposited electrochemically, by evaporation, or by sputtering. If, on the other hand, the semiconductor is mechanically polished or sandblasted, the junction will usually be ohmic regardless of how the metal is applied. This is because the mechanical action disturbs the semiconductor crystal structure sufficiently so that the idealized considerations given before do not apply.

7.6. Semiconductor Junctions. Another rectifying junction recently developed is one composed of two dissimilar semiconductors [Shb]. The understanding of the action of such a junction is basic to the understanding of transistor action.

Shown in Fig. 7.19 are the energy levels in a junction of an n-type and a p-type semiconductor. Such a junction is known as a p-n junction.

p-n junctions exist with various degrees of symmetry, i.e., the relative concentrations of the carriers in the two types of semiconductor may or may not be equal. This diagram shows only the part of the energy-band structure of interest. It must be remembered that in such a diagram only the holes and electrons are mobile; further, that electrons tend to run downhill, whereas holes tend to run uphill. The Fermi levels of the two semiconductors tend to stabilize at the same level. There will be a contact difference of potential and there will be an exchange of electrons

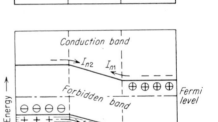

FIG. 7.19. Energy diagram of a p-n junction in equilibrium.

and holes in equilibrium. Some high-energy electrons will pass from the n- to the p-type material in an emissionlike action, and some high-energy holes will pass in the opposite direction. In addition, there will be a few electrons generated thermally in the p region that will run downhill into the n region, and likewise a few holes will be generated thermally in the n region that run uphill into the p region. This generation is associated with electron transitions across the entire forbidden band. Let us call the uphill electron current from the n region to the p region I_{n1} and the downhill electron current from the p region to the n region I_{n2}. Under equilibrium conditions, these will be equal.   Likewise, let us call the downhill hole current from the p region to the n region I_{p1} and the uphill hole current from the n region to the p region I_{p2}.   Under equilibrium conditions, these will also be equal.   The subscript 2 in each case is associated with the forbidden-band transition component.

In Fig. 7.20 is shown the situation for a forward bias of the junction. This occurs for the p-type material positive relative to the n-type.   For this condition, the size of the energy barrier between the two materials is reduced.   This makes it easier for the high-energy electrons and holes to

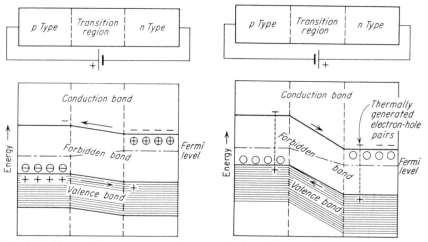

FIG. 7.20. Energy diagram of a p-n junction with forward bias.

FIG. 7.21. Energy diagram of a p-n junction with reverse bias.

be "emitted" from one material to the other, as shown.   Sizable currents may flow even when the gradient of potential between the sections is still retarding.

With a reverse bias, the situation is as shown in Fig. 7.21.   In this case, the height of the energy barrier is increased, with the result that only the very highest-energy electrons and holes can surmount the barrier to give a current component in the forward direction.   There will still be a small current in the reverse direction.   This latter is associated with thermally generated electron-hole pairs, as previously indicated.   The electrons generated in the p-type material and the holes generated in the n-type material will run to the other region.   Since the number of electron-hole pairs thus generated is independent of the bias voltage, the reverse current tends to saturate at a constant value.

The current-voltage characteristic of a typical p-n junction is shown in Fig. 7.22 on linear scales of voltage and current.   The same characteristic is redrawn in Fig. 7.23 on logarithmic scales.   These curves are consistent with a theoretical characteristic of the form

$$I = I_0(\epsilon^{eV/kT} - 1) \tag{7.11}$$

where V = potential difference across junction, positive for forward
     direction and negative for reverse

    T = absolute temperature

    k = Boltzmann's constant

    I_0 = sum of electron and hole currents $I_{n1} + I_{p1}$ for zero bias, as
     shown in Fig. 7.19[1]

Equation (7.10) results from the summation of all current components,
I_{n1}, I_{p1}, $-I_{n2}$, and $-I_{p2}$. The components I_{n1} and I_{p1} vary with the

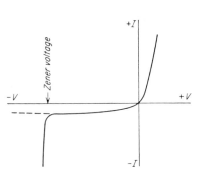

FIG. 7.22. Current-voltage characteristic of a p-n junction diode (linear
scales).

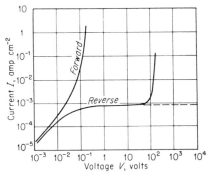

FIG. 7.23. Current-voltage characteristic
of a p-n junction diode (logarithmic
scales).

factor $\epsilon^{eV/kT}$, whereas the components $-I_{n2}$ and $-I_{p2}$ remain constant.
The front/back ratio of currents is seen to be high for moderate voltages.

For large back voltages, the reverse current suddenly increases rapidly.
This is known as the *Zener* effect. It is due to the production of electron-
hole pairs by a strong internal field within the materials. The effect and
the associated Zener voltage are quite stable and may actually be used
for voltage regulation.

7.7. Semiconductor Junctions (Continued). The subject of semiconductor junctions is of sufficient interest to justify saying something
more about the internal mechanism of rectification and current flow.

Shown in Figs. 7.19 to 7.21 are diagrams of the energy levels and current components within the p-n diode rectifier for the equilibrium condition and for forward and reverse voltages. These diagrams need to
be examined in more detail.

---

[1] I_0 has a value of $q(n_p Dn/Ln + p_n Dp/Lp)$, where the constants of the first term
apply to electrons in the p-type material, whereas the constants of the second term
apply to holes in the n-type material. As before, p_n and n_p are minority carrier
densities, D is diffusion constant, and L is mean diffusion length.

In Fig. 7.19 it is shown how the Fermi level in the p region adjusts itself to be at the same level as the Fermi level in the n region. This requires a step in the energy levels, as evidenced by the bottom of the conduction band and the top of the valence band. These band boundaries can be interpreted as relative potential-energy curves for electrons or as negative voltage. There is thus seen to be a *voltage* step *up* from the p region to the n region.

The voltage step in the p-n junction tends to displace the mobile charges, the electrons being displaced to the right and the holes to the left in accordance with their reaction to the field associated with the voltage step. This action leaves the transition region free of mobile charges, for which reason it is sometimes referred to as a space-charge-depletion layer. This depletion layer becomes narrower upon application of a forward external voltage and becomes wider upon application of a reverse external voltage. This will now be explained.

The potential step of Fig. 7.19 and the associated charge distribution must be related by Poisson's equation [see Eq. (3.18)]. For a one-dimensional variation of potential, Poisson's equation takes the form

$$\frac{d^2V}{dx^2} = -\frac{\rho}{\varepsilon}(x) \tag{7.12}$$

which can also be written

$$\frac{d^2(-eV)}{dx^2} = \left(\frac{e}{\varepsilon}\right)\rho(x) \tag{7.13}$$

where V = potential
$-eV$ = electron potential energy
x = distance
e = magnitude of electron charge
ε = dielectric constant
$\rho(x)$ = volume space-charge density

This equation says that the second derivative of potential with distance must be proportional to the negative of the space-charge density as a function of distance. In other terms, the second derivative of potential energy with distance must be proportional to the space-charge density as a function of distance. It may readily be verified by sketching that the second derivative of a voltage step function with rounded corners gives rise to a double layer of space charge with the two parts of opposite sign. This relation is shown graphically in Fig. 7.24a and d.

The double layer of space charge in Fig. 7.24 may be explained with reference to the equilibrium case (open-circuit diode). Shown in part (a) of the figure is the potential-energy step that results from the adjustment of Fermi levels and the associated movement of charge. In part (b) are shown the densities of the acceptors N_a on the p side and of the donors N_d on the n side. These are shown as having a fairly abrupt termination. The donors contribute to positive space-charge density, the acceptors to negative. Both are immobile, being frozen into the crystal. Shown in part (c) are electron and hole densities. The holes get pushed out of the transition region to the left and the electrons to the right by the electric field associated with the voltage step. The resultant net charge distribution is shown in part (d) for the equilibrium case. The double-layer charge distribution is seen to be flat-topped. This is because the displacement of the electrons and holes out of the

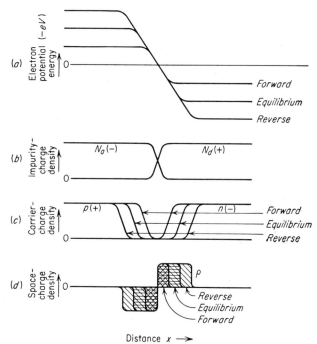

FIG. 7.24. Energy step and charge densities in a junction diode for equilibrium, forward, and reverse operation.

transition region leaves the donor and acceptor charges unneutralized, and the residual charge and densities are nearly constant.

For a forward voltage on the junction, the p-type region is made relatively positive, as shown in Fig. 7.20. This has the effect of lowering the potential energy of the p-type material and thus reducing the size of the voltage step within the diode, as shown in Fig. 7.24a. This has the further effect of reducing the region over which the electric field acts with an attendant reduction of the thickness of the space-charge-depletion layer.

For a reverse voltage on the junction, the p-type region is made relatively negative, as shown in Fig. 7.21. This increases the potential-energy step inside the diode at the junction and increases the region over

which charge is displaced.   This, of course, increases the thickness of
the space-charge-depletion layer and reduces the current and capacity.

It is next of interest to examine the electron and hole density within
the junction diode.   As an example, there will be taken a p-n junction of
p-type material with a conductivity of 100 ohm^{-1} cm^{-1} and an n-type
material with a conductivity of 10 ohm^{-1} cm^{-1}.   According to Fig. 7.6,
the hole and electron densities will be as shown by the solid lines in Fig.

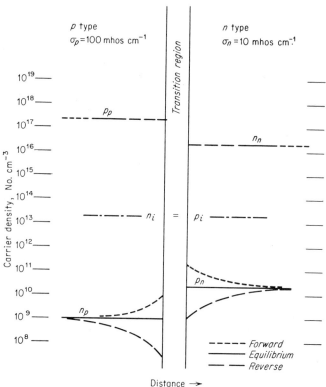

FIG. 7.25. Carrier densities in a p-n junction diode for equilibrium, forward, and
reverse operation.

7.25.   The p and n densities are seen to be more widely spaced in the
high-conductivity p-type material than in the lower-conductivity n-type
material.

If now a forward bias is applied, more holes will be able to cross the
reduced energy barrier from the p to the n region, and likewise more electrons will move from the n to the p region.   As a result, the density of
the holes in the n region just outside the transition region will be considerably increased.   The increased hole density at the transition boundary will cause the holes to diffuse to the right.   They will recombine with
electrons along the way so that the hole density will drop exponentially

to the equilibrium value. The hole density in the p region will be hardly affected because their density here is so high that the loss of some to the n region is relatively negligible. A similar action accounts for the shape of the electron-density curve.

If a reverse bias is applied, fewer holes make the transition from the p to n region, with the result that the hole density is reduced below the equilibrium value at the boundary of the transition region in the n portion. This causes holes to diffuse from right to left. Likewise, the electron density in the p-type region next to the transition is decreased.

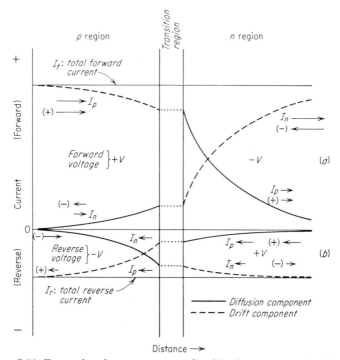

Fig. 7.26. Forward and reverse current densities in a p-n junction diode.

Away from the transition region, the electron density gradually rises to the equilibrium density.

The current components associated with the charge densities of Fig. 7.25 are shown in Fig. 7.26. In Fig. 7.26a are shown current components for forward bias and current flow. The negative gradient of hole density in the n region causes a diffusion component of hole flow to the right here. This component drops exponentially to zero because recombination of holes with electrons restores the hole density to the equilibrium value. Since the total current must be constant, there is also a component of electron flow from right to left in the n region, which gradually drops off in magnitude because of recombination with holes. This, however, is a drift component due to the gradient of potential. The sum of the electron and hole current must everywhere be equal to the total forward current, a constant. In the p region, the electron flow is a diffusion component to the left, while the hole flow is a drift component to the right.

The current components associated with the charge densities of Fig. 7.25 for reverse bias are shown in Fig. 7.26b. Because the gradient of hole density in the p region is positive, holes will move from right to left by diffusion, constituting a negative current component. Associated with this there will be electron movement from left to right. This is a drift component. The hole current *declines* in magnitude from right to left, but the electron current *grows* from right to left. This is possible because more electrons are created by thermal ionization than are lost by recombination near the junction, the hole density being below equilibrium value. Similar considerations explain the current components in the n region.

CHAPTER 8

ELECTRON EMISSION

8.1. Basic Aspects of Electron Emission.[1] Electron emission from a solid into a vacuum can occur in one of four ways, as follows: (1) thermionic emission, (2) photoelectric emission, (3) secondary emission, (4) field emission.

In all cases, emission occurs as a result of free electrons within the solid acquiring enough energy to overcome potential-energy barriers existing on the surface of the solid. The different forms of emission differ in the source of the energy. When the energy is supplied thermally, by heating the solid, the emission is called *thermionic*. This chapter will be concerned largely with thermionic emission. When the energy is received as radiant energy, the emission is *photoelectric*. Photoelectric emission will be discussed in a later chapter. When the liberating energy is received as the kinetic energy of a bombarding particle, the emission is called *secondary*, as distinguished from primary thermionic emission. Secondary emission will be discussed briefly at the end of this chapter. When the potential-energy barrier is lowered by a strong electric field, large electron emission may result at ordinary temperatures. This is called *field* emission. As yet, this has found limited application and will be discussed only briefly.

In 1883 Edison, working with evacuated incandescent lamp bulbs, found that, if a third electrode were placed in the bulb, a current could be drawn from it when it was positive relative to the incandescent filament but not when it was negative. He did not appreciate the significance of the effect, and it remained for others to discover the electron and determine the laws of electron emitters.

It was discovered early that filaments of various metals were good thermionic emitters of electrons in a vacuum. They might also be good in air; but usually the emitters would oxidize, and the few electrons emitted could not maintain a current flow in the relatively dense atmosphere. It was discovered that the total electron emission in a vacuum varied extremely rapidly with temperature. It was also found that some materials were good emitters and others not. All these aspects turned out to be part of a common basic picture.

[1] General references: [DaA, WrC].

The physical picture of thermionic emission is simply that as the temperature of the emitter is raised—usually by electrical heating—some of the electrons in the conduction band acquire a greater energy than others. The high-energy electrons may have velocities of sufficient magnitude and of suitable direction to permit them to surmount the surface potential-energy barrier. This action is very roughly equivalent to evaporation of molecules from a liquid as a function of temperature.

It has already been indicated that the distribution of energies among electrons in the conduction band of metals is a function of temperature and that there is a potential-energy barrier that electrons must overcome before they can escape. The relation between these ideas is shown in

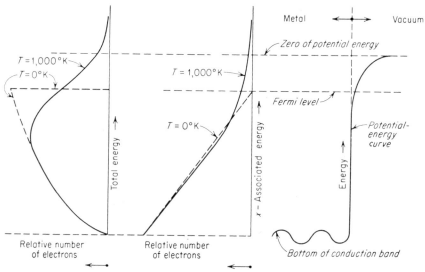

FIG. 8.1. Energy relations for free electrons at a metal-vacuum junction.

Fig. 8.1. At the right of this figure is shown the potential energy of electrons relative to a zero level outside the metal. At the left is the total-energy distribution as determined by the temperature and the assumption of a constant potential within the metal. At 1000°K it is seen that a few electrons have energies greater than the zero level of potential energy and hence have the possibility of escaping from the metal. However, not all electrons with energies greater than the zero level of potential energy can escape from the metal. It is only those with sufficient energy associated with the proper direction that can escape. Thus if the direction normal to the metal surface is the x direction, then only those electrons can escape which have velocities v_x such that $\frac{1}{2}mv_x^2$ is greater than the depth of the conduction band.

A curve for x-associated energy is shown in the middle of Fig. 8.1. The equation for this distribution is found to be (Appendix 6)

$$\frac{dn_x}{dv_x} = \frac{4\pi m^2 kT}{h^3} \ln\left(1 + \exp\frac{\mathcal{E}_f - \frac{1}{2}mv_x^2}{kT}\right) \tag{8.1}$$

Here dn_x is the number of electrons per unit volume in a velocity range dv_x having an x-associated energy $\frac{1}{2}mv_x^2$.

At zero temperature this function is a straight line from a finite number of electrons at zero energy to zero electrons at the Fermi level. For higher temperatures the curve extends its toe as shown. With this representation, half of the electrons with x-directed energies greater than the depth of the conduction band will be emitted. This distribution seems much more reasonable in the way it passes through the Fermi level than does the total-energy distribution curve, even though both are correct. However, it may seem strange at first glance that the number of electrons with x-directed energy equal to zero is finite. To see this, it is only necessary to remember that electrons with zero x component of velocity may have large y and z components of velocity and, as such, comprise a large group of electrons.

A theoretical analysis of the effect based on (8.1) gives a universal equation for electron-emission current as a function of temperature T and work function $e\phi$, of the form

$$J_e = A_e T^2 \epsilon^{-e\phi/kT} \qquad \text{amp cm}^{-2} \tag{8.2}$$

where J_e = current density of emitted current
$\quad A_e$ = a constant of theoretical value 120 amp cm^{-2} °K^{-2}
$\quad k$ = Boltzmann's constant, 1.38×10^{-23} watt-sec °K^{-1}
$\quad e\phi$ = work function, ev
$\quad T$ = temperature, °K

This is known as the Richardson-Dushman equation. The value of the current density is influenced most by the exponential term and is accordingly a sensitive function of the work function and the temperature. Figure 8.2 shows the relation between density of emitted current, temperature, and work function, assuming the constant A_e has a value of unity. Where the actual coefficient A_a is different from unity, the current density obtained from Fig. 8.2 must be multiplied by A_a. In this figure it is seen that a difference in the work function of only 0.5 ev can make a difference in the emission of more than a thousandfold. Similarly, increasing the temperature from 800 to 900°K can increase the emission a hundredfold.

Actually, the coefficient A_e in the emission equation will usually differ from the theoretical value of 120. This means that two constants must be known for each material in order to calculate the density of the emission current as a function of temperature, namely, the work function and the constant A_a. These quantities are best determined experimentally. Examination of (8.2) shows that if there be plotted log (J_e/T^2) vs. $1/T$

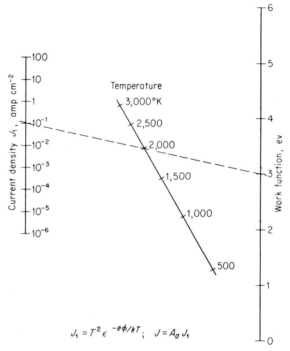

Fig. 8.2. Nomographic chart showing emitted current density as a function of work function and temperature. This chart assumes unity coefficient in the emission equation. Current density indicated here must be multiplied by the actual emission coefficient to get true current density.

for a measured curve of emission as a function of temperature, the resultant plot should be a straight line. Such a plot for typical emitters is shown in Fig. 8.3. In such a plot the value of the work function is proportional to the slope of the line, and the intercept of the extrapolated line to a zero value of $1/T$ gives the logarithm of A_a. Values of A_a and ϕ for the commonest emitters are listed in Table 8.1.

TABLE 8.1

Type	Material	A_a	ϕ, volts	Melting temp, °C
Metal..........	Tantalum	37	4.1	3269
Metal..........	Tungsten	72	4.52	3410
Metal..........	Platinum	32	5.32	1773.5
Atomic-film.....	Thoriated tungsten	3.0	2.62	
Atomic-film.....	Bariated tungsten (Lemmens)	1.0	1.6	
Oxide..........	Barium oxide–strontium oxide	0.01–0.05	1.0–1.5	

The departures of the values of the constant A_a from the theoretical value appear to be due to several causes. For metals, where the agreement should be good, it appears to be due to a slight variation of the work function with temperature, giving the effect of a different value of the constant. For metals $\phi = \phi_0 + \alpha T$, where α is of the order of $10^{-4}°K^{-1}$. In addition, there are some surface-reflection effects not considered in the

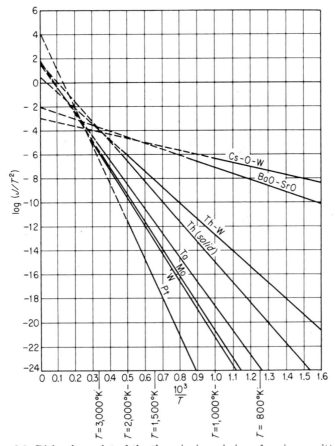

Fig. 8.3. Richardson plot of the thermionic emission of various emitters.

theory. For other than metal emitters, the departures are largely due to surface-charge effects resulting from the rearrangement of the atoms involved. For oxides (semiconductors) Eq. (8.2) is not very accurate so that constants derived from it are merely equivalent.

It should be explained at this point that the current predicted by (8.2) may not all reach a collector electrode or anode. Only when the cathode-anode voltage is sufficiently high will all the emitted current be collected. For relatively low anode voltage, only part of the emitted current will be collected owing to a limiting action associated with the mutual repulsion between electrons.   As a result of this action, the anode current for low anode voltages is a definite function of anode voltage and relatively independent of cathode temperature.   Accordingly, (8.2) should be considered as giving the total emission capabilities of the cathode.

Since the emitted electrons are the relatively high-energy electrons that have escaped from the emitter, it is expected that they will be emitted with initial velocities ranging from zero to infinity.   The actual distribution of velocities tends to be the same as that encountered in molecules of a gas, i.e., Maxwellian, since the electrons come from the tail end of the Fermi-Dirac distribution curve.   Because of the initial velocity, emitted electrons may reach a negative anode in varying amounts depending on its potential.   The electron-velocity distribution is conveniently related to the fraction of the emitted current that can overcome a retarding potential of a given size.   This relation is

$$\frac{I_r}{I_e} = \epsilon^{eV_r/kT} \tag{8.3}$$

where I_e = emitted current given by J_e of (8.2) multiplied by emitter area

I_r = current that can overcome a negative retarding potential V_r

e = electron charge

k = Boltzmann's constant

T = absolute temperature of emitter

A nomograph giving the fraction I_r/I_e as a function of cathode temperature and retarding voltage is shown in Fig. 8.4.   For the sample construction line shown, it is seen that for a cathode temperature of 1500°K, 50 per cent of the emitted electrons can overcome a retarding potential of 0.09 volt, which may thus be taken as the voltage equivalent of the average emission velocity.

As a result of the velocity of emission of thermally emitted electrons as given by (8.3), if a plot of logarithm of anode current vs. anode-cathode potential be made for a given tube, the curve will be a straight line with a large positive slope for negative voltages and a straight line of small positive slope for positive voltages.   If the intersection of these two straight-line segments does not coincide with zero voltage, the difference is due to contact difference of potential.

8.2. Thermionic Emission of Metals.   In general, the metals are good thermionic emitters.   The practical emitters are those listed in Table 8.1. When the work function and the emission constant A_a are known, the emission capabilities can be computed from the Richardson-Dushman equation [(8.2)] or from the curves of Fig. 8.2.   (See [Mia] for a tabulation of values of the work function of other metals.)

Various factors will limit the operation of metal emitters so that not all metals make good emitters.   Tungsten is a good emitter in spite

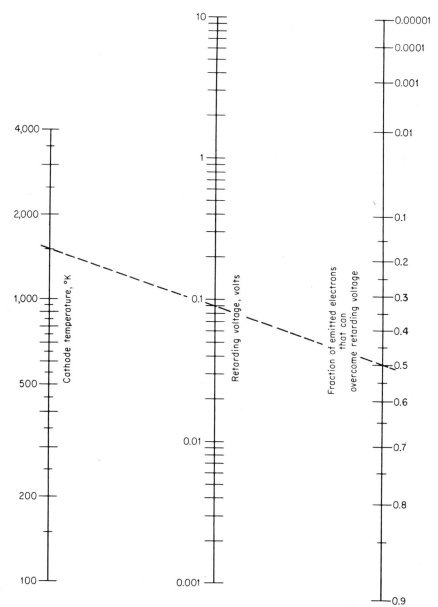

F<small>IG</small>. 8.4. Nomographic chart giving velocity distribution of thermionically emitted electrons. This chart shows the fraction of the emitted electrons from a cathode (at a given temperature) that can overcome a given retarding voltage.

of its high work function, 4.54 ev, because it can be raised to a high temperature (3370°C) without melting and its rate of evaporation is low. On the other hand, copper, which has a lower work function, about 4.1 ev, melts at 1083°C and vaporizes before it emits. In general, a compromise must be found in operating conditions between high emission and long life. The lower the temperature, the lower the emission but the lower the evaporation rate and hence the longer the life. The interaction between the various operating characteristics of an ideal tungsten filament is shown in Fig. 8.5 (data of [Jox]).

Platinum is sometimes used as an emitter, although usually only in special tubes or experimental equipment. The attractive feature of platinum is its chemical inertness. As a result, it does not contaminate readily and is thus useful in demountable vacuum systems. It is, however, a very-low-efficiency emitter, being even lower than tungsten in this regard. Emission efficiency is here measured in milliamperes of emission current per watt of heating power.

Tantalum, too, is sometimes used as an emitter. Tantalum is relatively more efficient as an emitter than tungsten. An attractive feature of tantalum is that it is available in sheets, which can be formed in special shapes. Tungsten, which must be swaged, i.e., hammered into shape, is available only in wire and bar form. Specially shaped cathodes must be indirectly heated.

In general, metal emitters are used in filament form because of the relatively high thermal efficiency of this form of cathode. Such filamentary cathodes are convenient because they give emission almost instantaneously compared to indirectly heated emitters. An associated disadvantage is that there is a voltage drop along the filament, which causes one end to have a different potential than the other. This gives a nonuniform action of the filament when used in a tube with a control grid. Where an alternating filament voltage is used to equalize emission, a hum component is introduced.

Metal emitters also have the advantage that they can be used in tubes operating up to the highest voltages, i.e., up to 50,000 volts or more, without suffering unduly from ion bombardment. No vacuum is ever perfect. As a consequence, molecules of the residual gas are ionized by the cathode. The positive ions formed are attracted to the cathode. These positive ions may bombard the cathode with energies sufficient to damage the emission of special emitting surfaces but metals suffer no ill effect.

8.3. Atomic-film Emitters. It has been found that a monatomic film of one metal on another has excellent emission characteristics in certain cases. It seems to be possible to coat a metal of a high melting temperature with another of a low work function and get the advantages of both.

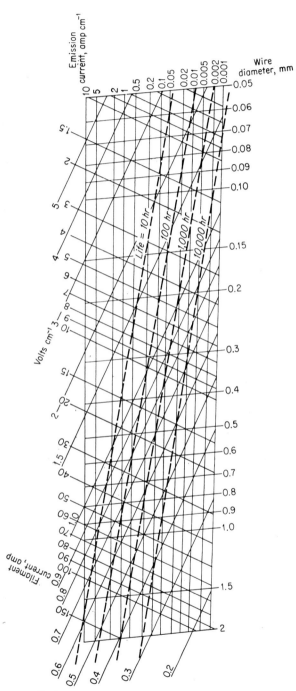

FIG. 8.5. Emission characteristics of an ideal tungsten filament.

The most extensively used atomic-film emitter is thoriated tungsten [Dac, Spc].   It has been found that the small amount of thoria, ThO_2, put into tungsten to reduce its tendency to crystallize and thus to become brittle would under certain conditions enhance the emission by a factor of 1,000.   What happens is that the $1\frac{1}{2}$ per cent of thorium oxide added is reduced by heating to give metallic thorium, which diffuses to the surface. Here it forms a monatomic layer, excess atoms evaporating.   The electrons in the thorium atoms rearrange themselves to give the molecule a dipole action with the positive pole outward.   This has the effect of changing the potential-energy distribution at the metal surface in such a way as to reduce the work function.   The potential-energy distribution

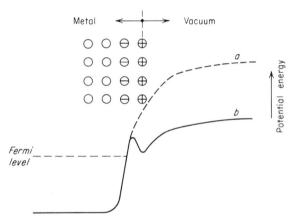

Fig. 8.6. Potential-energy curve at a thoriated-tungsten surface: a, Tungsten alone. b, Thorium on tungsten.

at the metal surface with and without the dipole layer of thorium atoms is shown in Fig. 8.6.

An interesting property of the thoriated tungsten is that successful operation may be had at a temperature nearly equal to the melting temperature of thorium, namely, 1900°K, without excessive evaporation of thorium.   This comes about because of electrostatic binding of the thorium atoms to the tungsten surface.   In addition, the work function of 2.62 ev is lower than that of either pure tungsten, 4.51 ev, or thorium, 3.4 ev.   This is the result of the reduction of the potential-energy barrier. The emission constant of thoriated-tungsten filaments is about $A_a = 3.0$ amp cm^{-2} °K^{-2}.

Thoriated-tungsten filaments are "carburized" to increase their life. This means that some of the tungsten is chemically transformed to tungsten carbide by heating the filament in an atmosphere of some hydrocarbon such as naphthalene, benzene, or xylene.   This process is usually carried out to the point where the conductivity of the filament is reduced to about 80 per cent of its original value [Wec, p. 61].

The emission of thoriated-tungsten surfaces depends upon an equilibrium between the generation of thorium plus its diffusion to the surface and evaporation from the surface. The emission can be impaired if the filament is overheated or if excessive currents are drawn. However, the emission can often be regenerated by flashing the filament for a few seconds at a higher temperature and then operating at normal temperature for a while without drawing current.

Another atomic-film emitter is bariated tungsten, which in fabricated form is known as the L cathode, after its inventor, H. J. Lemmens [EsB, HuB, Lec]. Whereas the thoriated-tungsten emitter is invariably in filamentary form, the L cathode is invariably in indirectly-heated-cathode form. The first form of the L cathode was a dispenser type, which had a reservoir or pellet of barium carbonate–strontium carbonate sealed behind a porous plug or pressed tungsten powder. The second is an impregnated type, in which barium oxide is dispersed throughout the pressed tungsten powder. The impregnated type has proved so successful that it has displaced the dispenser type. The two forms are shown in Fig. 8.7.

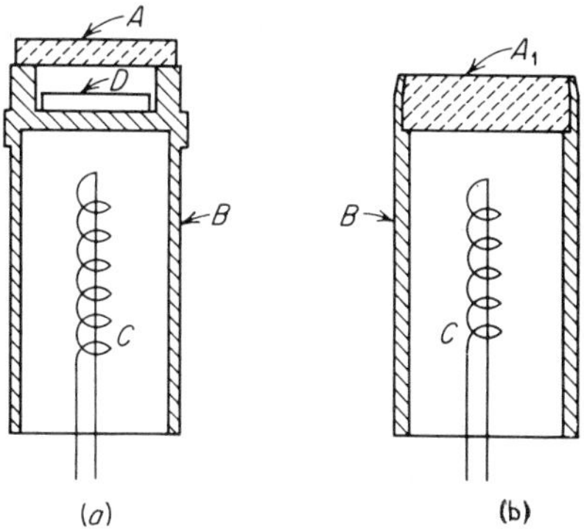

The impregnated type of L cathode has emission capabilities better than those of tungsten and thoriated tungsten with operating emission densities midway between those of thoriated-tungsten and oxide emitters. It can be machined and handled in air, which makes it useful for special and experimental tubes. It is easily activated and extremely rugged, being capable of standing the back bombardment of positive ions occurring at 3,000-volt operation.

FIG. 8.7. Forms of the L cathode: (a) Dispenser and (b) impregnated type. A, porous tungsten body. A_1, impregnated porous tungsten. B, molybdenum body. C, heater. D, cavity containing barium carbonate–strontium carbonate.

Reported values of the emission constants of the impregnated-type L cathode are a work function of 1.56 volts and an emission constant of 0.6 amp cm^{-2} °K^{-2}. Emission densities of close to 1 amp cm^{-2} at 1100°C and reasonable life at 1000°C have been reported.

8.4. Oxide Emitters. By far the most extensively used emitting surface is a mixture of barium and strontium oxides [Bll1, Bll2, Ble, Eic, HeAl, HeA2, NeB]. Such an oxide coating has an effective work function of the order of 1.0 to 1.5 ev and an emission constant A_a of the order of 0.01. Because of the very low equivalent work function, an emission density of 100 ma cm^{-2} may be obtained at a temperature of 1000°K with an efficiency of 20 ma watt^{-1} of heating current. To get the same emission density, a tungsten filament would have to be raised to 2300°K, giving an efficiency of 1 ma watt^{-1}. The oxide coatings may be applied either to an indirectly heated cathode surface or directly to a filament. Such coatings are particularly well suited to making unipotential cathodes of various shapes. The relatively low operating temperature permits the use of a base metal, such as nickel, that has a relatively low melting temperature and a relatively high vapor pressure.

As with the atomic-film emitters, the combination oxide emitter appears to have a lower work function than either of its component oxides or either of the metals involved. In addition, oxide coatings need to be activated; i.e., after being thermally formed, there is at first relatively little emission and there is required one of several procedures to develop the emission. These and other intriguing aspects of oxide emission are now largely explained on the theory that the oxides form an ionic crystal, which is at the same time an excess, or n-type, semiconductor.

Ba^{++} O^{--} Ba^{++} O^{--} Ba^{++}

O^{--} Ba^{++} O^{--} Ba^{++} O^{--}

Ba^{++} O^{--} Ba^{++} O^{--} Ba^{++}

O^{--} Ba^{++} O^{--} Ba^{++} O^{--}

Ba^{++} O^{--} Ba^{++} O^{--} Ba^{++}

FIG. 8.8. The crystal structure (perfect) of barium oxide.

Both barium and strontium oxides and a mixture of the two will form ionic crystals similar in structure to sodium chloride, as shown in Fig. 6.4. The metal atoms are doubly charged electropositive ions and the oxygen atoms are doubly charged electronegative ions. Under certain conditions, an excess of metal ions will develop. Actually, this excess of metal ions is due to an insufficiency of oxygen ions. When this occurs, the excess metal ions are found to have an action like that of donors in a metal semiconductor in that they contribute to the conduction band electrons that are subsequently emitted.

This action is best understood in terms of a single oxide component. In Fig. 8.8 is shown the structure of a perfect crystal of barium oxide. This figure shows only one plane of a three-dimensional lattice. Upon continued heating, some of the oxide will be reduced chemically by combination with other elements present or be dissociated thermally with subsequent electrolytic migration and liberation of the oxygen. When this happens, there appear vacancies in the lattice structure due to occasional absence of the electronegative oxygen ions, with an associated irregularity of the charge pattern as shown in Fig. 8.9. Here there is shown a neutral barium atom next to each vacant oxygen site. Such defects in the structure are known as *Schottky defects*. The neutral barium atom is in excess of the stoichiometric, or chemical, ratio of atoms. It is in this sense that there are excess barium atoms present. Such points are also sometimes known as F centers after the German word *Farbenzentren*, meaning "color centers." Such points play an important role in optical absorption and in fluorescence phenomena. Actually, any one of the six barium atoms next to the vacant oxygen site may be the neutral atom;

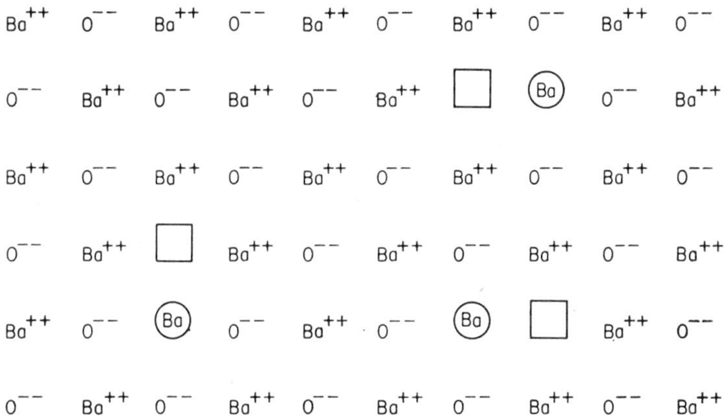

$$Ba^{++} \quad O^{--} \quad Ba^{++} \quad O^{--} \quad Ba^{++} \quad O^{--} \quad Ba^{++} \quad O^{--} \quad Ba^{++} \quad O^{--}$$

$$O^{--} \quad Ba^{++} \quad O^{--} \quad Ba^{++} \quad O^{--} \quad Ba^{++} \quad \square \quad \textcircled{Ba} \quad O^{--} \quad Ba^{++}$$

$$Ba^{++} \quad O^{--} \quad Ba^{++} \quad O^{--} \quad Ba^{++} \quad O^{--} \quad Ba^{++} \quad O^{--} \quad Ba^{++} \quad O^{--}$$

$$O^{--} \quad Ba^{++} \quad \square \quad Ba^{++} \quad O^{--} \quad Ba^{++} \quad O^{--} \quad Ba^{++} \quad O^{--} \quad Ba^{++}$$

$$Ba^{++} \quad O^{--} \quad \textcircled{Ba} \quad O^{--} \quad Ba^{++} \quad O^{--} \quad \textcircled{Ba} \quad \square \quad Ba^{++} \quad O^{--}$$

$$O^{--} \quad Ba^{++} \quad O^{--} \quad Ba^{++} \quad O^{--} \quad Ba^{++} \quad O^{--} \quad Ba^{++} \quad O^{--} \quad Ba^{++}$$

FIG. 8.9. The crystal structure of barium oxide with an excess of barium.

and, in fact, neutrality, or rather the local excess of negative charge, moves around the vacant oxygen site just as does the excess electron of an n-type impurity atom of a metal semiconductor, as shown in Fig. 6.16. This is also shown schematically in Fig. 8.10.

It is thus seen that excess barium atoms in a barium oxide crystal make it an n-type semiconductor. The activation process already referred to is simply one of producing the excess barium atoms. Just as in the impurity-type semiconductor, a certain number of donor electrons are elevated thermally into the conduction band. The conduction electrons are then available for emission if they have enough energy to overcome the potential barrier between the bottom of the conduction band and the potential outside the oxide.

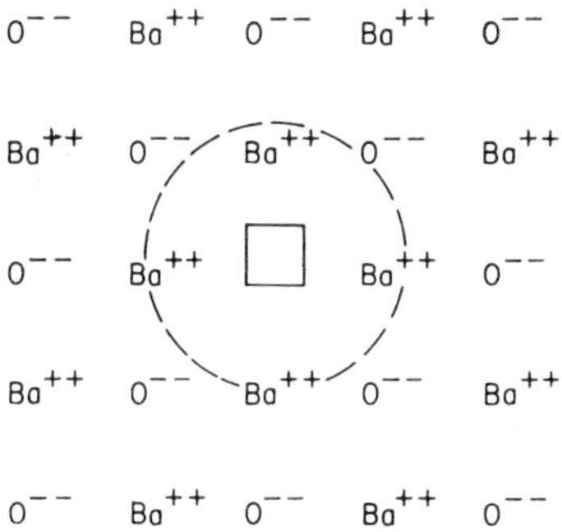

$$O^{--} \quad Ba^{++} \quad O^{--} \quad Ba^{++} \quad O^{--}$$
$$Ba^{++} \quad O^{--} \quad Ba^{++} \quad O^{--} \quad Ba^{++}$$
$$O^{--} \quad Ba^{++} \quad \square \quad Ba^{++} \quad O^{--}$$
$$Ba^{++} \quad O^{--} \quad Ba^{++} \quad O^{--} \quad Ba^{++}$$
$$O^{--} \quad Ba^{++} \quad O^{--} \quad Ba^{++} \quad O^{--}$$

FIG. 8.10. Schematic representation of the distribution of free electrons at a vacant oxygen site in a barium oxide crystal (see also Fig. 6.16).

The number of electrons available for emission can be determined as follows, with reference to Fig. 8.11: The number of electrons n_1 transferred in unit time to the conduction band from the impurity levels will be proportional to the number of excess metal atoms N_d and to an exponential factor. Thus,

$$n_1 = k_1 N_d \epsilon^{-\Delta \mathcal{E}_d / kT} \tag{8.4}$$

The number of electrons n_2 returning in unit time will be proportional to the number of electrons n_c in the conduction band and to the number of vacant impurity centers, which is also n_c.   Then

$$n_2 = k_2 n_c^2 \tag{8.5}$$

In equilibrium, n_1 and n_2 will be equal, giving

$$n_c^2 = k_3 N_d \epsilon^{-\Delta\varepsilon_d/kT} \tag{8.6}$$

or
$$n_c = k_4 N_d^{\frac{1}{2}} \epsilon^{-\Delta\varepsilon_d/2kT} \tag{8.7}$$

The emission will now be proportional to the product of n_c and an exponential factor based on the height of the potential-energy barrier relative

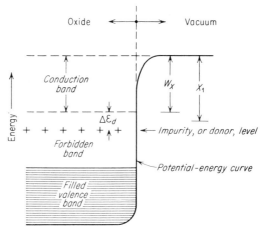

Fig. 8.11. Energy levels determining emission in an excess-impurity semiconductor such as barium oxide.

to the bottom of the conduction band, giving

$$J = k_5 n_c \epsilon^{-W_x/kT} \tag{8.8}$$

or
$$J = k_6 N_d^{\frac{1}{2}} \exp - \frac{1}{kT}\left(W_x + \frac{1}{2}\Delta\varepsilon_d\right) \tag{8.9}$$

where k_6 in a complete expression will include a temperature factor.   This expression shows a Fermi level halfway between the donor level and the bottom of the conduction band, a limit reached with n-type semiconductors *when the donor density is extremely high*.   The quantity W_x is often referred to as the external work function and $\frac{1}{2}\Delta\varepsilon_d$ as the internal work function.   The sum of the two is known as the total work function.

A confirmation of the above theory may be had by noting that both the conduction and the emission will be proportional to the conduction electron density.   Thus,

$$J = k_7 \sigma \epsilon^{-W_x/kT} \tag{8.10}$$

where σ is conductivity. Careful experiments have shown that the expectation of proportionality between conductivity and emission realized over a range of values of 1,000 to 1 [Hab2] is the result of a large number of measurements on a barium oxide–strontium oxide cathode subjected to repeated cycles of activation and deactivation (poisoning), as shown in Fig. 8.12. There can be no doubt about the proportionality between conductivity and emission.

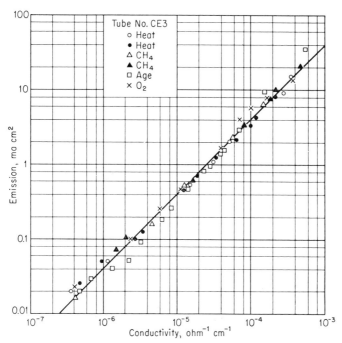

FIG. 8.12. Proportionality between emission and conductivity of a barium oxide–strontium oxide cathode while being activated or deactivated by various means. (*After Hannay, McNair, and White.*)

The remarks above have been partially confined to an emitter of a single oxide. The same remarks apply to mixtures of oxides, of which a mixture of 60 parts strontium oxide and 40 parts barium oxide gives the best results. In such mixtures there is a preferential evaporation of barium and barium oxide with the result that the emitting surface is made up mostly of strontium oxide. However, the excess barium atoms still give up electrons more readily than do excess strontium atoms. A 37:37:6 mixture of strontium, barium, and calcium oxides works even better.

There is a delicate equilibrium that determines the density of the excess barium atoms. They are created largely by chemical reduction of barium oxide by traces of reducing elements, such as titanium or silicon, in the

nickel base.   There will then be a diffusion of free barium into the coating.   Some of the free barium gets to the surface, where it evaporates.
It is the equilibrium between reduction, diffusion, and evaporation of
barium that controls the density of the impurity centers consisting of
the excess barium atoms.   The density of these centers is affected by the
cathode temperature and by the amount of current drawn.

The activation process referred to previously is that of producing the
excess barium atoms.   Activation occurs by one of three processes: (1)
chemical reduction of the barium oxide; (2) electrolytic dissociation due to

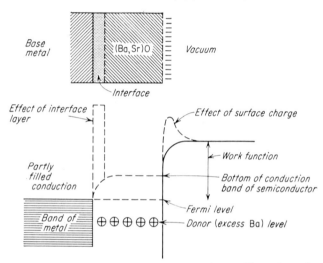

Fig. 8.13. Energy diagram of a barium oxide–strontium oxide emitter showing interface and surface-charge effects.

positive-ion bombardment; (3) in practice, heating of the cathode to a
temperature of 1200 to 1500°K for a short time without drawing current.
In the practical process, a tube is then operated slightly above 1100°K,
and an anode voltage of about 100 volts is applied through a protective
resistor, which will lower the anode potential as the current builds up.
An oxide cathode will also be fully active after thermal treatment only.
Subsequent aging by drawing current will stabilize and sometimes increase
emission.

The complete story on oxide emission from the impurity-semiconductor
point of view is more involved than the simplified explanation presented
above.   This is due principally to surface charges, which tend to decrease
the work function, and to the formation of a resistive interface layer
between the oxide and the base metal.   Here it is found that the very
elements that promote activation, such as traces of titanium or silicon
in the base nickel, also promote the growth of the interface layer and
shorten the life of the tube.   The interface layer ranges in thickness from

10^{-4} to 10^{-3} cm, increasing with time. It is composed of barium ortho-silicate, Ba_2SiO_4, and barium orthotitanate, Ba_2TiO_4, which have a resistivity about 1,000 times greater than the normal oxides. As a result, very pure electrolytic nickel is used as a base metal where long life is desired.

Considering the interface layer and surface charges, we find that the energy diagram of the entire cathode for no current drawn will be as in Fig. 8.13. The Fermi level in the oxide coating will equalize itself with the Fermi level in the base metal. The Fermi level of the oxide will be about halfway between the donor levels and the bottom of the conduction

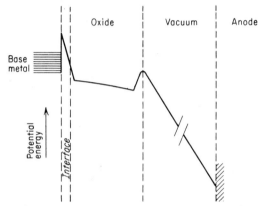

Fɪɢ. 8.14. Energy levels through a barium oxide–strontium oxide cathode when current is flowing.

band. The effect of the interface layer may be greater than that of the surface layer.

Because of the high resistivity of the interface layer, there will be a large voltage drop through the layer when current is drawn. This situation is shown in Fig. 8.14, which shows the potential-energy, or negative-potential, diagram of an entire diode drawing current. Where the interface layer is thick enough, it has an equivalent circuit composed of a resistance shunted with a capacity. The effects of these may be observed in the pulse response of the tube.

Another oxide emitter which is sometimes used is thoria, ThO_2. This was developed for magnetron tubes, where a combination of good thermionic emission and good secondary emission is desirable [Dab]. Such cathodes have good emission and better sparking and poisoning characteristics than barium oxide–strontium oxide and a lower rate of evaporation. Essential characteristics of thoria cathodes are given in the next section.

8.5. Relative Capabilities of Various Emitters. It is not possible to say which is the best emitter any more than it is possible to say that there is a best car or a best breed of dog. Emission applications generally involve a sufficient number of factors so that the emitter selection will depend upon many characteristics. The principal characteristics of interest are (1) operating temperature, (2) emission efficiency, (3) maximum emission capabilities, (4) resistance to back bombardment, (5) insusceptibility to poisoning, (6) life (active and shelf), (7) resistance to

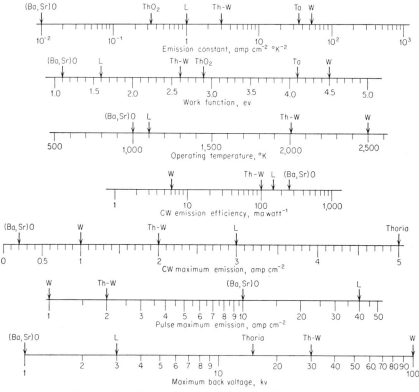

FIG. 8.15. Relative characteristics of various emitters.

physical shock, (8) ease of fabrication, (9) cost. It is possible to ascribe a definite numerical value to the first four factors but not to the others.

Figure 8.15 is a chart showing the relative values of some of the factors given above and some of the physical characteristics as well. These values cannot be given with precision. Different values are reported by different observers, and improvements are made with time. The maximum values shown are conservative.

The emission efficiency (a misnomer), usually given in milliamperes per watt, will be dependent not only on the emission properties of the surface but also on the cathode design. The emission always goes up with temperature, while at the same time the life decreases. The maximum bombardment energy that the cathode can stand depends upon the heat generated by the ion impact. This is not only a function of the voltage used in the tube but also of the degree of vacuum. The better the vacuum, the higher the voltage that can be used. Curves of emission

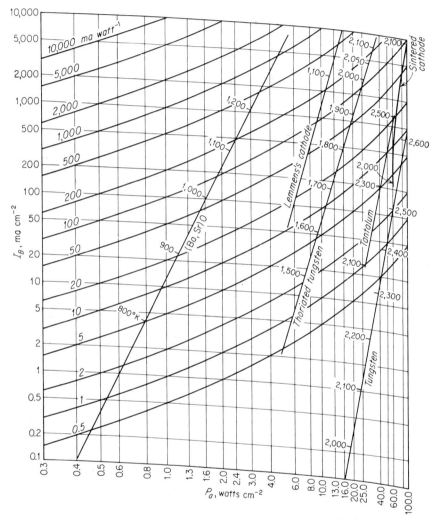

FIG. 8.16. Relative emission efficiencies of various cathodes.

density against temperature or heating power will not be straight lines even when logarithmic scales are used. However, it is possible to devise a special paper with warped coordinate lines on which curves of emission density vs. heating power per square centimeter of cathode area are straight lines. Such paper and curves for the common emitters are shown in Fig. 8.16. On this graph are also shown curves of constant emission efficiency and temperature scales for the different emitters. It is seen that the emitters in the order of their emission efficiency are the barium oxide–strontium oxide, L-cathode, thoriated-tungsten, thoria, and tungsten.   Unfortunately, though superior in its emission capabilities, the barium oxide–strontium oxide cathode is inferior in its ruggedness. As a result, for continuous emission, the oxide tends to be used for small tubes at low voltages, whereas the other emitters are used for higher voltages and powers.   For pulsed emission, oxide cathodes may be used to very high voltages.

8.6. The Schottky Effect.   One additional thermionic-emission effect of interest relates to a variation of emission with voltage or, more correctly, with voltage gradient at the cathode.   It will be shown in the next chapter that for low voltages and high temperatures the current collected by an anode is only part of the current emitted by the cathode. This results from a mutual repulsion between electrons, which produces a slightly negative gradient of potential at the cathode and causes some of the electrons to return to the cathode.   A consequence of this action is that the current to the anode varies as the three-halves power of the voltage difference between cathode and anode up to the point where the anode is receiving all the current that the cathode is emitting.   If now the voltage is increased further, the gradient of potential at the cathode becomes positive and the emission current tends to stay constant.   But it is not exactly constant; rather, it increases much more slowly with voltage.   This can be ascribed to a lowering of the energy barrier at the cathode because of the positive gradient of potential at the cathode.   This effect is commonly referred to as the Schottky effect.

This action may be understood by reference to Fig. 8.17.   Here is shown the potential energy in the absence of an external field.   This follows an inverse-square law except very close to the cathode.   A component of potential energy due to an external field is a straight line with a negative slope.   The sum of the two shows the resultant energy barrier with a maximum at a distance x_c from the cathode reduced in magnitude by an amount $e \, \Delta\phi$.   The distance x_c is a critical distance at which the force of attraction of the image charge and the force due to the external field on an electron are equal and opposite.   This has a value

$$x_c = \frac{1}{4} \sqrt{\frac{e}{\pi \varepsilon_0 V'}} \tag{8.11}$$

where V' is the gradient of potential.   At this distance the value of the potential-energy maximum below the zero reference value that existed in the absence of the external field is

$$e \, \Delta\phi = -\frac{e}{2} \sqrt{\frac{e V'}{\pi \varepsilon_0}} \tag{8.12}$$

This may be considered a component by which the work function has been reduced by the presence of the external field. It is seen to vary with the square root of the field. In the region where this action occurs, the current density relative to the zero field current will be

$$\frac{J_E}{J_0} = \exp \frac{4.40 \sqrt{V'}}{T} \qquad (8.13)$$

where J_E = current density in presence of field
J_0 = current density in its absence
V' = voltage gradient, volts cm^{-1}

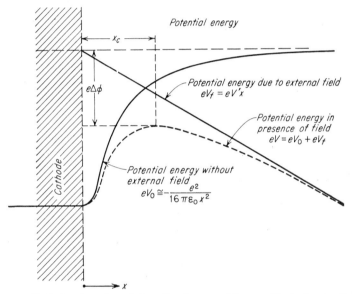

FIG. 8.17. Reduction of work function by a positive gradient of potential.

The resultant current-voltage characteristic is shown in Fig. 8.18. For low voltages the current is limited to a three-halves-power law by space charge. For higher voltages the current would be constant if there were no reduction of the energy barrier. The actual result is as shown. If a curve of logarithm of current vs. the square root of gradient be plotted, then in the upper region the curve will be a straight line with a slope $4.40/T$ in accordance with (8.13). The effect is observed in various degrees of conformity with the theory. Agreement is good for the metals. For the atomic-film and oxide emitters, the variation of current with gradient tends to be much greater than that given by the simple theory above.

8.7. Field Emission. It was shown in the last section that, if there is an electric field at an emitter surface, the emission is increased, giving the effect of a reduced work function, which can be considered as equivalent to an increased temperature. Accordingly, it is expected that, if the field is made strong enough, there may even be found emission of electrons at room temperature. This is indeed the case and such emission is called *field emission* [Duu, DyE].

Figure 8.17 will also apply to this situation except that the height of the potential-energy barrier will be reduced to nearly the Fermi level within the emitter and the *width* of the barrier above this level will be very

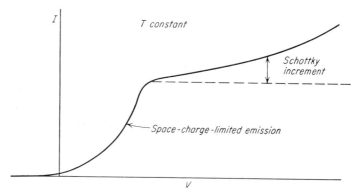

Fig. 8.18. Current-voltage characteristic of a typical metal emitter.

narrow. Since at room temperature the electrons in the emitter will not have enough excess energy to climb even a low barrier, emission will occur by diffusion *through* the barrier. This is known as the "tunnel" effect. A theoretical formula based on this concept and in keeping with experimental observations is similar to the thermionic-emission equation (8.2) but with temperature replaced by electric field.

$$J_f = B(V')^2 \epsilon^{-\alpha/V'} \qquad (8.14)$$

where V' = gradient of potential at emitter surface
B, α = constants of a given emitter

This type of emission requires extremely high gradients, of the order of 500,000 to 1,000,000 volts cm^{-1}, to give appreciable currents. Such can be obtained only with extremely fine points, say, with radii of the order of 1 μ. With such large gradients, the effect of temperature is nearly negligible. The emission is greatly influenced by traces of contamination.

A related topic is field-emission microscopy [AsA]. If a small-radius emitting point be put at the center of a transparent, conducting, spherical anode covered with fluorescent material, electrons from the point will move in straight lines to the anode, giving a magnified image of the emission surface. Effective magnifications of 10^5 have been obtained. Such a field-emission microscope has shown differences in emission from the different parts of a tungsten crystal and even made possible the determination of different emission constants associated with the different crystal faces. Shown in Fig. 8.19 is a fluorescent-screen pattern observed from the emission of a tungsten point.

To date, one of the few applications of field emission has been in high-voltage X-ray tubes [Slj]. Field emission will also be a limiting factor in power-tube design. Electrical breakdown in a vacuum will be limited by field emission to designs giving gradients of about 50,000 volts mm⁻¹.

8.8. Secondary Electron Emission. A third form of electron emission that will occur in a vacuum is *secondary emission* [Mcc, Poa]. The term secondary is used to distinguish it from primary emission (generally synonymous with thermionic emission). Secondary emission refers to the emission of electrons occurring as a result of other electrons striking a solid. It may occur for cold materials. It may occur for conductors, semiconductors, or insulators. It is roughly analogous to the spray of small water

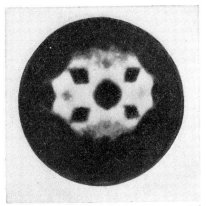

Fig. 8.19. Image of tungsten crystal structure produced by field emission from a tungsten point. (*Courtesy of Walter P. Dyke.*)

droplets, due to the impact of large raindrops, observed on the surface of a pool during a heavy rainstorm.

The most striking aspect of secondary emission is that the *number* of secondary electrons can be several times greater than the number of primary electrons. It is equally significant that it occurs for very low impact energies of the primary electrons down to a few electron volts. As a result, secondary electron emission is *virtually always* present in an electron tube. Under many conditions the secondary electrons will not go anywhere and will have little effect, as is the case with the droplets in the rainstorm analogy. However, under certain conditions they may have a very pronounced effect on the operation of a tube.

The first characteristic of interest with secondary emission is the ratio of the number of secondary electrons to the number of primary electrons, or simply the ratio of the secondary electron current to the primary electron current. When the ratio, generally indicated by the symbol δ, is measured, it is found that it first increases very rapidly with primary impact energy, reaches a maximum, and then with further increase of primary impact energy decreases very slowly. In fact, this action, at least for metals, seems to follow the universal curve shown in Fig. 8.20 [Baa, JoB]. However, different metals have different maximum ratios of secondary to primary emission and the maxima occur for different energies.   There is some correlation between the work function of the metals and the maximum value of δ, but the materials with the lowest work function seem to have the lowest secondary-emission ratio, contrary to expectation.   The curve for materials other than metals is similar.

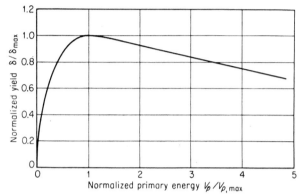

FIG. 8.20. Universal secondary-emission curve.   (*After Baroody.*)

In Table 8.2 are listed the maximum ratio and the primary electron energy at which this occurs.

The universal curve of Fig. 8.20 can be explained qualitatively as follows: For low primary energies, it is expected that the number of

TABLE 8.2

Material	Max ratio	Primary electron energy, ev
Carbon............................	0.6–1	
Iron..............................	1.32	400
Nickel............................	1.27	500
Copper............................	1.35	500
Molybdenum.......................	1.35	500
Tantalum..........................	1.35	600
Tungsten..........................	1.43	700
Gold..............................	1.47	700
Platinum..........................	1.78	700
Barium oxide–strontium oxide........	5–12	1,600
Cesium-silver......................	5–10	500–1,000
Quartz............................	2.9	440
Glass.............................	2.3	330–420

secondary electrons will increase with the impact energy on the basis that a high-energy particle can knock more electrons out of a material than one with low energy.   However, as the energy of the primary electron increases, it will bore deeper into the metal.   The energy transferred to surface electrons of the material, where the primary electron has high velocity, will be small; and the electrons of the material at greater depth that acquire more energy will have a harder time getting out of the metal. Accordingly, beyond a certain point the secondary-emission yield is expected to decrease with primary impact energy.

The fact that the number of secondary electrons can exceed the number of primary electrons by large factors indicates that most of the secondary electrons must have low velocities in order not to violate the principle of energy conservation. Measurement of the velocity distribution shows this to be the case. Generally, the secondary electrons fall into three groups with respect to velocity, somewhat as shown in Table 8.3. In the

TABLE 8.3

Group	Energy range, volts	Fraction of total
1	0–30	0.7–0.4
2	30–0.95V_1	0.2–0.3
3	0.95V_1–V_1	0.1–0.3

first group will be conduction and valence electrons that have been knocked out of the material by the primary electrons of energy eV_1. In the third are probably included mostly primary electrons that are elastically reflected. Since it is impossible to distinguish one electron from another, this is merely conjectural; but it is hard to see how electrons

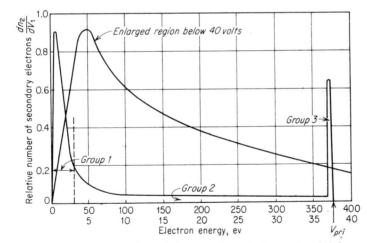

FIG. 8.21. Velocity distribution of the secondary electrons of molybdenum.

of the material bombarded can be given such large velocities in a direction opposite to that of the bombarding electron. In the second group are probably secondary electrons originating with the material bombarded. The higher the energy of the bombarding electrons eV_1, the greater the fraction included in group 3. In Fig. 8.21 is shown the velocity distribution of the secondary electrons of molybdenum.

Another secondary-emission property of interest is that the emission ratio increases by factors as much as 2 or 3 for glancing incidence of the primaries. The smaller the angle between the primary beam and the surface, the greater the ratio. The low-velocity electrons are emitted with what is nearly a cosine low distribution. The high-velocity electrons are predominantly emitted in a direction opposite to the primary velocity with a secondary maximum in a direction corresponding to normal reflection [BrD, JoA].

The secondary-emission characteristics of insulators are similar to those of conductors. However, since there is very low conductivity, insulator potentials change greatly under the influence of secondary emission. In most electron tubes, the glass walls will become charged positively to a considerable potential by the loss of secondary electrons.

Secondary emission is often undesirable, as was the case with the screen-grid tetrode, where it necessitated the addition of another grid to give the pentode. On the other hand, secondary emission has been used in certain current-multiplier tubes. It enhances the cathode emission in certain tubes such as the magnetron. Probably the most important occurrence is in cathode-ray tubes, where the circuit of the beam that strikes the fluorescent screen is completed through secondary electrons to a collector electrode. The collector electrode is the conducting film of graphite on the inside wall of the glass envelope.

CHAPTER 9

VACUUM AND SEMICONDUCTOR DIODES

9.1. Types of Diode. A diode is a two-terminal electron device with a nonsymmetrical current-voltage characteristic. Because of the nonsymmetry, the electrical resistance is much lower in one direction than in the other, and the device is capable of rectification. Ideally, a diode is an element with a voltage character-istic as shown in Fig. 9.1. Here the resistance in the forward direc-tion, as given by the reciprocal of the slope of the characteristic in the first quadrant, is low and constant, preferably zero. The slope in the third quadrant is high and constant, preferably infinite.

In actual devices, the ideal char-acteristic of Fig. 9.1 can be only approximated. Some realizable characteristics of physical diodes are shown in Fig. 9.2. In part (*a*) is shown the characteristic of one form of semiconductor diode. In part (*b*) is shown the characteristic of a vacuum diode. Semiconductor diodes may be formed by metal-semiconductor junctions. This group includes copper-oxide and selenium diodes. They may also be *p-n* junctions of germanium or silicon.

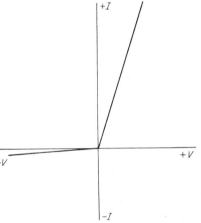

FIG. 9.1. Voltage-current characteristic of an ideal diode.

Diodes are used for rectification, detection, modulation, and wave shaping. Each application requires certain characteristics. The char-acteristics of most importance are forward resistance, backward resistance, power-handling capacity, peak inverse voltage strength to breakdown, temperature stability, linearity, and frequency response. It is the pur-pose of this chapter to describe the characteristics of the various types of diode and indicate their principal applications.

9.2. Vacuum Diodes. The vacuum diode consists of a cathode and an anode in an evacuated envelope. There is, of course, provision for bring-ing out leads and for heating the emitter. Cathodes are of two types:

directly and indirectly heated.   In the directly heated type, there is an
electric heater in the form of a tungsten filament, which may emit directly
or may be coated with emitting oxides.   The filament may also be of
thoriated tungsten for direct emission.   The indirectly heated cathode
consists of a nickel tube, which is coated with emitting oxides and which
is heated by a filament within.   The filament is invariably of tungsten

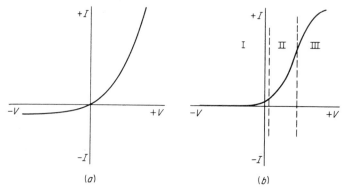

FIG. 9.2. Voltage-current characteristics of (a) a semiconductor diode and (b) a vacuum
diode.

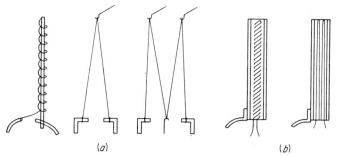

FIG. 9.3. Typical filament structures used in vacuum tubes: (a) Filamentary forms.
(b) Indirectly heated forms.

coated with insulation in the form of aluminum oxide.   As a result, the
vacuum diode is either a three-terminal device if the cathode is directly
heated or a four-terminal device if the cathode is indirectly heated.
Some typical filament structures are shown in Fig. 9.3.

In the directly-heated-cathode type, the filament is commonly heated
from a center-tapped transformer winding, the tap of which serves as
the cathode connection.   Such diodes are preferred in applications where
cathode emission efficiency is important and also in applications where
oxides are not rugged enough.   In diodes with indirectly heated cathodes,
the filament connections are brought out separately and permit the filament and cathode to be operated at different potentials, although this

potential difference cannot be much greater than 100 volts because of the danger of breaking down the insulation.   The indirectly heated cathode is a unipotential cathode, which gives more uniform emission than the directly heated type and also freedom from hum when the filament power is alternating.   Various diode filament connections are shown in Fig. 9.4.

Some typical vacuum diodes are shown in Fig. 9.5.   Such diodes may have either glass or metal vacuum envelopes.   The metal envelopes are used less than glass and do not serve as the anode but only as the vacuum

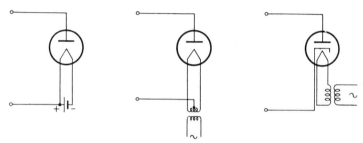

FIG. 9.4. Typical vacuum-diode filament connections.

FIG. 9.5. Some representative vacuum diodes: 6AX5GT, 6H6, 6W4GT.

envelope.   For low-power diodes, the metal envelope is iron, and glass envelopes of soft glass will also be used.   For medium- and high-power diodes, hard-glass envelopes such as nonex or pyrex are used.   For low-power diodes, the anodes or plates are of nickel, although in higher-power tubes molybdenum, tantalum, and sometimes carbon are used.   The envelopes are evacuated to a pressure of less than 10^{-6} mm Hg.   In small tubes, a "getter" is used to assist in producing the vacuum.   This is usually a pellet of barium or magnesium, which is vaporized by induction heating as the tube is being taken off the pump.   This produces the mirrorlike metallic coating seen on the inside of the glass envelopes.   The dispersed getter material captures the gas molecules that strike it and thus gradually improves the vacuum in the tube.

9.3. Current-Voltage Characteristics of Vacuum Diodes. A typical current-voltage characteristic of a vacuum diode has already been shown in Fig. 9.2. This characteristic is best discussed by dividing it up into three regions, as shown by the Roman numerals in the figure. The first region is that of negative and small positive anode potentials. The

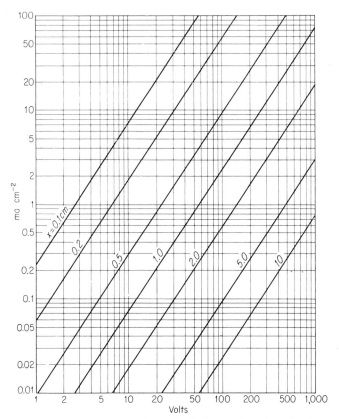

Fig. 9.6. Current density in a plane-electrode diode as a function of voltage and electrode spacing, as given by (9.1).

second region is that of moderate positive anode voltages, up to the rated anode voltage of the tube. In this region the characteristic has a positive curvature. The third region is that of excessive anode voltages, in which there is a saturation of current because the full emission capability of the cathode is being reached. Anode voltage is almost always measured relative to the cathode, which is taken as being at zero potential. Filament power is constant.

The most important region of the characteristic is the second. In this region the current is limited by the mutual electrostatic repulsion between the electrons in the stream. This repulsion, due to the negative charge of the electrons, has the effect of depressing the potential gradient in front of the cathode to the point where only electrons with emission velocities above a certain value can escape to the anode.   As a result, the current in a diode varies approximately as the three-halves power of anode voltage.   More specifically, current density is proportional to the three-halves power of anode voltage and inversely proportional to cathode-anode distance squared:

$$J = \frac{2.335 \times 10^{-3} V^{\frac{3}{2}}}{x^2} \qquad \text{ma (unit area)}^{-1} \qquad (9.1)$$

for positive voltages and plane electrodes (see Appendix 8).   Here J is current density, and V may be taken as cathode-anode voltage, in which case x is cathode-anode distance. Distance is measured in the same units as the area.   Shown in Fig. 9.6 is a family of curves giving current density as a function of anode voltage and electrode spacing for parallel plane electrodes.

The three-halves-power law resulting from space-charge limitation of emission can easily be demonstrated qualitatively.   Consider first that all electrons are emitted with velocities nearly zero.   Consider also that a potential is applied between the anode and cold cathode of a plane-electrode diode.   Then the potential distribution between cathode and anode will be a straight line, and the electric flux lines will be straight lines between cathode and anode, as shown in Fig. 9.7a.   If now the cathode is heated to the point where it emits a little, some electrons will be emitted that will be attracted toward the plate. In moving from cathode to plate, the electrons constitute a negative space charge that depresses the potential curve, as shown in Fig. 9.7b.   At the

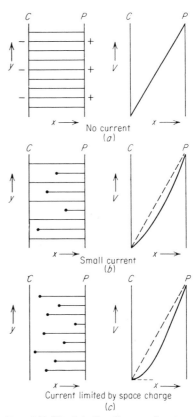

Fig. 9.7. Electric flux lines and potential distribution in a plane-electrode diode for various degrees of space charge.

same time some of the electric flux lines terminating at the plate will originate on electrons in flight rather than on the cathode.   A convention of one flux line per electron has been assumed in the figure for simplicity.

If now the cathode is heated further, the potential curve will be depressed more and more and at the same time more and more flux lines will originate on electrons in flight. This process can continue only until all the flux lines originate on electrons in flight. When this happens, the gradient of potential at the cathode will be zero as in Fig. 9.7c and the potential curve cannot be depressed further even though the cathode is heated to the point where it can emit more electrons than are being drawn.

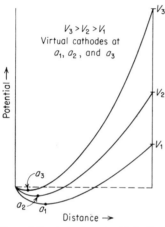

FIG. 9.8. Actual potential distributions in a plane-electrode diode, showing virtual cathode due to finite velocity of emitted electrons.

If the gradient should become negative at the cathode because of depression of the potential curve under the above conditions, then emission of most electrons will be prevented, the space charge will be reduced, and the potential curve will elevate itself until equilibrium is established.

Current density is proportional to the product of space-charge density and electron velocity. In a given plane parallel to the cathode, it is expected that the space-charge density will be proportional to anode potential since anode surface charge will be proportional to voltage, as in a simple capacitor. At the same time, the potential at any point will be proportional to anode voltage, giving electron velocity proportional to the square root of anode potential. Accordingly, current density, being the product of these two factors, will vary as the three-halves power of anode potential.

Let now the effect of cathode-anode distance be examined by increasing the spacing while observing reaction at, say, the mid-plane. With anode voltage kept constant, the total charge per unit area of anode that can originate flux lines will be reduced as electrode spacing is increased. At the same time, the volume charge density will be reduced because of the increased spacing, giving an inverse-square law of current with spacing.

The above argument was based upon an assumption of emission velocity nearly zero. Actually the emission velocities are larger than this and spread over a large range. It will be recalled from (8.3) that the velocity distribution of emitted electrons follows a negative-exponential law. Considering this, we see that there must be developed in front of the cathode, for equilibrium, a potential minimum at a voltage slightly negative relative to the cathode, as shown in Fig. 9.8. Such a minimum at a slight negative potential is known as a "virtual cathode" because the electrons that get to the plate appear to originate from it rather than from the actual cathode.   In such a situation, electrons emitted with low velocity will not be able to overcome the negative potential and will return to the cathode.   Only electrons with high enough velocity of emission will get to the plate.   As plate voltage is raised, more charge can exist between the virtual cathode and plate, the virtual cathode will move toward the cathode, and the size of the minimum will decrease. This will permit more electrons to overcome the minimum, and the plate current will increase.   Now the equilibrium mechanism is more evident. The current-voltage law will follow the three-halves-power law for voltages down to a few tenths of a volt, and also in the other direction until most of the emitted current is being drawn.

In the first region of Fig. 9.2b, the current will tend to be exponential with retarding voltage, as previously indicated in (8.3).   Currents for zero voltage will usually be small but in some applications large enough to be considered.

In the third region of Fig. 9.2b, there will be a saturation with a curve depending upon the Schottky effect of Sec. 8.5.   Most tubes are designed so that this saturation occurs only for voltages above rated values.   The saturation encountered here is known as emission saturation.

Thus although the three-halves-power law will hold over most of the range, it should always be remembered that departures are bound to occur for low and high values of voltage.   The three-halves-power law can be shown to hold with equal validity for *all* electrode geometries. The coefficient of the voltage factor will have to be determined in each case.

The vacuum diode, being a nonlinear device, has a resistance dependent upon the operating conditions.   Furthermore, the resistance to direct and alternating voltages will be different.   The resistance to direct voltage is called the *static* resistance and is simply the ratio of direct voltage to direct current.   Shown in Fig. 9.9 is a vacuum-diode characteristic following closely the three-halves-power law.   At an operating point a, the static resistance is

$$R_0 = \frac{V_0}{I_0} \quad \text{ohms} \quad (9.2)$$

corresponding to the operating direct voltage and direct current.   This is seen to be equal to the reciprocal of the slope of a straight line joining the origin with the point a.   Often alternating voltages are superimposed on direct voltages giving rise to alternating currents superimposed on direct currents.   Thus as seen in the figure, an alternating current I_1 is superimposed on I_0.   The ratio of the alternating voltage to current is called the dynamic plate resistance

$$r_p = \frac{V_1}{I_1} \quad (9.3)$$

This is seen to be equal to the reciprocal of the slope of the tangent to the static characteristic at the point a. The dynamic plate resistance, in general, is equal to

$$r_p = \frac{\partial V_0}{\partial I_0} \tag{9.4}$$

or the dynamic plate conductance is given by

$$g_p = \frac{1}{r_p} = \frac{\partial I_0}{\partial V_0} \tag{9.5}$$

If the current follows a three-halves-power law of voltage, as it generally does in the operating range, then the relation between the static and

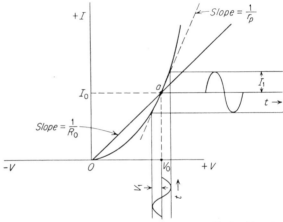

FIG. 9.9. Current-voltage characteristic of a vacuum diode, showing the relation between dynamic and static plate resistance.

dynamic resistances or conductances may be found by taking the derivative of current with respect to voltage. With this approach, it will be evident that

$$g_p = \tfrac{3}{2} G_0 \tag{9.6}$$

and

$$r_p = \tfrac{2}{3} R_0 \tag{9.7}$$

where $G_0 = I_0/V_0$. Thus the dynamic plate resistance is approximately two-thirds of the static plate resistance.

There has been considered the variation of diode current with anode voltage for constant filament temperature. If now filament temperature is allowed to vary with anode voltage constant, the curves of Fig. 9.10 are obtained. In this figure, T_3 is the normal operating temperature and T_2 and T_1 are lower values. The same curves are shown in Fig. 9.11 plotted against filament temperature for various values of anode voltage. The saturation observed here is known as space-charge saturation.

Regardless of the operating condition within the tube, the power consumed by it is the product of the plate voltage and the plate current. The energy so consumed appears as heat on the plate resulting from impact of electrons.   Each electron acquires a kinetic energy determined by the

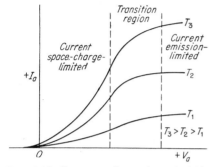

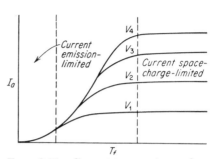

FIG. 9.10. Current-voltage characteristic of a vacuum diode for various temperatures, showing voltage saturation.

FIG. 9.11.   Current-temperature characteristic of a vacuum diode for various voltages, showing temperature saturation.

anode potential.   This energy is converted into heat when the electron strikes the plate.   The heat developed at the plate is often a limiting factor in the operation of diodes.

9.4. Semiconductor Diodes for Power Rectification.   Semiconductor rectifiers are extensively used for power rectification, being preferred to tubes in many cases.   The principal rectifier types are (1) copper oxide, (2) selenium, (3) germanium junction, (4) silicon junction.   The first two of these have been available for a long time.   The junction rectifiers

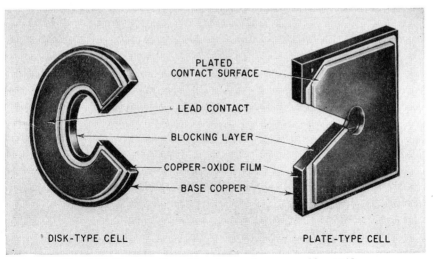

FIG. 9.12. Construction of two types of copper-oxide rectifier.

are relatively recent developments that have the possibility of displacing the older types if economic factors are favorable.

Copper-oxide Rectifiers. These are formed by oxidizing a base disk of pure copper to produce a layer of cuprous oxide, Cu_2O, in contact with the base copper. The copper base serves as one electrode. On the cuprous oxide there is plated nickel, silver, or gold to form the other electrode. This combination, shown in Fig. 9.12, forms the copper-oxide rectifier. This rectifier passes a large current from the plated electrode (positive) to the copper base (negative) and a relatively small current in the opposite direction [StA, Moc]. A back/front ratio of resistance of 1,000 is readily obtained.

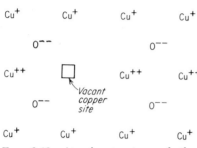

FIG. 9.13. Atomic structure of the p-type semiconducting oxide in a copper-oxide rectifier.

In this diode, the cuprous oxide is a semiconductor, and the rectifying junction is that between it and the base copper. Cuprous oxide is a semiconductor with a forbidden energy gap of about 0.7 ev. It will commonly have an excess of oxygen or a deficiency of copper. A typical arrangement of atoms with a vacant copper site is shown in Fig. 9.13. Since the absent copper atom has taken away an electron there will be a hole

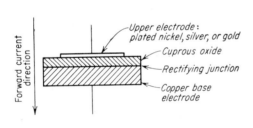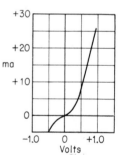

FIG. 9.14. Schematic diagram of copper-oxide rectifier and current-voltage curve.

for each vacancy. This hole probably resides on a copper ion, turning a cuprous ion into a cupric ion. Such holes move from one copper atom to another and account for the conductivity at ordinary temperatures. The vacant copper sides act as acceptors just as do indium atoms (valence 3) in a germanium (valence 4) crystal. We thus have in cuprous oxide a p-type, or defect, semiconductor. The energy gap between the valence band and the acceptor level as shown in Fig. 6.17 is about 0.13 ev.

With a p-type semiconductor such as cuprous oxide it is necessary to have a junction of the type shown in Fig. 7.16c to produce rectification.

Such a junction apparently exists between the cuprous oxide and the base copper. At the same time, it is necessary that the other junction be a nonrectifying one, as in Fig. 7.16d. This is had with a high-work-function metal, such as nickel, silver, or gold.

Shown in Fig. 9.14 are a schematic diagram and typical rectification characteristic. Copper-oxide rectifiers have a current capacity of from 0.1 to 0.25 amp in.$^{-2}$, depending upon the degree of cooling. The maximum back voltage per cell is limited to 5 volts. Cell resistance in either direction decreases with temperature. Cell temperature should not be allowed to increase more than 15°C above the ambient temperature. There is an aging effect during the first 6 to 12 months of operation, during which the resistance increases.

Selenium Rectifiers. These are similar to copper-oxide rectifiers but use a different combination of elements [StA, Clj]. Selenium rectifiers will commonly consist of a nickel-plated steel plate on which is deposited a thin layer of selenium, which is heat-treated to produce the crystalline form. On this is deposited a layer of a low-melting-temperature alloy such as Wood's metal (lead, 26 per cent; tin, 13 per cent; cadmium, 12 per cent; bismuth, 49 per cent), as shown in Fig. 9.15.

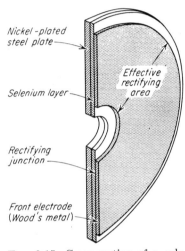

FIG. 9.15. Cross section of a selenium-rectifier plate. (*IT&T.*)

In this case, the selenium is believed to be the semiconductor, probably of the *p* type. The rectifying junction is between the selenium and the Wood's metal. The other junction between the selenium and the nickel is nonrectifying. Forward direction of current flow is from the selenium to the Wood's metal.

A typical current-voltage characteristic of a selenium rectifier is shown in Fig. 9.16. Selenium rectifiers can withstand a higher back voltage and operate over a greater temperature range than can copper-oxide rectifiers. As a result, copper-oxide rectifiers are used mostly for special purposes, as voltage limiters, instrument rectifiers, modulators, etc., whereas selenium rectifiers are used more as a-c to d-c converters. They are now available in small sizes suitable for power supplies in radio broadcast receivers [Chl]. Voltages up to 36 volts per cell permit the construction of high-voltage rectifiers with back voltages up to 8,000 volts.

Germanium-junction Rectifiers. These are a recent development, being to a large extent a by-product of transistor development [McD, RoEl, HaB, RoBl]. Germanium *p-n* junctions exhibit high current-carrying capacity of the order of 300 amp in.$^{-2}$ for the maximum current density. The back/front resistance ratio is likewise high, being about 400,000. Maximum back voltage per junction is about 200 volts, which is superior to both the copper-oxide and selenium types. The principal limitation of this rectifier is that it cannot operate at temperatures above

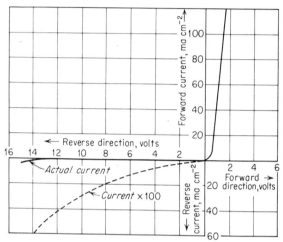

Fig. 9.16. Static forward- and reverse-current characteristics of a selenium rectifier. (*IT&T*.)

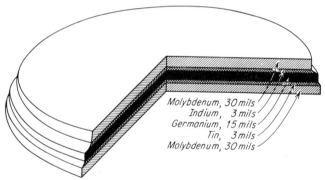

Fig. 9.17. Structure of a high-power germanium-rectifier disk. (*General Electric Co.*)

65°C. Above this temperature, the reverse resistance drops sharply. This is due to the intrinsic action.

Germanium-junction diodes are of several types. Small units are made by a diffusion process, whereby a pellet of, say, indium is placed upon a disk of germanium crystal and melted in [HaB, RoBl]. Large units use a disk of germanium crystal which may be 1 in. in diameter as the center layer of a five-layer sandwich [McD], as shown in Fig. 9.17. The top and bottom layers are of molybdenum, which has the same thermal expansion as germanium, has a high thermal conductivity, and serves to protect the inner layers. The center slice of germanium is n type. The germanium is soldered to the bottom molybdenum layer with pure tin and to the top molybdenum layer with pure indium. Some of the indium diffuses into the germanium, converting it to p type within a surface of penetration. This surface forms the p-n junction. The tin-germanium junction is nonrectifying.

A rectifying unit such as that of Fig. 9.17 can pass 200 amp with a voltage drop of only 0.63 volt. A typical current-voltage characteristic is shown in Fig. 9.18.

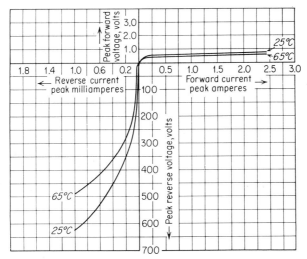

FIG. 9.18. Current-voltage characteristic of a germanium-junction rectifier.

Silicon-junction Rectifiers. Another recent development is the silicon-junction p-n diode, which is useful for certain special rectifier applications [PeB, PeD]. These special applications include cases in which very low reverse currents are desired and cases in which operation at higher temperature is desired.

Silicon-junction diodes are made by an alloy-diffusion process. Small-area diodes may be made by diffusing the end of an aluminum wire into silicon. Large-area diodes are made by diffusing boron over and into silicon at temperatures of more than 1000°C.

Silicon junction diodes have back/front resistance ratios of more than 10^6. Because of the large energy gap, 1.12 ev, silicon-junction diodes may operate at temperatures up to 150°C before large reverse currents develop because of intrinsic action. Such diodes have a pronounced Zener saturation at moderate reverse voltages, giving rise to a large region of voltage saturation. This is constant enough in voltage to be useful for voltage regulation. The Zener voltage may be adjusted from

40 to 300 volts.   Zener voltage is regulated by changing the conductivity of the silicon.   The higher the conductivity, the higher the Zener voltage. Some typical silicon-junction-diode characteristics are shown in Figs. 9.19 and 9.20.

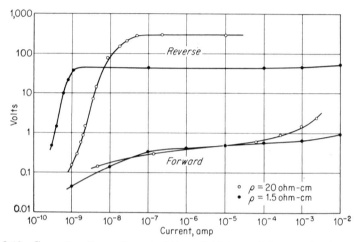

FIG. 9.19.   Current-voltage characteristics of high- and low-conductivity silicon-junction diodes, showing reverse voltage saturation, or Zener effect.   (*After Pearson.*)

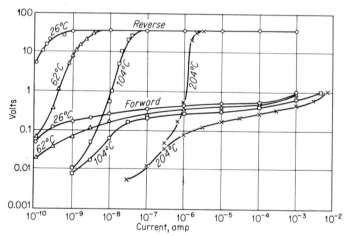

FIG. 9.20. Static characteristic of a silicon-junction power rectifier, showing the effect of temperature.   (*After Pearson.*)

Other special applications of silicon-junction diodes include back-to-back units with symmetrical current-voltage characteristics.   These have a high resistance at low voltage and a low resistance at high voltage. They are useful as voltage-surge protectors and nondestructible lightning protectors.   Silicon diodes may also be used in computers for capacitor storage applications. The reverse resistance of these diodes is so high that they may be used to charge and discharge capacitors without appreciable loss of charge through diode leakage.

Relative Capabilities of Semiconductor Rectifiers. The characteristics of the various diodes discussed above are listed in Table 9.1.

TABLE 9.1

Characteristic	Copper-oxide	Selenium	Germanium-junction	Silicon-junction
Back/front resistance ratio.........	10^3	10^3	4×10^5	10^6
Max current density, amp in.$^{-2}$.....	0.25	0.32	300	1,000
Max operating temp, °C............	60	100	65	150
Max back voltage per cell, volts.....	5	36	200	300

From the above tabulation it is seen that the germanium- and silicon-junction diodes are generally superior to copper-oxide and selenium diodes. They are also generally more expensive, especially the silicon units, which require processing at extremely high temperatures.

All the types of diodes have satisfactory back/front resistance ratios for power rectification, although the ratios for germanium and silicon are vastly superior and admit of other applications. Germanium and silicon are vastly superior in the matter of current-handling capacity. Germanium and copper oxide have the lowest temperature ratings. Germanium and silicon have the largest permissible back voltages, although the nature of the limitations is different. In the case of silicon, heating is not a factor; but back voltage is limited by the Zener effect in that greater back voltages simply cannot be developed. In the case of germanium, the back voltage listed is that which gives the maximum tolerable heating. The same is true for the other types. Germanium-junction diodes can actually be used to 500 volts of back voltage for short periods of time. Copper-oxide and selenium rectifiers also experience considerable aging during the first 6 months of operation before the characteristics stabilize.

A better idea of the possibilities of semiconductor rectifiers can be had by reference to Fig. 9.21. Here are shown the useful ranges of different types of rectifier. In part (a) of the figure are shown the different parts of the voltage-current field covered by all forms of rectifiers. Here it is seen that semiconductor rectifiers can cover all but a portion of the high-voltage area covered by machines. In part (b) of the figure are shown the areas covered by the various semiconductor rectifiers. Copper-oxide rectifiers are useful mainly in low-voltage applications. Selenium rectifiers are useful mainly in high-voltage–low-current applications. Germanium rectifiers cover the important medium-voltage–high-current region.   It is too early to predict the entire capabilities of silicon-junction rectifiers.   They will probably be useful in high-current applications at voltages above the limits of germanium rectifiers.

9.5. Semiconductor Diodes for Low-power Applications.   Semiconductor diodes are extensively used for many low-power applications. These include modulation, detection, wave shaping, and gate circuits. In the last category, modern digital computers will commonly use several times as many diodes as control elements.   New applications are being found daily as the units are improved in range and quality.   Semiconductor-diode production in the United States in early 1955 was about

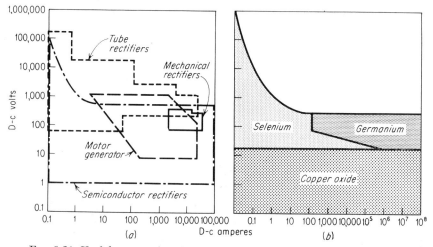

Fig. 9.21. Useful ranges of various types of rectifier.   (*General Electric Co.*)

$1\frac{1}{2}$ million units per month.   This was a 100 per cent increase over the value at the same time the previous year.

Germanium Diodes.   These are now available in a wide variety of forms for general-purpose work.   The internal workings of the diode generally consist of a tiny wafer (100 by 100 by 20 mils) of *n*-type germanium with a tungsten or phosphor-bronze cat whisker forming a point contact.   The forward direction of current is from the whisker to the germanium.   The diodes are hermetically sealed in a glass, ceramic, or metal-tube housing as shown in Fig. 9.22.   A typical characteristic is shown in Fig. 9.23.   Forward currents are of the order of 5 ma at 1 volt. Backward currents are of the order of 50 μa at -10 volts.   Forward resistance is of the order of 50 to 120 ohms at 1 volt.   Backward resistance is of the order of 0.5 to 2.5 megohms at -10 volts, at which voltage it has a maximum value.   The principal applications include functions as a rectifier, video detector, frequency-modulation discriminator, balanced modulator, and impulse noise limiter and various wave-shaping and clamping applications. The upper frequency limit is well up in the megacycles.

Silicon Diodes. These diodes were developed primarily as microwave crystal converters for use in radar receivers during the war. At that time, the crystals gave a better noise figure than any existing vacuum

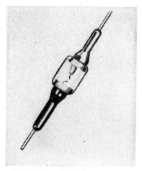

1N34A, 1N38A, 1N54A
1N55A, 1N56A, 1N58A
1N82

1N34, 1N36, 1N38
1N54, 1N55, 1N56
1N57, 1N58, 1N60

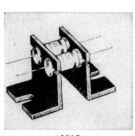

1N35

1N40, 1N42

1N71

FIG. 9.22. Various forms of germanium diodes.   (*Sylvania Electric Products, Inc.*)

tubes for frequencies above 2,000 Mc. The silicon diodes consist of a small wafer (50 by 50 by 10 mils) of p-type silicon with a 3- to 15-mil tungsten cat whisker. Forward direction of current flow is from the wafer to the whisker [Toc, Ste, Scd]. Silicon was chosen from among many rectifying materials because of superior over-all characteristics. The p-type silicon showed greater sensitivity and greater resistance to burn-out and was therefore preferred to the n type. Such p-type silicon is best obtained from nearly pure silicon to which are added traces of boron or aluminum, of the order of 10 ppm. (More recently, lower noise detectors have been developed of n-type germanium.)

The construction of microwave crystal converters is shown in Fig. 9.24. The silicon wafer and tungsten cat whisker are enclosed in a

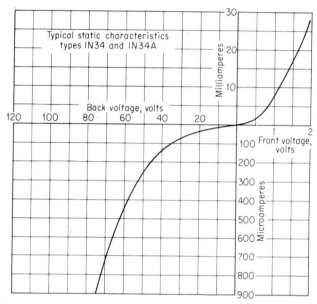

FIG. 9.23. Static characteristic of a germanium point-contact diode.   (*Sylvania Electric Products, Inc.*)

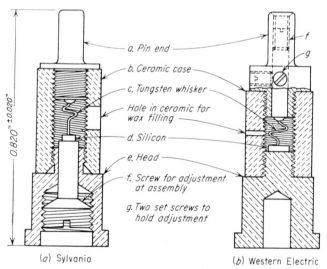

a. Pin end
b. Ceramic case
c. Tungsten whisker
Hole in ceramic for wax filling
d. Silicon
e. Head
f. Screw for adjustment at assembly
g. Two set screws to hold adjustment

(*a*) Sylvania   (*b*) Western Electric

FIG. 9.24. Construction of the 1N21B microwave crystal detector for 3,000 Mc.

ceramic sleeve.   Metal ends permit contact and adjustment of a cat whisker.   The point is applied under pressure and then formed for best results.   The whisker is then embedded in a low-loss plastic, which gives the crystal an astonishing resistance to shock and vibration.   This form of crystal may be used up to 10,000 Mc.

The equivalent circuit of the above crystal depends more on the characteristics of the point contact and of the silicon wafer than on that of the housing. A satisfactory equivalent circuit is shown in Fig. 9.25. It consists of a nonlinear resistance R_c corresponding to the contact resistance. This is shunted by a capacity C, which represents principally a capacity within the semiconductor in the vicinity of the point contact. The R_cC combination is in series with another resistance r_s, known as the spreading resistance. This is a linear resistance within the semiconductor resulting principally from the concentration of current flow in the vicinity of the point. The contact capacity is of the order of 0.2 to 1.0 $\mu\mu$f. This is by no means insignificant because at 3,000 Mc a capacity of 1.0 $\mu\mu$f has a reactance of 53 ohms. This can easily bypass the contact resistance. The spreading resistance has a value of the order of 20 ohms. The contact resistance cannot be specified exactly because of its nonlinearity. The current-voltage relation is found to conform to the static form of (7.11) for small voltages and may be written

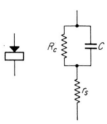

FIG. 9.25. Equivalent circuit of a point-contact-crystal diode.

$$I = I_0(\epsilon^{aV} - 1) \tag{9.8}$$

Here a is of the order of 2 to 20 volts^{-1} (theoretically 3.84 volt^{-1}), and I_0 is of the order of milliamperes. Typical values of current in the forward direction are 10 μa at 0.1 volt and 20 ma at 1.0 volt. Reverse currents are 1.0 μa at 0.1 volt and 4.0 μa at 1.0 volt.

For very small values of voltage, (9.8) will reduce to a linear term plus a quadratic term, etc.:

$$I = I_0\left(aV + \frac{a^2V^2}{2} + \cdots\right) \tag{9.9}$$

For a single frequency applied, this will give a rectified component

$$\Delta I = \frac{a^2V_1^2}{4} + \cdots \tag{9.10}$$

This shows that for small signals the action of the crystal detector follows a *square law*. Use of this property is made in many measurement devices.

For frequencies higher than 10,000 Mc, a coaxial form of crystal housing is used. This is done to improve the radio-frequency impedance characteristics of the device and permit the radio-frequency power to reach the contact easily. A cutaway view of a type 1N26 crystal is shown in Fig. 9.26. Such a crystal assembly is designed to operate from 16,000 to 24,000 Mc. There is also a type 1N53 crystal for use at 30,000 Mc and higher frequencies.

9.6. Detection with Diodes. One of the most important functions performed with diodes is that of detection or demodulation. Modulation is the process whereby an audio-frequency signal is impressed on a radio-frequency signal for transmission. Detection or demodulation is the process whereby the audio signal is separated from its radio-frequency carrier.

The commonest modulation system is called amplitude modulation. In this form the audio signal appears as a variation in the amplitude of

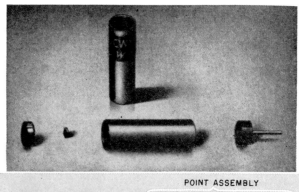

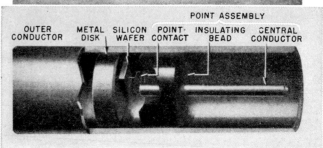

Fig. 9.26. Construction of the 1N26 microwave crystal detector for 24,000 Mc. (*Western Electric Co.*)

the radio signal. This results in a signal of the form shown in Fig. 9.27, which has the equation

$$v(t) = V_r(1 + m_i \cos \omega_a t) \cos \omega_r t \qquad (9.11)$$

where V is the symbol for voltage, subscript r means radio, subscript a means audio, ω is angular frequency, and m_i is an index of modulation giving the ratio of the audio variation of the envelope to the unmodulated radio-frequency wave. The radio-frequency component is called the carrier. It is seen that the audio signal appears as an amplitude variation of the carrier, giving rise to an envelope that varies with the audio-frequency signal. This is the kind of signal radiated by the average broadcast station. In a later chapter, the production of such waves will be discussed.   Here there will be discussed only the separation of the audio signal from the carrier.

The amplitude-modulated wave given above is equivalent to the superposition of three unmodulated radio waves.   This may be seen by trigonometric expansion of (9.11) to yield

$$v(t) = V_r \cos \omega_r t + \frac{m_i V_r}{2} \cos (\omega_r - \omega_a)t + \frac{m_i V_r}{2} \cos (\omega_r + \omega_a)t \quad (9.12)$$

The first term is called the carrier.   The other terms are called the lower and upper side band, respectively.   The existence of these three components may be demonstrated in the laboratory with the aid of a wave

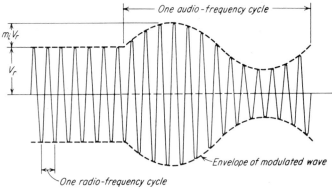

FIG. 9.27. Form and notation of an amplitude-modulated wave.

analyzer.   The equivalence of (9.11) and (9.12) may also be shown by combining the terms of the latter vectorially.   If the first term is taken as a reference vector, the second and third are terms of equal magnitude rotating in the clockwise and counterclockwise direction, respectively, at the audio frequency (relative to the carrier).   The sum of the last two terms is a vector variable in magnitude and always in phase with the carrier.

Assuming that an amplitude-modulated wave as described above is present, we wish now to discuss means of extracting the audio signal from it.   The first common means of doing this with a diode is known as *square-law detection*.   Square-law detection is illustrated in Fig. 9.28. It makes use of the fact that for small signals the diode characteristic is always continuous and can be represented by a power series at a given operating point as

$$i(v_1) = a_1 v_1 + a_2 v_1^2 + \cdots + a_n v_1^n + \cdots \quad (9.13)$$

where v_1 = increment of voltage about operating point
$a_1, \ldots, a_n$ = constants

If the increment v_1 is of the form of (9.12), the first term of (9.13) will give a replica of v_1 but the second—the square-law term—can give detection. Specifically, if (9.12) is squared, there will be found

$$i = a_2 m_i V_r^2 \left(\cos \omega_a t + \frac{m_i}{4} \cos 2\omega_a t \right) + \cdots \tag{9.14}$$

The first term here gives the audio signal linear with the modulation factor m_i. The second term represents a second harmonic distortion,

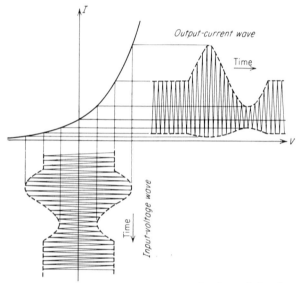

Fig. 9.28. Square-law detection of an amplitude-modulated wave.

which is always present, however, nonlinearly. For 100 per cent modulation, the second harmonic distortion is 25 per cent; for 40 per cent modulation, only 10 per cent. There will be other frequencies generated that are sometimes of interest though readily filtered out for detection. These are twice the carrier frequency, twice the carrier frequency plus and minus the audio, and twice the carrier frequency plus and minus twice the audio frequency. In spite of the limitations indicated above, small-signal square-law detection is often used. The circuit is simply a series connection between the voltage source, the diode, and a small resistor across which an output voltage proportional to current is taken.

A second form of diode detection makes use of a circuit that produces an output voltage following the envelope of the modulated wave. This form of detection is very extensively used and is sometimes referred to as envelope detection. It is a large-signal form of detection in contrast to square-law detection, which is a small-signal form of detection. In Fig. 9.29 is shown the circuit and resultant waveforms of such a detector.

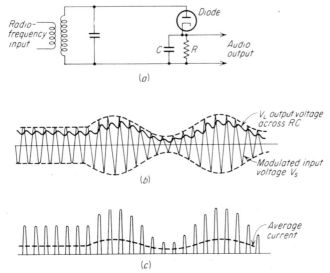

FIG. 9.29. Envelope detection by a diode-detector circuit: (a) Circuit of simple diode detector. (b) Input voltage applied to diode. (c) Current through diode.

After a short initial period, the capacitor will become charged to nearly the peak signal voltage, and diode current will flow only at the peak of the cycle. During each cycle between peaks, the capacitor will discharge a little only to be recharged at the next peak. The result is that the voltage across the RC combination follows the signal envelope and so gives an audio output when the signal is amplitude and modulated. The ratio of the magnitude of the output audio signal to the input-signal modulation will commonly be between 70 and 90 per cent, being higher the higher the resistance in series with the diode. This resistance cannot be made too high: The RC time constant will then be so high that the circuit cannot follow the modulation signal. Input impedance of the diode-RC series combination is approximately half the value of R divided by the detection efficiency, defined as the ratio of the output audio signal to the input-signal modulation [Ted, EvF]. Shown in Fig. 9.30 are

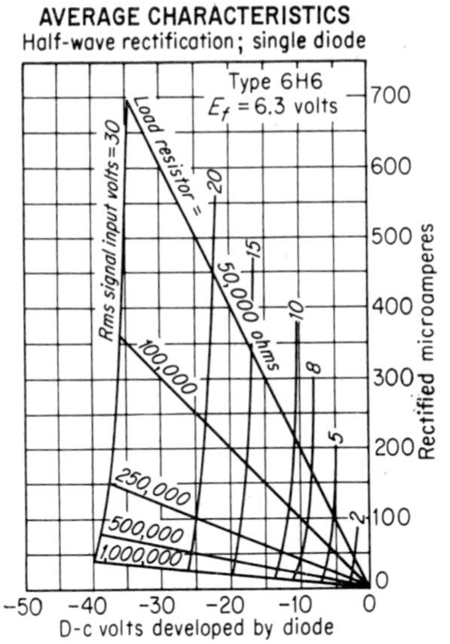

AVERAGE CHARACTERISTICS
Half-wave rectification; single diode

Type 6H6
$E_f = 6.3$ volts

FIG. 9.30. Peak envelope-detection characteristics of the 6H6 vacuum diode. (RCA.)

some actual operating characteristics of a common diode.   The linearity of
detection and the inverse dependence of rectified current on resistance are
evident.   This same diode-detection circuit is often used in peak-reading
vacuum-tube voltmeters.   The input impedance can be made quite high
by simply increasing the size of the output resistance.   The data of
Fig. 9.30 are replotted in Fig. 9.31 to show better the relation between the
peak signal voltage and the direct-voltage output.

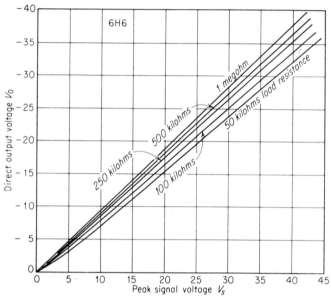

Fig. 9.31. Alternative representation of the detection characteristics of the 6H6
vacuum diode, showing linearity.

9.7. Diode Rectifiers for Power Supplies.   One of the most extensive
applications of diodes is in rectifier circuits converting alternating power
to direct power for power supplies.   This is a large subject and is extensively treated in many books.   Here there will be given some discussion of
single-phase systems only.

One or more diodes connected to convert an alternating voltage to a
pulsating unidirectional voltage constitute what is known as a rectifier
circuit.   When a filter is employed between the rectifier circuit and a load
to convert the pulsating output to a constant d-c output, we have what is
known as a *power supply*.

The three commonest single-phase rectifier circuits are shown in Fig.
9.32.   In part (a) are shown half-wave rectifier circuits.   These require
only one diode, which may be of any type.   The upper diagram shows a
vacuum diode and the lower a semiconductor diode.   Excitation is
invariably by means of a transformer.   The part of a circuit to the left

of the crosses is the rectifier circuit.   If a resistance load is connected
directly to the rectifier, a pulsating output waveform, consisting of alternate halves of a sine wave, will result.   The negative half waves are
almost completely rejected because of the high back resistance of the

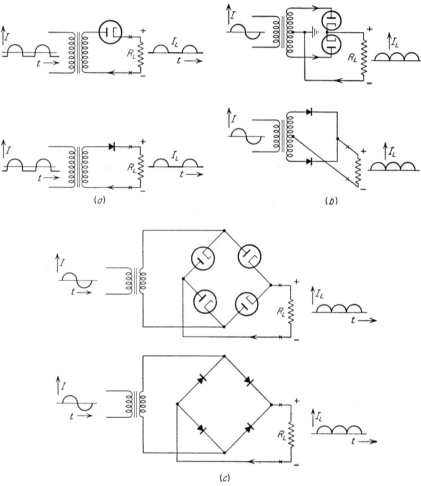

Fig. 9.32. Half- and full-wave diode power-rectifier circuits, showing output waveforms of current: (*a*) Half-wave rectifier circuits.   (*b*) Full-wave rectifier circuits
with center-tapped transformers.   (*c*) Full-wave bridge-type rectifier circuits.

diodes.   Shown are *current* waveforms in various parts of the circuits.
These will be evident from the fact that, in the vacuum diode, electrons
can pass only from cathode to anode.   In the semiconductor rectifier,
the current flow is predominantly in the direction of the triangle of the
rectifier symbol.   The current in the secondary circuit of the transformer

will be virtually unidirectional of the form shown.   The current in the primary of the transformer *must* have the same *form* as the secondary current but *cannot have a direct component*.   These two requirements are met by the fact that the zero level of primary current adjusts itself somewhat as shown with both negative and positive portions.   To get a steady direct current in a load, it is necessary to insert some form of filter between the rectifier and the load at the points marked with crosses.

In Fig. 9.32*b* are shown so-called full-wave rectifier circuits using center-tapped transformers.   These require two diodes.   The diodes conduct on alternate halves of the cycle and the circuits are such that the successive half waves combine with the same polarity in the load.   The effectiveness of these circuits is twice as great as that of the half-wave circuits though two diodes are required instead of one and essentially two secondary windings instead of one.   Again a filter needs to be inserted at the points marked with crosses in order to give a steady direct current in the load.

In Fig. 9.32*c* are shown bridge-type full-wave rectifier circuits.   These circuits put successive half waves through the load with the same polarity. They do not require center-tapped transformers but require two extra diodes.   It is not possible to use *two* vacuum-type double diodes unless one of them has separate cathodes insulated from each other, which is not the case with ordinary tubes.   These circuits produce twice the current given by the circuits of part (*b*) for the same total secondary voltage. Filament windings for both (*b*) and (*c*) must be insulated for the peak output voltage developed.

The characteristics of the rectifier circuits shown may be worked out for resistance loads on the assumption that the output pulses are sinusoidal.   This is not exactly true but is a good approximation.   This may be seen by considering the dynamic characteristic of a single diode with a resistance load, as shown in Fig. 9.33.   Here the relation between diode current i, signal voltage v_s, and diode voltage v_0 is

$$v_0 = v_s - iR_l \tag{9.15}$$

where R_l is the load resistance.   The dynamic characteristic may be determined graphically from the static characteristic of the diode (shown solid in the figure) by considering the voltage axis to be signal voltage and drawing a so-called *load line* through the value of signal voltage in question.   The load line is a straight line with a slope of $-1/R_l$.   Along such a line, the voltage-current relations will correspond to (9.15).   Where this line intersects the static diode characteristic will be found the value of diode voltage and the unique value of current that satisfies (9.15).   The current determined here can be projected over the corresponding signal-voltage values to give the dynamic characteristic.   For example, if the signal voltage has the value corresponding to point a, then the diode voltage and current will be given by the point a'.   Using the value of current at a'' above the signal voltage gives a point on the dynamic characteristic.   Similar construction for signal voltages b and c yields points b'' and c'', from which the dynamic characteristic can be drawn (shown dashed in the figure).   It is seen that the dynamic characteristic has much less curvature than the static characteristic, justifying the assumption of a sinusoidal output current for a sinusoidal signal voltage.

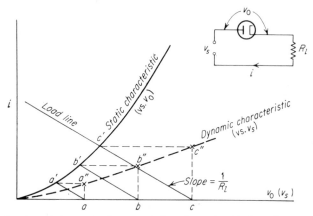

FIG. 9.33. Static and dynamic characteristics of a series diode-resistor combination.

In addition, to determine rectifier characteristics, it is necessary to know the frequency components of the various rectifier outputs.   For the half-wave rectifier giving a series of positive half sine waves spaced a cycle apart as in Fig. 9.32a, the Fourier-series expansion gives

$$i = I_m \left(\frac{1}{\pi} + \frac{1}{2} \cos \omega t + \frac{2}{3\pi} \cos 2\omega t - \frac{2}{15\pi} \cos 4\omega t + \cdots \right) \quad (9.16)$$

where I_m is the peak value of the half sine waves and ω is the angular frequency of the impressed signal.   The desired direct component of current is seen to be $1/\pi$ times the peak current while the lowest-frequency component is $\frac{1}{2}$ the peak current, giving a large alternating component to be filtered out.   The higher-frequency components are smaller and easier to filter out.

The current into a resistive load out of a full-wave rectifier as shown in Fig. 9.32b will be

$$i = I_m \left(\frac{2}{\pi} - \frac{4}{3\pi} \cos 2\omega t - \frac{4}{15\pi} \cos 4\omega t - \cdots \right) \quad (9.17)$$

where I_m is again the peak value of the half sine waves.   It is seen that the direct component is twice as big as in the previous case.   Also the lowest output frequency for balanced diodes is twice the input frequency, making the filtering problem easier.

It is the purpose of the filter connected between the rectifier circuit and the resistive load to reduce the alternating components of output indicated above to an unobjectionable size. Several types of filter are commonly used. These are shown in Fig. 9.34. The first of these, as shown in (a), is simply a capacitor shunted across the load. The second, at (b), is an L section with an inductance in series followed by a shunt capacitor. One or more such sections may be used. A third is an RC form of L section. Various combinations of these may also be used. In considering the action of such filters, we must take into account the influence of the first element on the waveform and the subsequent filtering action. If the input element is a capacitor, as in (a), the direct voltage developed will generally be higher than with (b). This is because

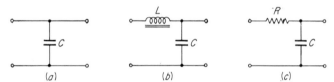

(a)   (b)   (c)

Fig. 9.34. Various types of simple rectifier filter sections.

the capacitor tends to charge up to the peak value of rectifier output voltage, whereas the inductance-input filter tends to work at the average value. At the same time, the regulation with capacitor input will be worse than with inductance input. This comes about because the capacitor will discharge rapidly between voltage peaks as the load resistance is decreased. The inductance-input filter, on the other hand, has relatively good regulation because the diode current waveform does not change much with load. The current drawn from the diodes will be in the form of pulses less than a quarter of a cycle in length in the case of the capacitor-input filter, whereas the diode current will approximate square waves for inductance-input filters. The RC filter of Fig. 9.34c is not nearly so effective or efficient as the LC filter but is sometimes used when considerations of economy, size, and weight overrule.

It is almost always necessary to use a capacitor-input filter in the case of the half-wave rectifier because the capacitor can hold the load voltage nearly constant over a cycle, whereas the inductance-input filter *cannot* hold the current constant because the circuit is effectively open half of each cycle. The largest values of L and C that considerations of cost and size will permit are used. Capacitors are invariably electrolytic, available up to 40 μf at 450 volts, and in smaller sizes for higher voltages. Filter inductances, commonly called chokes, are available with typical values such as 10.5 henrys at 110 ma or 16 henrys at 80 ma and with weights of $2\frac{1}{2}$ lb.

The filter circuit of Fig. 9.34b is essentially a reactance voltage divider. The usual values of reactance for the output frequencies encountered are such that the reactance of the inductance is large compared to the parallel combination of the capacitor and the load.   The capacitor reactance in turn is small in comparison with the impedance of the load.   To the extent that these assumptions are true, the current into the section will be the input alternating voltage divided by the inductive reactance ωL minus the capacitive reactance $1/\omega C$.   The output voltage will be the

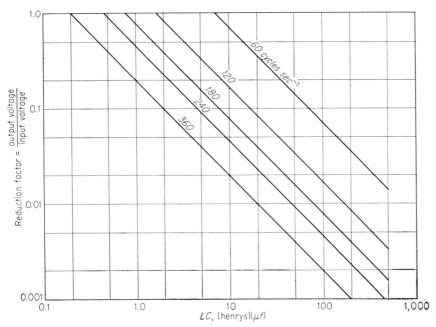

Fig. 9.35. Ripple-reduction curves for LC filter sections.

above current multiplied by the capacitive reactance $1/\omega C$.   Accordingly, the reduction of alternating components with angular frequency ω is given by

$$\frac{\text{Output alternating voltage}}{\text{Input alternating voltage}} = \frac{1}{\omega^2 LC - 1} \qquad (9.18)$$

This applies only to a single LC section.   It applies to any of the frequency components of the rectifier output.   A curve showing the reduction factor corresponding to this ratio is shown in Fig. 9.35.

The same considerations apply to the RC filter of Fig. 9.34c.   Here the reduction factor will be

$$\frac{\text{Output alternating voltage}}{\text{Input alternating voltage}} = \frac{1}{R\omega C} \qquad (9.19)$$

The curves for this case are shown in Fig. 9.36.

Examination of these last two figures reveals the essential characteristics of such filters.   The reduction factor of the *LC* filter decreases with the *LC* product.   It also decreases with ω^2 so that the higher harmonics are very effectively attenuated.   The reduction factor of the *RC* filter decreases with the *RC* product but only with the first power of frequency.   Thus the *RC* filter does not attenuate higher harmonics as well.   It might seem from these curves that the *RC* filter is nearly as

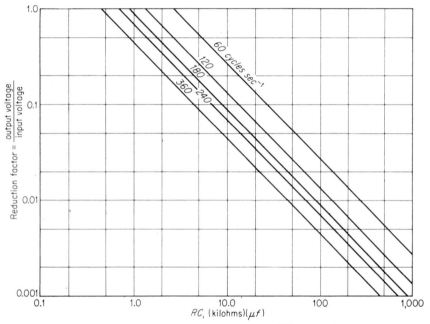

Fig. 9.36. Ripple-reduction curves for *RC* filter sections.

effective for the lowest-frequency component as the *LC* filter.   This is true as far as the lowest frequency is concerned, but it must be remembered that the *LC* filter gives very small reduction of direct voltage whereas the *RC* filter may give very large reduction of direct voltage as determined by potential-divider action of the resistances for constant currents.

Specific Power-supply Characteristics.   The simplest power supply is the half-wave rectifier with a shunt capacitor across a resistive load. This is used primarily for high-voltage low-current supplies.   Shown in Fig. 9.37 are the circuit and the voltage and current waveforms in various parts of such a supply.   Action here is similar to that in the diode detector.   The capacitor will charge to nearly the peak voltage of the transformer minus the drop in the diode at the peak of each cycle and then, if the time constant of the *RC* combination is large enough, discharge slowly over the next cycle. Current will flow again only when the transformer voltage is larger than the drop across the capacitor. The result is a series of narrow high-current pulses and a saw-toothed wave of output current and voltage. Shown in Fig. 9.38 is the characteristic of a typical half-wave rectifier.

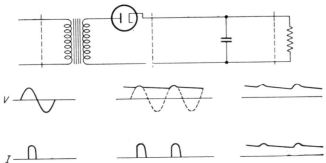

FIG. 9.37. Current and voltage waveforms in various parts of a half-wave rectifier circuit with a capacitor-input filter.

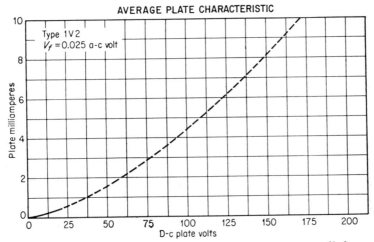

FIG. 9.38. Current-voltage characteristic of the 1V2 vacuum diode.

The full-wave rectifier with center-tapped transformer and inductance-input filter has the circuit, current, and voltage waveforms shown in Fig. 9.39. The output current of the rectifier will be determined principally by the effect of the series of positive half sine waves upon the input inductance. This will give a nonsinusoidal wave with a phase lag, as shown, superimposed upon the direct component of current. If the input inductance is sufficiently high, the ripple will be small and the transformer input-current waveform will be nearly square. The effect of the filter is to reduce the ripple as shown.

Some typical regulation characteristics of such a power supply are shown in Fig. 9.40. The regulation exhibited here is good except for low output currents. This is due to the fact that, for low currents, the alternating component of rectifier output may tend to exceed the d-c output, thus interrupting the continuity of current flow. When this happens the stabilizing influence of the input inductance is lost, giving poor regulation. Accordingly, there is a minimum output direct current or a maximum load resistance that should be used with such a power supply. These values may be determined from the fact that the peak

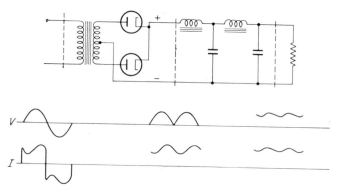

Fig. 9.39. Current and voltage waveforms in various parts of a full-wave rectifier circuit with inductance-input filter.

value of the alternating component of current is approximately proportional to the second term of (9.17) divided by the input inductive reactance, whereas the d-c component is proportional to the first term of (9.17) divided by the load resistance R.

$$\frac{\text{Peak alternating current}}{\text{Direct current}} = \frac{(4I_m/3\pi)/2\omega L}{(2I_m/3\pi)/R} = 1 \qquad (9.20)$$

This gives a minimum value of inductance

$$L_{\min} = \frac{R}{6\pi f} \qquad \text{henrys} \qquad (9.21)$$

where $L_{\min}$ = minimum filter input inductance, henrys
    R = effective load resistance, including choke, resistances, ohms
    f = input frequency, cycles sec^{-1}

The above limitation on regulation is generally overcome in one of two ways: The first is to connect a resistance in parallel with the load, which will ensure continuity of current. Such a resistance is known as a *bleeder* resistance. The second method is to use a choke with a specially designed magnetic circuit (with a smaller than usual air gap) whose inductance is high for low direct current and whose effective inductance to alternating components is low for larger direct currents. Such an inductance is called a *swinging choke*. Where the load on a power supply is rigidly fixed, it is, of course, not necessary to apply such methods because the regulation is not a problem.

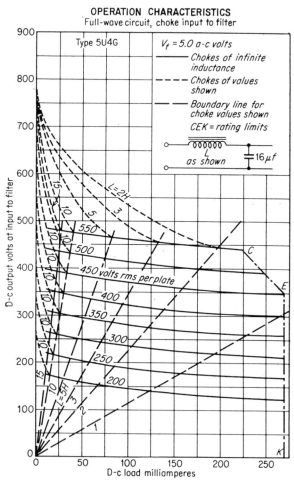

FIG. 9.40. Regulation characteristics of a type 5U4G double diode used in a full-wave rectifier circuit with inductance-input filter. (*RCA.*)

Shown in Fig. 9.41 are the circuit and the current and voltage waveforms of a full-wave rectifier with a center-tapped transformer, using a capacitor-input filter. This has the same general aspect as the half-wave rectifier with capacitor-input filter as shown in Fig. 9.37. The resulting regulation characteristics are shown in Fig. 9.42 for a typical tube. Such power supplies give higher voltage with the same transformer but have poorer regulation than can be obtained with inductance-input filters.

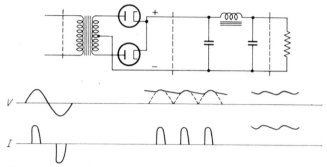

FIG. 9.41. Current and voltage waveforms in various parts of a full-wave rectifier circuit with capacitor-input filter.

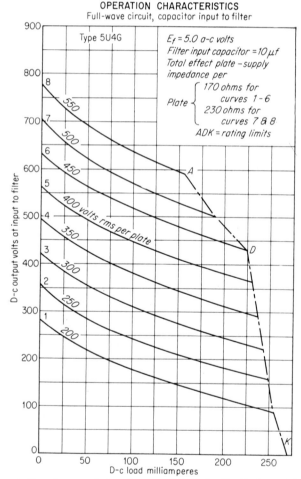

FIG. 9.42. Regulation characteristics of a type 5U4G double diode used in a full-wave rectifier circuit with a capacitor-input filter. (*RCA.*)

They are also subject to the limitation that very large current pulses may be drawn through the diodes.   As a result, gas diodes are almost never used with a capacitor-input filter because of the damage which may occur to such tubes if their current ratings are exceeded.

No section on power supplies should be concluded without reference to voltage-doubler and -multiplier circuits.   Shown in Fig. 9.43 are the circuits of a so-called voltage doubler and voltage quadrupler [Cos]. In part (*a*) of the figure is a form of bridge circuit giving nearly twice the peak transformer voltage.   This is essentially two half-wave rectifiers

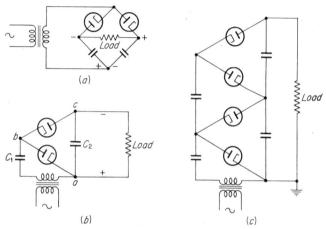

FIG. 9.43. Various rectifying voltage-doubler and -multiplier circuits.

of opposite polarity with outputs connected in series.   In part (*b*) is a type of voltage doubler using a tandem connection.   The operation of circuit (*b*) may be understood by first considering that the upper diode is disconnected at the point *b*.   Then the capacitor C_1 will charge up to almost the peak output voltage of the transformer, and the voltage of the point *b* will vary between zero and nearly twice the peak transformer output voltage.   If now the second diode is connected, the second capacitor will be charged up to nearly twice the peak transformer output voltage. This circuit has the advantage that one side of the output can be grounded. The polarity can be reversed by simply reversing the diode connections. This method of getting high voltage can be extended as shown in the quadrupler circuit of Fig. 9.43*c*.   In fact it can be extended almost indefinitely, subject to insulation limitations.   It has been used in certain types of high-voltage impulse generators.   Such circuits, however, have poor regulation and are suitable only for the production of small currents.

9.8. Diode Modulating Circuits.   Modulation is the process whereby intelligence at low frequency is impressed upon waves of higher frequency for the purpose of transmission.   Modulation is achieved in many ways, as will be discussed later, most frequently with control-type electron devices.

However, there are several basic diode modulation circuits deserving of mention.

The simplest type of diode modulator simply inserts two voltages in series with a resistor and diode and derives an amplitude-modulated radio-frequency signal from the nonlinear characteristic of the diode. This is shown in Fig. 9.44. The two voltages are an audio voltage V_a and a radio-frequency voltage V_r. This circuit is a small-signal modulator making

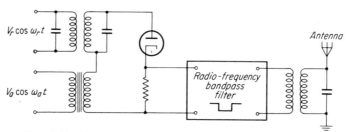

FIG. 9.44. Schematic diagram of a diode modulating circuit.

use of the nonlinearity of the diode characteristic, which may be written as in (9.13)

$$i(v_1) = a_1 v_1 + a_2 v_1^2 + \cdots + a_n v_1^n + \cdots \tag{9.22}$$

In this case, the applied voltage v_1 will be the sum of the radio and audio voltages:

$$v_1(t) = V_a \cos \omega_a t + V_r \cos \omega_r t \tag{9.23}$$

Applying this in (9.22),

$$\begin{aligned} i(v_1) = {} & a_1 V_a \cos \omega_a t + a_1 V_r \cos \omega_r t + a_2 V_a^2 \cos^2 \omega_a t + a_2 V_r^2 \cos \omega_r t \\ & + a_2 V_a V_r \cos (\omega_a + \omega_r)t + a_2 V_a V_r \cos (\omega_a - \omega_r)t + \cdots \end{aligned} \tag{9.24}$$

Here the first term is at the audio frequency. The third and fourth terms yield direct current and second harmonics of the audio and radio frequencies. However, the second, fifth, and sixth terms combine to give an amplitude-modulated wave, which consists of a carrier term (the second) and upper and lower side bands (the fifth and sixth). The other terms are not grouped around the carrier and may easily be filtered out. It is interesting to note that the simple series diode may be used either for modulation or demodulation (detection) of amplitude-modulated waves.

Another diode modulating circuit is a type of bridge circuit, of which a number of variations are shown in Fig. 9.45 [Cal]. Such circuits commonly employ copper-oxide rectifiers and are extensively used in carrier telephony. In such circuits the carrier voltage will generally be larger than the signal voltage and will serve to increase or decrease the diode resistances depending upon the polarity. Thus the diodes are essentially switches activated by the carrier voltage. The circuit of Fig. 9.45a is seen to place a short across the line on alternate half cycles. This yields

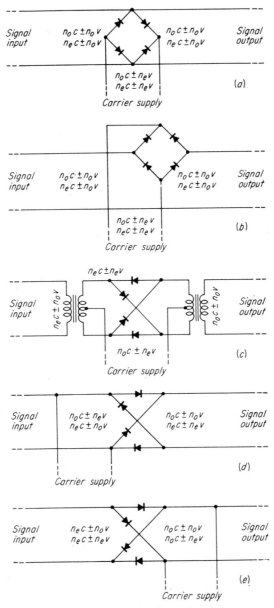

FIG. 9.45. Bridge-type diode modulating circuits. Frequency components present in each branch are indicated. Carrier frequency is c; signal frequency is v; n_o is any odd number; n_e is any even number or zero. (*After Caruthers.*)

a waveform as shown in Fig. 9.46a.   The circuit of Fig. 9.45b opens the
line on alternate half cycles.   The circuit of Fig. 9.45c is seen to give a
direct and a twisted connection between transformers every half cycle of
carrier voltage, resulting in the output waveform shown in Fig. 9.46b.
Filters must be used in both input and in the output circuits to separate
the various modulation components generated.   The circuits of Fig.
9.45d and e have the same general action as that of Fig. 9.45c.

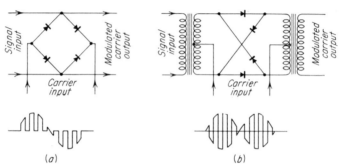

(a)   (b)

FIG. 9.46. Output-current waveforms of some bridge-type diode-modulator circuits.

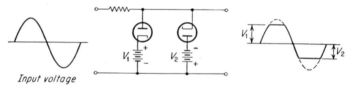

FIG. 9.47. Double-diode limiter circuit (clipper).

9.9. Wave-shaping Applications of Diodes.   The nonlinear characteristics of diodes make them useful for various wave-shaping functions
[Chb].   The most common of these for diodes is a limiting, or clipping,
action, which makes rectangular waves out of nonrectangular waves.
Such circuits make use of the fact that current flows essentially in only
one direction in diodes, and in this direction the use of a large voltage-
dropping resistor makes it possible to hold voltage at a reference level.
In the other direction the diode resistance is high enough to cause it to
act as an open circuit.   A double-diode limiting circuit is shown in Fig.
9.47.   In this circuit the left-hand diode conducts only for input voltages
greater than V_1, and for this condition the voltage drop through a large
resistor R limits the output to slightly more than V_1.   The right-hand
diode conducts only for voltages more negative than V_2, and again the
voltage is limited by the series resistance, giving the output voltage wave
shown in the case of a strongly overdriven input sine wave.   Successive
application of such circuits can be used to produce square waves from
sine waves.

Another application of diodes of interest is their use in fixing the relative level of waveforms. Often nonsinusoidal waveforms are passed through a coupling capacitor, with the result that the d-c reference value is lost and the waveform adjusts its position so that its average value is at zero potential. Frequently, however, there is desired a different level. This can be established with a diode in what is called a *clamping* circuit. Such circuits are shown in Fig. 9.48. In part (a) of the figure is shown the effect of passing an arbitrary rectangular pulse through a capacitor

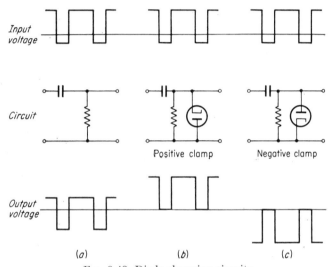

FIG. 9.48. Diode clamping circuits.

coupling circuit. The output wave in this case adjusts itself for equal positive and negative areas. In (b) is shown a positive clamp circuit, which has the effect of causing the wave to assume entirely positive values. In (c) is shown a negative clamp circuit, which causes the wave to assume entirely negative values. This action is easily explained by considering the diode a low resistance when it has a positive voltage on its plate and a high resistance when it has a negative potential on its plate.

9.10. Diodes in Computers. Diodes are extensively used in computers. There will generally be two or three diodes for every tube or transistor in a digital computer. Most of the diodes are used in wave-shaping, clamping, and limiting operations, but more interesting applications are found in the use of the diodes as electric switches. The diode can be used as an electric switch because it acts as a closed switch on forward polarity and as an open switch on reverse polarity. Modern diodes can be found with forward resistances of only a few tenths of an ohm and reverse resistance of the order of megohms. These values are comparable to an actual switch.

One such switching application is found in a capacitor-diode memory circuit, as shown in Fig. 9.49. In this simple circuit, any capacitor can be charged by applying a positive voltage between any "charge line" C

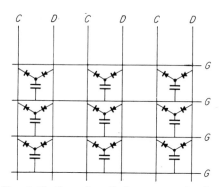

Fig. 9.49. Capacitor-diode memory circuit.

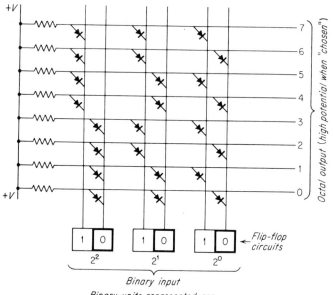

Fig. 9.50. Binary-to-octal conversion matrix.

and the proper "ground line" G. Likewise, any charged capacitor can be discharged by connecting the proper "discharge line" D to the corresponding ground line G. By this means, "bits" of information can be stored in a matrix of capacitors and diodes. It is now possible to find capacitors and diodes with such low leakage that a very long storage time may be achieved [Hoc].

Another use of the switching property of diodes makes possible the conversion of numbers from one digital form to another. Shown in Fig. 9.50 is a circuit capable of converting numbers from a binary to octal code. This is done with a matrix of 6 vertical cross bars, 8 horizontal cross bars, and 24 diodes.

The octal and binary codes are commonly used in computer work. They are related as shown in the tabulation below:

Octal	Binary
0	000
1	001
2	010
3	011
4	100
5	101
6	110
7	111

The matrix is activated by the three flip-flop circuits shown at the bottom, one for each digit of the binary code. A flip-flop circuit is an electrical circuit that has two stable states yielding either a high or low potential, a kind of electrical seesaw. Shown in the figure is the condition that the three flip-flops have their right side at high potential and their left side at low potential. The low-potential sides will short out various horizontal cross bars through the diodes. As a result, the 000 binary input will yield a 0 octal output at high potential, whereas all other octal output leads will be at low potential.

CHAPTER 10

CONTROL-TYPE VACUUM TUBES

10.1. Electric-field Control of Current Flow in Vacuum Tubes. One of the greatest engineering discoveries of modern times, the one that gave rise to the field of electronics, was the discovery by De Forest (1907) that current flow in a diode could be controlled by the field produced by a grid of fine wires between the cathode and the plate [Dez]. This occurs for the grid negative with respect to the cathode, under which condition it collects no electrons and thus indicates that its controlling action occurs by virtue of the electric field that it produces.

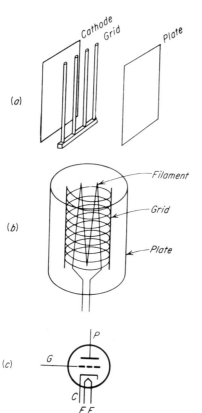

De Forest's original "audion" was the forerunner of the modern *triode*. This is a three-electrode tube, which, in idealized form, is shown in Fig. 10.1. Here is shown a plane cathode covered with emitting material heated electrically either directly or indirectly. The grid is a screen of parallel wires in a plane close to the cathode and between it and a plane anode or plate. The wires are interconnected so as to bring them all to the same potential. The grid has a shielding effect so that, for instance, if the cathode and grid are connected together at zero potential and the plate is at a positive potential, relatively few flux lines from the plate will penetrate the grid to reach the cathode. As a result, the positive gradient at the cathode surface will be small. Normally, however, the cathode is at zero potential, the grid at a slight negative potential, and the plate at a large positive potential. In this situation electrons will be emitted from the cathode

Fig. 10.1. (*a,b*) Form and (*c*) symbol of electrodes in the vacuum triode.

204

and be drawn to the plate through the spaces between the negative grid wires.

Actually the triode grid and plate may both draw current if both are positive. The region of interest, however, is that of positive plate potentials and small negative grid potentials. For this condition the grid has a sensitive influence over the emitted current, which all goes to the plate, giving a means of controlling current that uses virtually zero power.

To understand this, it is most helpful to examine the electric fields resulting from the presence of the grid at various potentials. In Sec. 4.6 it was mentioned that electric fields and electron paths could be observed

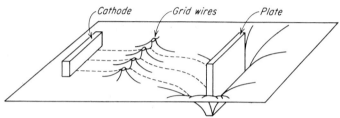

Fig. 10.2. Elastic-membrane model showing potential variation within a plane-electrode triode. Elevation corresponds to negative potential.

with a rubber-membrane model. In this model, a membrane is first stretched horizontally on a rectangular frame. Blocks shaped like the electrodes are then pressed against the membrane to represent their potential, *vertical displacement* being made proportional to *negative potential*. The resulting membrane configuration for positive plate potential (negative elevation relative to cathode) and slightly negative grid potential (slight positive elevation relative to cathode) is shown in Fig. 10.2. Here is shown a block representing the cathode electrode at the zero reference level of a supporting frame. The positive plate is represented by a block depressed into the membrane. The negative grid wires are represented by cylinders pushed against the membrane from below. It is possible to have a positive plate (negative displacement) and a negative grid (positive displacement), which gives a negative slope (positive gradient of potential) over the emitting surface of the cathode.

In the above model, little balls, corresponding to electrons, can roll from the cathode surface to the plate in the depressed space between the grid wires. It is seen that a small change in grid potential (elevation) will make a change in the slope (voltage gradient) in front of the cathode large in comparison to a similar change in the potential (elevation) of the plate potential. This, of course, is due to the fact that the grid is closer than the plate to the cathode and because the plate variations are masked (shielded) by the grid. It is also possible for the grid to be negative (high) enough to cause the gradient of electric potential to be negative (positive slope in the model). Under this condition, low-velocity electrons cannot escape the cathode and the conduction of the tube is cut off.

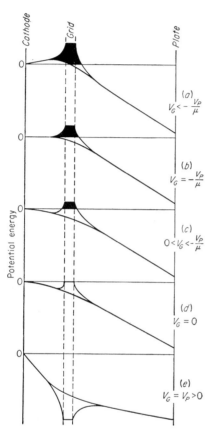

FIG. 10.3. Electron potential energy, or negative-potential profiles, of a plane-electrode triode with various grid voltages.

Between the cutoff condition and zero grid potential is a large region of operation in which the grid may control the plate current without at the same time intercepting any electrons from the cathode directly.

Actually the model of Fig. 10.2 gives answers that apply only to the cold-cathode triode; i.e., it gives the potential distribution in the absence of electrons. This is because the deformed elastic membrane can only represent charge-free potentials. However, whenever the slope of the membrane in front of the cathode is negative (gradient of potential positive), small balls will be able to roll from cathode to plate in the model, or current will be able to flow in the tube and will be simply related to the gradient, or more properly an equivalent potential, of the grid plane. Corrections for space charge in the form of depression of potential (elevation of membrane) are easy to apply; and so, for an initial qualitative study, space charge will be neglected and the subject will be examined in terms of the potential variations within the cold tube. The variations of potential within a triode corresponding to negative deformations of the elastic membrane can be represented in several ways. One type of diagram shows selected potential *profiles*. These are curves corresponding to intersections of the membrane with a vertical plane. The two planes which are most revealing are planes perpendicular to the cathode and plate and passing through (1) a grid wire and (2) a point midway between two grid wires. Shown in Fig. 10.3 are a series of such profiles for different grid potentials, considering the cathode at zero potential and the plate at a fixed positive potential. In this figure are shown values of *negative potential*, i.e., the normal diagram upside down. This representation is used here and in the rest of the book because it corresponds to *elevation* in the elastic-membrane model (also to potential energy of an electron) and because electrons will run *downhill* in such a diagram, making it easier to visualize electron paths and the amount of current flowing. The profiles in this figure show the effect on the gradient in front of the cathode of the combination of grid and plate potential starting with a very negative grid and making it more positive.

In Fig. 10.3*a* is shown the effect of a grid so negative that the gradient of potential in front of the cathode is negative. Under this condition the tube is said to be cut off and no current flows from the cathode. In part (*b*) is shown the value of grid potential that makes the gradient at the cathode just zero. This is the limiting condition between current flow and no current flow. The grid here is said to be at the *cutoff* value. Here a small negative grid potential annuls the effect of a large positive plate potential. The ratio of the positive plate potential to the negative grid potential for the cutoff condition is known as the *amplification factor* of the tube. This is because this same factor determines the relative effectiveness of the grid and plate in determining the gradient of potential at the cathode and hence also the cathode current. The amplification factor is indicated by the symbol μ. In Fig. 10.3 regions of negative potential are shown shaded. These are regions where electrons cannot enter.

In Fig. 10.3*c* the grid is negative but more positive than the cutoff value. The gradient of potential at the cathode is positive, permitting electrons to flow to the plate but not to the grid, which is still negative. It is in this condition that the majority of vacuum tubes operate and here that the control action of the grid is most effective. In part (*d*) of the figure the grid is at zero potential representing an upper limit for which the grid will draw no current and a maximum allowable continuous plate current for most tubes. In part (*e*) is shown an extreme condition in which the grid is as positive as the plate. Few tubes can be operated like this continuously without damage from the resulting high currents. Under this condition the plate draws a very large current and the grid intercepts a fraction of the total current roughly proportional to its area. This is a peak operating condition used in certain large-signal amplifiers, where, however, the grid will be positive only a small fraction of a cycle and the current will flow in short intense pulses.

Corresponding to the potential profiles of Fig. 10.3, equipotential diagrams can be drawn as in Fig. 10.4. These correspond to topographic maps showing equal-elevation contours and as such are the corresponding map for the elastic-membrane model. The five parts of this figure correspond to the parts of the previous figure. The areas at negative potential are again shaded, representing areas into which electrons *cannot* enter.

It is interesting to note that, except for the cutoff condition, the equipotentials near the cathode are nearly straight lines parallel to it so that the electrons tend to move normal to the cathode.

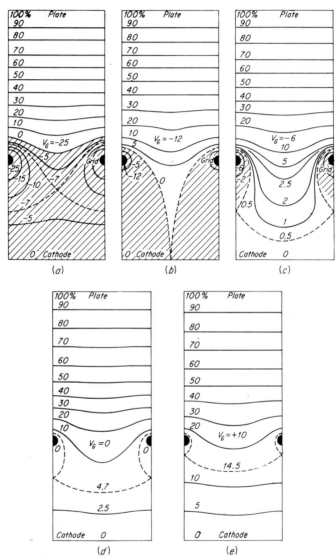

FIG. 10.4. Equipotential contours of a plane-electrode triode for various grid voltages.

The control effectiveness of the grid, or amplification factor, is expected to be greater as the cathode-grid spacing is made relatively smaller. Also one would expect the amplification factor to be greater as the grid spacing is decreased and as the size of the grid wire is increased. In practice, values of amplification factors between zero and several hundred are easily obtained.   In Fig. 10.5 is given a chart showing how the amplification factor of a plane-electrode triode depends upon its internal dimensions.   The amplification factor is one of the most important tube characteristics though, as will be shown shortly, it is only one of several that are of interest.   Accordingly, tubes are not always designed with the highest possible value of this factor.

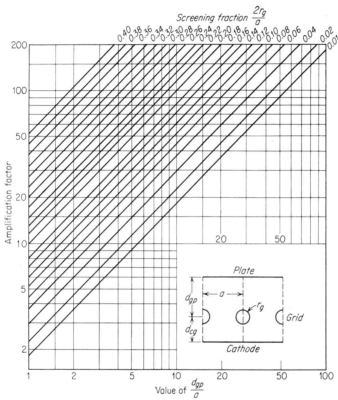

Fig. 10.5. Amplification factor of a plane-electrode triode as a function of electrode spacings.

This and the following section are concerned principally with triodes. There are many other kinds of control-type vacuum tubes, although generally each contains a triode section.   Thus if the operation of the triode is well understood, it is a simple matter to develop the characteristics of other tubes.

10.2. Triode Characteristics.   The easiest way to get an idea of triode current-voltage characteristics is to measure them and plot some curves. After the curves have been examined and their principal features observed, it will be possible to explain them more easily.   One word is interjected at the start.   In the past it has been the custom to ignore grid currents in elementary treatments. It is true that grid currents are much less important than plate currents and that the majority of applications permit only plate currents to flow. However, the modern electronic engineer will encounter transistors where the input current cannot be ignored. He should therefore get used at the earliest possible time to the idea that electron devices may have input as well as output current.

Although the electron device in its simplest terms, triode or transistor, has three active elements, it is invariably operated with one terminal common to input and output, making it a four-terminal device, as shown in Fig. 10.6. Here is shown the commonest connection, known as the grounded-cathode connection, and the associated assumed directions of current and voltage. It should be noted that this is not the only possible connection, i.e., grounded-grid and grounded-plate connections are also sometimes used. However, if the current-voltage characteristics for one connection are known, they may be easily constructed graphically for the other connections.

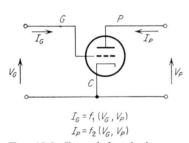

$$I_G = f_1(V_G, V_P)$$
$$I_P = f_2(V_G, V_P)$$

Fig. 10.6. Grounded-cathode connection of a vacuum triode and associated notation.

For the connection of Fig. 10.6 the following simple forms are applicable:

$$I_G = f_1(V_G, V_P) \qquad (10.1)$$
$$I_P = f_2(V_G, V_P) \qquad (10.2)$$

where the subscripts G and P refer to grid and plate, respectively. This is to say that there are four interrelated variables, two currents and two voltages. Each current is a function of the two voltages. The voltages are considered the independent variables and the currents the dependent variables, although this is a little arbitrary. It happens that the grid current is not a simple function of voltage and is seldom expressed so analytically. The plate current is, however, a simple function of the voltages over most of its useful range.

Space Current. Even more fundamental than the above two relations are the following, which hold for all operating conditions of all triodes:

$$I_S = I_G + I_P \qquad (10.3)$$

$$I_S = f\left(V_G + \frac{V_P}{\mu}\right) \qquad (10.4)$$

where I_S = total current transmitted from cathode to other electrodes, *space* current

μ = amplification factor, or relative control effectiveness of grid and plate

This last form results from the linear superposition of field effects within the tube. Actually the space current will follow a Child's-law type of behavior, as encountered in the diode, giving

$$I_S = G\left(V_G + \frac{V_P}{\mu}\right)^{\frac{3}{2}}$$ (10.5)

for $V_G + V_P/\mu$ greater than zero, where the factor of proportionality G is called perveance and depends only on the tube geometry, being independent of the operating voltages. The factor $V_G + V_P/\mu$ is an equivalent grid voltage. This means that a diode with an electrode spacing

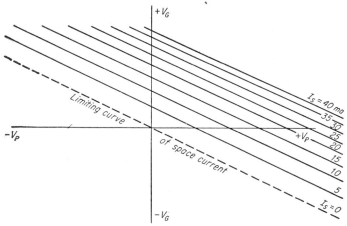

FIG. 10.7. Idealized curves of constant space current for a vacuum triode plotted against axes of plate and grid voltage relative to cathode.

about equal to the cathode-grid spacing of the triode and a plate voltage equal to the above equivalent grid voltage will pass the same current as the triode (see Appendix 9). This form is verified experimentally by measuring space current and plotting curves of constant space current as a function of grid and plate voltage. Such a plot is shown in Fig. 10.7 for a hypothetical tube. In accordance with (10.5) the curves are simply a set of parallel straight lines. In such a set the slope of the lines will be the negative reciprocal of the amplification factor. There is a limiting dashed line of zero current, which divides the region of current flow from the region of no current flow. Below this line no current flows. The spacing between the lines decreases as the current increases because of the exponent $\frac{3}{2}$.

In the curves of Fig. 10.7 there are four quadrants, and there may be indicated further subdivisions of two of the quadrants as shown in Fig. 10.8. The four quadrants are indicated with Roman numerals. Plate current can flow only when plate voltage is positive and so can occur only in the right half plane. Grid current can flow only when the grid is positive and so can occur only in the upper half plane. Current of any kind can flow only when the equivalent grid voltage $V_G + V_P/\mu$ is positive and so can occur only above and to the right of the dashed line, which is sometimes known as the cutoff curve. Combining these considerations and examining the sectors in reverse order of interest we note the following: In the third quadrant neither plate nor grid current may flow, and the space current is zero. In this area the tube is completely inactive. In the second quadrant plate current may not flow, but grid

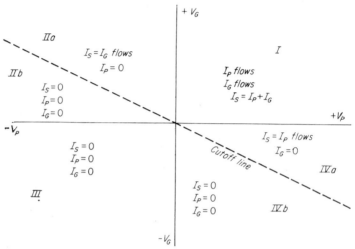

FIG. 10.8. Current-flow regions in the vacuum triode.

current may flow in part IIa, where it will comprise the entire space current. No current of any kind will flow in part IIb, which is below and to the left of the cutoff line. Quadrants II and III are of little interest and are frequently not even shown in constant-current diagrams.

In quadrant I both plate and grid current may flow, and the space current is the sum of the two. Triodes cannot ordinarily be operated continuously in this region because of the high currents drawn. In quadrant IV grid current may not flow, but plate current may. This it does in part IVa, where the equivalent grid voltage is positive. Below and to the left of the cutoff line in part IVb plate current is cut off, and no current of any kind flows. In part IVa the plate current is the entire space current; this is the region of greatest interest, and the one where the majority of tube applications occur. This is naturally the most desirable region of operation because the grid current and hence the grid power is zero, while at the same time the control action of the grid is present.

Constant-plate- and Grid-current Characteristics. It is desirable to show both grid and plate current in a representation like that of Fig. 10.8.

Such a separation is also shown in Fig. 10.9. In the fourth quadrant the space current is all plate current and the curves are approximately straight parallel lines. The second and third quadrants are not shown, being of little operational interest. In the first quadrant both plate and grid current may flow. The space current follows the law of (10.5) given earlier, but the space current divides between plate and grid in a way that is simple neither to describe nor to explain. The best representation is actually that of Fig. 10.9. Briefly it may be said that the ratio of plate

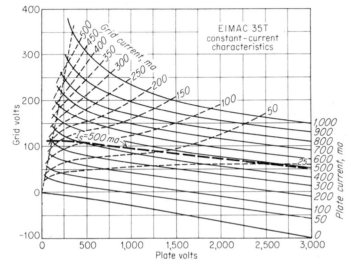

FIG. 10.9. Curves of constant plate and grid current of a vacuum triode against axes of plate and grid voltage relative to cathode.

to grid current in the absence of secondary emission depends only upon the ratio of plate to grid voltage. This is a consequence of the properties of electron paths discussed in Sec. 4.6, where it was pointed out that the form of the electron paths depends only upon the shape of the potential contours and not upon their magnitudes. For a constant ratio of plate to grid potentials the shape of the field within the tube stays constant as do the electron paths and hence the division of space current between grid and plate. Also in the absence of secondary emission the following approximations will hold: for $V_P > V_G$,

$$\frac{I_P}{I_G} \cong k_1 \sqrt{\frac{V_P}{V_G}} \tag{10.6}$$

for $V_P < V_G$,

$$\frac{I_P}{I_G} \cong k_1 \left(\frac{V_P}{V_G}\right)^2 \tag{10.7}$$

These relations result from a study of electron paths in the tube. When secondary emission exists, the grid current may have almost any value and the characteristics can only be represented by a set of curves [Spc].

Triode-plate-current Characteristics. Plate-current characteristics are more usually presented as a family of curves in one of two representations. These are shown in Figs. 10.10 and 10.11. The first of these shows plate current as a function of grid voltage. For a given plate voltage each curve of plate current has a very nearly linear variation with grid voltage except for low currents. As expected, the plate current increases rapidly as the grid voltage increases. This is the principal useful characteristic

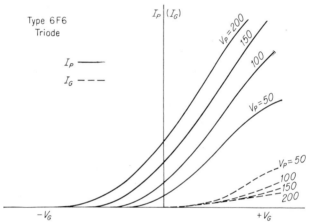

FIG. 10.10. Plate and grid current in a vacuum triode as a function of grid-cathode voltage.

of control-type tubes. Each curve has approximately the same shape, but the curves are successively displaced to the right as the plate voltage increases. For positive grid voltages the curves increase less rapidly with grid voltage because the grid draws some of the total current in this region. Also at higher values of plate current saturation effects sometimes begin to show themselves.

In Fig. 10.11 are shown the plate-current characteristics of the same tube presented as curves of plate current against plate voltage. For negative grid voltages the curves have the same aspect as the curves of Fig. 10.10. Plate current increases with plate voltage more or less linearly except for small currents. Increasing grid voltage displaces curves to the left, giving the effect of an increased plate current for a given plate voltage. For positive grid voltage the plate current increases with plate voltage more rapidly, giving curves with a negative instead of a positive curvature. This happens because here the space current is changing its division between plate and grid. As plate voltage increases, the space current increases and at the same time the fraction of the space current that goes to the plate also increases, giving two factors instead of one contributing to the increase in plate current.

Triode-grid-current Characteristics. Shown dashed in Figs. 10.10 and 10.11 are also curves of grid current. These are of less importance than curves of plate current and may be passed over by the reader until there is encountered an application requiring them. In Fig. 10.10 the grid current, assuming no secondary emission, is seen to increase with grid voltage in accordance with expectation. Grid current is, of course,

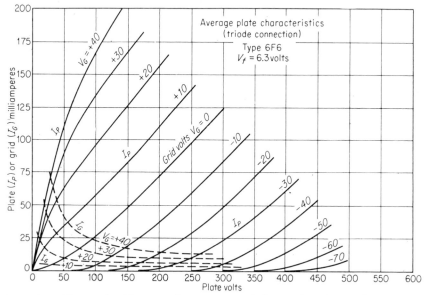

FIG. 10.11. Plate and grid current in a vacuum triode as a function of plate voltage.

encountered only for positive grid voltages. Somewhat contrary to expectations, the grid current decreases with increasing plate voltage. This results from the difference of two actions. In the first place, increasing the plate voltage increases the space current. However, as plate voltage is increased, the electrons are pulled more strongly toward the plate with the result that the *fraction* of the space current that goes to the grid is actually decreased. For the usual electrode dimensions, the latter action dominates, giving a grid current that decreases with plate voltage. Figure 10.11 gives grid current against plate voltage. Here the increase in grid current with grid voltage and the decrease with plate voltage are evident.

Triode Constants. In describing triodes it is not always practicable to exhibit curves of the entire current characteristics. It is more convenient to define certain figures of merit, which describe the principal characteristics of the tube. Interestingly enough these turn out to be numbers simply related to the current characteristics. Specifically, the so-called tube constants are given directly or inversely by slopes of the various current characteristics.

There are three so-called tube constants of principal interest. They are the amplification factor, the mutual conductance, and the dynamic plate resistance. The first of these, the amplification factor, has already been mentioned. It is a measure of the amplification of a tube into a high impedance circuit. The mutual conductance is a measure of the amplification of a tube into a relatively low impedance. The plate resistance is the resistance measured looking back into the plate and cathode terminals of the tube. These so-called tube constants are constant only in a relative sense. They all depend somewhat upon the direct components of voltage used with the tube. The amplification factor is most constant. The other two constants vary considerably with the current passed through the tube.

The subject of tube constants and their use in equivalent circuits will be discussed in more detail in a later chapter. For proper perspective it should be stated that the three constants mentioned are simply related so that there are in reality only two independent constants. Further, these two constants are concerned with the plate current. Two more concerned with the grid current may be found, but they ordinarily have a value of zero and so are seldom used. Also, speaking in general terms, the vacuum tube is generally used as an active four-terminal network. This means that it is like a passive four-terminal network with some internal generators. The passive four-terminal network requires three constants to describe its behavior. The active four-terminal network requires four. However, since two of these depend upon the input current and the input current of a vacuum tube for negative control grid is zero, this reduces to two. A combination of these two is sometimes used, with the result that there are apparently three constants. In reality there are only two for negative grid operation and four for positive grid operation.

The amplification of a tube may be defined as the *relative effectiveness of the plate and control grid in controlling the plate current*. Mathematically it is given by

$$\mu = -\frac{\partial I_P/\partial V_G}{\partial I_P/\partial V_P} = -\left(\frac{dV_P}{dV_G}\right)_{I_P=\text{const}} \tag{10.8}$$

This indicates that, if the plate voltage is *increased* a certain amount, the grid voltage must be *reduced* a corresponding amount to maintain the plate current constant. The amplification factor is seen to be the negative reciprocal of the slope of the constant-plate-current curves of Fig. 10.9. Here the relative constancy of the amplification factor can be seen from the uniformity of slope. At small grid voltages the amplification factor becomes lower. This occurs because there are some low-μ parts of the grid due to end effects in parallel with high-μ parts. The high-μ parts will cut off first, leaving a low-μ action. However, over most of the range the amplification constant is relatively constant.

Another tube constant is the so-called mutual conductance, or trans-conductance. *The mutual conductance is the rate of change of plate current with control-grid voltage.* This is written as

$$g_m = \left(\frac{\partial I_P}{\partial V_G}\right) = \left(\frac{dI_P}{dV_G}\right)_{V_P=\text{const}} \tag{10.9}$$

An increase in grid voltage results in an increase in plate current, which in the limit are in the ratio of g_m. The mutual conductance is by this definition the slope of the plate-current–grid-voltage characteristics of Fig. 10.10. The mutual conductance is seen to increase with plate current in the negative grid region. Mutual conductances are usually expressed in units of microamperes of plate current per grid volt. Typical values of this constant run around 1,000 to 10,000 μa volt^{-1}. Some specially designed tubes will have mutual conductances as high as 20,000 μa volt^{-1}.

The plate resistance of a tube, often qualified with the adjectives "dynamic" and "variational," is the impedance that would be measured in the plate circuit with an a-c bridge that did not disturb the d-c operating conditions. Plate resistance is the reciprocal of the rate of change of plate current with plate voltage

$$r_p = \frac{1}{\partial I_P/\partial V_P} = \frac{\partial V_P}{\partial I_P} = \left(\frac{dV_P}{dI_P}\right)_{V_G=\text{const}} \tag{10.10}$$

The plate resistance is seen to be the reciprocal of the slope of the plate-current–plate-voltage curve. Values of this constant for triodes run from 1,000 to 50,000 ohms. A typical value is 5,000 ohms.

The definitions given above for the three triode constants are general and apply to multielectrode tubes as well. Values of the mutual conductance are about the same for triodes and multielectrode tubes. However, the amplification factor of multielectrode tubes will be higher than that for triodes because of the shielding effect of the other grids. Similarly, the plate resistance of multielectrode tubes will be much higher than that in triodes.

Relation between Tube Constants. The relation between the tube constants may be shown by taking the differential of (10.2), which simply says that the plate current is a function of grid and plate voltage. This gives

$$dI_P = \frac{\partial I_P}{\partial V_G} dV_G + \frac{\partial I_P}{\partial V_P} dV_P \tag{10.11}$$

This says that a small change in plate current will be given by the change in grid voltage multiplied by the rate of change of plate current with grid voltage plus the change in plate voltage multiplied by the rate of change of plate current with plate voltage in the limit of small changes.

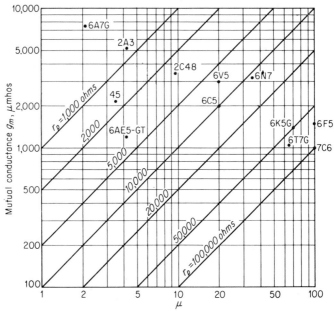

FIG. 10.12. Mutual conductance, amplification factor, and dynamic plate resistance of typical vacuum triodes.

Using the definitions of the constants previously given,

$$dI_P = g_m dV_G + \frac{1}{r_p} dV_P \qquad (10.12)$$

If the change in plate current is held to zero, then

$$g_m r_p = - \left(\frac{dV_P}{dV_G} \right)_{I_P=\text{const}} = \mu \qquad (10.13)$$

This shows that the product of the mutual conductance and the dynamic plate resistance is equal to the amplification factor for any given operating condition.   This is a general relation which applies to all tubes.   Shown in Fig. 10.12 is a plot of tube constants of various triodes.   Virtually any combination of the three constants is available.

There has already been given in Fig. 10.5 a set of curves showing how the amplification factor of a tube varies with electrode dimensions. Mutual conductance, by definition, is the rate of change of plate current with grid voltage.   Since the plate current varies approximately as the three-halves power of equivalent grid voltage, according to (10.5), for negative grid potentials, the mutual conductance will vary as the derivative of this, or as the one-half power of the equivalent grid voltage. But the one-half power of equivalent grid voltage is proportional to the cube root of plate current, also from (10.5), for negative grid voltages. Accordingly, *the mutual conductance of a given tube varies as the cube root of the plate current as the operating condition is changed.* Shown in Fig. 10.13 are curves showing how the constants of a typical triode vary with plate

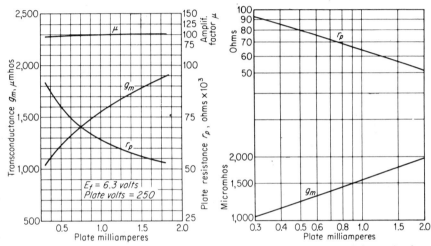

Fig. 10.13. Variation of mutual conductance, amplification factor, and dynamic plate resistance as a function of plate current in a typical vacuum triode.

current. The amplification factor is relatively constant. The mutual conductance increases with the one-third power of plate current; and since the plate resistance varies as μ/g_m, it varies approximately inversely as the one-third power of plate current. In Appendix 9 are listed equations for the amplification factor and mutual conductance of a triode in terms of electrode dimensions.

How Triodes Amplify. It is desirable to say at least a word at this point about how triodes amplify, to satisfy the curiosity of the reader who does not already know, since this subject is considered only several chapters later. Triodes may amplify either voltage, power, or current. We must also explain what we mean by amplify. Obviously a device cannot amplify power without violating the law of conservation of energy. This is not true of amplification of voltage and current. Actually, electron devices do not amplify power but control the flow of power from another source. More properly, electron devices *convert* power from one form to another. Usually this is from the form of direct current to that of alternating current. The British use the term "electric valve" to describe a vacuum tube. This is more indicative of the function of the device than the American expression. The triode is a type of electric valve in which a small voltage between the control grid and the cathode controls the flow of a large current and associated power from a source of power connected between the cathode and plate.

Usually vacuum tubes are called upon to amplify voltage. It has already been indicated that a variation in grid *voltage* causes a variation in plate *current*. If this current is made to produce a voltage by passing through an impedance, the voltage so developed can be applied to the grid of another tube and so on. One simple way in which this is often done is to put a large resistance in series with the plate and with the power supply that furnishes the plate current. Usually also, interest lies in amplifying an alternating component of voltage. Such alternating components are superimposed upon the direct voltages necessary to establish the operating point of the tube. Thus across the resistor in series with the plate there appears an amplified alternating component of voltage superimposed on a direct voltage. The alternating component is easily separated from the direct component by connecting the plate of the tube to the grid of a following tube through a large capacitor which will not transmit direct current but which has a relatively small impedance to the alternating component.

From the definition of the amplification factor, an alternating-signal voltage V_1 applied to the control grid will have the same effect as an alternating voltage of magnitude μV_1 in series with the plate circuit. The alternating current produced by the alternating voltage μV_1 will be determined by the series impedance of the plate circuit, namely, the load resistance R_l in series with the dynamic plate resistance r_p. This gives

$$|I_2| = \frac{\mu V_1}{r_p + R_l} \tag{10.14}$$

The alternating voltage developed across the load resistor will be the product of the current above and the value of resistance:

$$|V_2| = \frac{\mu V_1 R_l}{r_p + R_l} \tag{10.15}$$

The form of this expression shows clearly that the output circuit of a triode has an equivalent circuit that is simply a generator with an emf equal to μV_1 in series with a resistance r_p.

The amplification of a triode is equal to the ratio of the output voltage V_2 to the input voltage V_1, namely,

$$|A| = \left| \frac{V_2}{V_1} \right| = \frac{\mu}{1 + r_p/R_l} \tag{10.16}$$

There A is the *voltage* amplification of the triode. It is seen that the voltage amplification is equal to the amplification factor reduced by the factor $1 + r_p/R_l$, which will typically have a value of one and a half to two. Thus the amplifier gain will be from one-half to two-thirds the amplification factor. For multielectrode tubes the reduction is much greater. For grounded-cathode circuits there is a 180° phase shift through a single stage.

It may be thought that the amplification can be made equal to the amplification factor by simply making the load resistance very high, but this does not work. This is because a large series resistance in the plate circuit reduces the direct voltage on the plate and hence also the direct plate current. When this happens, the dynamic plate resistance r_p tends to increase more rapidly than the series plate load resistance R_l, thus defeating the intention.

10.3. The Screen-grid Tetrode. The screen-grid type of tetrode is seldom encountered these days. It is now mainly of historical interest. However, it was an important step in the development of the pentode, the most extensively used of all types of vacuum tube, and so it will be discussed briefly.

Early radio receivers, before the superheterodyne circuit was invented, used a series of ganged tuned radio-frequency amplifiers to amplify the signal before detection. At first there were only triodes available for this function. These were not too satisfactory because such tubes have a fairly high internal grid-plate capacity. This capacity introduces an electrostatic coupling between the input and output circuits of a given amplifier stage, which gives rise to a tendency for self-oscillation in the stage. To avoid this, it was necessary to use special circuits that neutralized the effect of the interelectrode capacity. These were usually a form of bridge circuit that introduced into the grid circuit a voltage equal and opposite to that resulting from the grid-plate capacity. Such "neutrodyne" circuits were

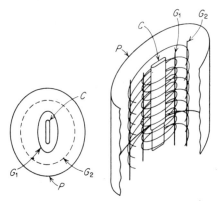

FIG. 10.14. Internal construction of a vacuum screen-grid tetrode.

hard to design in a way that would permit tuning over a large frequency band.

The screen-grid tetrode is a four-element tube having a cathode, control grid, and plate but also a second grid, known as the screen grid, between the control grid and plate, which is operated in such a way as to reduce the capacity between control grid and plate. Shown in Fig. 10.14 is a diagram of the construction of a screen-grid tetrode. The cathode and control grid are similar to those in the triode. The next grid, the so-called screen grid, will generally be of coarse mesh and will surround the control grid. The plate will often be cylindrical and surround the screen grid. The cathode potential is taken as zero, the control-grid potential is slightly negative, and the screen grid and plate will usually be at about the same positive potential. Shown in Figure 10.15 are profiles of negative potential through and between grid wires along lines running from cathode to plate. Also shown are representative

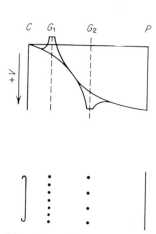

FIG. 10.15. Electron potential energy, or negative-potential profiles, in a plane-electrode vacuum screen-grid tetrode.

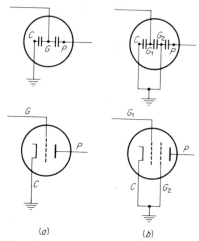

FIG. 10.16. Internal capacities in the triode and screen-grid tetrode showing the shielding action of the screen grid in the latter.

relative dimensions. Electrons can run from the cathode between negative grid wires toward the screen grid and the plate. Some electrons will be intercepted by the screen grid but most of them will pass on to the plate. None, however, can be intercepted by the negative control grid.

The screen-grid tube has a greatly reduced capacity between the plate and control grid by virtue of the fact that the screen grid is usually grounded through a large capacity. In Fig. 10.16 is shown a comparison of the interelectrode capacities in the triode and the screen-grid tetrode. Part (a) of the figure shows the detrimental capacity between the grid and the plate of a triode. Also shown is the cathode-grid capacity. Not shown is a small capacity between plate and cathode, usually of no significance. Because of the capacity divider action, voltages developed on the plate also appear on the grid, tending to give oscillation. In part (b) of the figure are shown the important interelectrode capacities of the screen-grid tube. Here the voltage on the plate can induce no voltage on the control grid because virtually all the lines of flux from the plate terminate on the screen grid G_2, which is grounded and thus can induce no voltage on the control grid G_1. Actually there is a small penetration of flux lines from the plate through the screen grid to the control grid, but the associated capacity will usually be smaller by a factor of 100 than the grid-plate capacity in a triode. Thus the insertion of the extra grid in the screen-grid tetrode is seen to serve its purpose of reducing the plate-to-control-grid capacity. Let us, however, determine if the resulting current-voltage characteristics are satisfactory.

The screen-grid tube, though a tetrode, is operated like a triode; i.e., the screen grid itself is kept at a fixed positive potential and, by means of a bypass capacitor, at ground potential as far as alternating voltages are concerned. The static characteristics will therefore be a family of plate-current curves that are dependent upon the control-grid and plate potentials. Control-grid current for positive control-grid potentials is of relatively little interest but will be similar to that in triode characteristics. With the assumption of a negative control-grid potential and a fixed positive screen-grid potential, the plate current in a screen-grid tube is expected to be relatively little influenced by plate potential because the field at the cathode is almost completely shielded by the extra screen grid. Actually this expectation is verified for the space current in the tube but not for the plate current.

The plate current is found to be strongly influenced by a new factor, namely, the secondary-electron interchange between the plate and the screen grid. Because the screen grid is kept at a fixed positive potential, it will intercept a small and nearly constant fraction of the primary space current. Secondary electrons will be produced at both the screen grid and the plate. Such secondaries as have a higher-potential electrode to go to will do so, while those which encounter a negative gradient of potential will return to the electrode from which they originated. Accordingly, if the plate is more positive than the screen grid, it will have its primary current increased by secondary electrons from the screen grid. If the plate potential is more negative than the screen grid, it will have its current reduced by its own secondaries, which it will lose to the screen grid.

The above secondary-electron action explains the measured screen-grid characteristics shown in Fig. 10.17. This shows the space current, which increases slowly with plate voltage but greatly with grid voltage. Plate current for high plate voltages is nearly equal to space current and is actually a little larger because of some extra secondary electrons from the screen. For plate voltages lower than screen-grid voltage, the plate voltage is greatly reduced and even becomes negative at times. This is due to loss of secondary electrons from the plate to the screen grid. The grid voltage varies the magnitude of the curves but not their shape. This is because it controls the space current, but the division of current between screen grid and plate is determined only by the ratio of plate to screen-grid voltage. The screen-grid current is a constant fraction of the space current at high plate voltages but is greatly increased by secondary electrons from the plate when the screen grid is more negative in potential than the plate.

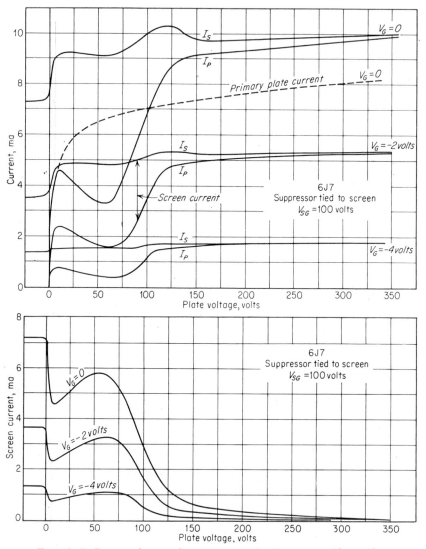

FIG. 10.17. Screen, plate, and space current in the screen-grid tetrode.

Because of the great distortions introduced into the characteristics of the screen-grid tube by secondary-emission action, much distortion in output-current waveforms may be encountered when the tube is used as an amplifier.   To avoid this, another grid has been added between the screen grid and the plate to suppress the secondary-emission interchange between the screen grid and the plate.   Such a tube is the pentode.

The amplification factor of screen-grid tubes will usually be so high as to have little significance.   It is not possible to capitalize on the potential amplification capabilities of this tube without encountering great distortion.   The μ factor is, of course, high because the cathode is shielded from the plate-potential variations not only by the control grid but by the screen grid as well.   The mutual conductance of the screen-grid tube will be determined by the electrode dimensions, considering the screen grid as the plate of an equivalent triode.   Values so determined will be about the same as those encountered in triodes.   The plate resistance in the region of nearly constant plate current will be very high, of the order of hundreds of thousands of ohms, because of the small slope of the current characteristic in this region.   As a result, in this region the screen-grid tube is nearly a constant-current generator.

At present, the screen-grid tube is little used.   It has been replaced almost entirely by the pentode, which has superior characteristics.   It is, however, of great historical interest, having led to the development of the pentode.   It is also of great interest in that it shows what may happen when secondary emission is not properly controlled.   It should be borne in mind that secondary emission always occurs whenever primaries strike a surface with energies of more than 5 to 10 ev.   However, in many cases—such as the triode—the secondary electrons created at the plate are always confronted by a negative gradient of potential and so returned to the electrode from which they came.

There is another form of tetrode, known as the *beam power tube*.   The beam power tube can best be understood after studying the pentode. Discussion of this tube will, therefore, be deferred until after the discussion of the pentode.

10.4. Pentodes.   The pentode, as its name implies, is a five-element tube.   It is like a screen-grid tetrode with another grid added between screen grid and plate.   The additional grid is called the *suppressor grid*. It is a coarse grid usually operated at cathode potential.   At this potential it will depress strongly the potential between screen grid and plate, which are usually operated at high positive potentials.   This causes both the screen grid and the plate to offer a negative gradient of potential to secondary electrons originating on them, thus suppressing them.   At the same time the passage of electrons from cathode to plate is not impeded by the suppressor grid because, being at cathode potential, its wires will correspond to potential hills that will deflect electrons away from it.

The action of the suppressor grid in a pentode is best understood by reference to a diagram of potential profiles within the tube, as shown in Fig. 10.18.   This figure shows the relative potentials and the relative dimensions of the tube.   The control grid is a fine-mesh grid close to the cathode.   It is usually operated at a slight negative potential.   The screen grid is a medium-pitch grid several times further out from the control grid.   It is usually operated at a fairly high positive potential.

The suppressor grid is a coarse grid operated at cathode potential. The plate is usually operated at the screen-grid potential. The profiles of the figure show *negative* potential along lines passing through the grid wires and also along lines midway between the grid wires. All potentials lie between the limiting profiles shown.

On the negative-potential diagram of Fig. 10.18, electrons will roll downhill. They are able to roll between the control-grid wires even though this grid is negative. They will then roll downhill toward the screen grid, where some few will be intercepted but the majority will continue to roll uphill toward the suppressor grid. Here they will be able to pass in the space between the suppressor-grid wires, and only a few will strike the suppressor grid itself. After passing the suppressor grid, the electrons move unimpeded to the plate. This action is repeated for other combinations of potentials. The only exception occurs at low plate potentials for which the electrons have a hill to climb, as shown dotted in the same figure. For this condition, electrons which have been strongly deflected sideways in passing through previous grids may find themselves lacking sufficient velocity in a direction normal to the plate, fail to make the grade, and roll back into the screen grid. Thus although the space current will be little affected as the plate potential is made to approach zero, the plate current will decrease suddenly to zero and the screen current will suddenly rise from a low value to the space current. Shown in Fig. 10.19 are electron paths in a pentode for a typical operating condition.

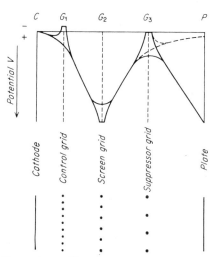

Fig. 10.18. Electron potential energy, or negative-potential profiles, in a plane-electrode pentode.

It is of particular importance to note in Fig. 10.18 the fact that, for normal voltages (solid profiles), the low-velocity secondary electrons created by the impact of primaries at the screen grid and plate are unable to climb the hill between them and the next electrode and so return to their point of origin. This suppression action is effective down to very low plate voltages. The notation G_1 for control grid, G_2 for screen grid, and G_3 for suppressor grid is used in this figure.

The resultant current-voltage characteristics are shown in Figs. 10.20 and 10.21. The first of these show plate and space current vs. grid voltage for several screen-grid potentials. Current vs. grid voltage is similar

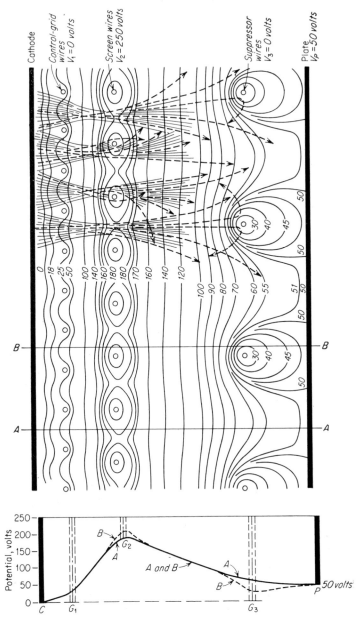

FIG. 10.19. Electrostatic field and electron paths in a plane-electrode pentode. (*After Schade.*)

to that in the triode. The conditions shown are for zero suppressor-grid voltage and moderately high plate voltage. The variation of plate current with plate voltage is so slight that it is not indicated in this figure. In Fig. 10.21 are shown plate, screen, and space current vs. control-grid voltage for zero suppressor-grid voltage. The space current

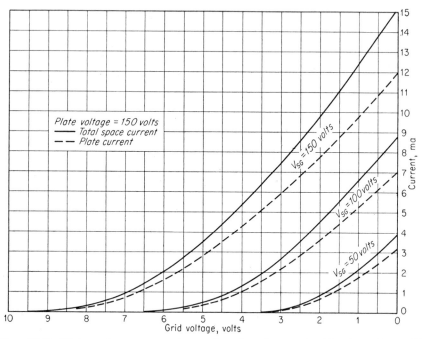

Fig. 10.20. Plate and space current as a function of control-grid voltage in a 6J7 pentode.

is seen to vary strongly with control-grid voltage and increase only slightly with plate voltage. Space current depends upon an equivalent control-grid potential, as in the triode, of the form

$$I_S = G\left(V_1 + \frac{V_2}{\mu_2} + \frac{V_3}{\mu_3} + \frac{V_P}{\mu_P}\right)^{\frac{3}{2}} \qquad (10.17)$$

where the voltages are those of the first, second, and third grid and plate, respectively, and the μ's measure the relative effectiveness of the indicated electrode in controlling plate current relative to the control grid. For the usual operating conditions the second term is constant and the third is zero, giving the simpler form

$$I_S = G\left(V_1 + k_2 + \frac{V_P}{\mu_P}\right)^{\frac{3}{2}} \qquad (10.18)$$

The factor μ_P is the plate amplification factor. It will be extremely high, of the order of 10,000 or more, because the cathode is shielded from the

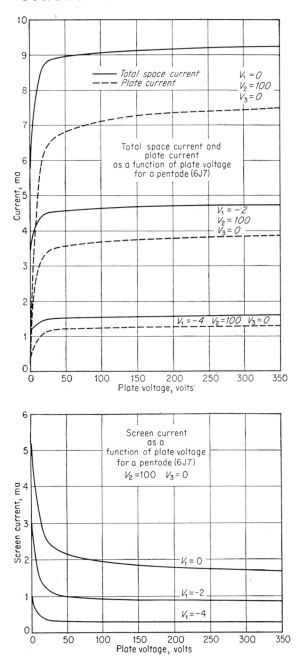

FIG. 10.21. Plate, space, and screen current as a function of plate voltage in a plane-electrode pentode.

plate by three grids. This means that 1 mv on the control grid has as much influence on the plate current as does 10 volts on the plate.

It is evident that all the space current does not go to the plate. The division of space current between plate and screen depends upon the voltages. It will in general depend only upon the ratio of plate to screen voltage, thus,

$$\frac{I_P}{I_2} = f\left(\frac{V_P}{V_2}\right) \qquad (10.19)$$

as expected from the fact that the shape of the electron paths depends only upon the ratio of electrode voltages. No simple analytical form of this function is known. It can be seen, however, that, when plate voltage is zero, all the space current goes to the screen and none to the plate. When the plate voltage equals the screen voltage, the ratio of plate to screen current will be nearly equal to the ratio of area between screen-grid wires to the projected area of the wires. Beyond this the ratio of currents will increase slowly with the ratio of voltages. For all conditions the sum of the plate and screen current must equal the space current. Thus the control grid changes the magnitude but not the shape of the plate- and screen-current curves as a function of plate voltage. This is differ- ent from what happens with the triode, where the plate-current vs. plate-voltage curves were nearly of the same shape but displaced to the left by more negative control-grid voltage.

Mutual conductance in pentodes will be about the same as in triodes. Plate resistance will be many times higher. Plate resistances of the order of megohms are possible. The high resistances correspond to the low slope of the plate-current vs. plate-voltage characteristic. The high plate resistance of the pentode causes it to act as a constant-current source. This means that, for a given input grid signal, the alternating component of plate current is nearly independent of the resistance in series with the plate.

The pentode is popular because of the large area of uniformity in its plate-current vs. plate-voltage characteristics. As seen in Fig. 10.21, there is a large region where the characteristics are nearly parallel straight lines. This contributes to low distortion of waveforms when alternating voltages are amplified. It will also be shown that, for a given mutual conductance, the pentode is capable of giving more voltage amplification than the triode. The pentode is also able to give more power amplifica- tion than the triode because its control-grid currents are smaller.

Pentodes are principally used for voltage amplifiers and constitute the bulk of the tubes in radio and television receivers. However, they may also be designed to serve as power amplifiers, though the construction of high-power pentodes is more difficult than is the construction of high- power triodes.

10.5. The Beam Power Tube. The beam power tube, sometimes known simply as the beam tube, is a tetrode with characteristics quite similar to the pentode. It is a tube in which an accentuated space charge due to electrons in motion from screen grid to plate produces a depression of potential between screen grid and plate similar to that produced by a suppressor grid. It is a tube designed to produce more power than a voltage amplifier. It is called a beam tube because the electrode design is such as to cause the electrons within the tube to move in sheetlike beams.

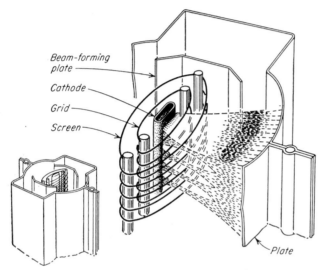

Fig. 10.22. Cutaway view of the 6L6 beam power tetrode. (*RCA.*)

Figure 10.22 shows a cutaway view of one form of beampower tetrode. The distinctive features of this tube are three: (1) The wires of the control grid and the screen grid are aligned so that the screen-grid wires are in the shadow of the control-grid wires as seen from the cathode. (2) Some large so-called beam-forming plates at cathode potential are used to keep the beam from spreading sidewise. (3) The spacing from the screen-grid to the plate is relatively large. In passing through the control grid, the electrons are squeezed by the negative control-grid wires to form parallel sheets of current. Beyond the control grid the mutual repulsion between the electrons causes these sheets to thicken and to spread sidewise. It is the purpose of the beam-forming plates to prevent the sidewise spread. Because of the alignment of the grids, relatively few electrons strike the screen grid so that the current can be made higher than is usual in multielectrode tubes.

The beam power tube achieves a high electron density in its beams by virtue of keeping the beam from spreading. This high electron density increases the negative space charge, which depresses the potential in the space between screen grid and plate to values substantially less than would be the case if the potential had a straight-line variation between them.   As a result, the potential encountered by an electron in moving from cathode to plate will be typically as shown in Fig. 10.23, which should be compared with Fig. 10.15 for the ordinary screen-grid tube. Shown are potential profiles between screen grid and plate with and without space charge.   Negative potential is again shown to facilitate visualization of electron motion.   Electrons move downhill from the cathode between the normally slightly negative control-grid wires, where they are squeezed together in the potential valley between the wires. They then move down the steep hill toward the screen grid.   Relatively few electrons will be intercepted by the screen grid.   They then coast

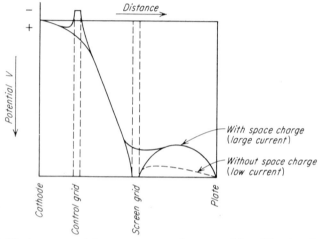

FIG. 10.23. Electron potential energy, or negative-potential profiles, in a beam power tetrode.

over the potential hill produced by the space charge and on to the plate. The potential hill between screen grid and plate presents a retarding gradient of potential to secondary electrons from either plate or screen grid, which is as effective as though it were produced by the suppressor grid of Fig. 10.18.   Some have suggested that the beam power tube is really a pentode in which the beam-forming plates constitute a very-low-pitch suppressor grid.   This is not quite true because, without the high density of space charge, the depression in potential between screen grid and plate produced by the beam-forming plates would be relatively slight.

It is important to understand the mechanism whereby the space charge depresses the potential.   This is the same as the effect encountered in space-charge limitation of current in a diode except that in this case the injected current is constant and the potential adjusts itself without changing the current except in special cases.   The presence of negative charge causes the potential to be more negative.   This is a consequence of Poisson's equation, which in one dimension is given by

$$\frac{d^2 V}{dx^2} = -\frac{\rho}{\varepsilon_0} \tag{10.20}$$

where ρ = space-charge density [see (3.18)]

ε_0 = dielectric constant of free space, a constant required for mks units

In the case of a space charge due to electrons, the quantity ρ is negative and the right-hand term is positive. This equation may be interpreted as indicating that the curvature of a potential profile will always be positive for electrons and proportional to the space-charge density. This means that, for electrons, the curve of positive potential will always be concave upward since the sign of the curvature is determined by the sign of the second derivative. Since the end points of the potential profile in this case are fixed, the more current that is injected, the higher the negative space charge, the greater the curvature of the curve of positive potential, and the greater the depression of potential between the end points.

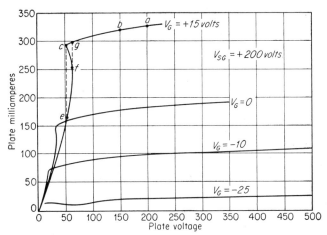

FIG. 10.24. Plate current as a function of plate voltage in a beam power tetrode.

The measured plate-current vs. plate-voltage characteristics of a beam power tube are shown in Fig. 10.24. These curves have the same general aspect as the curves of a pentode except that the shoulder of the curves is sharper. Secondary-emission distortion of the characteristics is effectively eliminated except for the curves of the lowest plate current corresponding to control-grid voltage close to cutoff, where a small inflection of the curves is evident. Some other features of these curves are also interesting. For relatively high control-grid voltages the curves exhibit a slight overlap and also a very steep rise with plate voltage, culminating in a slight cutback before continuing to rise at a slow rate.

To understand the last above-mentioned effect, let us trace backward one of the large current curves, e.g., the curve for zero control-grid voltage. This value of control-grid voltage permits a large current to flow from the cathode toward the plate. As the plate voltage is made more negative, the electrons get slowed down more and more in passing from screen grid to plate, and as a result, the space-charge density increases and the depression of the potential profile becomes more pronounced, as in going from curve a to b in Fig. 10.25. As the plate potential decreases further, the potential of the minimum decreases at an increasingly faster rate that may, if the current is sufficiently high, lead to an instability, which causes the minimum to jump to zero, as shown in the change from c to the dashed curve of d.

When the condition of d exists, a so-called virtual cathode is formed at the point of zero potential. Some of the electrons will get past this point and the rest will be reflected toward the screen grid. Electrons that go on to the plate observe the diode space-charge law; and since the current is decreased by reflection though the potential difference between the virtual cathode and the plate stays fixed, the distance between the virtual cathode and the plate must increase. This causes the curve to move to the left to some position such as e. Corresponding points are shown on the current-voltage characteristic of Fig. 10.24. Further decrease in plate voltage increases the reflected current and moves the curve farther to the left. The plate current drops very rapidly in this region because the action is the same as that in a diode in which the plate voltage is being decreased at the same time as the cathode-plate spacing is being decreased.

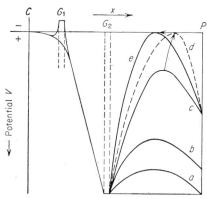

FIG. 10.25. Electron potential energy, or negative-potential profiles, in a beam power tetrode.

Upon an increase of the plate voltage, the virtual cathode will move to the right, with a continuous decrease in the reflected current. This can continue to the point d in Fig. 10.25. At a certain point the rate of increase of current with voltage may become infinite, and the current will tend to jump from f to g, as shown in Fig. 10.24. Current transmission is now complete and the current will increase slowly with plate voltage beyond this point as shown. Actually, the jumps and the resultant hysteresis loop will occur only under ideal conditions. Because the electrons have a small spread in velocity, the characteristic will exhibit an S-shaped reverse kick as shown.

The beam power tube is designed specifically for power production. It is a little simpler to build than the pentode and has a larger area of uniform characteristics. However, if the voltage-current excursions take the operating point out of the region of uniform characteristics, the distortion increases much more rapidly than with the pentode.

CHAPTER 11

TRANSISTORS

11.1. Nature of Transistors and of Transistor Operation. Transistors are crystal amplifiers invented in 1948 as a result of a study of surface states in semiconductors. They are the equivalent of vacuum tubes in their operation. Although many forms of transistors now exist, there are two principal types. The first type, invented by Bardeen and Brattain, is the so-called point-contact transistor [Bab]. This is essentially a crystal detector with two closely spaced cat whiskers. With proper bias conditions, power amplification may be obtained by using one whisker or the base as an input terminal, the other whisker as output terminal, and the third terminal as common to input and output. A second type of transistor, known as the junction transistor, was invented in 1949 by Shockley [Shb]. This is essentially a sandwich of a thin layer of n-type semiconductor (usually germanium or silicon) between two layers of p-type semiconductor or vice versa, with connections to the three layers. In this type of transistor the thin center layer corresponds to the base of the point-contact transistor, and the two outer layers correspond to the cat whiskers. Both of these types are triodes.

Transistors are quite small and are commonly enclosed in a sealed capsule or cartridge about the size of a pea. Shown in Fig. 11.1 are some representative transistors. The small size of transistors is due largely to the fact that the device requires no filament or cathode for its operation. The active volume of a transistor will ordinarily be only a few cubic millimeters.

The transistor is, like the vacuum tube, a device that owes its amplifying characteristics to electric-field control of current within the device. Like the vacuum triode, the transistor triode is a species of double diode. The vacuum triode exhibits a diode action between cathode and grid or cathode and plate. The transistor triode exhibits a diode action between any two of its three terminals.

The terminology for designation of transistor-triode electrodes is derived from the form and action of the point-contact transistor. The base to which the semiconductor wafer is soldered forms one electrode and is called the *base*. One of the cat whiskers is called the *emitter* because, with proper bias, it emits minority carriers into the semicon-

235

ductor.   The other cat whisker is usually biased so that it collects most
of the minority carriers injected by the emitter.   For this reason it is
called the *collector*.   Several analogies between vacuum triodes and
transistor triodes may be drawn.   No analogy is perfect in all respects,
but one of the best is that the emitter corresponds to the cathode, the
base corresponds to the grid, and the collector corresponds to the plate.

The vacuum triode is short-circuit-stable and open-circuit-unstable.
The latter comes about because a free electrode, such as the grid, will

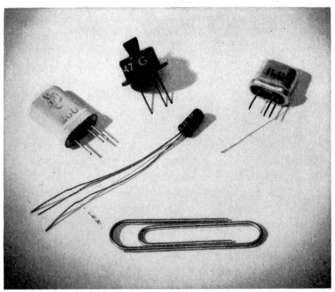

Fig. 11.1. Some representative types of transistors.

collect electrons and thus may bias the tube negatively beyond cutoff.
Some transistor triodes, on the other hand, as will be shown, tend to be
open-circuit-stable and short-circuit-unstable.   As a result, transistors
work well when connected to high-impedance or constant-current sources
of bias, whereas the vacuum triode works best when connected to low-
impedance or constant-voltage sources of bias.

Because of their short-circuit stability, vacuum-tube characteristics
are usually shown in the form of curves of current as the dependent variable vs. voltage as the independent variable.   Transistors, on the other
hand, because of their open-circuit stability, commonly have their
characteristics shown as curves of voltage as dependent variable vs.
current as independent variable.

Vacuum-triode characteristics are most commonly shown as curves of
plate current vs. either grid voltage or plate voltage with constant values
of the other voltage assumed in each case to give a family of curves.
Similar curves of grid current can be drawn but are not needed for the

majority of applications because grid current is zero for negative grid voltages that still permit control of plate current. In the case of transistor triodes, both input and output voltage and current must be shown for a complete representation because none of the voltages or

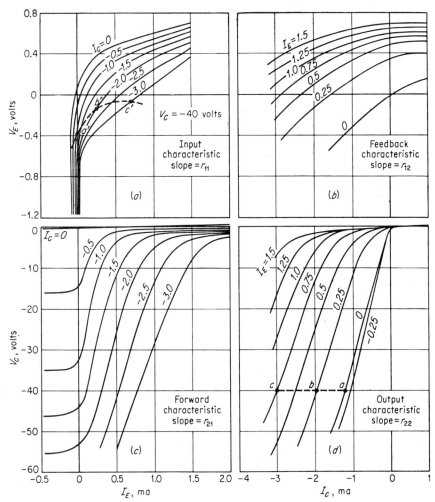

FIG. 11.2. Characteristics of the first point-contact transistor, Western Electric type M1689. (*The Bell System Technical Journal.*)

currents is zero or constant as is the case with grid current for negative bias operation. Shown in Fig. 11.2 is a set of characteristics for an early (*n*-type point-contact) transistor. Here are shown four families of curves, two self and two mutual. Actually, when any two of these families are given, the other two may be derived from them.

Vacuum triodes, when used as amplifiers, are operated with their input circuit biased in the reverse direction, i.e., in the direction of low-current flow, and with their output biased in the forward direction, i.e., in the direction of most current flow.   For small-signal-amplifier applications, transistors are *always* biased in the opposite sense to that employed with tubes.   Thus transistors have their input circuits biased in the forward, or high-current, direction, whereas their outputs are biased in the reverse, or low-current, direction.   The result of the biasing arrangements discussed above is that tubes in amplifier circuits have relatively high input

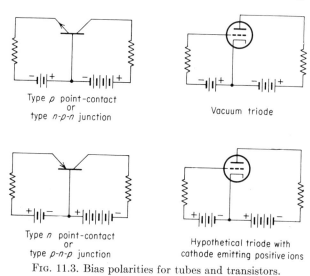

Type *p* point-contact
or
type *n-p-n* junction

Vacuum triode

Type *n* point-contact
or
type *p-n-p* junction

Hypothetical triode with
cathode emitting positive ions

Fig. 11.3. Bias polarities for tubes and transistors.

impedance and relatively low output impedance.   In contrast, transistors in amplifier circuits have low input impedances and relatively high output impedances.

The *polarity* of transistor bias will be determined by the type of material used since this determines the polarity of the charge carriers.   A *p*-type contact transistor will be biased with the same polarity as a vacuum triode.   This will also be true for an *n-p-n* junction transistor.   On the other hand, an *n*-type point-contact transistor or a *p-n-p* junction transistor will be biased with the opposite polarity to a vacuum triode but in the same direction as a hypothetical vacuum tube whose cathode emits positive ions instead of electrons.   These polarities are shown in Fig. 11.3.   In this figure grounded-base transistors are compared with grounded-cathode tubes.   The base and cathode are logical reference electrodes for potential.   This does not imply that their functions are analogous.   The arrow in the emitter lead of the transistor symbol points in the direction of current flow.

The diode action in a transistor is seen in Fig. 11.2a.   Here, for collector current zero, the emitter current-voltage characteristic is a simple diode characteristic. Various amounts of collector current displace this curve. Likewise, in part (d) of the figure, there is shown another diode characteristic for emitter current zero, the reverse portion of this curve being most prominently displayed. Various amounts of emitter current displace this curve.

As yet the materials used in making transistors are limited in number. Germanium is quite extensively used. It is relatively easy to process and permits precise control of its characteristics. In addition its electron and hole mobilities are higher than those for other materials. Silicon transistors only appeared several years after germanium transistors. This is because the melting temperature of silicon is quite high and the element is very active chemically at high temperatures. Silicon transistors do, however, have better high-temperature characteristics than germanium transistors because of a larger energy gap between the valence band and the conduction band. Other semiconducting compounds and alloys have been tried but to date are all inferior to silicon and germanium. It is entirely possible that with further research and development there may be found other materials as good as germanium and silicon for transistors.

The transistor is as yet a very young device. It will certainly revolutionize many aspects of electronics, although it will probably never entirely replace the vacuum tube. Although the characteristics of the transistor are not yet fully established, it appears to be superior to the vacuum tube in the following respects: (1) weight, (2) size, (3) efficiency, (4) power consumption, (5) ruggedness, (6) life. On the other hand, the vacuum tube appears to be superior to the transistor in the following respects: (1) cost, (2) power output, (3) frequency range, (4) freedom from noise, (5) stability with temperature, (6) gain, (7) variety of forms.

The above serves to give a preliminary idea of the relative usefulness of tubes and transistors. In the next section there will be given an explanation of transistor characteristics.

11.2. Minority-carrier Injection and the Filamentary Transistor.[1] Historically the point-contact transistor was developed before the junction transistor. Junction transistors have since experienced such tremendous improvements that they now outperform point-contact transistors in almost every respect and as a result have almost completely displaced point-contact transistors in many applications. In addition, the theory of the junction transistor is quite well developed while that of the point-contact transistor is not. Accordingly the point-contact transistor could almost be dismissed as an interesting historical development. However, it is believed that a study of point-contact transistors will greatly aid the understanding of the operation of transistors in general. But even

[1] Notation in this and the following sections is that of IRE Standards.

more than this, there is an inexorable logic to historical developments that is worth retracing.

All transistors are critically dependent upon minority-carrier action. This is particularly apparent in the point-contact transistor. Minority-carrier action has already been described in an elementary fashion in Sec. 7.5 and in Fig. 7.18 in connection with metal-semiconductor junctions. There it was shown that when a metal is in contact with an n-type semiconductor and when the metal is positive with respect to the semiconductor, electrons will run from the semiconductor to the metal but also holes will originate at the junction and run into the semiconductor.

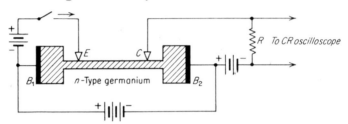

Fig. 11.4. Filamentary-transistor experiment, showing minority-carrier action.

The first experiments with n-type point-contact transistors indicated that the hole, or minority-carrier, flow played an important part in the operation. Accordingly, some ideas of operation were formed, which were tested with a classic experiment whose understanding is helpful in explaining point-contact-transistor action [Hab1]. This is known as the Haynes-Shockley experiment. This experiment will now be described briefly.

Consider the device shown in Fig. 11.4. Here there is shown a long, narrow, and thin strip of n-type germanium with an electrode on each end and a battery attached to produce an electric field along the strip. This field will tend to send electrons within the strip from right to left and holes within the strip from left to right. Two point contacts are connected to the filament through an external circuit and battery. The point contact on the left is called the emitter and is biased positively with respect to the left-hand terminal of the filament. The point contact at the right is called the collector and is biased negatively with respect to the right-hand terminal of the filament through a resistor permitting observation of current variations.

When the switch in series with the emitter electrode is closed, electrons will flow from the semiconductor into the point and holes will flow from the point into the semiconductor, as discussed in Sec. 7.5. Under these conditions the holes are said to be *emitted* by the point contact, and it is for this reason referred to as the emitter. Holes are emitted or injected at the point E but not at the base B, even though these both have the same polarity relative to the filament. Holes are emitted at the point largely because of the very high gradient of potential due to the small point radius, which gradient is large enough to tear electrons from the valence band of the semiconductor, thus giving rise to holes. Few holes are emitted by the base B, because this is usually an ohmic junction formed by mechanically polishing or sandblasting the surface of the semiconductor and then soldering on the base electrode. The high gradient of potential is also not present at the base-semiconductor junction. Furthermore, there is a large volume in which the few holes created may recombine with electrons before entering the filament.

If now the reaction at the collector terminal is observed with an oscilloscope, the result shown in the lower part of Fig. 11.5 occurs. Immediately upon closing the switch S a change in voltage is observed at the collector. This change is due to the electron flow and is the same as would be observed if the filament were a conductor rather than a semiconductor. This occurs because electrons are distributed throughout the filament and start migrating in unison when the switch is closed. A short time after the switch is closed, a further change in voltage in the same direction is observed at the collector. This is due to a component of current associated with the arrival of holes at the collector. These holes come from the emitter and take an observable time to get to the collector, where some of them will be taken out of the filament, giving rise to the

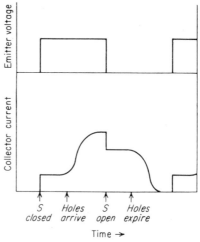

Fig. 11.5. Collector current response in the Haynes-Shockley experiment due to an emitter voltage step.

name collector for that point contact. Even though the number of holes entering the collector is smaller than the number of electrons that began leaving it when the switch S was closed, the increase in voltage upon arrival of holes may be larger than the first step. This occurs not only because the current through the collector is increased by the holes collected but also because the flow of holes into the collector point neutralizes, in part, a negative space charge due to electron flow out of the collector and thus permits more electrons to flow out.

When now the switch S is opened, there is an immediate drop in voltage due to interruption of electron flow into the emitter. The hole flow out of the emitter is interrupted at the same time, but the effect is not noted at the collector until a bit later when all the holes between the emitter and collector are swept past the latter, restoring the original voltage.

An even better indication of the carrier action is obtained if a short positive pulse of voltage is applied through the switch S.   The reaction at the collector is then as shown in Fig. 11.6.   A pulse of electron current shows identical in form to the voltage pulse and simultaneous in time followed by a pulse of hole current. The hole pulse is reduced in magnitude and spread out in time because of diffusion effects.   This method has been used to measure hole and electron mobility and is considered more accurate than other methods [PrC, PrD].

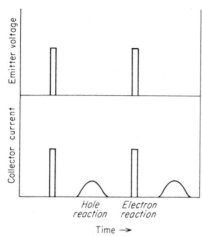

Fig. 11.6. Collector current response in the Haynes-Shockley experiment due to an emitter voltage pulse.

Using a similar device but with only a point-contact emitter as shown in Fig. 11.7, a simple form of transistor known as the *filamentary* transistor results.   Here the right-hand filament terminal acts as collector and will collect all holes emitted by the emitter.   The emitter is biased in a forward direction, which permits electrons to flow from the filament into the point and holes to flow in the opposite direction.   Now when the emitter current is increased, the collector current is increased by the increased hole current.

Measurements show that, for a typical n-type germanium sample, the emitter current is nearly 100 per cent hole current.   For a typical p-type

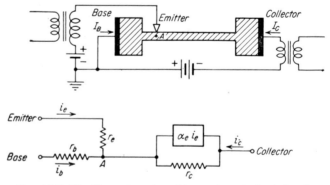

Fig. 11.7. The filamentary transistor and equivalent circuit.

sample, the emitter current is about 60 per cent electrons.   The percentage of hole and electron currents in the two cases decreases exponentially with movement down the filament because of recombination with the majority carriers.   Transit times for the minority carriers are of the order of microseconds.

An equivalent circuit in the form of a T section with a constant-current generator in parallel with the element in the collector branch can be drawn as also shown in Fig. 11.7. The point A corresponds to a point in the filament below the emitter contact. The three resistances correspond to the ohmic resistance associated with electron flow between the point A and the three terminals. The constant-current generator produces an extra component of current $\alpha_e i_e$ directed toward the collector junction. The factor α_e may be greater than unity because of the change in filament conductance with emitter current. Even if it is not greater than unity, it is possible for such a device to give power amplification if the dynamic collector output impedance is greater than the dynamic emitter input impedance. This may well be the case because the latter is a diode biased in the forward, or low-impedance, direction.

Whereas the filamentary transistor works in principle, it is inferior to other types of transistor because the transit time is low and hence the frequency response is poor and because the ratio of output impedance to input impedance is too low due to the large output-terminal area. It does, however, serve to indicate some principles of operation useful in understanding better forms of transistors. In particular it reveals a mechanism of amplification critically dependent upon minority-carrier injection and flow.

11.3. The Point-contact Transistor.[1] The point-contact transistor is an electron device similar to the microwave crystal detector but with two points making contact a few thousandths of an inch apart on a small block of germanium, as shown in Fig. 11.8. A third contact is made to the crystal semiconductor through a large-area ohmic contact, known as the base, on the bottom of the block. One of the point contacts, known as

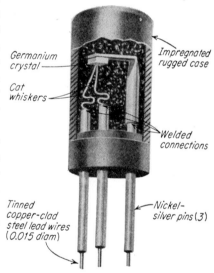

FIG. 11.8. Construction of an early transistor of the point-contact type (CBS Hytron).

the emitter, is biased in the forward direction, positive for n-type germanium, and passes a relatively large current. The other point contact is known as the collector, is biased in the reverse direction, negative for n-type germanium, and passes a relatively small current. The operation

[1] This section is included primarily for completeness and for historical value. Since point-contact transistors are now little used, this section can be omitted if not of interest.

of the device depends upon the fact that a change in current through the emitter causes an equal or greater change of current through the collector. Power amplification results largely from the fact that the input impedance is much less than the output impedance for current changes of about the same order [S1B, S1C].

In Fig. 11.9 is a diagram showing the flow of electrons and holes within a point-contact transistor. There will be a large flow of electrons from base to emitter. There will also be electron flow from collector to base

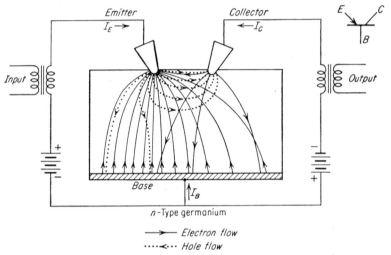

FIG. 11.9. Electron and hole flow in the point-contact transistor.

but much smaller because the collector is biased in the reverse direction with respect to the base. Then in addition there will be a hole flow from the emitter, which will go in small part to the base but mostly to the collector.

In Fig. 11.10 is given a simplified and idealized electron-potential-energy diagram showing the motion of electrons and holes between an emitter positive with respect to base and a collector negative with respect to base. In such a diagram electrons run downhill and holes float upward. There is a large electron flow from base to emitter and a smaller electron flow from collector to base. In addition there is a hole flow mostly from emitter to collector. In the absence of holes a negative space charge builds up around the collector because of the negative electron concentration, which raises the potential-energy profile and limits the electron flow, as shown by the dashed profile. The holes, however, neutralize this negative space charge in large part so that the collector current is increased not only by the amount of the hole flow but by an additional amount of electron flow made possible by the reduction of the negative space charge. This makes possible a current-amplification factor (analogue of the voltage-amplification factor in vacuum tubes and slightly different from the α_c of the previous section) greater than unity. This will be defined as

$$\alpha = -\left(\frac{\partial i_c}{\partial i_e}\right)_{v_C = \text{const}} \tag{11.1}$$

The negative sign comes about because the direction of currents is assumed to be into the emitter and *into* the collector whereas an increase

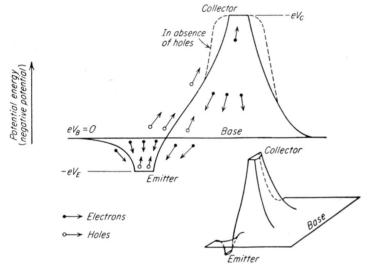

Fig. 11.10. Electron-potential-energy diagram for the point-contact transistor.

of current into the emitter causes an increase in current *out of* the collector. The factors α and α_e are nearly equal and are related by the equation

$$\alpha_e = \alpha + (\alpha - 1)\frac{r_b}{r_c} \tag{11.2}$$

or

$$\alpha = \frac{r_b}{r_b + r_c} + \frac{\alpha_e r_c}{r_b + r_c}$$

Shown in Fig. 11.2a is a curve of emitter current for constant collector voltage superimposed upon the normal characteristic. It is seen that for a fixed value of emitter voltage, two values of emitter current may exist for large collector currents. This explains the short-circuit instability of the point-contact transistor previously referred to. This effect is most prevalent in point-contact transistors.

The subject of equivalent circuits of tubes and transistors will be treated in the next chapter. One possible equivalent circuit has been shown for the filamentary transistor in Fig. 11.7. It also applies to the point-contact transistor.   Typical values of the constants in this equivalent T section are given by those of the Bell System M1729 point-contact transistor and are $r_e = 120$ ohms, $r_b = 75$ ohms, $r_c = 15{,}000$ ohms, and $\alpha = 2.5$ for the grounded-base connection.   It is seen that the input resistance is low and the output impedance relatively high.   The appreciable mutual resistance r_b will be seen later to cause an additional increment of amplification with an attendant loss in stability.

The equations representing the alternating components of voltage resulting from alternating components of current can be written

$$V_e = r_{11}I_e + r_{12}I_c \tag{11.3}$$
$$V_c = r_{21}I_e + r_{22}I_c \tag{11.4}$$

Here the resistance coefficients correspond to the short-circuit admittance coefficients of passive-quadripole theory.   Unlike the passive quadripole, however, the mutual resistances r_{12} and r_{21} need not be equal.   The resistance coefficients may be defined in terms of partial derivatives of voltage with respect to current, of the form

$$r_{12} = \left(\frac{\partial v_e}{\partial i_c}\right)_{i_E = \text{const}} \tag{11.5}$$

and the like.

By the above definitions the resistance coefficients are seen to correspond to the slopes of the various parts of Fig. 11.2, as indicated on the figure.   All the resistance coefficients are positive.   Shown in Fig. 11.11 are contours of constant values of the resistance coefficients.   From these contours can be seen the effect of changing the operating bias.

An alternative representation of transistor characteristics is given in Fig. 11.12.   This shows curves of constant emitter and collector voltage. These are the analogues of the vacuum-tube constant-current curves of Fig. 10.9.   The slope of the constant-collector-voltage curve is a function of the forward-current-amplification factor.   The slope of the constant-emitter-voltage curve is a function of the inverse-current-amplification factor.   The forward-current-amplification factor is seen to be largest for small forward values of emitter current.   This forward-current-amplification factor is also seen to be larger than the inverse-current-amplification factor.

The subject of equivalent circuits of transistors will receive a fuller treatment in the next chapter.   However, it is desirable to show now the simplest and most commonly used equivalent circuits along with the relations between the quantities involved.   This is done in Fig. 11.13.   The circuit of Fig. 11.13a goes directly with (11.3) and (11.4).   It is not the most convenient form since it involves two voltage generators.   The circuit of Fig. 11.13c has already appeared in Fig. 11.7 for the filamentary transistor.   The circuit of Fig. 11.13b is obtained from that of Fig. 11.13c

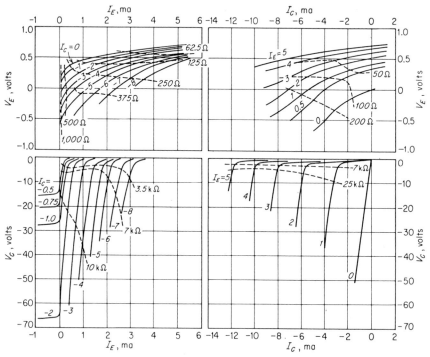

FIG. 11.11. Contours of constant resistance for the resistance coefficients of a point-contact transistor.

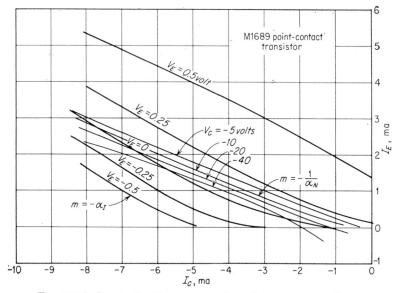

FIG. 11.12. Constant-voltage curves of a point-contact transistor.

by replacing the parallel combination of a constant-current generator and a resistor by the series combination of a constant-voltage generator and the same resistor. Relations between the parameters are tabulated in the figure.

It would be desirable to find formulas relating transistor dimensions and constants to the parameters of Fig. 11.13. To date, it has not been possible to do this completely for the point-contact transistor. This is because the theory of this device is not completely developed. In

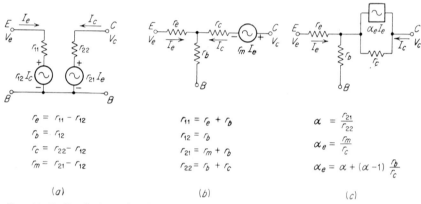

$$r_e = r_{11} - r_{12} \qquad r_{11} = r_e + r_b \qquad \alpha = \frac{r_{21}}{r_{22}}$$

$$r_b = r_{12} \qquad r_{12} = r_b \qquad \alpha_e = \frac{r_m}{r_c}$$

$$r_c = r_{22} - r_{12} \qquad r_{21} = r_m + r_b$$

$$r_m = r_{21} - r_{12} \qquad r_{22} = r_b + r_c \qquad \alpha_e = \alpha + (\alpha - 1)\frac{r_b}{r_c}$$

(a)   (b)   (c)

FIG. 11.13. Equivalent circuits for transistors and relationships among parameters.

particular, it is difficult to account for the high values of the current-multiplication factor α sometimes encountered. It has already been mentioned that these can be partly explained in terms of space-charge neutralization of electrons by holes. This can account for α's of the order of about 2 or 3, but higher values are often realized.

The situation on the theory of point-contact transistors is complicated by the fact that the point contacts are commonly subjected to a process called "forming." This consists of passing a short, intense pulse of current through the point in the direction opposite to that in which current will normally flow. Forming is more critical for the collector than for the emitter. Passing short, intense reverse pulses of current through the collector lead has the effect of raising the value of α and reducing the collector current for the normal polarity of reverse bias. Forming has the effect of changing the nature of the semiconductor in the immediate vicinity of the points. Thus in the n-type semiconductor, the material just under the emitter point is changed to p type, and the material next to the collector is changed to a layer of n type (next to the point) surrounded by a layer of p type, as shown in Fig. 11.14. This double layer is capable of explaining the high α values by a so-called p-n hook theory, which will be discussed later [Sha, DaD].

The emitter resistance r_e of a point-contact transistor is essentially the diode resistance of the emitter. This will consist of two parts, as shown in Fig. 11.15. The first of these is the nonlinear *junction resistance r_j*, due to the rectifying action. The second is the ohmic resistance between the very small area of contact and the base, the so-called *spreading resistance r_s*. This latter is due to the fact that the current is concentrated around the point contact.

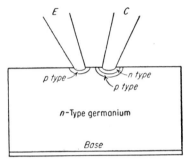

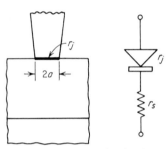

FIG. 11.14. The effect of forming in an *n*-type point-contact transistor.

FIG. 11.15. Equivalent circuit of a point-contact rectifier.

The junction component of resistance may be obtained from the diode law of (7.11). Since the emitter is usually biased in the forward, or high-current, direction, the exponential term will be large compared to unity and the conductance can be found by taking the derivative of current with respect to voltage. Junction resistance will be the reciprocal of junction conductance and has the form

$$r_j = \frac{kT}{eI_E} \quad \text{ohms} \tag{11.6}$$

where k = Boltzmann's constant
  T = absolute temperature
  e = electron charge
  I_E = direct emitter current
At room temperature (300°K), kT/e has a value of 38.6 volts, so that

$$r_j = \frac{1}{38.6I_e} \quad \text{ohms} \tag{11.7}$$

Thus for an emitter current of 1 ma, the theoretical emitter junction resistance is 25.9 ohms.

If the contact is regarded as a circular disk of radius a, then the spreading resistance is

$$r_s = \frac{1}{4\sigma a} \quad \text{ohms} \tag{11.8}$$

where σ is the conductivity per ohm per centimeter if a is the radius in centimeters. If the contact surface is a hemisphere of radius a, then

$$r_s = \frac{1}{2\pi\sigma a} \quad \text{ohms} \tag{11.9}$$

These equations assume that the base thickness is many times greater than the contact radius. The spreading resistance is independent of the base thickness because most of the voltage drop occurs in the high-current-density region next to the point. Thus for a circular-disk contact of radius 0.001 in. and a conductivity of 0.1 ohm^{-1} cm^{-1}, the spreading resistance is 983 ohms. Spreading resistance can be measured at large forward currents where the junction resistance is negligible. Measured values are generally lower than theoretical values given by (11.8) and (11.9). This is believed to be due to the fact that hole injection gives greater hole densities and hence greater conductivity than normal.

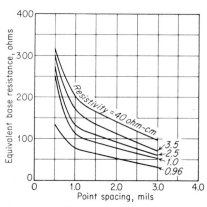

FIG. 11.16. Base resistance of a p-type point-contact transistor as a function of resistivity and point spacing. (After Slade.)

The total emitter resistance will, of course, be the sum of the junction and spreading resistances as given by the above formulas:

$$r_e = r_j + r_s \tag{11.10}$$

It would be expected that the base resistance r_b of a point-contact resistance will depend upon the point spacing and upon the base thickness [VaB, HuD]. An approximate formula is

$$r_b \cong \frac{\rho}{2\pi s}\left(1 - 0.693\,\frac{s}{w}\right) \tag{11.11}$$

where ρ = resistivity of base material, ohm-cm
s = emitter-collector spacing, cm
w = base thickness, cm

Measured values look like those of Fig. 11.16. These have the form predicted by (11.11).

One of the most important considerations with point-contact transistors is the high-frequency limit. This is imposed principally by the transit time of the minority carriers from emitter to collector [Sha, HuD, VaF]. An approximate formula for transit time is

$$\tau = \frac{s^3\sigma}{\mu I_E} \quad \text{sec} \tag{11.12}$$

where s = point spacing, cm

σ = conductivity, ohm^{-1} cm^{-1}

μ = minority-carrier mobility, cm^2 volt^{-1} sec^{-1}

I_E = emitter current, amp

This transit time cannot be measured directly but is expected to be the reciprocal of the current-amplification-factor cutoff frequency. This is the frequency at which the value of α drops 3 db (70.7 per cent of its low-frequency value). The above formula predicts cutoff frequencies that run several times higher than measured values. This discrepancy is due partly to the fact that the high-frequency cutoff is affected by forming in a way which is not understood. The average path length of minority carriers is also probably longer than assumed in deriving (11.12).

Measured values of high-frequency cutoff have the form illustrated in Fig. 11.17 [see also S1B, and S1C]. Experimentally the cutoff frequency varies as the -2.3 power of spacing. The limiting frequencies of n type and p type are approximately in the ratio of the minority-carrier mobilities. The p-type transistors work to higher frequencies because their minority carriers are electrons, which have a higher mobility than the holes of the n-type material. Some p-type transistors have been made to oscillate up to 425 Mc. Ordinary point-contact transistors will operate up to frequencies of the order of 20 to 50 Mc. In

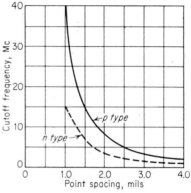

FIG. 11.17. Cutoff frequency of the current-amplification factor of point-contact transistors as a function of point spacing. (*After Slade.*)

switching applications, turn-on times are of the order of 0.2 μsec, and turnoff times are of the order of 2 μsec.

Unfortunately, no simple formula or theory is available to give values of α or collector resistance. A typical value of α for p-type transistors is 2.0, whereas that for n-type transistors is 2.8. Collector resistance will often be determined by surface leakage since the collector is operated in the reverse, or low-current, direction where the theoretical junction resistance is extremely high. A typical value of collector resistance for p-type transistors is 6,400 ohms, whereas that for n-type is 10,000 ohms.

Point-contact transistors initially had superiority over junction transistors in having a higher frequency limit, but this advantage has been largely overcome in recent years. Point-contact transistors suffer from greater noise and a lower power-handling capacity than junction transistors. They will probably be most extensively used in switching circuits.

11.4. The Junction Transistor. The junction transistor consists of a sandwich of alternate layers of n- and p-type germanium or silicon. There are n-p-n and p-n-p transistors. A lead is connected to each layer of the material. The two outer layers serve as emitter and collector, while the center layer serves as base. The center layer is very thin, commonly only about 10^{-3} in. thick.

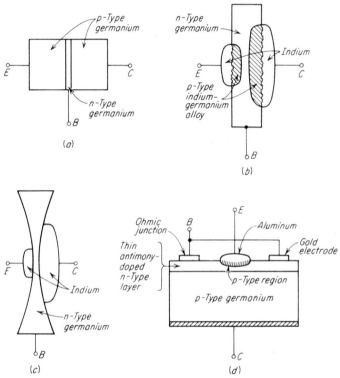

FIG. 11.18. Various forms of junction transistors: (a) grown-junction transistor, (b) alloy-junction transistor, (c) surface-barrier transistor, (d) diffused-base transistor.

Junction transistors are made in several ways. They may be cut from a single crystal grown by pulling a seed crystal very slowly from a reservoir of molten germanium or silicon. The composition of the melt or the rate of growth may be varied periodically to produce alternate layers of n- and p-type material. Such transistors are known as grown-junction transistors. Junction transistors may also be formed by an alloying process. In this process a wafer of germanium or silicon is used on which is placed a pellet of a metal of appropriate valence. Indium is commonly used with n-type germanium. The wafer and pellet are then heated until some of the pellet melts and diffuses into the germanium. Since indium is a p-type impurity, a p-n junction is formed upon cooling and recrystallization [LaB, SaB]. Transistors may also be made by electrochemical etching and subsequent electrochemical deposition of metal on the surface of germanium [BrC]. Such transistors are known as surface-barrier transistors, so named after an early theory of operation. They have junction-transistor characteristics. Shown in Fig. 11.18 are diagrams of various forms of junction transistors. That of Fig. 11.18*d* is known as the diffused-base transistor, to be discussed later.

The junction transistor works by a combination of carrier emission across its junctions and diffusion plus drift across the various layers. To understand this action it is necessary to know the electric potential within

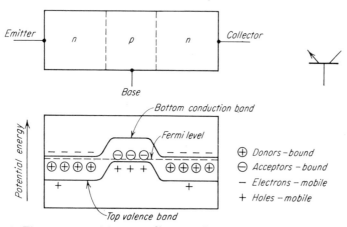

FIG. 11.19. Electron-potential-energy diagram of an *n-p-n* transistor under thermal equilibrium with all terminals open.

the transistor. Shown in Fig. 11.19 is an electron-potential diagram of an *n-p-n* transistor under a condition of thermal equilibrium with all terminals open. Under these conditions, the center *p*-type layer will assume a potential slightly negative with respect to the *n*-type layers. The Fermi levels of the three sections will become the same, under which conditions the electron and hole exchange between the layers is in balance. It should be borne in mind that in the diagram of Fig. 11.19 electrons tend to run downhill and holes float uphill in response to electric fields. However, electrons can be "emitted" from the outer *n*-type layers into the center *p* layer by thermal action. Likewise, holes may be emitted from the center *p* layer to the outer *n* layers.

Carrier Action. The *n-p-n* junction transistor is biased for amplification as shown in Fig. 11.20. Here the emitter is slightly negative with respect to base while the collector is considerably positive with respect to base. Under these conditions, relatively many electrons will be emitted from the *n*-type emitter layer to the *p*-type base layer, while relatively few electrons will be emitted from the *n*-type collector layer to the center

p-type base layer.   Most of the electrons emitted into the base layer from the emitter will diffuse across the thin base layer and "fall" into the collector layer.   Some of the electrons will recombine with holes in making a transit of the base layer, and this will require that more holes enter the base layer through the base connection.   The probability of recombination is reduced by making the center p layer of lower conductivity than the n-type emitter layer.   As a result, the p layer has a relatively low density of holes, whereas the n-type emitter layer has a relatively high density of electrons.   The number of electrons that are

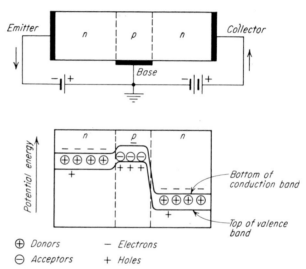

FIG. 11.20. Electron potential energy and carriers in an n-p-n junction transistor with normal bias.

emitted into the base will be an exponential function of the emitter-base potential difference: the smaller the difference, the more will get across the junction.

The above action is quite similar to that which would occur in a tetrode with control grid and screen grid at the same low negative potential with respect to cathode.   The plate is positive with respect to cathode.   It is interesting to draw side by side the structures and the electron-potential-energy diagram of the n-p-n transistor triode and the vacuum triode formed by the above tetrode connection.   This is done in Fig. 11.21. In the triode-connected tetrode, high-velocity electrons from the cathode will be able to ascend from cathode to control grid.   They will then move at constant velocity through the equipotential region between control and screen grid, after which they will fall into the plate.

Shown in Fig. 11.22 is a diagram showing how current is carried within an n-p-n junction-transistor triode.   Current in the n-type emitter is

carried principally by electrons. Most of these electrons will cross the
p-type region having the base connection and will be taken out by the
collector lead. Accordingly, the cur-
rent in the p-type section connected
to the collector lead will be carried
mostly by those electrons which have
originated in the emitter region. The
base current will be small, being the
difference between the emitter and the
collector current. This difference in
current will consist largely of holes from
the base lead flowing into the base
p-type region to replace those lost by
recombination with electrons. Some
of these holes will be emitted into the
emitter region, where they will recombine with electrons.

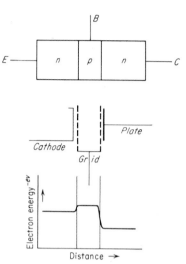

FIG. 11.21. Comparison of energy
levels in an n-p-n junction-transistor
triode and a triode-connected vacuum tetrode.

Carrier Action in More Detail. A
more quantitative description of the
above carrier action requires a knowledge of the carrier densities in various
parts of the junction transistor. (This
and the following paragraphs may be
omitted on a first reading.) Carrier densities for a junction-transistor
triode with all electrodes disconnected are shown dashed in Fig. 11.23a.

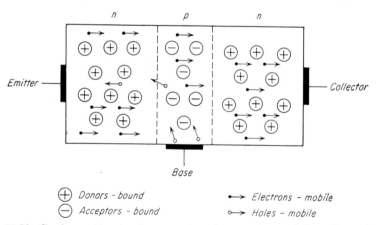

FIG. 11.22. Carrier motion in the n-p-n junction-transistor triode. The principal
action is due to electrons that are emitted from the emitter into the base and then
diffuse across the base and fall into the collector.

Densities here are shown on a logarithmic scale. Quantities with
subscripts represent equilibrium values with the transistor totally

disconnected. Thus n_p is the equilibrium electron density in the p region, and so on. The densities shown are correct only for the conductivities specified. These conductivities are chosen to simplify the diagram but are not too different from those used in alloy-junction transistors. In accordance with Fig. 7.6, the equilibrium electron density in the n regions will nearly equal the donor density since only one type of impurity is present and the donor density determines the conductivity; and likewise for the majority carriers in all the regions. The equilibrium minority carrier density is determined by the relation previously given at the end of Sec. 7.2

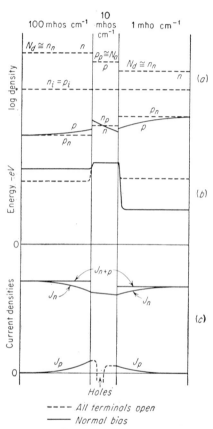

$$n_n p_n = n_p p_p = n_i p_i = n_i^2 \quad (11.13)$$

which states that the product of the electron and hole densities is always the same and specifically equal to the square of the intrinsic electron density. The latter is determined only by the energy gap of the material and the temperature in accordance with (6.1).

Now when bias voltages are applied to the junction-transistor triode, the majority carrier densities are hardly changed at all but the minority carrier densities may be changed appreciably. The minority carrier densities at a junction will be determined only by the equilibrium value and the voltage across the junction

Fig. 11.23. Carrier densities in the junction-transistor triode.

$$n = n_p \epsilon^{eV/kT} \quad (11.14)$$

and

$$p = p_n \epsilon^{-eV/kT} \quad (11.15)$$

where V is the voltage difference between the adjacent material and the material in question [Sha, p. 312]. To determine n in the p-type base section at the emitter junction, the voltage V is the positive emitter-to-base potential. This causes the electron density here to be higher than the equilibrium value. To determine n in the p-type base section at the collector junction, the voltage V is the negative collector-to-base voltage.

This causes the electron density at this point to be lower than the equilibrium value. Similarly, the hole density at the base junction in the emitter region is greater than the equilibrium value, and the hole density at the base junction in the collector junction is less than the equilibrium value. The resultant carrier densities are shown by the solid lines in Fig. 11.23a. The assumed potential values are shown in Fig. 11.23b.

The majority carrier densities are altered slightly at each junction to maintain charge neutrality, but this change is hardly visible on a logarithmic scale.

Once the minority carrier densities are known at the junctions, their values at other points will be determined by the diffusion equation (6.19). Solutions of this in the steady state allow the left-hand member to go to zero and yield exponential variations as shown.

Knowing the carrier densities of Fig. 11.23, the principal components of current flow can be determined from the gradient of charge density by (6.12). The negative gradient of electron density in the base region yields a nearly constant negative electron current to the left, corresponding to an electron migration to the right. The electron currents must be continuous across the junctions and so establish the electron current values just across the junctions. This gives the principal feature of operation, namely, electron injection from emitter to base with migration across the base to collector. Second-order effects include hole current from right to left in the emitter region dying out exponentially. Similar action occurs in the collector region.

Since the total current in the emitter and collector regions must remain constant, the electron current densities decline from terminals inward. This corresponds to electrons being lost by recombination with holes. Since the hole current from base to collector is less than that from emitter to base, the difference must be supplied in the form of a hole current from the base lead. These components are shown in Fig. 11.23c.

Current-Voltage Characteristics of the Junction Triode. As a result of the action described above, the current-voltage characteristics of the junction-transistor triode have the form shown in Fig. 11.24. These curves are for an *n-p-n* transistor. Curves for a *p-n-p* will be similar but with polarities reversed. These curves are seen to be much more regular than those of the point-contact transistor. In particular, the curves have the aspect of a series of displaced diode characteristics, as indeed they are. The uniform portions of these characteristics tend to be parallel straight lines.

The curves of Fig. 11.24 are for the common-base connection. The portion of these most commonly shown are the collector-voltage vs. collector-current curves. The part of these characteristics displayed is the reverse, or low-current region. The forward, or high-current, region is mostly out of the picture. The tetrode- or pentodelike character of these curves may be seen by plotting current vertically and voltage horizontally. The individual curves are labeled with different values of emitter current instead of grid voltage. From the slope of the curves it may be seen that the output resistance is quite high. The collector current is also seen to be only slightly less than the emitter current. This indicates a value of the current-amplification factor α close to unity.

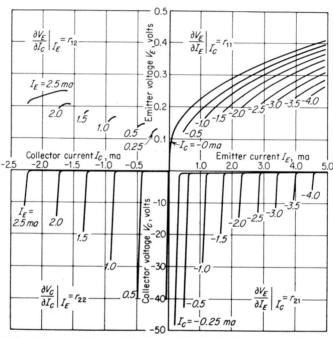

FIG. 11.24. Junction-transistor-triode characteristics for the common-base connection. (*Johns Hopkins University, Applied Physics Laboratory.*)

Likewise, the emitter-voltage vs. emitter-current curves reveal diode action in the forward, or high-current, direction. These are again quite regular and indicate a low input resistance by their slope. Emitter current-voltage curves are similar to collector current-voltage curves.

The junction-triode characteristics examined can be represented by a simple set of equations. These are obtained from a consideration of junction and diffusion effects within the transistor [StB, EbD] and give quite closely the behavior of an idealized, or "intrinsic," transistor. Actual physical transistors follow these equations quite closely. The equations are

$$I_E = a_{11}D(V_{EB}) + a_{12}D(V_{CB}) \qquad (11.16)$$
$$I_C = a_{21}D(V_{EB}) + a_{22}D(V_{CB}) \qquad (11.17)$$

where the currents and voltages are d-c values for the common-base connection. The function $D(V)$ is a diode function given by

$$D(V) = \epsilon^{eV/kT} - 1 \tag{11.18}$$
$$= \epsilon^{V/38.6} - 1 \tag{11.19}$$

at room temperature (300°K). In Eqs. (11.16) and (11.17) V_{EB} is voltage drop from emitter to base, and V_{CB} is voltage drop from collector to base. The coefficients a_{nm} have the dimensions of current and are simply related to transistor characteristics as follows:

$$a_{11} = - \frac{I_{E0}}{1 - \alpha_n \alpha_i} \tag{11.20}$$

$$a_{22} = - \frac{I_{C0}}{1 - \alpha_n \alpha_i} \tag{11.21}$$

$$a_{12} = \frac{\alpha_i I_{C0}}{1 - \alpha_n \alpha_i} \tag{11.22}$$

$$a_{21} = \frac{\alpha_n I_{E0}}{1 - \alpha_n \alpha_i} \tag{11.23}$$

where α_n = normal- (forward-) current-amplification factor
α_i = inverse-current-amplification factor, collector and emitter roles reversed
I_{E0} = saturation current of emitter junction with zero collector current
I_{C0} = saturation current of collector junction with zero emitter current

The theory indicates that

$$a_{12} = a_{21} \tag{11.24}$$

with the result that

$$\alpha_n I_{E0} = \alpha_i I_{C0} \tag{11.25}$$

Inversion of Eqs. (11.20) to (11.23) shows that

$$\alpha_n = - \frac{a_{21}}{a_{11}} \tag{11.26}$$

$$\alpha_i = - \frac{a_{12}}{a_{22}} \tag{11.27}$$

$$I_{C0} = \frac{a_{12}a_{21}}{a_{11}} - a_{22} \tag{11.28}$$

$$I_{E0} = \frac{a_{12}a_{21}}{a_{22}} - a_{11} \tag{11.29}$$

Equations (11.16) and (11.17) are a truly remarkable set of equations. Nothing so simple or complete can be written for point-contact transistors or for vacuum tubes. They give the complete low-frequency picture of operation, including nonlinear effects. All this is given in terms of three quantities at a given temperature. These equations show that all the current-voltage curves are of the same form, differing merely in scale and position.

If the diode factor of V_{CB} is eliminated between (11.16) and (11.17), there results

$$I_E = -\alpha_I I_C - I_{E0} D(V_{BE}) \tag{11.30}$$

Likewise, if the diode factor of V_{EB} is eliminated, there results

$$I_C = -\alpha_N I_E - I_{C0} D(V_{CB}) \tag{11.31}$$

These relations show a linear relation between emitter and collector current for constant values of either emitter or collector voltage.

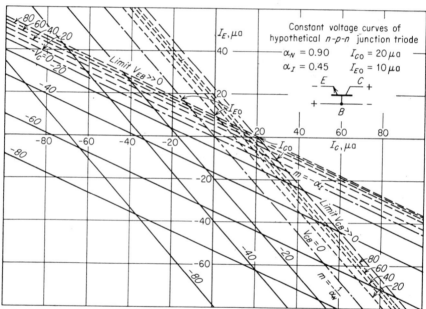

FIG. 11.25. Constant-voltage curves of an ideal junction-transistor triode with the common-base connection.

It will be recalled that, in the discussion of vacuum tubes, it was found that curves of constant plate current and constant grid current on axes of plate and grid voltage were very revealing. In the same manner, it is expected that transistor-triode curves of constant emitter voltage and constant collector voltage on scales of emitter current and collector current will be of interest. This is indeed the case. Equations for such curves are those of (11.30) and (11.31).

The desired constant-voltage curves are shown in Fig. 11.25 for the case of an ideal junction-transistor triode. This is a very interesting representation. The constant-voltage curves are families of straight lines. The slope of the constant-V_{CB} curves is $-1/\alpha_N$. The slope of the constant-V_{EB} curves is $-\alpha_I$. The saturation currents I_{E0} and I_{C0} are easily identified intercepts. It is clear which are the allowed and unallowed areas of current flow. In effect, this representation shows the relation between all voltages and currents on superimposed coordinates of voltage and current. As such, it is one of the simplest and clearest possible. There can be seen at a glance the effect of changing any voltage or current.

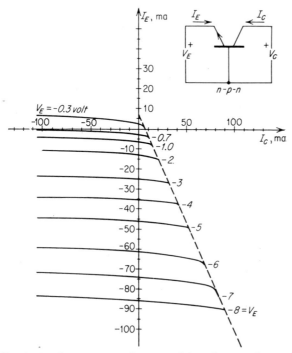

Fig. 11.26. Constant-voltage curves of an actual junction-transistor triode with the common-base connection.

The equations and curves discussed above are deficient mainly in that the ohmic resistance of the various parts of the transistor was not accounted for. This can be corrected by adding appropriate resistances external to the ideal, or intrinsic, transistor. The most important of these will be the base resistance, which must be added in series with the base lead. This introduces some regeneration (positive feedback) into the circuit. Next in importance is the collector leakage, which can be represented by a resistance connected from the collector to the base electrode. Emitter-leakage effects are small for forward bias.

Measured constant-emitter-voltage curves of an actual, rather than ideal, junction-transistor triode are shown in Fig. 11.26 (compare with Fig. 11.12). Such curves are rather difficult to obtain experimentally because voltage sources with impedances less than those of the transistor biased in the forward direction are required.

Other forms of junction-transistor-triode characteristics are of interest too. The commonest representation is that of collector current vs. collector voltage for the common-base connection. This has pentodelike characteristics and has already been shown in Fig. 11.24. Common-emitter operation is also often used; so it is of interest to show collector current vs. collector voltage for this connection. This is done in Fig. 11.27. These curves correspond to plate-current vs. plate-voltage curves

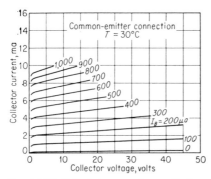

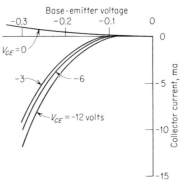

Fig. 11.27. Collector-current vs. collector-voltage characteristics of a junction-transistor triode for the common-emitter connection. Curves are for a *p-n-p* junction transistor, type 2N45. (*General Electric Co.*)

Fig. 11.28. Collector current vs. base-to-emitter voltage of a junction-transistor triode for the common-emitter circuit.

of the grounded-cathode vacuum triode. They show a decidedly lower plate resistance than that for the common-base connection and look like the positive grid portion of ordinary vacuum-triode characteristics.

Also of interest are some other forms of transfer characteristics than those shown in Fig. 11.24. Shown in Fig. 11.28 are the collector current vs. base-to-emitter voltage of a junction-transistor triode with a common-emitter connection. These curves correspond to the plate-current vs. grid-voltage curves of the vacuum triode with the usual common-cathode connection. The slope of these curves is a mutual conductance for transistors, the exact counterpart of the same quantity for vacuum tubes. The transconductances that can be realized are much higher than those which can be had with tubes. Theory and measurement show that the transconductance/emitter-current ratio in a transistor is about 39 at room temperature. Theoretically, tubes have a ratio of about 12 but practical values rarely exceed 2 [GiB]. Thus the transistor has about 20 times the transconductance of vacuum triodes. Corresponding power gains are about the same, however, because the vacuum triode has more favorable input and output impedance values than the transistor has.

Temperature Variation of Junction-transistor Characteristics. An important limitation of transistor operation is their temperature stability. In general this is much poorer than that of vacuum tubes because the equivalent circuit constants of transistors vary considerably with temperature, whereas those of tubes do not. Germanium transistors are most sensitive to temperature changes. Silicon transistors are much more stable with temperature than germanium transistors. The temperature instability of transistors at higher temperatures results from

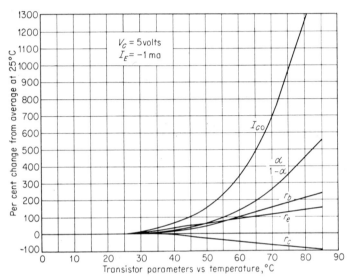

FIG. 11.29. Variation of germanium-junction-transistor-triode characteristics with temperature. Data are for the TI-200 series of grown *n-p-n* transistors. (*Texas Instruments, Inc.*)

intrinsic action due to the small total-energy gap. Germanium has a total energy gap of 0.75 ev. Its density of intrinsic carriers doubles about every 15°C. Silicon has a total-energy gap of 1.12 ev so that its rate of change of density is somewhat greater with temperature; but its intrinsic carrier density is smaller than that of germanium by more than a thousand so that it can be used to higher temperatures. The reader should also refer back to Fig. 6.21 for an impression of the effect of temperature on resistivity.

Shown in Fig. 11.29 is the variation of germanium-junction-transistor-triode characteristics with temperature. The quantities r_b and r_e increase slightly with temperature. This is in accord with both the diode law and Fig. 6.21. The collector saturation current I_{C0} increases very rapidly with temperature. This is due to reverse carriers across the base-collector junction in an emissionlike action. This increase in reverse current is accompanied by a slight reduction in r_C. The factor $\alpha/(1 - \alpha)$ is seen to increase considerably with temperature. This is because the factor α becomes more nearly equal to unity as temperature increases. This in turn is due to the fact that the mean recombination length increases with temperature, and as a result, fewer minority carriers are

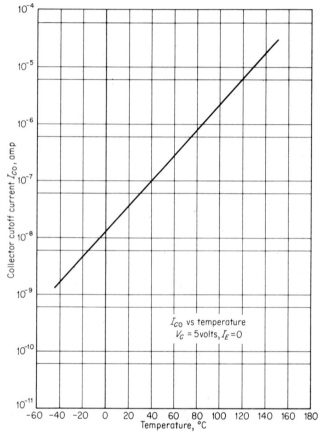

FIG. 11.30. Variation of reverse collector saturation current in a silicon-junction transistor as a function of temperature. Current increases by a factor of 10 every 42°C. (*Texas Instruments, Inc.*)

lost by recombination on traversing the base region. Because of these changes of characteristics with temperature, notably that of I_{C0}, germanium transistors are rarely operated at temperatures above 65°C.

With silicon transistors, as previously indicated, the collector reverse cutoff current is much lower than in germanium transistors but increases more rapidly with temperature. This situation is shown in Fig. 11.30. The current is seen to increase by a factor of 10 every 42°C. Shown in Fig. 11.31 is the variation of the factor $1 - \alpha$ with temperature. This is seen to decrease as the recombination length increases with temperature.

In Fig. 11.32 are shown the variation of some other silicon-junction-transistor-triode parameters with temperature. These parameters are given in terms of the so-called hybrid, or h, parameters, which will be

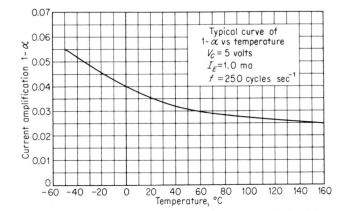

FIG. 11.31. Variation of $1-\alpha$ of a silicon-junction-transistor triode with temperature. (*Texas Instruments, Inc.*)

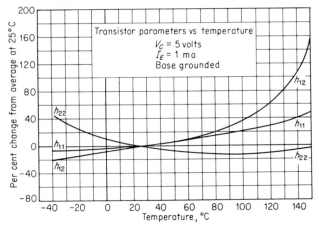

FIG. 11.32. Variation of silicon-junction-transistor-triode characteristics with temperature. (*Texas Instruments, Inc.*)

described in the next chapter. The defining relations for the h parameters are

$$V_e = h_{11}I_e + h_{12}V_c \tag{11.32}$$
$$I_e = h_{21}I_e + h_{22}V_c \tag{11.33}$$

where the capital letters indicate the alternating components of voltage and current. The quantity h_{12} is a voltage-amplification factor in the reverse (collector-to-emitter) direction. It is seen to increase with temperature. The quantity h_{22} is the reciprocal of the output open-circuit

impedance. It is seen to drop slightly with temperature out to 100°C
and then rise again. As a consequence, r_b, which is the quotient of h_{12}
and h_{22}, rises with temperature. The quantity h_{11}, which is the reciprocal
of the short-circuit input admittance, is seen to rise slightly with temperature. This is the major component of r_e. In short, transistor characteristics change appreciably with temperature, requiring special circuits to
give compensating action. Silicon transistors are superior in being able
to work at temperatures as high as 150°C, as compared with about 65°C
for germanium.

Frequency Limitations of Junction-transistor Triodes. The high-frequency performance of junction transistors is limited by several factors:
the transit time of the minority carriers in moving through the base
section, the capacity across the base-collector junction, and the base
resistance r_b in the circuit of Fig. 11.13b and c. The α factor tends to
follow a frequency variation of the form

$$\alpha = \frac{\alpha_0}{1 + jf/f_{c\alpha}} \tag{11.34}$$

as a result of minority-carrier transit-time effects. Here α_0 is the low-
frequency value of α, and $f_{c\alpha}$ is a reference frequency known as the α
cutoff frequency. The capacity across the base-collector junction shunts
out the equivalent current generator of Fig. 11.13c progressively as frequency increases. The base resistance introduces a regenerative action
(positive feedback), which narrows the frequency band, just as degenerative action (negative feedback) widens the frequency band. This subject
is discussed in more detail in Sec. 13.10.

Small junction transistors, having a dissipation of 50 mw or so, can
operate at frequencies up to tens of megacycles. Higher-power transistors with dissipations of the order of watts will operate only up to frequencies of the order of tens or possibly hundreds of kilocycles. This
lower-frequency limit results from the increased size with attendant
increase in transit time and base-collector junction capacity.

Power Limitations of Junction-transistor Triodes. The power-handling
capabilities of transistors will be determined by the maximum temperatures at which the materials can be used. As previously indicated, these
are about 65°C for germanium and 150°C for silicon. At higher temperatures the desired carrier densities are upset by intrinsic action. Temperatures can be kept low in several ways. An obvious method is to
enlarge the structures [HaB]. Another method is to conduct heat away
by making a good thermally conducting path between the transistor and a
heat sink, such as a chassis. One such design is shown in Fig. 11.33.
Here the metal envelope of the transistor is connected to the collector.
The major portion of the heat will be developed in either the base or the
collector, whichever has the highest resistivity. Where the collector

must be insulated from the chassis, as shown, good thermal conductivity is still obtained by using a thin mica washer on one side lubricated with a high-temperature silicone and a neoprene washer on the other side [MoE].

There is, however, a limit to what can be achieved by simply making electrodes larger in area. The base layer must always be kept thin in

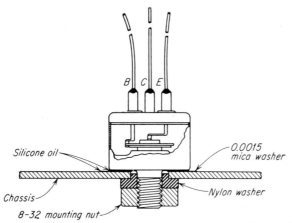

FIG. 11.33. Construction of type 2N57 high-power junction transistor. (*Minneapolis-Honeywell Regulator Co.*)

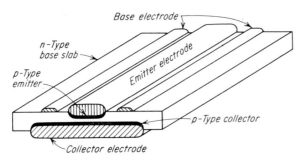

FIG. 11.34. Linearized type of high-power junction transistor.

order to keep the frequency limit high and the current-amplification factor high. As the electrodes are enlarged in area, it is found that the major portion of current flows around the edges of the electrodes so that improvement is achieved only as the first, rather than the second, power of dimension. This dictates a linearized structure as shown in Fig. 11.34 [FlE]. Such a structure can be made quite long. It is usually preferable to close the base electrode around a strip of emitter electrode and then use several such units in parallel on the same base slab. In 1957 there were transistors available with dissipations up to 7 watts in air and up to 55 watts when connected to a heat sink. Transistors using the geometry of Fig. 11.34 have the possibility of going to 50 watts dissipation at present. Further developments will undoubtedly give even higher-power transistors.

Junction-transistor Design Formulas. Theoretical values of the coefficients of (11.16) and (11.17) have been determined [Shb, StB, EaB, EaC, GiD2]. A complete tabulation and discussion of these formulas is beyond the scope of this book. However, a brief discussion of the most important relations is important.

Emitter conductance will be given closely by the diode formula

$$g_e = \frac{1}{r_e} = \frac{eI_E}{kT} \tag{11.35}$$

This indicates that input resistance is inversely proportional to emitter current. As such, it is subject to a measure of control simply by changing the bias. Current will depend upon voltages according to (11.16) with the a_{11} coefficient dominant. This in turn will be determined by diode considerations as

$$a_{11} = e\left(\frac{D_p p_n}{L_p} + \frac{D_n n_p}{L_n}\right) = I_0 \tag{11.36}$$

where e = electron charge
$\quad D_p$ = diffusion constant for holes in n region
$\quad p_n$ = hole equilibrium density in n region
$\quad L_p$ = diffusion length for holes in n region (and correspondingly for other quantities representing electron characteristics in p region)

The coefficient a_{11} is also equal to the I_0 of (7.11). The first term of (11.36) represents the current due to holes moving from the p to the n region. The second represents the current due to electrons moving from the n to the p region. The ratio of the two terms of (11.36) is equal to the square root of the conductivities of the adjacent sections. Carriers flow principally from the high-conductivity to the low-conductivity material. Being an equilibrium current, a_{11}, as given by (11.36), applies for either p-n or n-p junctions and likewise serves to give emitter resistance for either n-p-n or p-n-p transistors.

One of the parameters of most interest is the forward-current-amplification factor. This is given by

$$\alpha = \beta\gamma \tag{11.37}$$

that is, as the product of two factors. The first of these is a so-called transport factor, which gives the fraction of the injected minority carriers that succeed in diffusing across the base. For either type of transistor this is

$$\beta = \text{sech} \frac{w}{L_b} \tag{11.38}$$

where sech (w/L_b) = hyperbolic secant of w/L_b
$\quad\quad w$ = base thickness
$\quad\quad L_b$ = diffusion length of minority carriers in base
For small values of w/L_b this can be written as

$$\beta \cong \frac{1}{1 + \frac{1}{2}(w/L_b)^2} \tag{11.39}$$

This factor will usually be only a few per cent less than unity.

The second factor of (11.37) is known as the injection efficiency and represents the fraction that the injected minority carriers are of the total carriers making up the emitter current. It is given by

$$\gamma = \frac{1}{1 + (A_e/A_b)(\sigma_b L_b/\sigma_e L_e) \tanh (w/L_b)} \tag{11.40}$$

where A_e = area of emitter-base junction
$\quad\quad A_b$ = effective base area
$\quad\quad \sigma$ = conductivity
$\quad\quad L$ = minority-carrier diffusion length
$\quad\quad w$ = base width
The function $\tanh (w/L_b)$ is the hyperbolic tangent, which equals the argument for small values of the argument and so could have been replaced by w/L_b. The injection-efficiency factor will usually be even closer to unity than the β factor. This is because the emitter conductivity is usually greater than the base conductivity, the base thickness is small compared to the diffusion length L_b, and in the alloy-type transistor the area A_e is smaller than the effective base area A_b. The above equations can also be used to calculate the inverse current-amplification factor simply by replacing emitter values by collector values.[1]

No simple formulas are available for base resistance r_b and collector resistance r_c. The base resistance will depend upon the base resistivity and also upon the geometry of the transistor, which will differ from type to type. The collector resistance will depend more upon surface leakage and recombination effects than upon base-collector junction back resistance.

11.5. Some Special Forms of Junction-transistor Triodes. It is probably too early to do more than mention a few interesting special forms of the junction-transistor triode and indicate their general features. The transistor is a very young device, and there will undoubtedly be many striking developments that will revolutionize ideas and forms. Some of these have already appeared. There are several forms of both three- and four-element transistor triodes that are worth mentioning.

One interesting form of transistor triode is the so-called surface-barrier transistor [BrC]. This transistor is formed by etching electrolytically a

[1] See also [MoD, WeD].

thin wafer of germanium with jets of electrolyte directed at the two sides. The wafer can be etched to a thickness of 2×10^{-4} in. with good control. By reversing the polarity of the batteries connected to the jets it is then possible to deposit emitter and collector electrodes electrolytically. By this means transistors have been made which will amplify up to 50 Mc and oscillate to 100 Mc. It is not known whether the electrodes deposited on the base wafer form p-n or metal-semiconductor junctions— hence the name. Static characteristics are similar to those of junction transistors.

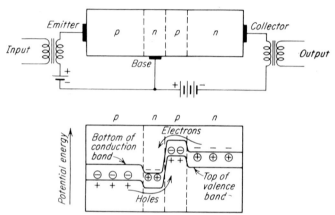

Fig. 11.35. Circuit connections and energy levels of the p-n-p-n junction-transistor triode.

Another three-element junction triode is the diffused-base transistor [LeF, TaF]. This is made by first diffusing antimony into one side of a p-type germanium wafer from a vapor of the metal at high temperature. A layer of antimony less than 10^{-4} in. thick and having a negative exponential variation of density with penetration is thus produced. On this is evaporated an aluminum emitter electrode in the form of a strip with a gold base electrode on each side. These are then alloyed into the antimony layer by heating. The resulting transistor has an α cutoff frequency as high as 600 Mc. This process may revolutionize the construction of transistors and make them competitive with vacuum tubes in cost.

An interesting four-element transistor triode is the n-p-n-p or p-n-p-n transistor. As the name implies, this consists of a succession of alternate layers of n- and p-type materials. In the p-n-p-n transistor, the emitter electrode is connected to the first p layer. The base electrode is connected to the adjacent n layer. The next p layer is left floating, and the last n layer has the collector electrode connected to it as shown in Fig. 11.35 [ShA2, EbB]. Connections and bias are as for the p-n-p transistor. With this bias condition the energy diagram is as shown in the same figure.

The center p- and n-type slices must both be very thin for successful operation. The collector is biased so that a few electrons from the final n-type section can climb the energy hump of the center p-type section to fall into the base. Otherwise the operation is like that of the p-n-p transistor with holes being injected from the emitter p-type region into the center n-type section connected to the base and with most of the holes diffusing through this section toward the p-n junction at the right.

However, in the p-n-p-n transistor triode, those holes passing through the center n-type section, instead of passing on to the collector lead immediately, tend to collect momentarily in the center p-type section, where there is a *potential-energy hook* to trap them. The accumulation of holes in the center p-type region produces a positive space charge that depresses the potential-energy curve and thus permits more electrons to flow from collector to base. Thus an additional component of collector current is triggered by the injected hole current. With such an arrangement, current-amplification factors of 2 or 3 or even more are readily obtained. Results are in agreement with the "p-n hook" theory. This same theory probably also explains how the current-multiplication factor of point-contact transistors can be greater than unity. It has been established that certain forming procedures for point-contact-transistor collector electrodes result in a double layer of opposite types of impurity next to the collector electrode. One can examine p-n-p-n transistor action by appropriate interconnections between an n-p-n and a p-n-p transistor.

Another four-element transistor triode is the p-n-i-p (or n-p-i-n) transistor [EaD]. This device overcomes the high-frequency limitation of ordinary junction-transistor triodes, caused by the large capacity across the base-collector junction, by interposing a layer of intrinsic material between base and collector. The other characteristics of the p-n-i-p transistor do not differ appreciably from those of p-n-p transistors, but the reduction of the base-collector capacity has made possible oscillator operation up to 400 Mc.

11.6. Junction-transistor Tetrodes. Several forms of tetrode have already appeared on the transistor scene. The first of these was the p-n-p-n tetrode. This has the same structure as the triode of Fig. 11.35 but has an electrode connected to each layer. The connection to the floating layer of the triode is used only for d-c bias and permits no a-c voltage to be developed. The principal feature of this type of tetrode is that it is possible to obtain a variation in the current-amplification factor by varying the bias on the third element. It is possible to get an action akin to that of a variable μ tube, making automatic gain-control operation possible.

Another tetrode is the one shown in Fig. 11.36. This is known as the double-base junction-transistor tetrode [WaB]. This is essentially a three-layer transistor with a normal base connection on one side of the base layer and an additional one on the other. The symbol and equivalent circuit are also shown. The equivalent circuit is the same as for the transistor triode. The second base is biased so as to cause the minority carriers to flow away from it and to flow close to the first base. The

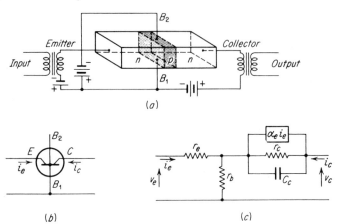

(a)

(b)   (c)

FIG. 11.36. (a) The double-base junction-transistor tetrode; (b) its symbol; (c) equivalent circuit.

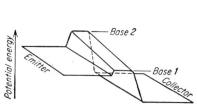

FIG. 11.37. Electron-potential-energy diagram of the double-base transistor tetrode.

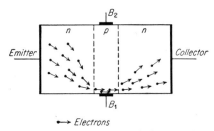

FIG. 11.38. Flow pattern of electrons in a double-base transistor tetrode.

negative bias applied to the second base in the case shown has the effect of producing a potential-energy surface as in Fig. 11.37. On such a surface, the electrons, which are the minority carriers, tend to roll downhill. Electrons are emitted from emitter to base by thermal action. Their general flow pattern will be as in Fig. 11.38. Because the electrons are concentrated near the first base, the equivalent base resistance r_b of Fig. 11.36 is greatly reduced. The effective base-collector capacity is also reduced. Because of these effects, experimental double-base transistor tetrodes have oscillated up to 800 Mc.

CHAPTER 12

EQUIVALENT CIRCUITS
OF TUBES AND TRANSISTORS

12.1. Basis for Equivalent Circuits. In the previous chapters were described the current-voltage characteristics of various tubes and transistors. In general such devices have pronouncedly nonlinear characteristics when viewed as a whole. However, if attention is restricted to small variations of voltage and current about a given operating point, the variations are found to be almost linear. This makes possible a large field of application of electron devices such as small-signal amplifiers and oscillators. In such cases the devices are biased to a suitable operating point. This requires application of constant direct input and output voltages, giving components of constant input and output current, which flow all the time. Small alternating voltages may then be superimposed upon these direct components without interrupting them. This is done in various ways. It may be done with transformers in series with the input and output that will pass alternating components of voltage and current but not direct current or voltage. It may be done with capacitors having a relatively low impedance to alternating voltage but not passing direct currents. It may also be done by using large inductances or chokes in series with the direct-voltage supplies. These will pass direct current but offer a high impedance to alternating currents.

In the study of the action of electron devices in response to small variations of current or voltage, it is found that the responses are nearly linear in the limit of small variations. This makes possible the use of certain equivalent circuits to describe the behavior *of the alternating components only*. These, however, are commonly the components of most interest.

The linear nature of the curved characteristics may be shown in several ways. If one quantity is a single-valued function of another, then the function may be expanded into a Taylor's series about a point, yielding a constant plus a linear term plus higher-order terms. If attention is restricted to the first two terms, it is seen that the curve of the function is approximated by a straight line tangent to the curve at the reference point. For small departures from the reference point, the straight line is a good approximation to the curve.

In the characteristics of electron devices, we deal with *functions of two variables.* Input and output current may be expressed as functions of input and output voltage or vice versa. Of the four quantities involved, any two may be taken as independent variables and the other two as dependent variables. A quantity which is a function of two variables may be represented geometrically as a surface. It is still possible to expand the function about any point in a Taylor's series [Pie]. In this case there results a constant plus a term linear with each variable plus higher-order terms. The geometrical significance of this is that the surface representing the function is approximated by a plane tangent to the surface at the reference point. For small departures from the reference point, the plane is a good approximation to the surface.

FIG. 12.1. Four-terminal-network notation.

12.2. General Equations. In application, the operating point of an electron device is established by applying constant current or constant potential to the input and output. Signals are then superimposed, usually in the form of small alternating components of current or voltage. Thus the input voltage of a tube consists of a direct-potential bias plus a small alternating component of voltage.

For the general circuit of Fig. 12.1, representing what is commonly called a quadripole,[1] we may write

$$i_1 = f_1(v_1, v_2) \tag{12.1}$$
$$i_2 = f_2(v_1, v_2) \tag{12.2}$$

or

$$v_1 = f_3(i_1, i_2) \tag{12.3}$$
$$v_2 = f_4(i_1, i_2) \tag{12.4}$$

for *total* currents and voltages.

Corresponding differential expressions are of the form

$$di_1 = \frac{\partial i_1}{\partial v_1} dv_1 + \frac{\partial i_1}{\partial v_2} dv_2 \tag{12.5}$$

$$di_2 = \frac{\partial i_2}{\partial v_1} dv_1 + \frac{\partial i_2}{\partial v_2} dv_2 \tag{12.6}$$

and

$$dv_1 = \frac{\partial v_1}{\partial i_1} di_1 + \frac{\partial v_1}{\partial i_2} di_2 \tag{12.7}$$

$$dv_2 = \frac{\partial v_2}{\partial i_1} di_1 + \frac{\partial v_2}{\partial i_2} di_2 \tag{12.8}$$

for *small variations* of current and voltage from fixed values.

[1] Quadripole is the general terminology for a four-terminal network. Other designations are two-terminal pair and two-port network. Actually, vacuum and transistor triodes are three-terminal networks with one terminal common to input and output.

If now the increments of current and voltage are taken as *small alternating components*, represented by capital letters,

$$I_1 = y_{11}V_1 + y_{12}V_2 \qquad (12.9)$$
$$I_2 = y_{21}V_1 + y_{22}V_2 \qquad (12.10)$$
and
$$V_1 = z_{11}I_1 + z_{12}I_2 \qquad (12.11)$$
$$V_2 = z_{21}I_1 + z_{22}I_2 \qquad (12.12)$$

These expressions will apply only to alternating components, and the z and y factors will be constant for fixed direct values of the operating voltages and currents.

Here

$$y_{nm} = \left(\frac{\partial i_n}{\partial v_m}\right)_{v_n=\text{const}} \qquad (12.13)$$

has the dimensions of admittance but will usually be conductive for electron devices at low frequencies, and

$$z_{nm} = \left(\frac{\partial v_n}{\partial i_m}\right)_{i_n=\text{const}} \qquad (12.14)$$

has the dimensions of impedance but will usually be resistive for electron devices at low frequencies.

In (12.9) and (12.10) the admittance coefficients apply to short-circuit conditions. Thus y_{11} is the input short-circuit admittance; i.e., it is the input admittance when the output is short-circuited to alternating components. Likewise y_{12} is known as a short-circuit transfer admittance; i.e., it is a ratio of alternating current in the input to alternating voltage in the output when the input is short-circuited to alternating components.

Similarly, in (12.11) and (12.12) the coefficients apply to open-circuit conditions. Thus z_{11} is the input open-circuit impedance to alternating voltage; i.e., it is the input impedance when the output circuit is open. Likewise, z_{12} is known as an open-circuit mutual impedance; i.e., it is the ratio of input alternating voltage to output alternating current when the input is open-circuited to alternating currents and an alternating component of current is applied to the output.

Since the admittance coefficients apply to short-circuit conditions while the impedance coefficients apply to open-circuit conditions, y_{11} is *not* the reciprocal of z_{11}. The reader may easily establish the following relations between the coefficients:

$$z_{11} = \frac{y_{22}}{Y^2} \qquad z_{12} = -\frac{y_{12}}{Y^2}$$
$$\qquad (12.15)$$
$$z_{22} = \frac{y_{11}}{Y^2} \qquad z_{21} = -\frac{y_{21}}{Y^2}$$

$$Y^2 = y_{11}y_{22} - y_{12}y_{21} \qquad (12.16)$$

Likewise,

$$y_{11} = \frac{z_{22}}{Z^2} \qquad y_{12} = -\frac{z_{12}}{Z^2}$$

$$y_{22} = \frac{z_{11}}{Z^2} \qquad y_{21} = -\frac{z_{21}}{Z^2}$$

(12.17)

$$Z^2 = z_{11}z_{22} - z_{12}z_{21} \tag{12.18}$$

Here Y^2 and Z^2 are the determinants of their respective coefficients expressed in a notation indicating the dimensionality. It is further evident that

$$Y^2 = \frac{1}{Z^2} \tag{12.19}$$

Up to this point, the relations are quite general and apply to either passive quadripoles, i.e., without internal generators, or active quadripoles, i.e., quadripoles containing energy sources. The four admittance coefficients are independent of each other as are also the four impedance coefficients, although the two groups are related. As we shall see, in the case of the negative-grid vacuum triode, two of the admittance coefficients are zero and the ratio of the other two is given a separate name. This leads to the common misconception that there are three independent circuit parameters associated with an active quadripole. Actually, there are four in the most general case as with the transistor triode and the positive-grid vacuum triode.

It has already been indicated that the admittance coefficients appear as short-circuit parameters; i.e., they are the ratios of a current to a voltage when the other voltage is shorted out. Likewise, the impedance coefficients appear as open-circuit parameters; i.e., they are the ratio of a voltage to a current when the terminals associated with the other current are open. This interpretation is easy to apply to passive quadripoles. Active quadripoles such as electron devices cannot have their input or output terminals open- or short-circuited without changing their characteristics. Accordingly, the above ideas must be generalized so that open circuit means extremely high impedance to alternating voltage and short circuit means extremely low impedance to alternating voltage. Associated resistances to direct current will usually be normal at the same time.

12.3. Equivalent Circuits for the Passive Quadripole. Equations (12.9) to (12.12) above are the same as the equations of a passive quadripole [Gup2]. For the passive quadripole, by which is meant one with passive linear bilateral elements, $y_{12} = y_{21}$ and $z_{12} = z_{21}$. The equality of the mutual admittances and impedances occurs for passive circuits because the reciprocity law holds for such circuits. The reciprocity law does not hold in general for active circuits such as are used to represent alternating components in electron devices, and as a result the mutual admittances and impedances in the two directions are different. Equations (12.9) and (12.10) are readily identified with the π section of Fig. 12.2, where the mutual admittance is given as y_{12}. Although these equations can also be represented by a T section, the section representation is simplest when current is expressed as a function of voltage.

Similarly, (12.11) and (12.12) are readily identified with the T section of Fig. 12.3, where the mutual impedance is given as z_{12}. It should be noticed that in both cases the passive quadripole is uniquely described in terms of three parameters. Accordingly, an electron device that requires four parameters to describe it cannot be represented by a *passive* T or π.

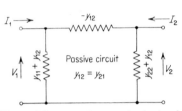

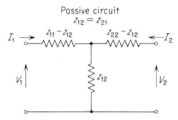

FIG. 12.2. Π-section equivalent of general four-terminal network.

FIG. 12.3. T-section equivalent of general four-terminal network.

12.4. Equivalent Circuits for the Active Quadripole. When the mutual impedances or, correspondingly, the mutual admittances of a quadripole are not equal, as is the case with active quadripoles, then slightly more complicated equivalent networks than the equivalent T or π are needed [Pec]. Among the simplest of these are the two-branch circuits shown in Figs. 12.4 and 12.5. Figure 12.4 represents (12.9) and (12.10), while Fig. 12.5 represents (12.11) and (12.12). Each circuit is seen to consist

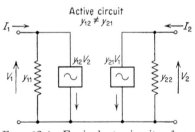

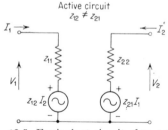

FIG. 12.4. Equivalent circuit of an active four-terminal network using two constant-current generators.

FIG. 12.5. Equivalent circuit of an active four-terminal network using two constant-voltage generators.

of two branches and two equivalent generators. In the case of Fig. 12.4, the two generators are constant-current generators represented by the sine wave inside the square box. In the case of Fig. 12.5, the two generators are constant-voltage generators represented by the sine wave inside the small circle. The constant-current and constant-voltage generators are assumed to have infinite and zero impedance, respectively.

These generators are constant only in the sense that, if located in the input portion of the circuit, their strength is independent of input conditions. Such generators will, however, have strengths dependent upon circuit output conditions. There is no direct coupling apparent between input and output in either case, although actually such coupling is provided by the generators, whose strengths are proportional to the strength of current or voltage in the other branch. Such equivalent circuits are quite adequate and correct though it is not always most convenient to use a circuit with two generators, especially when other external connections between input and output are made. As will be seen, it is possible to represent the active quadripole with an equivalent circuit consisting

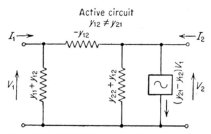

FIG. 12.6. Equivalent circuit of an active four-terminal network using a single constant-current generator.

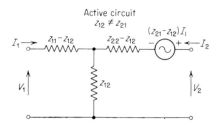

FIG. 12.7. Equivalent circuit of an active four-terminal network using a single constant-voltage generator.

of *three passive impedances and one equivalent generator*. This will be considered in the next paragraph.

For the purpose of obtaining an equivalent circuit with only one equivalent generator, let (12.10) be rewritten as

$$I_2 = y_{12}V_1 + y_{22}V_2 + (y_{21} - y_{12})V_1 \tag{12.20}$$

This, taken with (12.9) unmodified, is seen to be the same as the equations for the passive quadripole except for the last term of (12.20), which may be taken as representing a constant-current generator, as in Fig. 12.6. This circuit is seen to be the same as that of Fig. 12.2 except for the constant-current generator in the output circuit. The negative sign of the transfer admittance y_{12} need cause no concern. In passive circuits, this element will actually be positive and the signs of the mutual terms in the current equations will be negative instead of positive because of the assumed directions of the input and output current. In the positive-grid vacuum triode, the transconductance corresponding to this element is negative; so the equivalent circuit element is positive.

In a similar manner, (12.12) may be written

$$V_2 = z_{12}I_1 + z_{22}I_2 + (z_{21} - z_{12})I_1 \tag{12.21}$$

This is seen to be the same as the corresponding equation for the passive quadripole except for the last term, which may be considered as representing a constant-voltage generator in the output circuit, as shown in Fig. 12.7. This is seen to be the same as the passive quadripole equivalent of Fig. 12.3 except for the addition of the constant-voltage generator in the output circuit.

Thus it is seen that relatively simple equivalent circuits consisting of three passive impedances and one generator may be used to represent active quadripoles with complete generality. Two other forms are possible, which are simply related to these last two. In the circuit of Fig. 12.6, the parallel combination of the output branch and the constant-current generator may be converted into a series combination of an impedance and a constant-voltage generator by Thévenin's theorem (see Appendix 10). This form is extensively used for vacuum triodes. Likewise, in the circuit of Fig. 12.7, the series combination of impedance and constant-voltage generator can be converted to a parallel combination of impedance and constant-current generator by Norton's theorem (see Appendix 10). This form is extensively used for transistor triodes.

12.5. Equivalent Circuit for the Vacuum Triode. Vacuum-triode relations are most conveniently and logically written in the form of (12.9) and (12.10) based on (12.5) and (12.6):

$$I_g = \frac{1}{r_g} V_g + g_{12} V_p \tag{12.22}$$

$$I_p = g_m V_g + \frac{1}{r_p} V_p \tag{12.23}$$

for the common-cathode connection, where the subscripts g and p refer to grid and plate, respectively. Here g_m is the grid-plate mutual conductance, sometimes known as the grid-plate transconductance, defined as

$$g_m = \left(\frac{\partial i_p}{\partial v_g}\right)_{v_p=\text{const}} \tag{12.24}$$

from (12.6). The constant r_p is known as the dynamic plate resistance and is defined as

$$r_p = \left(\frac{\partial v_p}{\partial i_p}\right)_{v_g=\text{const}} \tag{12.25}$$

from (12.6). The constant g_m is recognized as the slope, at an operating point, of the plate-current vs. grid-voltage characteristics of the triode. Likewise, $1/r_p$ is the slope, at an operating point, of the plate-current vs. plate-voltage characteristic.

Similarly, r_g and g_{12} are the dynamic grid resistance and the plate-grid transconductance, with corresponding definitions. Here $1/r_g$ will be the slope, at an operating point, of the grid-current vs. grid-voltage characteristics of the vacuum triode. Likewise, g_{12} will be the slope, at an operating point, of the grid-current vs. plate-voltage characteristics of the vacuum triode. These last two coefficients are so seldom used that there is no standard notation for them. They are seldom used because the vacuum triode, when used for small-alternating-signal operation, invariably has a negative grid bias, for which i_g is zero and accordingly $1/r_g$ and g_{12} are both zero. However, for a general treatment of the positive-grid triode, they must be included. Thus the equivalent circuit of the positive-grid triode assumes the form of Fig. 12.8, where it is to

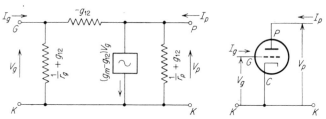

FIG. 12.8. Equivalent circuit of the positive-grid triode.

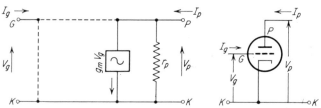

FIG. 12.9. Equivalent circuit of the negative-grid triode using a constant-current generator.

be remembered that, in the absence of secondary emission, r_g, r_p, and g_m are positive, whereas g_{12} is negative since an increase in plate voltage produces a decrease in grid current. Here the branch conductance values must be determined or measured for each operating condition since they are not constant.

For the *negative-grid* triode, $1/r_g$ and g_{12} are zero so that the equivalent circuit simplifies to that of Fig. 12.9, which is a good approximation for frequencies sufficiently low so that the currents through the interelectrode capacities are negligible. This figure gives *the vacuum-triode equivalent circuit reduced to an equivalent plate circuit* in which the grid control action is represented by a constant-current generator. This same form may also be used to represent multielectrode tubes and is preferred in such cases because the plate resistance of such tubes is frequently so high that the current through it may be neglected and the tube acts very nearly as a constant-current generator as far as its output circuit is concerned. In all the above, it should be remembered that the remarks *apply only to the determination of alternating currents and voltages.* To determine the direct currents resulting from the application of direct voltages, other considerations must be applied, usually the circuit and actual tube characteristics.

The parallel combination of plate resistance and current generator of Fig. 12.9 may be converted by Thévenin's theorem into the series combination of a resistance and a voltage generator whose emf is μv_g and is downward when the grid voltage is upward. Use has been made here of the relation

$$\mu = g_m r_p \tag{12.26}$$

where μ is the amplification factor of the tube, defined by

$$\mu = -\left(\frac{\partial v_p}{\partial v_g}\right)_{i_p=\text{const}} \tag{12.27}$$

The above relations are obtainable directly from (12.6) for $di_2 = 0$.

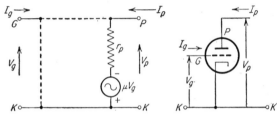

FIG. 12.10. Equivalent circuit of the negative-grid triode using a constant-voltage generator.

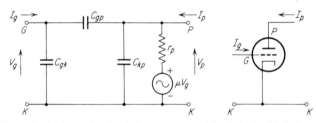

FIG. 12.11. Equivalent circuit of the negative-grid triode for high frequencies.

The significance of the negative sign in (12.27) is that a *decrease* in control-grid voltage is needed to offset an *increase* in plate voltage in keeping plate current constant. The equivalent circuit of Fig. 12.10, which results from the above conversion, is preferred for vacuum triodes, where the plate resistance is relatively low. In contrast, the equivalent circuit of Fig. 12.9 is preferred for vacuum pentodes, where the plate resistance of the tube is extremely high.

At moderately high frequencies, the currents through the interelectrode capacities must be considered. This is done simply by including the interelectrode capacities in parallel with previous circuits, as shown in the example of Fig. 12.11. Such a circuit works well up to frequencies of the order of 10 Mc, where electron transit times become an appreciable part of a cycle. Here it found that there appears a component of input conductance in the grid circuit that is closely proportional to frequency squared. This calls for a resistance shunted across the input circuit. This situation will be discussed further in Chap. 13.

12.6. Equivalent Circuit for the Transistor Triode. The basic equations for the transistor triode in terms of small alternating currents and voltages are conveniently written

$$V_e = r_{11}I_e + r_{12}I_c \tag{12.28}$$
$$V_c = r_{21}I_e + r_{22}I_c \tag{12.29}$$

where the subscripts e and c refer to emitter and collector, respectively, and the *base* is common to input and output. Accordingly, the equivalent circuit of Fig. 12.7 can be used simply by changing the notation to fit

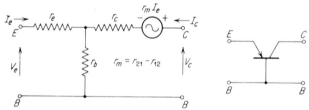

Fig. 12.12. Equivalent circuit of the transistor triode using a constant-voltage generator.

the above equations, as has been done in Fig. 12.12. In this figure, the following notation has been introduced:

$$r_e = r_{11} - r_{12} \tag{12.30}$$
$$r_b = r_{12} \tag{12.31}$$
$$r_c = r_{22} - r_{12} \tag{12.32}$$
$$r_m = r_{21} - r_{12} \tag{12.33}$$

This figure is the direct equivalent of Fig. 12.7 except that the impedance coefficients are resistive up to a megacycle or so. In this case, *none* of the resistance coefficients is negligible, as was the case with the negative-grid triode.

It is sometimes convenient to convert the series combination of a resistance and a voltage generator to a parallel combination of a resistance and a current generator. When this is done, the equivalent circuit has the form given in Fig. 12.13. Here a new symbol has been introduced,

$$\alpha_e = \frac{r_m}{r_c} = \frac{r_{21} - r_{12}}{r_{22} - r_{12}} \tag{12.34}$$

This is nearly equal to α, which is the current-amplification factor for transistors analogous to the voltage-amplification factor μ for vacuum tubes and is defined by

$$\alpha = -\left(\frac{\partial i_c}{\partial i_e}\right)_{v_c=\text{const}} = \frac{r_{21}}{r_{22}} \tag{12.35}$$

The relation between α and α_e is readily shown to be

$$\alpha_e = \alpha + (\alpha - 1)\frac{r_b}{r_c} \tag{12.36}$$

making α_e slightly different from α.

Some typical values of equivalent circuit constants for a junction

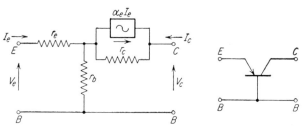

FIG. 12.13. Equivalent circuit of the transistor triode using a constant-current generator.

transistor are given below for the common-base-connection General Electric type 2N45 junction transistor $(p\text{-}n\text{-}p)$:

$r_{11} = 432$ ohms $r_e = r_{11} - r_{12} = 32$ ohms
$r_{12} = 400$ ohms $r_b = r_{12} = 400$ ohms
$r_{21} = 0.98 \times 10^6$ ohms $r_c = r_{22} - r_{12} = 10^6$ ohms
$r_{22} = 10^6$ ohms $r_m = r_{21} - r_{12} = 0.98 \times 10^6$ ohms

$\alpha = \dfrac{r_{21}}{r_{22}} = 0.98$ $\alpha_e = 0.98$

12.7. Hybrid Circuit Parameters. In some applications of transistors it is most convenient to use input current and output voltage as independent variables. This follows because the input, for the common-base connection, is commonly biased in the forward direction. As a result it is easier to adjust the operating point by setting input current rather than input voltage. The output is commonly biased in the reverse direction. As a result, it is easier to adjust the operating point by setting output voltage rather than output current. This makes the total-current-voltage functions assume the forms

$$v_1 = f_5(i_1, v_2) \tag{12.37}$$
$$i_2 = f_6(i_1, v_2) \tag{12.38}$$

which are to be compared with (12.1) to (12.4). The incremental, or small-alternating-signal, forms then become

$$V_1 = h_{11}I_1 + h_{12}V_2 \qquad (12.39)$$
$$I_2 = h_{21}I_1 + h_{22}V_2 \qquad (12.40)$$

in which the h coefficients are known as hybrid parameters.

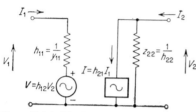

The relations of (12.39) and (12.40) may be represented by another simple equivalent circuit, as shown in Fig. 12.14. This is a two-branch two-generator circuit. The input branch has a single impedance and a constant-voltage generator in series as shown. The output branch has a single impedance and a constant-current generator in parallel as shown. This is another general form of circuit which may be used for tubes as well as for transistors.

FIG. 12.14. Equivalent circuit for the hybrid-parameter relations of (12.39) and (12.40).

The coefficients of (12.39) and (12.40) must be used with care because their dimensions are different. Thus h_{11} has the dimensions of impedance and h_{22} has the dimensions of admittance, whereas h_{12} and h_{21} are dimensionless. The above relations can be written in terms of previously developed concepts by recognizing that

$$h_{11} = \frac{1}{y_{11}} \qquad h_{12} = \mu_{12}$$

$$h_{21} = -\alpha \qquad h_{22} = \frac{1}{z_{22}} \qquad (12.41)$$

These relations are implicit in (12.39) and (12.40), as may be seen by allowing either I_1 or V_2 to be zero. Thus h_{11} is the input impedance when the output is shorted, and h_{22} is the output admittance when the input is open-circuited. The factor h_{21} is the negative of the normal forward-current-amplification factor. Likewise, the factor h_{12} is the negative of the reverse-voltage-amplification factor as used in tube studies.

There is nothing new about these hybrid parameters. They have been used in circuit analysis for a long time [Gup2]. The relations between the coefficients in the three systems so far discussed are readily obtained by straightforward algebraic operations. They are as follows:

$$h_{11} = \frac{|z|}{z_{22}} = \frac{1}{y_{11}}$$

$$h_{12} = \frac{z_{12}}{z_{22}} = -\frac{y_{12}}{y_{11}}$$

$$h_{21} = -\frac{z_{21}}{z_{22}} = \frac{y_{21}}{y_{11}} \qquad (12.42)$$

$$h_{22} = \frac{1}{z_{22}} = \frac{|y|}{y_{11}}$$

$$z_{11} = \frac{|h|}{h_{22}} = \frac{y_{22}}{|y|}$$

$$z_{12} = \frac{h_{12}}{h_{22}} = -\frac{y_{12}}{|y|}$$

$$z_{21} = -\frac{h_{21}}{h_{22}} = -\frac{y_{21}}{|y|} \tag{12.43}$$

$$z_{22} = \frac{1}{h_{22}} = \frac{y_{11}}{|y|}$$

$$y_{11} = \frac{1}{h_{11}} = \frac{z_{22}}{|z|}$$

$$y_{12} = -\frac{h_{12}}{h_{11}} = \frac{z_{12}}{|z|}$$

$$y_{21} = \frac{h_{21}}{h_{11}} = -\frac{z_{21}}{|z|} \tag{12.44}$$

$$y_{22} = \frac{|h|}{h_{11}} = \frac{z_{11}}{|z|}$$

where the quantity between verticals is the value, not the magnitude, of the determinant $|z| = z_{11}z_{22} - z_{12}z_{21} \cdots$. Other general relations are

$$\frac{h_{22}}{h_{11}} = |y| = |z|^{-1} \tag{12.45}$$

$$|h|^{-1} = \frac{y_{11}}{y_{22}} = \frac{z_{22}}{z_{11}} \tag{12.46}$$

The relations given above are more general than those usually given in circuit books because they apply for active circuits where reciprocity does not apply, that is, $z_{12} \neq z_{21}$, etc. There are given above the relations between only three out of five commonly used sets of coefficients. The relations between these five sets of coefficients are given in Appendix 11.

12.8. Dual Aspects of Tubes and Transistors. A comparison of the characteristics and equivalent circuits of tubes and transistors reveals some dual aspects. This is to say that there exists a similarity but in an inverse sense. Thus the vacuum tube is essentially a voltage amplifier, whereas the transistor is more of a current amplifier. The input circuit of a tube is normally biased in a reverse direction so that no current flows, whereas the input circuit of a transistor is normally biased in a forward direction so that current flows easily. On the other hand, the output circuit of a tube is normally biased in a forward direction, permitting current to flow easily, whereas in the transistor the output circuit is biased in a reverse direction so that only a small current flows. This results in a tube being a device with a high input impedance and a relatively low output impedance while the transistor is a device with a low input impedance and a relatively high output impedance. There is then an equivalence if current in one device is compared with voltage in the other and vice versa. This duality is to be taken in a general rather than a literal sense. Transistor characteristics are *not exactly* the dual of tube characteristics [WaA].

Duality is a subject well established in the field of circuit analysis [Gai, LeB, GuC]. A circuit whose current-voltage characteristics are the same as the voltage-current characteristics of another circuit is said to be its *dual*. The duality applies not only to electrical quantities but also to circuit elements, connections, and generators. The correspondence between the following quantities and their duals is apparent:

Quantity	*Dual*
Current	voltage
Resistance	conductance
Inductance	capacity
Mesh	node pair
Series connection	parallel connection
Constant-voltage source	constant-current source

It is easily established on the basis of the above relations, which work in either direction, that the dual of a series *RLC* circuit is a parallel connection of a resistance, a capacity, and an inductance. Further, if the ratio of the resistance in the first circuit to the conductance in the second circuit, the ratio of inductance in the first circuit to capacity in the second circuit, and the ratio of capacity in the first circuit to inductance in the second circuit are all equal, then the impedance of the first as a function of frequency will be the same as the admittance of the second as a function of frequency except for a constant factor.

According to the ideas of duality, the commonly used equivalent circuit for transistors of Fig. 12.12 is the dual of the general vacuum-tube equivalent circuit of Fig. 12.8. This comes about because of the general method of constructing the dual of a circuit. To do this, a node or connection point is placed inside each mesh of the given circuit, and an extra node, known as the datum node, is placed outside the circuit. The nodes are then connected by drawing through every element or generator

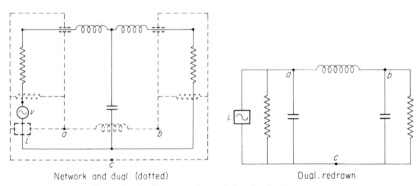

Network and dual (dotted)   Dual, redrawn

Fig. 12.15. Construction of the dual of a network.

in the given circuit a branch containing the dual of the element or generator thus traversed. This process is illustrated in Fig. 12.15. Here is
constructed the dual of the T section of a low-pass filter consisting of two
series inductances and a shunt capacity and having a resistance load as
its output and at its input a generator consisting of a constant-voltage
source, indicated by the circle, and a series resistance. Three nodes a,
b, and c are drawn. The nodes a and b are in the two meshes of the circuit, and the node c is the datum node outside. If we consider meshes as
identified by the areas outlined by the branches, there are actually three
meshes—two inside the network and one outside. The nodes are then
connected as indicated above and as indicated by the dashed circuit of
Fig. 12.15. When this is redrawn, it is seen to yield a low-pass section

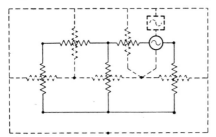 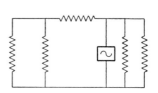

Network and dual (dotted) (see Fig. 12.12)   Dual redrawn (see Fig. 12.8)

FIG. 12.16. Construction showing the duality of transistor and vacuum-tube circuits.

having a resistance load at its output and a generator consisting of a
constant-current generator, indicated by the square, in parallel with a
resistance.

The process indicated above for finding the dual of a network works
only when the given network is a so-called *flat* network, i.e., one which
can be drawn on a plane or a sphere without any of the connections
crossing. This group of flat networks includes the majority of important
applications.

The manner in which the dual of Fig. 12.12 is constructed and shown
to be the circuit of Fig. 12.8 is shown in Fig. 12.16. The circuit configurations are potentially dual. The numerical values of the elements
must be properly adjusted for them to be truly dual. Tubes and transistors are dual only in the approximate sense. This is to say that, roughly
speaking, the current-voltage characteristics of one are about the same
as the voltage-current characteristics of the other.

12.9. Equivalent Circuits of Multiterminal Electron Devices. The
vacuum and transistor triode, as described above, are three-terminal
devices that are, however, used as four-terminal devices by the simple
expedient of allowing one terminal to be common to input and output.
These are then the so-called active quadripoles. In the case of vacuum
tubes there have long since been developed multielectrode tubes, such as

the pentode, which have significant advantages over the triode.   There have also been developed some transistor tetrodes, and more multi-electrode transistors may be expected.   In general these will correspond to multielectrode tubes and will be operated in the same general way.

Multielectrode tubes and transistors may perform operations more complex than amplification; but when used for amplification, they will be used in the same manner as triodes.   One electrode will be common to input and output.   Only three terminals will carry alternating currents. The others will be biased and bypassed so as to have constant voltage and current.

The static characteristics of multiterminal devices will, of course, be different from those of the vacuum triode, but the same four-terminal equivalent circuits can still be used.   Values of the self- and mutual-impedance factors will be different from device to device.   This means that a multielectrode tube, such as the pentode, when operated as a negative-grid amplifier, can be represented by the same equivalent circuit of Fig. 12.9 as is used for the triode.   Likewise, a four- or more terminal transistor used as an amplifier is capable of representation by the circuit of Fig. 12.12 or 12.13.

CHAPTER 13

SMALL-SIGNAL AMPLIFIERS
USING ELECTRON DEVICES

13.1. Introduction. The subject of this chapter is a very large one and embodies one of the major applications of electron devices. Here there can only be discussed principles of operation. Readers interested in a more extensive treatment leading to design should consult the various books devoted to this subject [Sea2, BoC, VaC]. A unified treatment of vacuum-tube and transistor amplifiers will, however, be attempted here.

The function of amplification is one in which the electron device holds an unchallenged position of superiority. It can give amplification of voltage, current, or power over larger ranges of these quantities and of frequency than any other device. However, mention should be made of other devices, often competitive, that can be used for amplification. These include the magnetic amplifier [GeD] and the dielectric amplifier [MaD]. These have almost the same range in voltage, current, and power as electron devices but are limited in frequency to about 10 kc or less. Another device is the Amplidyne, which is a sensitively controlled rotating-armature electric generator [FiB]. This device has small amplification but large power output and is limited to zero or very low frequencies. It is often used as a link between electronic systems and electromechanical systems requiring considerable power.

Amplifiers are of many types and admit of several classifications. A first, common classification originated with vacuum tubes, is related to their operating conditions, but is also applicable to transistors. It depends upon the no-signal operating point and the size of the input and output signals as follows:

1. *Class A Amplifier.* One in which the operating point is such that current flows over the entire cycle of operation. Signals are small enough so that the operation is linear. Vacuum-tube amplifiers are called Class A_1 if the grid is biased negatively, current flows for the entire cycle, and no grid current flows. If the grid swings positive, so that grid current flows for part of the cycle, the operation is called Class A_2. Such amplifiers are usually low-power or -voltage amplifiers and form the principal subject of this chapter. Theoretical maximum efficiency is 50 per cent.

2. *Class AB Amplifier.* One in which the voltage swings are large enough to get off the linear portion of the characteristics and the bias is such that the current flows less than a full cycle but more than a half cycle. Such operation requires the combination of two devices to reproduce a sine wave. With vacuum tubes, the subscript 1 is again used if the grid does not swing positive and the subscript 2 if it does. Theoretical maximum efficiency is between 50 and 78 per cent.

3. *Class B Amplifier.* One in which the input of the device is biased on the edge of current flow in the output circuit or to so-called cutoff. Voltage excursions are fairly large and result in output-current pulses which are nearly half sine waves. Two devices are needed to combine half waves of opposite polarity to produce a complete sine wave. Theoretical maximum efficiency is 78 per cent.

4. *Class C Amplifier.* One which is biased so that no output current flows in the absence of input signal. Voltage excursions are large, and the output current flows in pulses of less than a half-cycle duration. Theoretical maximum efficiency is 100 per cent.

Actual practical efficiencies in all types run about four-fifths of the theoretical maximum but may be approached more closely in special cases.

Figure 13.1 is a diagram showing the relation of the operation point and signal amplitude to the output current for an applied sinusoidal input current for the different types of amplifiers defined above.

Amplifiers may also be classified according to their function, such as (1) voltage amplifiers, (2) current amplifiers, (3) power amplifiers. Devices are likewise classified as to their suitability for operation in such amplifiers; the forms for the different functions require rather different designs.

A further classification is less definite but relates to frequency, circuit form, or method of operation. Thus there are encountered d-c, audio-frequency, video, radio-frequency amplifiers, on the one hand, and direct-coupled, transformer-coupled, tuned radio-frequency amplifiers, on the other.

Another aspect of the subject to be emphasized in this chapter is the relation between the various possible circuit connections. If an electron device is considered as a three-terminal device that can be connected between input and output terminal pairs, there are six different connections possible by using one terminal of the device common between input and output. This is shown schematically in Fig. 13.2. Vacuum tubes are specially designed for operation in one direction, i.e., with the plate always in the output circuit. This means that the most useful connections are of this form. This group includes the grounded-plate connections for vacuum tubes. The grounded-plate connection is more often referred to as the cathode follower because the potential of the cathode follows

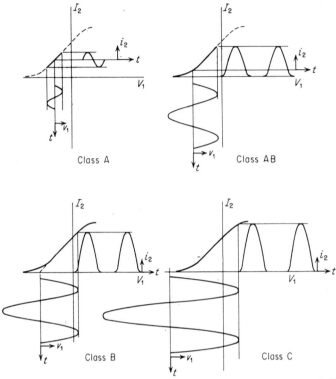

FIG. 13.1. Operating conditions and waveforms for Classes A, AB, B, and C amplifier operation.

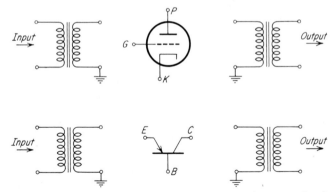

FIG. 13.2. Electron devices in relation to input and output circuits.

that of the grid. It is essentially a circuit that transforms impedance from a high to a low value with input and output voltage nearly equal. These circuits are shown in Fig. 13.3.

Only one of the reverse connections with vacuum tubes is at all used. This is the so-called inverted amplifier of Fig. 13.3*d*. It has a voltage gain of less than unity and is principally used for measurement or observation of voltages too large to be applied to instruments directly.   In Fig. 13.4 is shown a chart indicating the usefulness of the various connections for vacuum tubes.

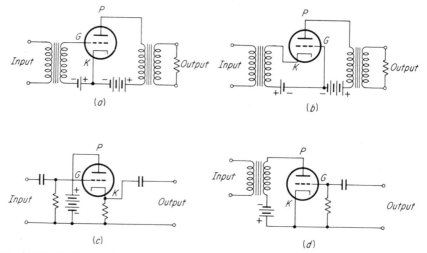

FIG. 13.3. Useful vacuum-tube connections: (a) Grounded cathode.   (b) Grounded grid.   (c) Grounded plate, or cathode follower.   (d) Inverted amplifier.

Transistors admit of more connection possibilities than vacuum tubes. In the case of the junction transistor, there is often a symmetry between emitter and collector which permits these terminals to be interchanged. As a result, the junction transistor may transmit in either direction. With point-contact transistors, it is found that, for current-amplification

	Input			
		K	G	P
Common ground	K	×	U	N
	G	U	×	S
	P	N	U	×

K = cathode
G = control grid
P = plate
X = not possible
U = useful
S = good for special application
N = not useful

	Input			
		E	B	C
Common ground	E	×	U	P
	B	U	×	P
	C	U	P	×

E = emitter
B = base
C = collector
X = not possible
U = useful
P = possible

FIG. 13.4. Connection chart for vacuum tubes.

FIG. 13.5. Connection chart for transistors.

factors greater than unity, the transistor may simultaneously transmit in the backward as well as the forward direction for the grounded-base and grounded-collector connections [RyB].   In Fig. 13.5 is shown a connection chart giving the various connection possibilities of transistors. Needless to say, the various connections exhibit substantially different characteristics.   This will be the subject of some of the following sections.

13.2. Separation of Alternating and Direct Components of Current and Voltage. In practical circuits for electron devices, it is usually necessary to separate direct and alternating components of current and voltage. This is because direct values of current and voltage are used to establish operating conditions but carry no information since they remain fixed. Information is carried on small alternating components superimposed on the direct values. Thus a tandem connection of similar units must be isolated for direct components since these are not amplified, whereas the alternating components are.

It is necessary at this point to certify a notation that distinguishes clearly between direct and alternating components and can be applied to *both* vacuum tubes and transistors. The notation used previously and in the rest of the book follows closely the standards recommended by the IRE [IrF] and conforms to the following plan:

1. Instantaneous varying-component values are indicated by lower-case letters with lower-case subscripts, for example, i_p.

2. Average, or direct, values are indicated by capital letters with capital subscripts, for example, V_B.

3. Rms or effective varying-component values are indicated by capital letters with lower-case subscripts, for example, I_e.

4. Instantaneous total values are indicated by lower-case letters with capital subscripts, for example, v_E.

5. Supply voltages are indicated by repeating the electrode subscript. The reference electrode may then be designated by the third subscript, for example, V_{EE}, V_{GGK}.

6. Alternating components of input and output voltages and currents are often indicated by subscripts 1 and 2. Positive current direction is assumed to be *into* the device. Positive voltage is *upward*, for example, V_1, I_2.

7. Electrode currents are usually indicated by single subscripts, associated with the electrode according to the notation

k, cathode	b, base
g, grid	e, emitter
p, plate	c, collector

8. Interelectrode voltages and currents may use a double subscript with a subscript sequence conforming to the mathematical convention for writing determinants from a set of fundamental Kirchhoff equations. The first subscript designates the electrode at which the current is measured or where the electrode potential is measured with respect to the reference electrode, or circuit node, designated by the second subscript. When the reference electrode or circuit node is understood, the second subscript may be omitted, where its use is not required to preserve the meaning of the symbol.

TABLE 13.1

		Symbol	
		i, v, p	*I, V, P*
Subscript	*k, b* *g, e* *p, c*	Instantaneous varying-component values	Rms or effective varying-component values
	K, B *G, E* *P, C*	Instantaneous total values	Average (d-c) values

9. The subscript s is used for signal or source values, l for load values.

10. Magnitudes are indicated by italic: E. Space vectors are indicated by boldface roman type: **E**. Complex numbers are indicated by boldface italic: ***E***.

The conventions of the first four points in the above list are conveniently summarized in Table 13.1.

Shown in Fig. 13.6a is a grounded-cathode vacuum-triode amplifier using capacitor coupling in both output and input circuits to separate alternating from direct components. All the direct currents and voltages are confined to the parts of the circuit between the capacitors C_1 and C_2. Shown in Fig. 13.6b is a grounded-base-transistor amplifier with a capacitor input coupling and a transformer output coupling to separate alternating and direct components.

In Fig. 13.6a is shown a means commonly used for obtaining negative grid bias. This is a resistance in the cathode. Current flowing through this resistance results in the cathode end of the resistor being at a higher potential than the grounded end connected to the grid. For this condition the grid will be negative with respect to the cathode, and there will be no current flow in the grid circuit. This is known as self-

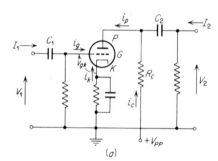

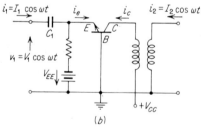

Fig. 13.6. Circuit diagram illustrating notation for electron devices: (a) $i_g = \sqrt{2}\,I_g \cos \omega t + I_G$; $v_g = \sqrt{2}\,V_g \cos \omega t + V_G$; $v_p = -\sqrt{2}\,V_p \cos \omega t + V_{PP}$; $V_P = V_{PP} - I_C R_c$; $v_{gK} = -V_K + V_1 \cos \omega t$. (b) $i_e = \sqrt{2}\,I_e \cos \omega t + I_E$; $i_c = -\sqrt{2}\,I_c \cos \omega t + I_C$; $v_{eb} = -V_{EE} + \sqrt{2}\,V_{eb} \cos \omega t$; $v_{cb} = V_{CC} - \sqrt{2}\,V_{cb} \cos \omega t$.

bias.   The biasing resistor is usually bypassed with a large capacitor so that the a-c impedance of the parallel combination is much lower than the resistance.

When pentodes are used, the effort is made to operate an entire amplifying stage off a single power supply.   This is done as in Fig. 13.7.   The positive terminal of the power supply is connected to ground.   Both the plate and the screen grid, which require considerable positive voltage, are connected to the power supply through voltage-dropping resistors. In the case of the plate the alternating voltage is developed across the resistor R_c, known as the coupling resistor.   In the case of the screen grid an alternating component of voltage is not desired, and the dropping resistor R_s is bypassed to the cath-

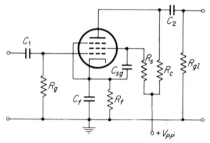

ode through the capacitor C_{sg}. The resistance R_s is used to keep the screen-grid direct voltage at or below that of the plate.   The suppressor grid, No. 3, is directly con-nected to the cathode.   Bias of the control grid, No. 1, is obtained through the parallel combination of R_f and C_f.   Input voltage is devel-oped across the voltage R_g since practically no grid current flows in

Fig. 13.7. Practical pentode amplifier circuit.

the negatively biased pentode.   Output voltage is developed across the parallel combination of R_c and R_{gl}, the latter being the so-called grid-leak resistance, usually several times the size of the former.   Coupling capacitors C_1 and C_2 are used to pass alternating currents but isolate against direct-voltage differences.

13.3. Units of Gain : the Decibel.   Before discussing amplification, it is desirable to define gain.   Gain is a measure of amplification expressed as a ratio of output power to signal input power.   Because of conversion of energy from other sources, this may be many times greater than unity. Gain is commonly expressed in logarithmic units to avoid the use of very large numbers.   The most commonly used logarithmic unit is the *decibel* (db), which is defined as

$$\text{No. of decibels} = 10 \log \frac{P_2}{P_1} \qquad (13.1)$$

where P_2 = output power
  P_1 = input power
Thus a power amplification of 100 is expressed as a gain of 20 db.   A power amplification of 2,000 is expressed as 33 db.   The decibel unit may also be used to express current and voltage ratios.   Since power varies as the square of voltage or current,

$$\text{No. of decibels} = 20 \log \frac{V_2}{V_1} \tag{13.2}$$

or

$$\text{No. of decibels} = 20 \log \frac{I_2}{I_1} \tag{13.3}$$

Thus a voltage amplification of 100 is a gain of 40 db. A current amplification of 2,000 is a gain of 66 db. This has the same significance as when taken with respect to power *only* when the input and output voltages and current are measured across or through *the same value of resistance.* Shown in Fig. 13.8 is a chart giving the number of decibels corresponding to a given power, voltage, or current ratio.

The decibel is one-tenth of an older unit known as the bel, which is simply the logarithm to the base 10 of the ratio of power levels. Thus a

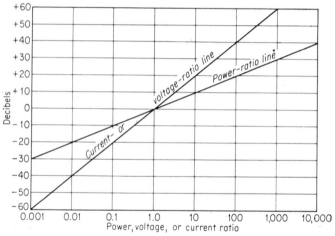

Fig. 13.8. Chart relating decibels and ratios of current, voltage, and power.

ratio of power levels of 100 corresponds to 2 bels or 20 db. The bel unit is too large for most purposes, and so the decibel is preferred. The logarithmic unit of power levels is more than merely convenient. Human sensory perceptions tend to be logarithmic according to the Weber-Fechner law, which says that the increment of stimulus needed to give a certain response is proportional to the level of the stimulus. Visual and aural responses are nearly perfectly logarithmic. A further justification for the use of the unit of the decibel is that it corresponds to the smallest detectable aural response. One decibel corresponds to a 26 per cent change in power level or a 12 per cent change in voltage or current level.

Another logarithmic unit of level is the neper. This was formerly used in telephone transmission engineering. The neper is given by

$$\text{No. of nepers} = \ln \frac{I_2}{I_1} \tag{13.4}$$

and is thus the natural logarithm of the ratio of currents. Because of the difference in definitions,

$$1 \text{ neper} = 8.68 \text{ db} \tag{13.5}$$

The above relation makes it possible to convert many relations involving the naperian base $\epsilon = 2.718$ to decibels.

It should be remembered that the decibel is a measure of *relative* power level rather than of absolute level. This is because it is determined by the logarithm of the *ratio* of powers. However, in many fields arbitrary reference power levels are assumed, making possible a power-level interpretation. In telephone work a zero level of 1 mw of power is used. This same level is also sometimes used for microwave-receiver signal levels. In radio systems a zero level of 6 mw is used. In acoustic measurements a zero level of 10^{-16} watt cm^{-2} is used.

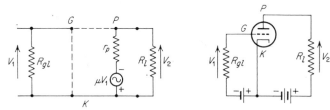

Fig. 13.9. Grounded-cathode vacuum-triode amplifier and equivalent circuit.

13.4. Grounded-cathode and Grounded-emitter Amplifiers.

The grounded-cathode connection is the vacuum-tube connection most extensively used. For that reason it will be discussed first. Because transistor grounded-emitter operation is very similar, it will be discussed at the same time. The amplification properties of these amplifiers are quite easily determined from their equivalent circuits as given in the previous chapters.

For negative-grid vacuum-tube amplifiers the equivalent circuits of Figs. 12.9 and 12.10 are used. If Fig. 12.10 is redrawn to include a load resistance R_l, as shown in Fig. 13.9, it is seen that there is a voltage amplification given by

$$\left| \frac{V_2}{V_1} \right| = \frac{I_2 R_l}{V_1} = -\frac{\mu R_l}{r_p + R_l} \tag{13.6}$$

This assumes that the frequency is low enough so that the currents between the grid and other electrodes through the interelectrode capacities are negligible. This will be true for audio frequencies and higher frequencies up to the order of 500 kc. The above equation shows two things: (1) There is a reversal of phase in the amplifier; (2) the voltage amplification is equal to the amplification factor of the tube multiplied by $R_l/(r_p + R_l)$, a factor which is always less than 1. Thus the voltage amplification is always less than the amplification factor of the tube. The reduction factor can be made larger by making R_l larger, but a practical limitation exists.   Usually the direct plate current flows through this resistor.   If it is made too large, the direct plate voltage is reduced with an attendant reduction of mutual conductance and an increase in plate resistance.   This latter increase rapidly becomes large enough to offset the increase in load.   In a typical triode-amplifier case a reduction factor of about two-thirds in (13.6) seems to be a practical upper limit. In a pentode amplifier a value of about one-tenth is an upper limit.

The vacuum-tube amplifier can also be analyzed in terms of the equivalent circuit of Fig. 12.9, as shown in Fig. 13.10.   Here, again neglecting currents through the interelectrode capacities, there is a constant-current

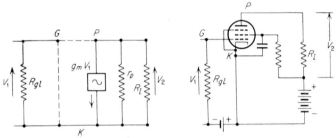

FIG. 13.10. Grounded-cathode vacuum-pentode amplifier and equivalent circuit.

generator of strength $g_m V_1$ putting current through the parallel combination of plate and load resistance.   This results in an output voltage

$$V_2 = - \frac{g_m r_p R_l}{r_p + R_l} V_1 \tag{13.7}$$

Here the current through the load resistor is $-g_m V_1 r_p/(r_p + R_l)$, which is multiplied by the load resistance R_l to give the output voltage.   Accordingly, the amplification is

$$\left| \frac{V_2}{V_1} \right| = - \frac{g_m r_p R_l}{r_p + R_l} \tag{13.8}$$

Noting that $g_m r_p = \mu$, we see this to be the same result as in (13.6). The above relation can be put into the form

$$\frac{V_2}{V_1} = - \frac{g_m r_l}{1 + (r_l/r_p)} \tag{13.9}$$

This form is particularly useful for pentodes, where the plate resistance is large compared to the load resistance.   Here it is seen that the amplification is $-g_m r_l$ divided by a factor slightly larger than 1.   The same formula can, of course, also be used for the triode except that the factor in the denominator will be of the order of 2 or 3 instead of slightly larger than 1.

Voltage gains of the order of 10 to 50 (20 to 34 db) result with vacumn triodes.   Voltage gains of the order of 50 to 300 (34 to 49 db) result with vacumn pentodes.   With small-signal voltage amplifiers having input signals of the order of a few tenths of a volt or less to which the above equivalent circuit considerations apply, it is preferable to speak of voltage rather than power amplification.   This is because the negative grid of a vacuum tube controls plate current by electrostatic action, with the result that the control, or input, power is negligible.   In an actual amplifier some power will be consumed in the grid-leak resistor, which serves to drain off any electrons hitting the negative grid to keep it from acquiring a negative charge.   However, this resistor is commonly of the order of 1 megohm in resistance so that even an input voltage of 1 volt corresponds to an input power of only 1 μw.   Yet such an input power may be sufficient to give output powers of the order of watts with some tubes, corresponding to power gain of the order of 60 db per stage.   This is an exceptionally high value of power amplification, which is not representative.   For voltage amplifiers, considering also the fact that the input and output resistances may be different, it is preferable to quote a decibel gain given by the voltage ratio but to bear in mind that the corresponding power amplification will not always apply.   When tubes are used to amplify powers of the order of a few tenths of a watt or more, then the power gain must be specified; and the gains will be of the order of 10 to 20 db per stage.

With transistors, on the other hand, power amplification must be considered, including the effect of different input and output resistances. For the grounded-emitter-transistor amplifier the circuit of Fig. 12.12 is convenient to use, although that of Fig. 12.13 will, of course, give the same answers.   In Fig. 12.12 it must be remembered that

$$r_m = r_{21} - r_{12} = \alpha(r_c + r_b) - r_b = r_b(\alpha - 1) + \alpha r_c$$

With the equivalent circuit of Fig. 12.12, which is redrawn to show a signal generator and load in Fig. 13.11, it is an easy matter to write two circuit mesh equations as follows:

$$I_1(R_s + r_b + r_e) + I_2 r_e = V_s \qquad (13.10)$$
$$I_1 r_e + I_2(R_l + r_c + r_e) - I_e r_m = V_l$$
or $\qquad I_1(r_e + r_m) + I_2(r_c + r_e + R_l + r_m) = V_l \qquad (13.11)$

since $I_e = -(I_1 + I_2)$.   Now to determine the power gain, it is necessary to determine the output power, which is $I_2^2 R_l$, and the input power, which is I_1^2 times the input resistance.   In the above equations are included both a signal voltage V_s and a voltage V_l in series with the output.   The former is used alone to calculate the forward gain, and the latter is used alone to calculate a possible backward gain.   Resistances are used instead of impedances in the equivalent circuit, which restricts

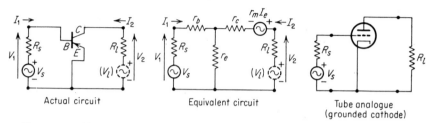

| Actual circuit | Equivalent circuit | Tube analogue (grounded cathode) |

FIG. 13.11. Characteristics of the grounded-emitter transistor-triode amplifier.

Circuit equations:
$$V_s = I_1(R_s + r_b + r_e) + I_2 r_e$$
$$V_l = I_1(r_e + r_m) + I_2(R_L + r_e + r_c + r_m)$$

Circuit determinant:
$$\Delta = (R_s + r_b + r_e)(R_l + r_e + r_c - r_m) + r_e(r_m - r_e)$$

Currents:
$$I_1 = \begin{vmatrix} V_s & r_e \\ V_l & r_e + r_c - r_m + R_l \end{vmatrix} \frac{1}{\Delta}$$

$$I_2 = \begin{vmatrix} R_s + r_b + r_e & V_s \\ r_e - r_m & V_l \end{vmatrix} \frac{1}{\Delta}$$

Input and output resistances:
$$R_{in} = r_b + r_e + \frac{r_e(r_m - r_c)}{r_e + r_c - r_m + R_l}$$

$$R_{out} = r_e + r_c - r_m + \frac{r_e(r_m - r_c)}{R_s + r_b + r_e}$$

Current gain:
$$\frac{I_2}{I_1} = \frac{r_m - r_e}{r_e + r_c - r_m + R_l} \cong \frac{\alpha}{1 - \alpha + R_l/r_c}$$

Voltage gain:
$$\frac{V_2}{V_1} = \frac{R_l(r_e - r_m)}{r_b(r_e + r_c - r_m + R_l) + r_e(r_c + R_l)} \cong \frac{-\alpha R_l}{r_e + (1 - \alpha)(r_b + R_s)}$$

Forward transducer gain:
$$G_F = \frac{4(r_m - r_e)^2 R_s R_l}{\Delta^2}$$

Reverse transducer gain:
$$G_R = \frac{4 r_e^2 R_s R_l}{\Delta^2}$$

Actual power gain:
$$G = \left(\frac{I_2}{I_1}\right)^2 \frac{R_l}{R_{in}} = \left|\frac{I_2 V_2}{I_1 V_1}\right|$$

Typical values:

Quantity	Junction	Point-contact
r_e, ohms.	25	150
r_b, ohms.	500	120
r_m, kilohms.	960	60
r_c, kilohms.	1,000	40
R_l, kilohms.	20	20
R_s, ohms.	500	0[1]
α.	0.96	1.5
R_{in}, ohms.	925	720
R_{out}, kilohms.	63.4	13.3
I_2/I_1.	16	3
V_2/V_1.	−346	−167
$\|I_2 V_2/I_1 V_1\|$.	5,520	500
	(or 37.4 db)	(or 27 db)

[1] To give maximum R_{out}.   Point-contact transistors tend to be unstable in this type of operation.

the results to low frequencies. For a more general treatment it is necessary to use impedances.

It is convenient in determining input and output power to have available an expression for the circuit determinant, which is the determinant appearing in the denominator of expressions for current. This is

$$\Delta = (R_s + r_b + r_e)(R_l + r_e + r_c - r_m) + r_e(r_m - r_e) \quad (13.12)$$

This expression must be greater than zero for stability since, if the value is zero or negative, oscillations may build up without applied voltages. However, the circuit may be unstable for other reasons even if the expression is positive, as will be seen; so this condition is necessary but not sufficient for stability. It is also convenient to have expressions available for input and output impedances at the transistor terminals with the generator at the other end always inactive. These are

$$R_{in} = r_b + r_e + \frac{r_e(r_m - r_c)}{R_l + r_e + r_c - r_m} \cong r_e + r_b(1 - \alpha) \quad (13.13)$$

for $R_l \ll r_c$. This is seen to be the resistance measured looking into the base-emitter terminals with the output generator inactive. It is equal to $V_s/I_1 - R_s$. Likewise,

$$R_{out} = r_c + r_e - r_m + \frac{r_e(r_m - r_c)}{R_s + r_b + r_e} = r_c \frac{r_e + r_b(1 - \alpha) + R_s}{r_e + r_b + R_s} \quad (13.14)$$

for $r_b \ll r_c$. This is the resistance looking into the collector-emitter terminals with the input generator inactive. It is equal to $V_l/I_2 - R_l$. The input resistance R_{in} is generally positive. The output resistance R_{out} is positive for junction transistors but may be negative for point-contact transistors.

It is customary to describe transistor power gain as a so-called *transducer gain*, which is defined as the ratio of the actual output power to the available power from the signal source. The *available* power from the signal source is that which it will transmit into a resistance equal to its own internal resistance R_s and is the *maximum* that a *given* signal source can deliver. It has a value

$$P_{sm} = \frac{V_s^2}{4R_s} \quad (13.15)$$

remembering that V_s is rms value. The output power is equal to the output current squared times the load resistance

$$P_{out} = \left(\frac{r_m - r_e}{\Delta}\right)^2 V_s^2 R_l \quad (13.16)$$

The ratio of these last two expressions gives the transducer gain in the forward direction as

$$G_F = 4R_s R_l \left(\frac{r_m - r_e}{\Delta}\right)^2 = \frac{4R_s R_l \alpha^2}{[r_c + R_s + r_b(1 - \alpha)]^2} \qquad (13.17)$$

for $R_l \ll r_c$.

The forward operating gain given above is not necessarily the highest that can be attained. The highest gain occurs when $R_l = R_{out}$ and when $R_s = R_{in}$. It should be borne in mind that the highest gain is not always desirable because this sometimes brings the circuit determinant near to a value of zero and thus the amplifier close to a condition of oscillation. A lower gain gives a larger value of the circuit determinant, farther from the value of zero, with higher associated stability.

Backward transducer gain is evaluated in a manner similar to that used in determining forward gain. It has a value

$$G_R = 4R_s R_l \left(\frac{r_e}{\Delta}\right)^2 \qquad (13.18)$$

This will usually be small compared to the forward gain.

An idea of the operation of transistors is best gotten by some examples. Typical values are given for Fig. 13.11 to show the comparative properties of the different circuit connections. Shown in the same figure is an analogous vacuum-tube circuit, a grounded-cathode circuit. By this analogue the cathode corresponds to the emitter, the grid to the base, and the plate to the collector. When α is close to unity, the analogy is fairly good in that the input impedance is comparatively high, the output impedance is higher, and there is a 180° reversal of phase on transmission.

The matter of stability in transistors is much more of a problem than with vacuum tubes. Transistor circuits will *always* be unstable if the circuit determinant is zero or negative. In addition, the circuit may be unstable if the input or output impedance has a negative-resistance component because then the net resistance may be negative. Circuits are not necessarily unstable if, for instance, the input resistance is negative. It is possible to have stable negative-resistance elements [LiC, Gif]. However, it is generally desirable to have the generator resistance larger than the magnitude of the input resistance if the latter is negative. Under these conditions, the circuit will not be unstable. In transistor circuits, the circuit determinant and the input and output resistances are sensitive functions of the generator and load resistances. So also are the power, voltage, and current gain. Accordingly, the effect of the source and load resistances upon the circuit determinant, the input, and the output resistances as well as upon the gain must be considered. Because of the complexity of the equations, this is best done by numerical computation. Generally, the source and load resistances chosen must be such as to give a compromise between stability and gain.[1]

13.5. Grounded-grid and Grounded-base Amplifiers. The grounded-grid vacuum-tube amplifier has characteristics substantially different from the grounded-cathode amplifier. It has a relatively low input impedance instead of a high one. It is a power rather than a voltage amplifier. It has no reversal of phase. It can be used to higher frequencies because the grid effectively acts as a shield between the input cathode connection and the output plate connection.

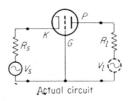

Actual circuit

To see how these characteristics come about, we need only look at the equivalent-circuit diagram with a grounded grid. Such a diagram, based on Fig. 12.10, is shown in Fig. 13.12. This is a simple series circuit with an input generator and an output generator shown. The equivalent of the cathode-plate circuit contains an internal generator whose emf is equal to the product of the μ of the tube and the cathode-grid voltage. The latter is equal to the negative of the input voltage.

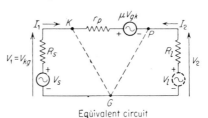

Equivalent circuit

Fig. 13.12. Grounded-grid vacuum-triode amplifier and equivalent circuit.

Considering that only the signal generator is active, the equations for this equivalent circuit are

$$V_s - \mu V_{gk} = I_1(R_s + R_p + R_l) \tag{13.19}$$
$$V_{kg} = - V_{gk} = V_s - I_1 R_s \tag{13.20}$$

Solving for V_{kg} and dividing by I_1, we find the input impedance

$$R_{in} = \frac{r_p + R_l}{1 + \mu} \tag{13.21}$$

This is seen to be a relatively small number.

The voltage gain is found from the ratio of the voltage drop across the load to the input voltage V_{kg}. This is

$$\frac{V_2}{V_1} = \frac{R_l(1 + \mu)}{r_p + R_l} \tag{13.22}$$

---

[1] See [StC1; GiC; CoC, pt. IX; ShB2] for a more detailed treatment of the various transistor-amplifier circuits.

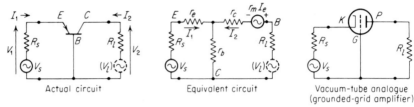

Fig. 13.13. Characteristics of the grounded-base transistor-triode amplifier.

Circuit equations:
$$V_s = I_1(R_s + r_b + r_e) + I_2 r_b$$
$$V_l = I_1(r_b + r_m) + I_2(r_b + r_c + R_l)$$

Circuit determinant: $\Delta = (R_s + r_e + r_b)(r_b + r_c + R_l) - r_b(r_b + r_m)$

Currents:
$$I_1 = \begin{vmatrix} V_s & r_b \\ V_l & r_b + r_c + R_l \end{vmatrix} \frac{1}{\Delta}$$
$$I_2 = \begin{vmatrix} R_s + r_e + r_b & V_s \\ r_m + r_b & V_l \end{vmatrix} \frac{1}{\Delta}$$

Input and output resistances:
$$R_{in} = r_e + r_b - \frac{r_b(r_m + r_b)}{r_b + r_c + R_l} = r_e + r_b(1 - \alpha)$$
$$R_{out} = r_b + r_c - \frac{r_b(r_b + r_m)}{R_s + r_e + r_b}$$

Current gain:
$$\frac{I_2}{I_1} = -\frac{r_m + r_b}{r_b + r_c + R_l} = -\frac{\alpha}{1 + R_l/(r_c + r_b)}$$

Voltage gain:
$$\frac{V_2}{V_1} = \frac{(r_m + r_b)R_l}{r_e(r_b + r_c + R_l) + r_b(r_c - r_m + R_l)} = \frac{\alpha R_l}{r_e + R_s + r_b(1 - \alpha)}$$

Forward transducer gain:
$$G_F = \frac{4(r_m + r_b)^2 R_s R_l}{\Delta^2}$$

Reverse transducer gain:
$$G_R = \frac{4r_b^2 R_s R_l}{\Delta^2}$$

Actual power gain:
$$G = \left(\frac{I_2}{I_1}\right)^2 \frac{R_l}{R_{in}} = \left|\frac{I_2 V_2}{I_1 V_1}\right|$$

Typical values:

Quantity	Junction	Point-contact
r_e, ohms	25	150
r_b, ohms	500	120
r_m, kilohms	960	35
r_c, kilohms	1,000	15
R_s, ohms	500	500
R_l, kilohms	20	20
α	0.96	2.3
R_{in}, ohms	25	150
R_{out}, kilohms	532	9.66
I_2/I_1	−0.94	−1.0
V_2/V_1	346	133
G	325	133
	(or 25.1 db)	(or 21.24 db)
G_F	114	160
G_R	3.0×10^{-6}	1.9×10^{-6}

which is almost the same as for the grounded-cathode tube except that there is no reversal of phase. In practical cases the voltage amplification will be about half of the tube amplification factor.

The fact that the ground-grid amplifier has such a low input impedance means that it takes considerable power to drive the tube. Accordingly, the power amplification has more significance than the voltage amplification in this case. Since the input and output current are the same in magnitude, the power amplification is simply the load resistance divided by the input resistance given in (13.21):

$$G_p = \frac{R_l}{R_{in}} = \frac{R_l(1 + \mu)}{r_p + R_l} \tag{13.23}$$

which, interestingly enough, has the same value as the voltage amplification. Note that one can take only the decibel measure of the power gain because the input and output impedances are not equal. The expression for the actual gain above is simpler in this case than the expression for the transducer gain previously defined.

To find the output impedance, consider only the output generator active. It follows that the impedance looking back into the grid-plate terminals is

$$R_{out} = r_p + R_s(1 + \mu) \tag{13.24}$$

This will generally be several times the plate resistance.

The grounded-base-transistor amplifier has many characteristics similar to those of the grounded-grid amplifier. The equivalent circuit in this case is based on Fig. 12.12 and is shown in Fig. 13.13. Here also are the expressions for the various operating parameters. The grounded-base-transistor amplifier is characterized by the same properties possessed by the grounded-grid amplifier, namely, low input impedance, high output impedance, and no reversal of phase on amplification. In this case both the input and output resistances are positive for high and low values of α, and the other characteristics are likewise stable.

The grounded-base connection is particularly prone to instability because of a negative value of the circuit determinant if the value of either α or R_b is too large. This is because of an inherent regenerative effect through the base resistor common to input and output. Thus the larger α, the smaller the value of R_b that will give instability. It is particularly important not to use external resistance in the base lead. Increased values of source and load resistances generally improve the stability at the price of a reduction in gain.

13.6. Grounded-plate and Grounded-collector Amplifiers. The grounded-plate vacuum-tube amplifier is called the *cathode follower*. This is because the potential of the cathode follows very closely the potential of the grid. The circuit has a high input impedance, a low output impedance, and a voltage gain of nearly unity without reversal of phase. These properties are easily shown with reference to the equivalent circuit of Fig. 13.14.

Reference to the output current in the equivalent circuit of the cathode follower shows that

$$I_2(r_p + R_l) = -\mu V_{gk} \tag{13.25}$$

Summing voltages around the outside of the network,

$$-V_{gk} = I_2 R_l + V_s \tag{13.26}$$

since the current in the grid circuit is zero for Class A operation. Combining these last two equations,

$$\frac{V_2}{V_1} = -\frac{I_2 R_l}{V_s} = \frac{R_l}{r_p + R_l(1 + \mu)} \tag{13.27}$$

which is more simply written as

$$\frac{V_2}{V_1} = \frac{1}{1 + 1/\mu + 1/g_m R_l} \cong 1 \tag{13.28}$$

which shows that the gain is slightly less than unity without a reversal of phase. The value of the cathode resistance R_l is not at all critical if only it is not too large or small relative to the plate resistance. If the value is too small, then the current increases strongly and the voltage ratio rises in accordance with the formula because of the increase in g_m. If it is too large, the current falls strongly, causing a drop in the amplification factor, and the voltage ratio drops.

The input impedance at frequencies low enough so that currents through the interelectrode capacities are negligible will be very high, of the order of megohms. The output impedance must be determined

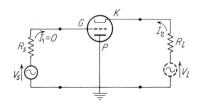

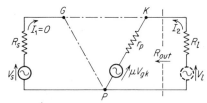

FIG. 13.14. Grounded-plate (cathode-follower) vacuum-triode amplifier and equivalent circuit.

by circuit analysis but will be rather low, of the order of $1/g_m$ of the tube. Reference to Fig. 13.14 shows that with the input generator V_s inactive the output generator will create a current

$$I_2 = \frac{V_l - V_{gk}}{r_p + R_l} \tag{13.29}$$

But
$$V_{gk} = I_2 R_l - V_l \tag{13.30}$$

Substituting and solving for R_{out},

$$R_{out} = \frac{V_l}{I_2} - R_l = \frac{r_p}{1 + \mu} \cong \frac{1}{g_m} \qquad (13.31)$$

Numerically, this may be as low as 20 ohms for a g_m of 50,000 μa volt^{-1}. Again the operating values are critical only to the extent to which they affect the direct plate current and hence the mutual conductance.

Consideration of (13.31) and (13.28) shows that the vacuum-tube cathode follower has the property of transforming impedance from a high input value to a low output value while at the same time preserving a 1:1 voltage ratio. This is a combination of characteristics that is not attainable with a passive network [Reg].

The situation with the grounded-collector transistor is decidedly more complicated but still subject to analysis by standard methods based upon the circuit equations derived from the equivalent network. Figure 13.15 presents the actual and equivalent circuit along with the basic equations and relations. Also given are some typical values.

The characteristics of the grounded-collector connection are dependent upon the value of the current-amplification factor α. When $\alpha \leqq 1$, the characteristics are quite similar to the grounded-plate electron tube. For this condition the transistor circuit has a high input impedance and a low output impedance without a change in polarity. The circuit will also give a fairly large gain in the reverse direction. If, however, $\alpha > 1$, then again the circuit amplifies in both directions and gain in the reverse direction may be greater than in the forward direction. Also the input and output impedances become negative, introducing a problem of stability. In any event the voltage gain is always a little less than unity [StC2].

13.7. Circuit Influence on Frequency Response. Previous discussion of amplifiers has been limited to cases in which circuit reactances play a negligible role. Actually the equations given will apply in all cases if the circuit resistances are replaced by impedances. In actual physical cases the frequency response is always limited by circuit or device reactances. At low frequencies transformers and coupling capacitors lose their effectiveness. At high frequencies distributed capacities and device interelectrode capacities shunt the circuit with low reactances limiting the gain. Further interest in the subject arises from the fact that electron-device amplifiers have as one of their principal abilities that of producing a prescribed frequency response.

A complete discussion of this subject is not possible in a book of this type. However, it forms the principal theme of a number of well-known textbooks. Here there can only be pointed out some general principles illustrated in a few special cases. A complete discussion includes the case of internal coupling between input and output or feedback. This

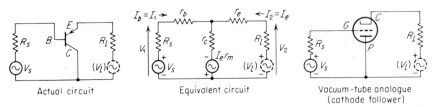

FIG. 13.15. Characteristics of the grounded-collector transistor-triode amplifier.

Circuit equations:
$$V_s = I_1(R_s + r_b + r_c) + I_2(r_c - r_m)$$
$$V_l = I_1 r_c + I_2(R_l + r_e + r_c - r_m)$$

Circuit determinant: $\Delta = (R_s + r_b + r_c)(R_l + r_e + r_c - r_m) - r_c(r_c - r_m)$

Currents:
$$I_1 = \begin{vmatrix} R_s + r_b + r_c & V_s \\ r_c & V_l \end{vmatrix} \frac{1}{\Delta}$$

$$I_2 = \begin{vmatrix} V_s & r_c - r_m \\ V_l & R_L + r_e + r_c - r_m \end{vmatrix} \frac{1}{\Delta}$$

Input and output resistances:
$$R_{in} = r_b + r_c + \frac{r_c(r_m - r_c)}{R_l + r_e + r_c - r_m} = r_b + \frac{r_c}{1 + (1 - \alpha)(r_c + r_b)/(R_l + r_e)}$$
$$R_{out} = r_c - r_m + r_e + \frac{r_c(r_m - r_c)}{R_s + r_b + r_c} = r_e + \frac{(1 - \alpha)(r_c + r_b)}{1 + r_c/(R_s + r_b)}$$

Current gain:
$$\frac{I_2}{I_1} = -\frac{r_c}{R_l + r_e + r_c - r_m} \cong \frac{1}{1 + [(r_b + R_s)/R_l](1 - \alpha)}$$
$$\frac{V_2}{V_1} = \frac{r_c R_l}{r_b(R_l + r_e + r_c - r_m) + r_c(r_e + R_l)} \cong 1$$

Forward transducer gain:
$$G_F = \frac{4R_s R_l r_c^2}{\Delta^2}$$

Reverse transducer gain: $G_R = \dfrac{4R_s R_l (r_m - r_c)^2}{\Delta^2} = (1 - \alpha)^2 G_F$

Actual power gain:
$$G = \left(\frac{I_2}{I_1}\right)^2 \frac{R_l}{R_{in}} = \left|\frac{I_2 V_2}{I_1 V_1}\right|$$

Quantity	Junction	Point-contact
r_e, ohms..............	25	150
r_b, ohms..............	500	120
r_m, kilohms...........	960	35
r_c, kilohms...........	1,000	15
R_s, ohms..............	500	0[1]
R_l, kilohms...........	10	30
α......................	0.96	2.3
R_{in}, kilohms...........	200	45
R_{out}, ohms.............	65	50
I_2/I_1..................	−20	−1.5
V_2/V_1.................	0.996	0.998
G......................	20	1.5
	(or 13 db)	(or 1.76 db)

[1] R_{out} is negative for all but very small R_s. Point-contact transistors tend to be unstable in this connection.

will be the subject of the next section. This section will be concerned only with the effect of coupling circuits working in combination with electron devices that are assumed to have characteristics independent of frequency.

If the frequency-sensitive circuit elements exist only between electron devices as a coupling circuit, then it is generally possible to develop a

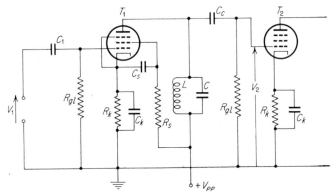

Fig. 13.16. Circuit of a simple tuned radio-frequency pentode amplifier.

simple approximate equivalent circuit which readily gives the frequency response. The approximations are usually the key to the understanding and design of the circuit because a detailed consideration of the interaction of all elements usually leads to great complications. This is best illustrated in the case of some simple vacuum-tube amplifiers, although the same considerations will apply to transistor amplifiers.

A first simple example is that of an amplifier which is desired to pass a narrow band of frequency. Such an amplifier in its simplest form may have the circuit of Fig. 13.16.

The essential features of this amplifier are two pentodes T_1 and T_2 and a parallel resonant LC circuit shunted across the connection between the tubes. These essential elements for the alternating components of current and voltage are

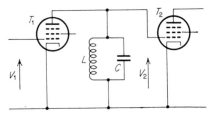

Fig. 13.17. Schematic circuit of tuned radio-frequency amplifier.

shown in Fig. 13.17. The other elements in Fig. 13.16 are for the purpose of separating alternating and direct components and for applying the proper direct voltages to the tubes. These other elements have little influence on the frequency response of the amplifier.

The control grid of the first tube is connected to the cathode through resistors R_{gl} and R_k. The plate current of the first tube flows through R_k, of the order of a few thousand ohms, which causes the cathode to be a few volts positive to ground. The control grid is connected to ground through R_{gl}, through which virtually no direct current flows. Hence the control grid is negative with respect to cathode, as is required for Class A operation. The resistance R_{gl} is known as the grid-leak resistance. This is because it is a high resistance, of the order of half a megohm, that permits accumulated charge from any electrons hitting the grid to leak off. If the grid-leak resistance were omitted, the grid would gradually build up a negative charge, which would finally cut off the plate current.

The capacity C_1 applies the input alternating voltage V_1 to the control grid without disturbing the d-c bias. It is necessary that the reactance of the capacitor C_1 be low compared to the resistance of R_{gl}. In this manner the voltage between control grid and ground will be only slightly less than the input voltage V_1.

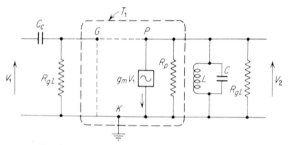

Fig. 13.18. Equivalent circuit of tuned radio-frequency amplifier.

The capacitor C_k serves to pass alternating components of current around the resistor R_k, which develops the control-grid bias. Its reactance must be small compared to R_k. The capacitor C_s between cathode and screen grid prevents the screen grid from developing an alternating voltage across the resistor R_s, which limits the screen-grid voltage. The capacitor C_c serves to apply to the control grid of tube T_2 the alternating component of voltage developed across the LC circuit while preventing the large positive direct voltage on the plate of T_1 from also being applied. The grid-leak resistance and cathode-bias elements with the second tube serve the same function as for the first tube.

An equivalent circuit for small alternating components, based on Fig. 12.9, is shown in Fig. 13.18. The elements corresponding to T_1 itself are enclosed by a dashed line. It is assumed that the cathode resistor is perfectly bypassed. In this form the input voltage V_{gk} to the tube T_1 is substantially equal to V_1. The essential circuit then consists of the constant-current generator putting out a current proportional to the input voltage into a parallel combination of the LC circuit and the plate and grid-leak resistance. It is again assumed that the reactance of C_c is small compared to R_g over the frequency range of interest.

It is well known that the impedance of a parallel combination of inductance and capacity has the shape of a resonance curve. The existence of resistors in parallel with this will reduce the Q, or sharpness, of resonance but not change the character of the curve. The voltage developed across this circuit will then be the product of the injected current $g_m V_1$ and the impedance $\mathbf{Z}_p$.

$$V_2 = g_m \mathbf{Z}_p V_1 \qquad (13.32)$$

where $\mathbf{Z}_p$ is the impedance of the parallel combination of L, C, r_p, and R_{gl} as a function of frequency. The ratio V_2/V_1 will then have the amplitude and phase characteristics shown in Fig. 13.19. This figure shows some universal characteristics derived from the theory of parallel resonant circuits for large Q. The magnitude of the gain is seen to follow a resonance

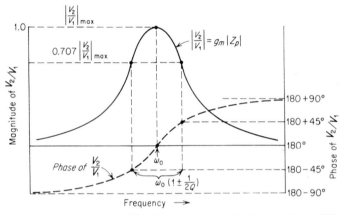

FIG. 13.19. Universal amplification characteristic of a tuned amplifier.

curve. The phase increases over a range of 180°, having a resonant frequency value of 180°. The incremental frequency between the 70.7 per cent points is $1/Q$ times the resonant frequency, and the phase shift at these points is $\pm 45°$ relative to the phase shift at resonance. Another representation of the voltage-amplification characteristics of this amplifier is Fig. 13.20, which shows the vector locus of voltage amplification as a circle with a maximum value of $g_m Z_{res}$, where Z_{res} is the impedance of the equivalent parallel resonant circuit at resonance. Gain is given by the vector from the origin to a point on the circle determined by the frequency scale as shown. The phase shift at resonance is seen to be 180°. The 45° departures from resonance correspond to 70.7 per cent of maximum gain.

Another example that may be used to show circuit influence on resonant frequency is the well-known R-coupled amplifier designed to give uniform amplification over a wide band of frequencies. Such a circuit is shown in

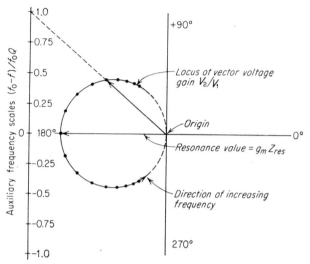

Fig. 13.20. Vector locus of amplification of a tuned radio-frequency amplifier.

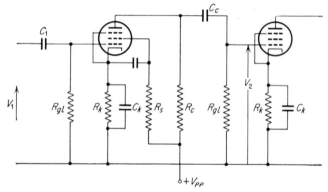

Fig. 13.21. Practical circuit of a two-stage RC-coupled pentode amplifier.

Fig. 13.21.   This circuit contains a large number of elements serving to separate direct and alternating components of current and voltage.   The essential elements determining the frequency response and gain are shown in Fig. 13.22.   Shown dotted here are some interelectrode and distributed capacities important at high frequencies.   It is also necessary to include the coupling capacity C_c, which is important at low frequencies.   In the middle of the

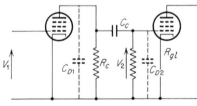

Fig. 13.22. Schematic circuit of a two-stage RC-coupled pentode amplifier.

frequency band the distributed and interelectrode capacities can be omitted and the coupling capacity can be considered as a short circuit.

These considerations lead to the equivalent circuit of Fig. 13.23. The capacities and the resistances are of such size that at mid-band frequencies the switch s_1 can be considered closed and the switches s_2 considered open. This yields a simplified equivalent-circuit diagram valid for mid-frequencies, as shown in Fig. 13.24b. This is simply a constant-current

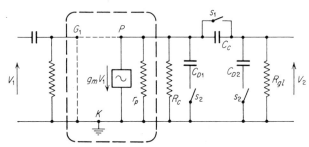

FIG. 13.23. General equivalent circuit of a two-stage RC-coupled tube amplifier. All switches are open at low frequencies and are closed at high frequencies. At mid-frequencies s_1 is closed, s_2 are open.

generator working into a parallel combination of r_p, R_c, and R_{gl}. The corresponding voltage gain is approximately

$$\frac{V_2}{V_1} = g_m R_1 \tag{13.33}$$

where $1/R_1 = G_1 = g_p + G_c + G_{gl}$, that is, R_1 is the value of r_p, R_c, and R_{gl} in parallel.

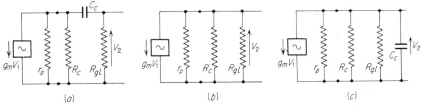

FIG. 13.24. Approximate equivalent circuits for RC-coupled tube amplifier for various frequency ranges: (a) for low frequencies, (b) for mid-frequencies, (c) for high frequencies.

At low frequencies the switches in Fig. 13.23 may all be considered open. This is because the reactances of the distributed capacities are so small that they have no effect, but the reactance of the coupling capacitor is so large that it must be considered. The resulting approximate equivalent circuit for low frequencies is shown in Fig. 13.24a. For this circuit the voltage gain will be

$$\frac{V_2}{V_1} \cong - \frac{g_m R_1}{1 - j(f_1/f)} \tag{13.34}$$

where R_1 = resistance of parallel combination of three resistances involved

f_1 = frequency at which reactance of C_c equals resistance of R_{gl} in series with parallel combination of r_p and R_c

This is complex gain, including magnitude and phase. The minus sign takes care of the 180° phase shift at mid-frequency. For frequencies below f_1 the phase shift tends toward a relative 90° lead, and the amplification is proportional to frequency. For frequencies above f_1 the amplification and phase shift approach the mid-band value [Ted].

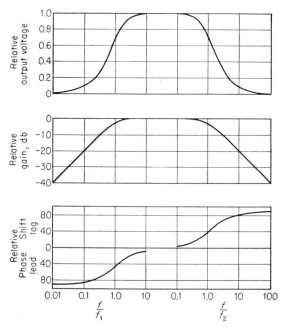

Fig. 13.25. Universal voltage-gain characteristics of an RC-coupled amplifier.

At high frequencies the switches in Fig. 13.23 may all be considered closed. This is because the reactance of the coupling capacitor will be so low as to constitute a near short, but the reactance of the shunting capacities cannot be neglected. The resulting approximate equivalent circuit for high frequencies is shown in Fig. 13.24c. For this circuit the complex voltage gain will be

$$\frac{V_2}{V_1} = -\frac{g_m R_1}{1 + j(f/f_2)} \tag{13.35}$$

where f_2 is the frequency at which the reactance of all the shunting capacity is equal to the resistance of the parallel combination of r_p, R_c, and R_{gl}, namely, R_1. The minus sign again takes care of the 180° phase shift at mid-frequencies. When f equals f_2, the gain is 70.7 per cent of the mid-frequency value and the phase shift lags the mid-frequency phase shift by 45°. For frequencies above f_2 the voltage gain tends to vary inversely with frequency, and the relative phase shift approaches 90° lag. For frequencies below f_2 the gain and phase shifts tend toward the mid-frequency value. The over-all characteristics are shown in Fig. 13.25 [Ted].

Shown in Fig. 13.26 is the vector locus of voltage gain for this case. This is seen to be a circle of diameter $g_m R_1$. Gain is the vector from the origin to the circle as determined by the frequency scales. Two frequency scales are needed in this case. The first is for low frequencies in terms of f_1. The second is for high frequencies in terms of f_2. It should be noted that the phase progression with frequency is in the opposite direction to that in Fig. 13.20.

Using the properties given above it is easy to make RC-coupled amplifiers having voltage gains up to 45 db and covering the audio range from 40 to 15,000 cycles sec^{-1} [Raa]. Also intimated above is a general property of coupling networks. It was found that when the voltage amplification varies inversely with frequency, i.e., 6 db per octave, the relative phase shift will be constant at 90° lag. In general when the amplification falls at a uniform rate

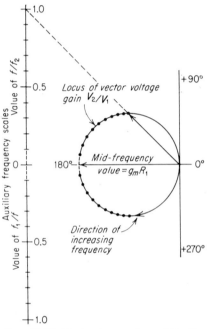

FIG. 13.26. Vector locus of amplification of a RC-coupled amplifier.

of k db per octave, the relative phase shift will be constant at $15k°$ of lag. For voltage amplification increasing with frequency, the same relation will hold with the relative phase shift leading.

Transistor-amplifier circuits can be handled in the same manner as for the vacuum-tube-amplifier examples given above. It must be borne in mind that transistor equivalent circuits will be resistive only to about 1 Mc, whereas vacuum-tube equivalent circuits are resistive to about 10 Mc.

13.8. Feedback Principles. Reference has already been made to a regenerative action in some transistor circuits that increases gain but reduces stability. This is a particular type of action known as feedback, which occurs when a part of the output voltage of an amplifier is introduced into the input. Such feedback action will be termed positive, or direct, when the portion of the output voltage fed back is in such phase as to increase the input voltage. When this is the case, the gain is increased but the other characteristics of the amplifier are made worse. When the phase of the feedback voltage is such as to reduce the input voltage, the feedback is said to be negative, or inverse (degenerative action), and the gain of the amplifier is reduced but other characteristics, such as stability, distortion, freedom from noise, are improved. Negative feedback is now extensively used to improve amplifier characteristics at the expense of a reduction in gain [Blg, Bof]. Feedback principles apply not only to electronic amplifiers but also to servomechanism types of control, biological, and economic systems.

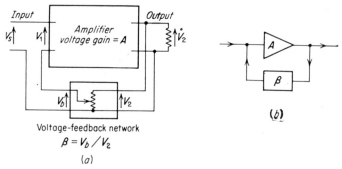

FIG. 13.27. Schematic circuit of an amplifier with voltage feedback.

A schematic diagram of a feedback amplifier is shown in Fig. 13.27. The double-line form of part (a) is more revealing than the single-line form of part (b), although both are extensively used. Let the complex voltage amplification of the amplifier be A and the complex transmission of the feedback network be β. Then

$$\frac{V_2}{V_1} = A \tag{13.36}$$

but

$$V_1 = V_s + \beta V_2 \tag{13.37}$$

Then

$$A_f = \frac{V_2}{V_s} = \frac{V_2}{V_1 - \beta V_2} = \frac{A}{1 - A\beta} \tag{13.38}$$

where A_f = complex voltage gain with feedback
  A = complex voltage gain without feedback
  β = complex transmission of feedback network

This means simply that all the factors include magnitude and phase and are to be treated as complex numbers. The sign convention is such that when the feedback voltage opposes the input voltage, β is negative. As a result, for amplifiers with negative feedback, the denominator of (13.38) will normally be positive.

Understanding of the above equations is improved by reference to a simple numerical example. Let the factor $A\beta$ have a value of $-10 = 10\underline{/180°}$, corresponding to a moderate amount of negative feedback. Let this be the result of a value of A of 100 and a value of β of $-\frac{1}{10}$. Then for a 1-mv value of V_1 at the internal-amplifier input there will be an output of 100 mv and a feedback voltage of -10 mv. Accordingly the value of input signal V_s must be 11 mv to produce 1 mv at the grid of the first tube. Accordingly the voltage gain with feedback is $V_2/V_s = \frac{100}{11} = 9.09$, compared to a voltage gain of 100 without feedback.

The above reduction in gain is compensated for by a corresponding increase in stability. Under the conditions of the last paragraph, if the voltage gain without feedback drops from 100 to 90, then by (13.38)

$$A_f = \frac{90}{1 + 9} = 9.00$$

This shows that a 10 per cent drop in the voltage gain in the internal amplifier without feedback (from 100 to 90) causes only a 1 per cent drop (from 9.09 to 9.00) in the amplifier with feedback. For larger feedback factors the effect is even more pronounced. The cited drop in internal gain may have been the result of tube aging, voltage variation, or change of some component value. Negative feedback is thus seen to reduce greatly variations in amplifier performance. Correspondingly, positive feedback increases amplifier instability. More generally it can be shown by differentiation that amplifier stability is modified by

$$\frac{\Delta A_f/A_f}{\Delta A/A} = \frac{1}{1 - A\beta} \tag{13.39}$$

Nonlinear distortion is also reduced by negative feedback. Such distortion produces harmonic components, which can be represented by a generator with a distortion-component output D in the output circuit. The amount of this voltage fed back to the input is βd, where d is the resultant distortion with feedback. This amount is amplified to combine with the internal distortion to give

$$d = D + A\beta d \tag{13.40}$$

or

$$\frac{d}{D} = \frac{1}{1 - A\beta} \tag{13.41}$$

Thus distortion is reduced by the same factor by which gain is reduced and by which stability is improved. In the case cited above, distortion is reduced by a factor of 11. Generally, then, negative feedback will make amplifier characteristics much more linear.

If there is some noise generated internally within an amplifier without feedback, this noise will be amplified and appear in the output. If now a feedback circuit is closed, this component of output noise will be reduced by the factor $1 - A\beta$. So, however, is also any signal component present. As a consequence, signal/noise ratios are not greatly reduced by feedback [Vac]. Signal/noise ratios are, however, altered by other effects of feedback. These include principally the alteration of the input impedance and bandwidth, which will control the noise admitted at the input and affect the signal/noise ratio. Other effects include noise introduced in the feedback resistors themselves and the way in which various types of noise combine. In general, each problem of feedback involving noise must be studied individually with the general expectation that improvement of noise characteristics by feedback will not be great.

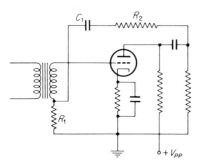

Fig. 13.28. Simple one-stage amplifier using negative voltage feedback.

In spite of its many advantages, feedback is not without its problems. The principal problem in using feedback is that of achieving stability over the complete frequency range. If the phase of $A\beta$ should become zero and the magnitude unity, then the quantity $1 - A\beta$ in the denominator of (13.38) will become zero and the amplification with feedback will become infinite; this will cause oscillation at the frequency for which $A\beta = 1$. Oscillations will also generally occur if $A\beta$ is greater than unity. To understand how this comes about, it is helpful to examine some specific circuits and the behavior of the $A\beta$ factor.

Shown in Fig. 13.28 is a single-stage amplifier with negative feedback. The feedback is supplied over the elements C_1 and R_2. The capacity C_1

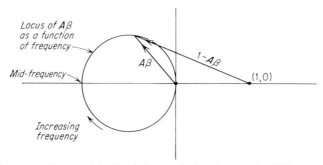

Fig. 13.29. Locus of feedback factor $A\beta$ for the circuit of Fig. 13.28.

is an isolating capacitor and is large enough so that its reactance is negligible. Accordingly, the feedback factor β is simply $R_1/(R_1 + R_2)$. The factor β is a scalar rather than a phasor here because the input and output voltages across the resistance divider are in phase. This is negative feedback because of the 180° phase shift through the tube and the fact that the voltage fed back is not reversed in phase. Although the feedback factor β is essentially constant, the amplification factor A will undergo the variation with frequency indicated in Fig. 13.26. As a result, a diagram showing the variation of the complex value of $A\beta$ with frequency will have the form shown in Fig. 13.29. Here we see illustrated a circular locus for the phasor $A\beta$ and the associated phasor $1 - A\beta$ for a particular frequency. Such a diagram is known as a Nyquist diagram after H. Nyquist, who proposed a general criterion for stability, to be discussed later [Nys]. In this case, it is evident that the phasor $1 - A\beta$ can never be equal to zero, and hence the circuit is stable and cannot oscillate.

The circuit of Fig. 13.28 makes use of what is known as *voltage feedback*. This name is given because the feedback circuit applies to the input a voltage proportional to the voltage across the output. Figure 13.30 shows a simple single-stage amplifier with *current feedback*. Here the feedback is supplied through the unbypassed cathode resistor. This is current feedback because there is introduced into the input circuit a voltage proportional to the current in the output circuit. The feedback factor in

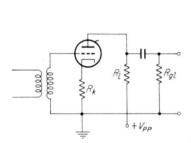

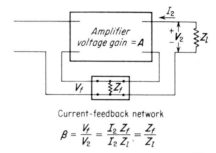

Current-feedback network

$$\beta = \frac{V_f}{V_2} = \frac{I_2 Z_f}{I_2 Z_l} = \frac{Z_f}{Z_l}$$

FIG. 13.30. One-stage amplifier with internal negative current feedback.

FIG. 13.31. Schematic circuit of amplifier with current feedback.

this case is R_k/R_2, where R_2 is the value of R_l and R_{gl} in parallel. This ratio is of such a size that the amplification with this kind of feedback is about one-third of the amplification with the cathode resistor bypassed. This gives a simple means of introducing a small amount of feedback with no attendant stability problems. The general method of introducing current feedback is shown schematically in Fig. 13.31. Combinations of positive and negative feedback may also be used.

A two-stage RC-coupled amplifier with negative voltage feedback is shown in Fig. 13.32. The feedback factor here is again $R_1/(R_1 + R_2)$ when the reactance of C_1 is low compared to the sum of R_1 and R_2. The feedback to be negative must be introduced into the cathode circuit of the first stage. If the feedback voltage is introduced into the grid circuit, as in Fig. 13.28, the feedback will be positive because of the additional 180° phase shift introduced by the second stage. With the circuit of Fig. 13.32 the circuit is stable, although a regenerative tendency shows itself at high and low frequencies. This is seen in the Nyquist diagram of Fig. 13.33. Here the $A\beta$ polar diagram has a cardioidlike shape because the phase of this factor may be as much as 180° more or less than the mid-frequency value. This comes about because each coupling circuit may introduce $\pm 90°$. Here it is seen that at high and low frequencies the value of $1 - A\beta$ may be less than unity, i.e., the $A\beta$ contour lies within the circle of unit radius about the point $(1,0)$, shown dotted. When

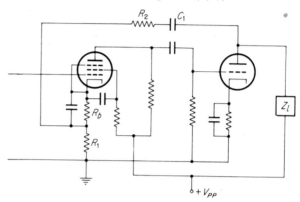

FIG. 13.32. Two-stage amplifier with negative voltage feedback.

this happens, the feedback is positive and the voltage amplification with feedback will be greater than without, as shown in Fig. 13.34. This shows that feedback may be positive over part of the frequency range though negative over the major portion of the range. This circuit is still stable because the value of $1 - A\beta$ cannot be zero, although it may be less than unity at the ends of the frequency band.

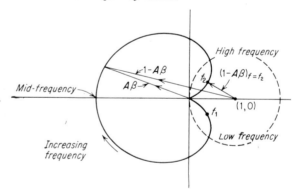

FIG. 13.33. Locus of feedback factor $A\beta$ for the circuit of Fig. 13.32.

Shown in Fig. 13.35 are some Nyquist diagrams for an amplifier of three *identical* RC-coupled-amplifier stages with negative feedback (at mid-frequencies) for small and large values of β. Here the phase shift may be $\pm 270°$ relative to that at mid-frequency. For small values of β, as shown by the solid contour, the value of $1 - A\beta$ cannot equal zero, i.e., the point $(1,0)$ lies outside the contour. As a result, the circuit is stable, although the feedback will be positive at high and low frequencies.

For larger values of β, as shown by the dotted contour, the $A\beta$ contour may pass through or enclose the point (1,0). If the contour passes through the point (1,0), the value of $1 - A\beta$ will be zero and the circuit will oscillate at a frequency corresponding to this condition. Nyquist has shown that, if the contour includes the point (1,0), oscillations will build up and, because of the nonlinear tube characteristics, the internal amplification will decrease, causing the contour to shrink until it passes through the point (1,0), resulting in a steady amplitude and frequency of oscillation corresponding to a point of intersection. *The Nyquist criterion for stability then is that the $A\beta$ contour shall not include the point (1,0).*

Those readers familiar with the theory of electric-circuit transients can understand the Nyquist criterion for stability by considering that

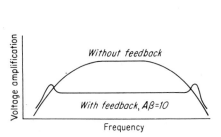

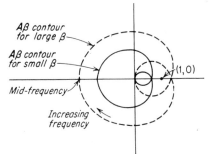

FIG. 13.34. Voltage-amplification characteristic of the circuit of Fig. 13.32 with and without feedback.

FIG. 13.35. Nyquist diagram of an amplifier of three identical RC-coupled stages for small and large values of feedback factor.

the $A\beta$ contour is a transformed frequency axis. In transient problems the imaginary axis of the complex-impedance plane is commonly taken as the frequency axis with frequency increasing from bottom to top. Terms in the denominator of the expression for impedance that have the possibility of going to zero for complex values of frequency correspond to parallel resonances. If the point for which the denominator goes to zero lies to the left of the frequency axis, then transients are damped sine waves. If the point lies on the frequency axis, the transient is an undamped sine wave corresponding to steady oscillation. If the point lies to the right of the frequency axis, the transients are exponentially growing sine waves. The same will apply to the Nyquist diagram. The point (1,0) corresponds to an incipient oscillation. If the point lies outside the $A\beta$ contour (to the left of the transformed frequency axis), transients will be damped sine waves giving ultimate stability. If the point (1,0) lies within the $A\beta$ contour, the transients will be growing sine waves, which will finally come to a condition of stable oscillation.

A three-stage RC-coupled amplifier may be made stable by making two of the stages identical with a moderate-frequency band and high gain and the third with a large-frequency band and a low gain [Ted]. The relative phase shift then will be less than 180°, owing to negligible contribution from the wide-band stage, until frequencies such that the amplification has dropped to a value low enough to ensure a value of $1 - A\beta$ less than unity. The control of the $A\beta$ contour to avoid inclusion of the point (1,0) is the major problem of feedback-amplifier design [Bof].

A final aspect of feedback is its influence on input and output impedance of amplifiers. Where voltage feedback is used, the effect of the feedback is to make the output voltage for a given signal input more constant with variations in output impedance. This improves the output regulation of the amplifier and gives the effect of a reduced effective output impedance. The output impedance is generally reduced by the factor $1 - A\beta$. Where current feedback is used, the effect of the feedback is to make the output current more constant. This has the effect of increasing the output impedance [Mal]. Input impedance of amplifiers may also be affected by feedback, although the effects are more difficult to generalize upon. It has already been observed that the input impedance of transistor amplifiers may be negative under certain conditions.

Thus it is seen that feedback may be used to stabilize amplifiers, the price paid being a reduction of gain. Frequency characteristics may be improved, distortion reduced, and output impedance controlled in a desirable fashion. Conditions for over-all stability are, however, more complex and must be studied with care.

13.9. High-frequency Effects in Vacuum Tubes. Previous discussions of electron devices have ignored interelectrode capacities and transit-time effects. In vacuum-tube amplifiers, this can be done without error up to frequencies of about 0.1 Mc. However, in the range of 0.1 to 10 Mc, interelectrode capacities make an observable difference in the tube behavior and must be included in the equivalent circuit. From about 10 to 150 Mc, electron transit time affects the input admittance of tubes. Fortunately, the effect can be accounted for by the addition of a single resistance to the equivalent circuit. For frequencies above 150 Mc, different equivalent circuits must be used to describe the tube behavior.

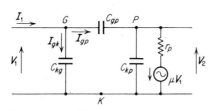

FIG. 13.36. Equivalent circuit of a grounded-cathode vacuum-tube amplifier including interelectrode capacities. This circuit is useful in the range of 0.1 to 10 Mc.

High-frequency Effects in Vacuum Tubes: 1 to 10 Mc. The equivalent circuit of a grounded-cathode vacuum tube at high frequencies, including the interelectrode capacities, is shown in Fig. 13.36. The input current will consist of two components, one through each of the two capacities having the grid as a common terminal. It has the value

$$I_1 = V_1 Y_{gk} + (V_1 - V_2) Y_{gp} \qquad (13.42)$$

where V_1, V_2 = input and output voltage, respectively
$\qquad Y_{gk}$ = admittance of grid-cathode capacity
$\qquad Y_{gp}$ = admittance of grid-plate capacity
The input admittance is the quotient I_1/V_1,

$$Y_1 = Y_{gk} + Y_{gp}(1 - A/\theta) \qquad (13.43)$$

where $A/\theta = +V_2/V_1$ is the complex gain of the amplifier. It is considered that the phase in the middle of the operating band is 180°, as indicated by the positive sign, and that θ is the phase departure from this condition. Thus $-90° < \theta < +90°$. It is apparent that the input admittance is that of an equivalent capacity

$$C_1 = C_{gk} + C_{gp}(1 + A \cos \theta) \qquad (13.44)$$

in parallel with a conductance

$$G_1 = -\omega C_{gp} A \sin \theta \qquad (13.45)$$

From the first of the above two equations, it is seen that the input capacity of the tube in operation is increased by the grid-plate capacity multiplied by $1 + A \cos \theta$. This comes about because the phase of the output voltage relative to the input encourages an additional reactive current component to flow into the input of the tube. The increase will be between 1 and $1 + A$ times the grid-plate capacity of the tube and may double or triple the cold input capacity.

In addition, Eq. (13.45) shows an input conductance which may be positive or negative depending upon the phase angle θ. For capacitive loads, the angle θ is negative and the input conductance is positive. This means that some power is required to drive the tube. For inductive loads, the angle θ is positive and the input conductance is negative. This means that the tube may supply power to the driving source with the attendant possibility of instability. The above variations in input impedance due to input-output coupling through the grid-plate capacity are known as the Miller effect.

In the case of vacuum tubes, the interelectrode capacities have a principal effect on the input admittance. Because of the negative-conductance component of this which may exist, the amplifier may oscillate if the effect is large enough. For this reason, radio-frequency triode amplifiers as sometimes used in broadcast transmitters must be neutralized, i.e., provided with some compensating feedback to prevent oscillation. Interelectrode capacities have a secondary influence on voltage

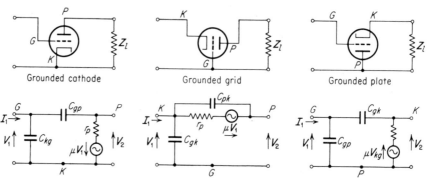

FIG. 13.37. Equivalent circuits for vacuum-tube amplifiers for frequencies in the range of 0.1 to 10.0 Mc.

Grounded-cathode amplifier:

Voltage gain

$$\frac{V_2}{V_1} = A = -\frac{\mu Z_l}{r_p + Z_l} \qquad (A \text{ negative when real; } C_{gp} \text{ neglected})$$

Input admittance

$$Y_{in} = \frac{I_1}{V_1} = j\omega C_{gk} + j\omega C_{gp}(1 - A) \qquad (Z_L \text{ includes } C_{pk})$$

Grounded-grid amplifier:

Voltage gain

$$\frac{V_2}{V_1} = A = \frac{(1 + \mu)Z_l}{r_p + Z_l} \qquad (A \text{ positive when real; } C_{pk} \text{ neglected})$$

Input admittance

$$Y_{in} = j\omega C_{gk} + j\omega C_{pk}(1 - A) + \frac{1 + \mu}{r_p + Z_l} \qquad (Z_l \text{ includes } C_{gp})$$

Grounded-plate amplifier (cathode follower):

Voltage gain

$$\frac{V_2}{V_1} = A = \frac{\mu Z_l}{r_p + (1 + \mu)Z_l} \qquad (A \text{ positive when real; } C_{gk} \text{ neglected})$$

Input admittance

$$Y_{in} = j\omega C_{gp} + j\omega C_{gk}(1 - A) \qquad (Z_l \text{ includes } C_{pk})$$

gain, though this is usually small. Output impedance is relatively unaffected, since the load impedance level is usually low.

Other amplifier circuits, such as the grounded grid and grounded plate, may be treated by the same method, as indicated above. Shown in Fig. 13.37 are expressions for the voltage amplification and input admittance of the three amplifier connections possible. The grounded-grid circuit will have its input capacity increased and admits of a negative conductance as does the grounded-cathode circuit. The grounded-plate (cathode-follower) circuit has the same characteristic. Any of these circuits then admits of negative input conductances with the possibility of attendant instabilities at high frequencies.

High-frequency Effects in Vacuum Tubes: 10 to 150 Mc. As frequencies are increased from high to very high, two additional effects must be considered beyond currents through the interelectrode capacities. The first of these is that there will be introduced a conductive component of input admittance due to feedback through the cathode-lead inductance. This conductance increases approximately as frequency squared. The second effect is due to electron transit times between cathode and grid plane and also introduces a conductive component of input admittance, which increases with frequency squared.

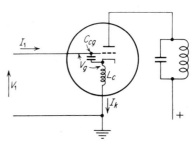

FIG. 13.38. Equivalent circuit, showing feedback effect due to cathode-lead inductance in the triode at very high frequencies.

The Miller effect described above is most pronounced in triodes, where the grid-plate capacity is high. In pentodes, the effect is much smaller. In consequence, as frequency is raised, the Miller effect will predominate in triodes but the effects described above will begin to dominate in pentodes only at higher frequencies.

The cathode-lead inductance effect can be understood by reference to Fig. 13.38. The effect described results from the following assumptions:

$$V_1 = V_g + j\omega L_c I_k \tag{13.46}$$
$$I_k = g_m V_g \tag{13.47}$$
$$V_g = \frac{I_1}{j\omega C_{cg}} \tag{13.48}$$

Combining,

$$Y_{in} = \frac{I_1}{V_1} = \frac{j\omega C_{cg}}{1 + j\omega L_c g_m} \cong j\omega C_{cg}(1 - j\omega L_c g_m) \tag{13.49}$$

The first term of the input admittance will be recognized as the normal capacitive susceptance of the tube. The second term is a real positive term representing a conductive component of input admittance and having the value

$$G_L = \omega^2 L_c C_{cg} g_m \tag{13.50}$$

The input conductance of (13.50) corresponds to a resistance that varies inversely with frequency squared in parallel with the input capacity. This resistance represents a power input increasing as the square of the frequency for a given magnitude of driving voltage. This driving power is simply transmitted to the plate circuit.

In addition to the input conductance due to cathode-inductance feedback, there is a component of input conductance due to electron-transit-time effects, which also increases as the square of the frequency [Spc]. This comes about because the grid voltage releases a sinusoidal cathode current, which in turn induces a grid charge sinusoidal with time. Because of the finite transit time of the electrons, the grid charge

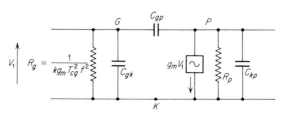

FIG. 13.39. Equivalent circuit for a vacuum tube at very high frequency, showing interelectrode capacities and input conductance due to transit-time loading.

will lag the grid voltage slightly in phase. As a result, the grid current will fail, by a small angle, to lead the grid voltage by 90°. The small component of grid current in phase with the grid voltage corresponds to a component of input conductance of the form

$$G_g = kg_m T_{cg}^2 f^2 \qquad (13.51)$$

where k = constant, of the order of 4
$\quad g_m$ = mutual conductance
$\quad T_{cg}$ = cathode-grid transit time
$\quad f$ = frequency

This is seen to be similar to the component of (13.50) due to cathode-lead inductance but will usually be larger. An equivalent circuit is then simply that of Fig. 13.36 but with a resistance shunted across the input (which varies inversely with frequency squared), as shown in Fig. 13.39. The circuit of Fig. 13.39 shows a constant-current generator in the plate circuit, as indicated by a square, whereas that of Fig. 13.36 shows a constant-voltage generator, as indicated by a circle.

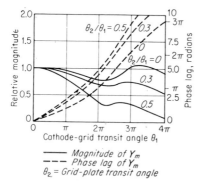

FIG. 13.40. Components of complex mutual conductance at very high frequencies as a function of frequency. (From Donald R. Hamilton, Julian K. Knipp, and J. B. Horner Kuper, "Klystrons and Microwave Triodes," McGraw-Hill Book Company, Inc., New York, 1948.)

High-frequency Effects in Vacuum Tubes: Above 150 Mc. At even higher frequencies still more elements are required in the equivalent circuit. The principal effect encountered here is that the mutual conductance becomes complex. As frequency increases, it tends to decrease in magnitude and acquire an increasing negative phase angle, as shown in

Fig. 13.40. The transit angles shown are simply ω times the transit times. With these values of complex mutual admittance, it is possible to use the circuit of Fig. 13.39 by including an additional resistance in parallel with C_{cp} and allowing for the high-frequency value of R_p [Pec]. It is also possible to use the T section of Fig. 13.41 [Llg] to represent triodes at very high frequencies. This representation, though superseded by the one just described, is interesting in that it resembles commonly used equivalent circuits for transistors. Here Y_m is complex mutual admittance

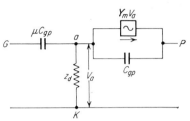

Fig. 13.41. Equivalent circuit of a triode at very high and ultrahigh frequencies. (*After Llewellyn and Peterson.*)

as given by Fig. 13.40. The point a is presumed to be a point in the electron stream midway between grid wires. The potential V_a is

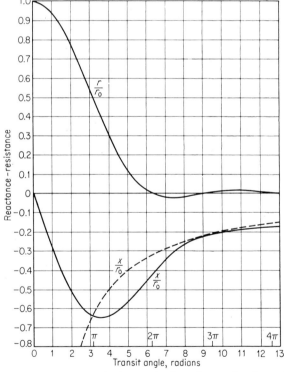

Fig. 13.42. Components of the equivalent series impedance of a plane-electrode diode, considering space charge and finite electron transit time. (*After Llewellyn.*)

given by a generalized expression for the equivalent grid-plane potential similar to that quoted in Appendix 9, i.e., (A9.2). The impedance z_d is a generalized expression for diode impedance between the cathode and the equivalent grid plane, as shown in Fig. 13.42 [Lll]. Here are shown series resistance and reactance components of diode impedance, considering space charge and finite transit time normalized against the zero transit-time value of dynamic diode resistance. The resistance component is seen to drop rapidly with transit time, even becoming slightly negative. The reactance is capacitive, rising at first and then falling somewhat like a constant capacity (shown dashed). To a first approximation, the diode impedance approximates a resistance in series with a capacity that is three-fifths of the cold capacity for small transit times.

13.10. High-frequency Effects in Transistors. Transistors suffer reduction in amplification at much lower frequencies than tubes, and hence the subject is one of paramount importance because the extension of the frequency range is almost always a problem. Among the factors to be considered are the following:

1. Refinements in low-frequency concepts, including widening of the space-charge layer at the collector junction and variation of α with emission current
2. Transit time and attendant recombination effects
3. Collector-junction capacity
4. External base resistance, including the effect of the three-dimensional geometry
5. Surface effects, including leakage and recombination

These topics will now be discussed briefly in the above order.

There is always a space-charge-depletion layer at transistor junctions, as discussed in connection with Fig. 7.24. The depletion layer at the emitter-base junction is normally thin because the emitter is usually biased in the forward direction. The depletion layer at the base-collector junction will, however, normally be thick because the collector is usually biased in the reverse direction. Further, the layer becomes thicker as the reverse bias is made greater. This effectively reduces the thickness of the base layer as the collector is biased more strongly in the reverse direction. As a result, the concentration gradient of the emitter minority carriers in the base is increased, permitting more of the base majority carriers to collect at the emitter-base junction and thus be propelled back into the emitter. (There must be a majority-carrier gradient equal to the minority-carrier gradient to maintain space-charge neutrality.) The over-all result is that there is a second-order effect of collector voltage on emitter current in the direction of increasing the emitter current slightly as the collector is biased more strongly in the reverse direction [EaC, EaD].

Another effect relates to the magnitude of the injected current from the emitter to the base.   The principal effect here is an increase in the base conductivity that decreases the emitter efficiency and increases recombination in the base.   These effects tend to reduce α as the emitter current is increased, except at very small emitter currents, where surface recombination leads to an opposite effect [WeD].

Transit-time effects become important at relatively low frequencies. Since the emitter majority carriers diffuse slowly across the base, many do not succeed in getting across in the time of one cycle as frequency is increased.   As a result, they are slowed down as the density gradient in the base is reduced on the low-emitter-voltage portion of the cycle, and more are lost by recombination.   There is also a phase lag, which develops for those carriers which do succeed in getting to the collector. An analysis of this effect along the lines of previous discussion shows that the β factor of the $\alpha = \beta\gamma$ relation follows the law

$$\beta = \operatorname{sech} BF = \frac{1}{\cosh BF} \tag{13.52}$$

where B is a dimensionless base-thickness factor

$$B = \frac{w}{L_b} \tag{13.53}$$

and F is a complex time factor

$$F = (1 + j\omega\tau_b)^{\frac{1}{2}} \tag{13.54}$$

Here, as before, w is the base thickness, L_b is the mean recombination distance of the base minority carriers in the base, τ_b is the mean recombination time of the base minority carriers in the base, and ω is radian frequency [StB, PrB, Shb, GiD2].   The above equations take into account transit time for space-charge layer widening and recombination effects but not the others listed at the beginning of the section.   The emitter efficiency γ is given by (11.40) and is independent of frequency. Hence the frequency variation of α is entirely contained in the transport factor β.

Equation (13.52) will be seen to reduce to (11.38) at low frequencies, as it should.   The general form of (13.52) is hard to work with since it involves the hyperbolic secant of the square root of a complex number.   A fair approximation to (13.52) has the simple form

$$\beta \cong \frac{\beta_0}{1 + j(\omega/\omega_a)} \tag{13.55}$$

where β_0 is given by (11.38) or (11.39) and ω_a is a reference frequency called the α cutoff frequency, given by

$$\omega_a \cong \frac{2L_b^2}{w^2\tau_b} = \frac{2D_b}{w^2} \tag{13.56}$$

since $L_b^2 = D_b \tau_b$, where D_b is the diffusion constant of the base minority carriers (emitter majority carriers) in the base.[1]   The α cutoff frequency is seen to vary inversely as the square of the base thickness.   For p-n-p germanium transistors, the α cutoff frequency is about 2.5 Mc for a base thickness of 1 mil.   For n-p-n germanium transistors, the α cutoff frequency is about 5.6 Mc for a base thickness of 1 mil [PrB].

The approximation (13.55) will be recognized as being similar to that encountered with RC-coupled vacuum-tube amplifiers, as given in (13.35). As a result, the same sort of falling off of amplification with frequency is

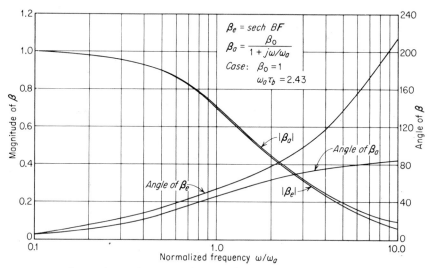

Fig. 13.43. Comparison of exact and approximate values of transport factor as a function of frequency, as obtained from (13.52) and (13.55).

expected with transistor amplifiers as with vacuum-tube amplifiers but for a different reason.   Actually, the approximation (13.55) may not be good enough for some purposes because it predicts a phase lag of 45° when the magnitude of β has dropped to 70.7 per cent of the low-frequency value, whereas the exact function of (13.52) predicts a phase lag of 58°. Where values more accurate than those given by (13.55) are desired, it is necessary to evaluate the exact form of (13.52), which can be done because the hyperbolic secant is the reciprocal of the hyperbolic cosine and the hyperbolic cosine of a complex number is given by

$$\cosh (a + jb) = \cosh a \cos b + j \sinh a \sin b \qquad (13.57)$$

(See [EvF].)   A comparison of values obtained from (13.52) and (13.55) is shown in Fig. 13.43.   Examination of this figure shows that the magni-

---

[1] Equation (13.56) gives the first approximation for ω_a.   A more accurate value is $\omega_a = 2.43[1 + 0.469(w/L_b)^2]D_b/w^2$.   This tends to be 25 per cent higher than the value given in the text above [HaD].

tude of β is well approximated out to the cutoff frequency. The approximate value of phase is consistently low, being 22 per cent low at the cutoff frequency and still lower beyond.

Owing to the same transit-time effects as above, other elements in the equivalent circuit of a transistor, as given in Fig. 12.12 or 12.13, also experience variation with frequency. The coefficients of (12.9) and (12.10) have the approximate form

$$\mathbf{y}_{11} \cong g_{11} \frac{1 + j\omega/\omega_a}{1 + j\omega/3\omega_a} \tag{13.58}$$

$$\mathbf{y}_{12} \cong - \frac{g_{22}}{1 + j\omega/3\omega_a} \tag{13.59}$$

$$\mathbf{y}_{21} \cong - \frac{g_{11}}{1 + j\omega/3\omega_a} \tag{13.60}$$

$$\mathbf{y}_{22} \cong g_{22} \frac{1 + j\omega/\omega_a}{1 + j\omega/3\omega_a} \tag{13.61}$$

where
$$g_{11} = \frac{e}{kT} \gamma I_E$$

$$g_{22} = \frac{\gamma}{w} \left| \frac{\partial w}{\partial V_C} \right| I_E = \frac{\gamma}{w} \frac{x_m}{2V_C} I_E$$

ω_a is given by (13.56), w is effective base width, $\partial w/\partial V_C$ is the rate of variation of effective base width with collector voltage, x_m is space-charge-depletion-layer width, I_E is emitter current, and γ is emitter efficiency, as given by (11.40) [EaC].[1] The factors $\mathbf{y}_{11}$ and $\mathbf{y}_{22}$ are seen to grow in magnitude with frequency and acquire a positive angle. The factors $\mathbf{y}_{12}$ and $\mathbf{y}_{21}$ are seen to decrease in magnitude with frequency and acquire a negative angle.

The effects encountered here are best understood by reference to an example:

Example. Given a germanium *p-n-p* transistor for which

$$D_n = 93 \text{ cm}^2 \text{ sec}^{-1} \qquad L_n = 0.1523 \text{ cm}$$
$$D_p = 44 \text{ cm}^2 \text{ sec}^{-1} \qquad L_p = 0.1 \text{ cm}$$
$$w = 1 \text{ mil} = 0.00254 \text{ cm}$$

where the subscript *n* applies for electrons in the *p*-type emitter region and the subscript *p* applies for holes in the *n*-type base region

$$\tau_n = \frac{L_n^2}{D_n} = 252.5 \ \mu\text{sec}$$

$$\tau_p = \frac{L_p^2}{D_p} = 227 \ \mu\text{sec}$$

[1] More exact expressions are given in terms of hyperbolic functions as

$\mathbf{y}_{11} = g_{11}BF/\tanh \ BF, \ \mathbf{y}_{12} = -g_{22}BF/\sinh \ BF, \ \mathbf{y}_{21} = -g_{11}BF/\sinh \ BF, \ \mathbf{y}_{22} = g_{22}(BF)/\tanh \ BF$

See [EaC, StD, MiE].

$$\omega_a = \frac{2D_p}{w^2} = 16.6 \times 10^6$$

$$f_a = \frac{\omega_a}{2\pi} = 2.64 \text{ Mc}$$

$$F = \sqrt{1 + j\omega_a \tau_p} = 43.3 + j43.3$$

$$B = \frac{w}{L_p} = 2.54 \times 10^{-2} \qquad BF = 1.102 + 1.102$$

Let $\gamma = 0.992$, $I_E = 1 \text{ ma} = 10^{-3} \text{ amp.}$

$$\left|\frac{\partial w}{\partial V_C}\right| = 2 \times 10^{-5} \text{ cm volt}^{-1}$$

$$g_{11} = \frac{e}{kT}\gamma I_E = 38.4 \times 10^{-3} \text{ mho}$$

$$g_{22} = \frac{\gamma}{w}\left|\frac{\partial w}{\partial V_C}\right| I_E = 7.82 \times 10^{-6} \text{ mho}$$

$$\beta_0 = \frac{1}{1 + \frac{1}{2}(w/L_p)^2} \cong 1.000$$

Then for $\omega = \omega_a$, that is, at the α cutoff frequency,

$$y_{11} = g_{11}\frac{1 + j\omega/\omega_a}{(1 + j\omega/3\omega_a)} = (46.2 + j23.1) \times 10^{-3} \text{ mho}$$
$$= 1.342 g_{11} \underline{/26.6°}$$

$$y_{22} = g_{22}\frac{1 + j\omega/\omega_a}{1 + j\omega/3\omega_a} = (9.38 + j4.69) \times 10^{-6} \text{ mho}$$
$$= 1.342 g_{22} \underline{/26.6°}$$

$$y_{12} = -\frac{g_{22}}{1 + j\omega/3\omega_a} = -(7.05 - j2.35) \times 10^{-6} \text{ mho}$$
$$= -0.949 g_{22} \underline{/-18.42°}$$

$$y_{21} = -\frac{g_{11}}{1 + j\omega/3\omega_a} = -(34.5 - j11.52) \times 10^{-3} \text{ mho}$$
$$= -0.949 g_{11} \underline{/-18.42°}$$

For comparison, the y coefficients will also be computed by the more exact hyperbolic formulas:

$$y_{11} = \frac{g_{11}BF}{\tanh BF} = \frac{38.4 \times 10^{-3}(1.102 + j1.102)}{1.14 + j0.147}$$
$$= (41.5 + j30.9) \times 10^{-3} = 1.352 g_{11} \underline{/36.6°}$$

where use has been made of the relation

$$\tanh(a + jb) = \frac{\sinh 2a + j \sin 2b}{\cosh 2a + \cos 2b}$$

Similarly,

$$y_{22} = g_{22}\frac{BF}{\tanh BF} = 7.82 \times 10^{-6}(1.08 + j0.805) \text{ mho}$$
$$= (8.51 + j6.30) \times 10^{-6} = 1.352 g_{22} \underline{/36.6°}$$

$$y_{12} = -\frac{g_{22}BF}{\sinh BF} = -\frac{7.82 \times 10^{-6}(1.102 + j1.102)}{0.66 + j1.50}$$
$$= -(6.93 - j2.70) \times 10^{-6} \text{ mho} = -0.952 g_{22} \underline{/-21.2°}$$

where use has been made of the relation

$$\sinh (a + jb) = \sinh a \cos b + j \cosh a \sin b$$

Similarly,

$$y_{21} = -\frac{g_{11}BF}{\sinh BF} = -38.4 \times 10^{-3}(0.888 - j0.345)$$
$$= -(34.1 - j13.24) \times 10^{-3} \text{ mho} = -0.952g_{11}\underline{/-21.2°}$$

A comparison of the two sets of values above shows that the approximate formulas are, with few exceptions, accurate to within 10 per cent.

The above relations give the frequency effects in what is often called the *intrinsic transistor*, i.e., the ideal one-dimensional transistor in which all currents are conduction and diffusion currents due to electrons and holes. However, in addition to the above effects there are displacement currents, and the transistor is never a one-dimensional device. This means that additional elements of the equivalent circuit must be considered. These include capacitances across the junctions and a resistance between a hypothetical point on the base of the intrinsic transistor and the external base lead, constituting an external base resistance.

The capacitances across the junctions are those associated with the space-charge-depletion layers. That across the emitter-base junction can often be ignored because it is across the emitter resistance of Fig. 12.13, which is quite low. The capacitance across the base-collector junction cannot be neglected because it is across the large collector resistance or, more properly, across the collector and base terminals of the intrinsic transistor. As a result, the intrinsic transistor must be supplemented with external circuit elements as shown in Fig. 13.44.

The junction capacitances of Fig. 13.44 are nonlinear capacitances. Their capacity varies inversely as the square root of the d-c voltage across the junction.[1] Accordingly,

$$C_j = A \sqrt{\frac{\varepsilon_s e}{2V}\left(\frac{1}{n_n} + \frac{1}{p_p}\right)} \qquad \text{farads} \qquad (13.62)$$

where C_j = junction capacity

A = junction area

ε_s = dielectric constant of semiconductor, 16 for germanium, 12 for silicon

e = electron charge

n_n, p_p = equilibrium majority carrier densities on the two sides of the junction

V = *total* voltage across the junction, including internal voltage step as well as external applied voltage

The junction capacitances are generally in the range of 5 to 500 $\mu\mu$f. The emitter-junction capacity will usually be several times as large as the col-

[1] Applies to step junctions. The capacity of graded junctions varies as $C = A(ea\varepsilon_s^2/2V)^{\frac{1}{3}}$, where a is the gradient of the impurity density.

lector-junction capacity because the large back voltage on the collector increases the thickness of the space-charge-depletion layer at the collector junction.

The external base resistance will be of the order of a few ohms and will depend upon the transistor geometry [MoD]. External base resistance in alloy types will be lower than in grown-junction types because of the physically larger base electrode. This resistance exists because the current from the base lead must flow into the base layer, and as a result, there is an ohmic voltage drop associated with it. Another way of looking at this is that there is some hypothetical point within the base layer that is at base potential and that it is necessary to connect this point with an external lead through the base material. The external base resistance is very difficult to determine theoretically but is easy to measure.

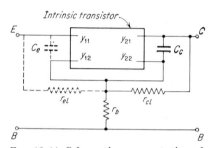

There are some surface effects also entering into the determination of the equivalent circuit. The first of these is leakage, which has the effect of a resistance shunted across the collector-to-base junction as shown in Fig. 13.44. The leakage resistance r_{cl} around the collector junction will usually be smaller than the collector resistance r_c of the intrinsic transistor. There will also be a leakage resistance r_{gl} across the emitter junction. However, this resistance will usually be large compared to the emitter resistance r_e of the intrinsic transistor [ChD, LaD].

Fig. 13.44. Schematic representation of a junction transistor in a grounded-base connection, showing external circuit elements needed to supplement the intrinsic transistor.

Another surface effect influencing transistor behavior is recombination [MoD]. Energy conditions on most surfaces is such that the minority carriers which flow toward it are lost by recombination on arrival. As a result, it is found that the α of alloy-junction transistors is maximum when the collector area is 2 to 9 times the emitter area because surface recombination occurs chiefly at the edge of the layer junctions and the above area ratio keeps the dense base current away from the collector-junction edge.

All the above effects must be integrated to obtain a simple satisfactory equivalent circuit for high frequencies. Such a circuit will preferably have circuit elements independent of frequency and will in addition have to be a compromise between simplicity and accuracy. The simplest circuit that gives a reasonably accurate representation of high-frequency effects is shown in Fig. 13.45. All the circuit elements are constant, being independent of frequency. The current-amplification factor α, however, will vary with frequency, as in (13.52), which means that (approximately)

$$\alpha = \frac{\alpha_0}{1 + j\omega/\omega_a} \tag{13.63}$$

This means that the determination of ω_a either by (13.56) or by measurement is required. In addition, it is required to know the values of three resistances and one capacity. The resistances and α_0 may be determined from low-frequency measurement. The capacity can be measured at some intermediate frequency. Thus four low-frequency quantities and two high-frequency quantities are needed to establish this circuit.

The correctness of the circuit of Fig. 13.45 requires a little justification. It was shown earlier that the impedances of the intrinsic transistor varied considerably with frequency. The emitter impedance tends to be low and can be represented to a first approximation as a parallel combination of a resistance and a capacity. Since the resistance is quite low, the capacity can usually be neglected and is shown dotted in the figure. The base resistance tends to be mostly ohmic and thus can be left as is. The collector resistance tends to vary with frequency but is shunted by the leakage resistance, which is generally lower, and so can be represented by a simple resistance. Since the base resistance is lower than the collector-to-base leakage resistance, which in turn is lower than the collector junction resistance, the circuit shown suffices. The approximation is aided by the fact that load resistances commonly used will usually be smaller than the resistance r_c. The values used in this equivalent circuit are best determined by measurement since a number of factors, such as leakage and ohmic base resistance, are not capable of theoretical determination.

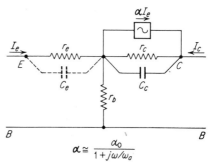

Fig. 13.45. Approximate equivalent circuit of a junction transistor suitable for high frequencies. The current-multiplication factor α is complex and is given approximately by (13.63).

Some typical values of the constants for the equivalent circuit of Fig. 13.45 are listed below:

$$70 < r_e < 200 \text{ ohms}$$
$$0.1 < r_c < 1.0 \text{ megohms}$$
$$35 < r_b < 450 \text{ ohms}$$
$$0.900 < \alpha_0 < 0.995$$
$$0.5 < f_a < 5.0 \text{ Mc}$$
$$15 < C_c < 400 \ \mu\mu\text{f}$$

CHAPTER 14

SMALL-SIGNAL OSCILLATORS

14.1. Effect of Signal Level on the Operation of Electron Devices.   In dealing with electron devices it is important to remember that they are essentially electric valves which can control the flow of electric energy. Hence in their circuit applications they are converters, not generators, of power.   An amplifier cannot really amplify a signal without having available a source from which to draw power.   In reality an amplifier is a device in which a signal from a first source controls the flow of power from a second source to produce an enlarged signal of the first form.   Likewise an oscillator receives energy from a d-c source and converts *part* of this energy into an alternating form of a definite frequency.   It does not generate electrical energy but merely converts it from one form to another.

In discussions of the previous chapters it was assumed that the signals were small enough so that the relations between the various quantities were linear.   Accordingly linear circuit analysis could be used.   Electron devices may also operate with large voltage and current excursions. Under these conditions operation is strongly nonlinear and other methods of analysis must be used.   In general the operation of electron devices falls into three classes, somewhat as follows:

1. *Linear, or Small-signal, Operation.*   This includes low-level amplifiers and the *initiation* of oscillations.   Such operation involves small excursions from an operating point and can be handled by ordinary circuit analysis.

2. *Slightly Nonlinear Operation.*   This includes Class A *power* amplifiers and small-signal oscillators.   The excursions here are large enough to bring in second-order effects resulting in generation of harmonics or changes in the values of the so-called constants of the electron devices. Such operation can be handled by some modifications of the linear circuit analysis but involve corrections rather than large modifications.

3. *Highly Nonlinear, or Large-signal, Problems.*   These include Class B or C amplifiers and oscillators, pulse cricuits, and switching circuits. Here the excursions are so large that different conditions exist for different parts of the cycle of operation.   Methods tend to be special for each problem.   Characteristics may sometimes be approximated by a combination of straight-line segments.

The material of Chaps. 12 and 13 falls into the first class above. The material of this chapter and the following falls into the second class. A later chapter will deal with large-signal applications. The subject of even small-signal *oscillators* falls into the second class because no completely linear device can give stable oscillation. Oscillators always require at least a small nonlinearity to stabilize the magnitude of the voltage and current excursions and to give attendant frequency stability. Thus if an amplifier is caused to oscillate by applying part of its output to its input in proper phase, it will produce sine waves if the amplifier is sufficiently nonlinear and has sufficient frequency selectivity. If, however, the amplifier is not strongly frequency selective and is nearly linear over a considerable range of amplitudes, it may produce square waves.

14.2. Types of Oscillators. Oscillators may be classified in many ways. They may be classified as small- or large-signal oscillators, as discussed in the previous section. They may also be classified in terms of their frequency range, as for instance audio-frequency, radio-frequency, etc. They may also be classed according to some specific feature, as for instance piezoelectric, velocity-modulated, electron-coupled, etc. They may be classified according to specific circuit form, as Hartley, Colpitts, tuned-plate–tuned-grid, etc.

Small-signal oscillators may also be classified as follows for convenience of analysis: (1) external-feedback oscillators, (2) direct-coupled oscillators, (3) negative-conductance oscillators. This classification will be used as a basis for discussion in the material of this chapter. In fact the above classification can be used fairly successfully for all types of oscillators.

By an external-feedback oscillator is meant an amplifier in which part of the output is fed back into the input. Conditions of oscillation may be determined from feedback-amplifier theory. This principle may be applied to give carefully controlled conditions of oscillation.

By a direct-coupled oscillator is meant one which has direct coupling between input and output but which cannot be easily converted into an amplifier by simply opening certain terminals. This classification is obviously a little arbitrary. Feedback may actually be external as well as internal and is generally through more than one element. Operation cannot be described simply by feedback-amplifier theory. Consequently, there are placed in this class oscillators not falling into the other two classes.

A negative-conductance oscillator is one formed by connecting a passive resonant circuit to an active electronic circuit which exhibits a negative conductance over a certain frequency range. If the magnitude of the conductance of the resonant circuit is less than that of the active negative conductance, the parallel combination of the two will be a negative conductance and the combination will oscillate. Certain tube and transistor

circuits exhibit negative conductance at a pair of terminals and will oscillate if connected to a suitable parallel resonant circuit. Oscillators may
also be built about negative transconductances.

14.3. External-feedback Oscillators. The requirements for an external-feedback oscillator are three: (1) There must be a frequency-sensitive
circuit that will determine the frequency of oscillation. (2) There must
be a feedback circuit supplying to the input of the device a voltage of
proper phase and sufficient in magnitude to permit oscillation. (3) For
amplitude stability there must be some mechanism such that any increase
in voltage amplitude will produce a decrease in gain around the feedback
loop to prevent the voltages from
running away and building up to
undesirable amplitudes.

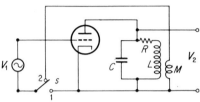

Shown in Fig. 14.1 is the schematic
diagram of a simple circuit known
as the tuned-plate oscillator, which
embodies the above elements. This
is a simple triode amplifier with a
parallel resonant circuit as a load and

Fig. 14.1. Tuned-plate-oscillator circuit.

a coil coupled to the output resonant circuit to provide a feedback voltage.
When the switch s is on position 1, the circuit acts as an amplifier. With
the switch s on position 2, oscillations may occur if the phase of the fed-
back voltage is right and if the mutual inductance M is sufficiently large.

Consider first the operation of the circuit as an amplifier. According
to (13.9), the gain of the amplifier will be

$$A = \frac{V_2}{V_1} = -\frac{g_m Z_l}{1 + Z_l/r_p} \cong -g_m Z_l \tag{14.1}$$

where A = voltage amplification
   V_1, V_2 = input and output voltage, respectively
   g_m = mutual conductance
   r_p = dynamic plate resistance
   Z_l = complex load impedance as a function of frequency
The approximate equality at the right holds only if Z_l is small in magnitude compared to r_p for all frequencies. This assumption will be made in
the following discussion to simplify the equations.

Let us examine this last expression for amplification. It depends upon
the complex impedance Z_l. The impedance of the parallel resonant circuit shown in Fig. 14.1 is given by

$$Z_l = \frac{jX_c(R + jX_l)}{R + j(X_l + X_c)} \tag{14.2}$$

Here $X_l = \omega L$, and $X_c = 1/\omega C$. Making these substitutions and assuming R is small compared to X_l,

$$Z_l = \frac{L/C}{R + j(\omega L - 1/\omega C)} \tag{14.3}$$

Since the resonant frequency is given by $\omega_0 = 1/\sqrt{LC}$, this is easily put into the form

$$Z_l = \frac{L/C}{R + j\omega_0 L(\omega/\omega_0 - \omega_0/\omega)} \tag{14.4}$$

If now we let $\omega = \omega_0 + \Delta\omega$ and then let $\delta = \Delta\omega/\omega_0$, we find

$$Z_l = \frac{L/C}{R + j\omega_0 L[1 + \delta - 1/(1 + \delta)]} \tag{14.5}$$

One final substitution of $Q = \omega_0 L/R$, and the assumption that δ is small compared to unity, makes possible the following extremely simple form

$$Z_l \cong \frac{R_0}{1 + 2jQ\delta} \tag{14.6}$$

where $R_0 = L/CR$ is the maximum value of Z_l, a large resistive value at resonance. This expression produces the well-known resonance curve of impedance. For Q's of the order of 20 or more, this expression is accurate to points well down on the skirts of the resonance curve. Note that the new frequency variable δ has a value of zero at resonance and $\pm 1/2Q$ at the 70.7 per cent points. The complex impedance Z_l itself has the form of a circle in the impedance plane. Various representations of (14.6) are shown in Figs. 14.2 and 14.3. That of Fig. 14.2 is conventional and fairly well known. It shows components of resistance and reactance and magnitude of impedance as a function of frequency. The impedance curve has the well-known form. The resistance component is similar, although smaller away from resonance. The reactance is inductive at frequencies below resonance

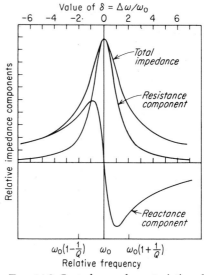

Fig. 14.2. Impedance characteristics of a parallel-resonant circuit as a function of frequency.

and capacitive above, passing through zero at resonance. At resonance the impedance is all resistive and has a maximum value. At frequencies $1/2Q$ times the resonant frequency above and below resonance, the resistance and reactance components are equal and each is equal to half the maximum resistance value.

Shown in Fig. 14.3 is the locus of complex impedance in the impedance plane. This, for large enough values of $Q = L/RC$, is nearly a circle through the origin with center on the resistive axis except at very high

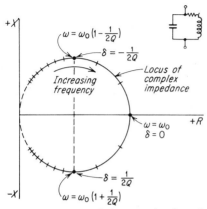

and very low frequencies, where the approximation is not so good. Frequency progresses in a clockwise direction around the circle from low to high frequencies. Frequency progression is nonuniform, being slow for low frequencies, then increasing greatly in the vicinity of resonance, and slowing down again at high frequencies. Resonance occurs at maximum value of impedance corresponding to the diameter on the resistive axis. The conventional half-power reference points (constant voltage applied) occur at the highest and lowest points on the

Fig. 14.3. Locus of the complex impedance of a parallel-resonant circuit.

circle and demonstrate the reason for the relation between the resistance and reactance of these points and the resistance at resonance cited above.

If we know from the above the nature of Z_l, the nature of the voltage amplification A, as given in 14.1, is easily indicated. The locus of voltage amplification will also be a circle but rotated 180° from the position of the locus of Z_l by the minus sign and multiplied in magnitude by g_m. The locus of A is thus a circle through the origin with its center on the negative real axis; i.e., the circle lies in the left-hand plane.

To study now amplification with feedback and the possibility of oscillation, it is necessary to evaluate the feedback factor β. The feedback voltage is given by

$$V_{fb} = -j\omega M I_l = -\frac{j\omega M V_2}{j\omega L} \tag{14.7}$$

since $I_l = V_2/j\omega L$, it being assumed that the inductive reactance is large compared to the series resistance in that branch. The sign of the feedback voltage has been chosen to correspond to positive feedback, i.e., to give a feedback voltage in phase with the input voltage. The feedback may be made negative simply by reversing the connections to the coupling coil. Accordingly, the feedback factor is in this case a scalar quantity given by

$$\beta = \frac{V_{fb}}{V_2} = -\frac{M}{L} \tag{14.8}$$

This factor will depend upon the value of M, which is adjustable. However, the β factor is independent of the voltages in the circuit.

The over-all feedback factor $A\beta$ is now seen to be

$$A\beta = g_m Z_l \frac{M}{L} \tag{14.9}$$

where g_m is nearly constant but will decrease in value as signal amplitude increases and is independent of frequency. The impedance Z_l is independent of signal level but is a function of frequency, and M/L is independent of both frequency and signal amplitude.

Consider now the operation of the circuit of Fig. 14.1 when the switch is in the lower position, giving amplification without feedback. The response will then be something like that shown in Fig. 14.4 by the curve marked A. If now the circuit switch is thrown into the upper position to include a positive feedback voltage, it being further assumed that

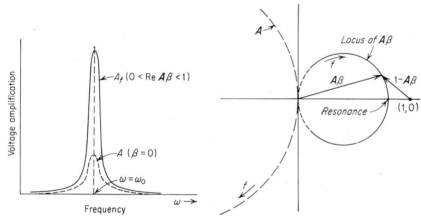

FIG. 14.4. Amplification of the circuit of Fig. 14.1 with and without feedback.

FIG. 14.5. Locus of the feedback factor $A\beta$ for the amplifier of Fig. 14.1 in a non-oscillating condition.

$A\beta$ is at first less than unity at its maximum, then the response is as shown by the curve A_f. This is seen to give a higher amplification and a sharper resonance. It may be understood by reference to (13.38) and Fig. 14.5. A diagram showing the locus of $A\beta$ is called a Nyquist diagram [Nys]. Amplification with feedback is given by

$$A_f = \frac{A}{1 - A\beta} \tag{13.38}$$

Shown in the figure are the circles of A and $A\beta$. To determine the gain with feedback, it is necessary to divide A by $1 - A\beta$. Shown also are phasors $A\beta$ and $1 - A\beta$ for a particular frequency slightly below resonance. It is evident that the phasor $1 - A\beta$ is quite small in the vicinity of resonance. Accordingly, since this quantity appears in the denominator of the expression for gain, the gain will be greatly increased in that region of frequency. The closer the value of $A\beta$ approaches the value unity, the larger the gain at resonance. If the $A\beta$ circle passes through the point (1,0), then theoretically the gain will be infinite at the resonant frequency. This is a limiting condition for self-contained oscillations. The extremely high gain realized with positive feedback under these conditions is accompanied by an attendant loss of stability. The effects with positive feedback are just the opposite of those encountered with negative feedback.

As long as the magnitude of $A\beta$ is less than unity, oscillations cannot occur even though the gain may become extremely high. This may be seen by noting that a pulse involving a distribution of energy over a small range of frequency will be amplified by a factor A on first passing through the amplifier. The pulse amplitude will then be reduced by the factor $A\beta$ on being fed back; and if $A\beta$ is less than unity in magnitude, the pulse will reenter the amplifier with an amplitude smaller than the initial one. On successive round trips over the amplifier and feedback circuit, the pulse amplitude will be further reduced, showing that the amplitude of signal cannot build up to a condition of oscillation.

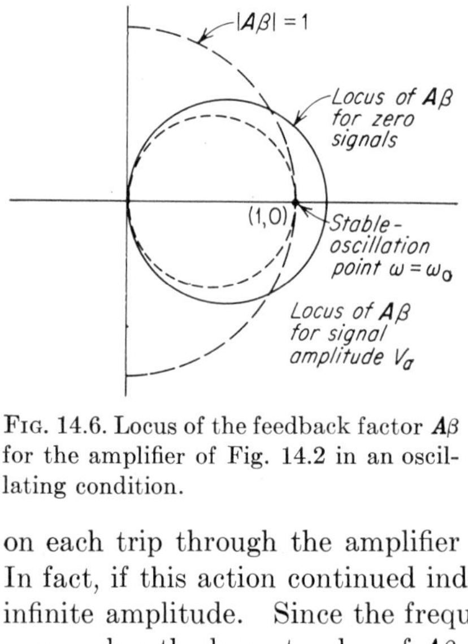

FIG. 14.6. Locus of the feedback factor $A\beta$ for the amplifier of Fig. 14.2 in an oscillating condition.

If, however, the value of $A\beta$ is greater than unity so that the $A\beta$ circle encloses the point (1,0), then oscillations may build up. This comes about because in the vicinity of resonance, as shown in Fig. 14.6, the magnitude of $A\beta$ will be greater than unity. Hence a pulse of energy with frequencies centered at the resonant frequency has the possibility of becoming slightly greater on each trip through the amplifier and back around the feedback loop. In fact, if this action continued indefinitely, the pulse would build up to infinite amplitude. Since the frequency component at the resonant frequency has the largest value of $A\beta$, the pulse will finally become a signal of that single frequency, adjacent frequencies having finally relatively smaller amplitudes.

Oscillations will, however, not build up to infinite amplitude because, as the magnitude of the circulating signal increases, the effective mutual conductance of the tube decreases and hence the factor A decreases in magnitude according to (14.1). This may be seen by reference to Fig. 14.7, showing static and dynamic plate-current vs. grid-voltage curves of the vacuum tube. The static characteristics are those which apply for zero load impedance. The dynamic characteristic is that which exists for a given load impedance and takes account of the fact that the voltage at the plate of the tube decreases as the instantaneous current increases because of the voltage drop in the load impedance.   The dynamic characteristic will always have a lower

slope than the static characteristic. The curvature of the dynamic characteristic is exaggerated to show the principle involved.   The effective mutual conductance is the slope of a tangent to the dynamic characteristic at the point o for zero signal amplitude.   For signals of the amplitude shown, the effective mutual conductance is approximately the slope of a line through the points a and b.   The slope of the line ab will be less than that of the tangent at o.   This means that, as the signal amplitude increases, the effective mutual conductance decreases.

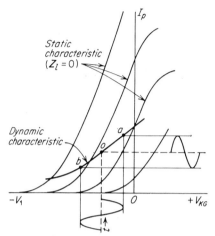

Fig. 14.7. Dynamic characteristic of a vacuum-tube amplifier, showing how the effective mutual conductance decreases as the signal level increases.

The decrease in effective mutual conductance and hence of over-all feedback factor $A\beta$ with input signal is shown in Fig. 14.8.   If the feedback factor for zero signal is greater than unity, then any disturbance will build up at the resonant frequency until the signal level has the amplitude Oa in Fig. 14.8, at which point the $A\beta$ factor has dropped to unity and the oscillations will be stable.   At the same time the $A\beta$ circle of Fig. 14.6 will shrink until it passes through the point $(1,0)$.   If at this point the oscillations should increase, the effective mutual conductance would decrease further and limit the oscillations.   If the oscillations should decrease, the effective mutual conductance would increase, tending to restore equilibrium.   The stability of the oscillator will depend upon the slope of the $A\beta$ characteristic of Fig. 14.8 at a value of

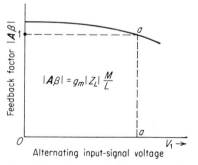

Fig. 14.8. Curve showing how the magnitude of the feedback factor $A\beta$ decreases as signal amplitude increases.

unity.   If the slope is low, the stability will be low.   If the slope is high, i.e., more negative, the stability will be greater.   Nonlinear elements, such as thermistors or light bulbs, are often introduced into oscillator circuits to increase the magnitude of the negative slope [Tel].   Also, circuits are easily devised which change the bias in the proper direction with changes in oscillation level.

The above example was chosen for detailed discussion primarily because it had a simple Nyquist diagram. The significant elements were feed-back from output to input, a frequency-selective circuit, and a nonlinear

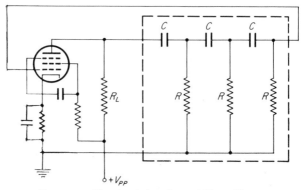

Fig. 14.9. Circuit of the phase-shift oscillator.

action for stabilizing the magnitude of oscillation. The frequency-selective circuit need not be a resonant circuit composed of inductance and reactance but may be a bridge circuit of resistances and capacities [Tel]. Such RC bridge circuit has a very low effective Q; but if the phase shift is rapid enough, the operation is quite stable.

Another circuit in this class is the phase-shift oscillator [Gij]. The circuit of such an oscillator is shown in Fig. 14.9. This is a single-stage

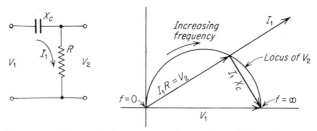

Fig. 14.10. Locus of the output voltage of an RC section.

pentode amplifier with a feedback circuit shown enclosed by a dotted box consisting of three RC sections. The transmission factor (i.e., ratio of output to input voltage) of a single RC section has a complex locus, which is a semicircle through the origin giving zero voltage and 90° phase angle leading at zero frequency and output equal to input with zero phase shift at infinite frequency. This assumes a low-impedance input genera-tor and a high-impedance load. The locus of a single section is shown in

Fig. 14.10. The product of three such semicircles is a spiral. This gives rise to an $A\beta$ spiral as shown in Fig. 14.11. The phase shift associated with the amplification is 180°. Accordingly, the spiral starts with zero magnitude and a phase angle of +90°. As the spiral grows, the phase angle first decreases to zero and then increases through negative values from zero to −180°. When each RC section has a 60° phase shift, the total phase shift of the circuit will be 180°. Taken with the 180° phase shift through the amplifier tube, the total phase shift will be 360° or zero, a value permitting oscillation. The spiral locus of the $A\beta$ factor crosses the positive real axis for this condition; and if the amplification is large enough, the

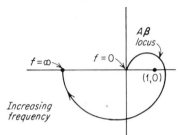

Fig. 14.11. Locus of the $A\beta$ factor in a phase-shift oscillator.

spiral will enclose the point (1,0) and the circuit will oscillate. The phase progression is rapid enough to give stable oscillation.

The above explanation is a simplified one which assumes that each RC section works between a low-impedance generator and a high-impedance load. For equal values of R and C, this is not quite the case, although the principles are the same. Computation of the exact value of phase shift shows that the phase shift through the β section is 180° for

$$f = \frac{1}{2\pi \sqrt{6}\ RC} \tag{14.10}$$

At the same time, the voltage is attenuated to $\frac{1}{29}$ its input value. Accordingly, the amplifier must have a gain of at least 29 in voltage to sustain oscillation.

Some external-feedback oscillators of a more conventional type are shown in Fig. 14.12. In part (a) is shown a tuned-plate oscillator. This has a tuned circuit L_2C_2 in the plate circuit. Feedback coupling is provided through mutual inductance M to inductance L_1 from the plate to the grid circuit. Grid bias is provided by a cathode resistor for small-signal oscillators. A large resistance is used in series with the grid bias to permit grid-voltage variation. The tuned-plate circuit is isolated from the direct plate voltage by the capacitor C_p, which does not, however, impede the flow of alternating currents. Direct plate voltage is supplied through the radio-frequency choke L_p, which does not pass alternating currents. The simplified schematic circuit shows the connections for a-c components. The oscillating frequency is nearly the resonant frequency of the plate circuit. There also exists a tuned-grid oscillator in which the tuned circuit is at the input of the tube and the plate circuit is an untuned inductance.

In Fig. 14.12b is shown the tuned-plate tuned-grid oscillator. This has two tuned circuits, one in the output and one in the input. Both are tuned to the same frequency. Coupling is provided through the inter-electrode capacity C_{gp}. This circuit has no means of controlling the feedback factor and generally operates best as a large-signal oscillator.

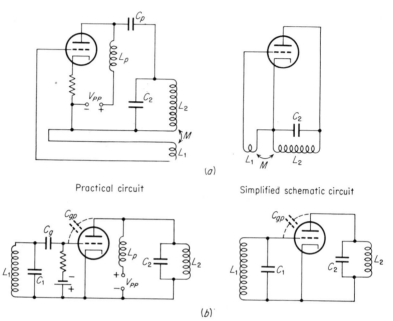

Practical circuit   Simplified schematic circuit

(b)

Fig. 14.12. Common types of external-feedback oscillators: (a) Tuned-plate oscillator. (b) Tuned-plate tuned-grid oscillator.

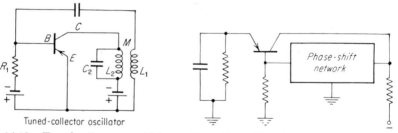

Tuned-collector oscillator

Fig. 14.13. Tuned-collector oscillator. This should be compared with Fig. 14.12a.

Fig. 14.14. Transistor phase-shift oscillator. Compare with Fig. 14.9.

The same principles annunciated above will also apply to transistors [OsB, Ryb, ShB2]. Shown in Fig. 14.13 is the transistor analogue of the tuned-plate oscillator. Current is amplified through the transistor with a reversal in phase. There is another 180° phase shift through the transformer, coupling output to input. Since the current gain is approximately $\alpha/(1 - \alpha)$, the circuit will oscillate if the current step up from collector to base is greater than the reciprocal of the amplification.

The transistor analogue of the phase-shift oscillator is shown in Fig. 14.14. This may be considered a grounded-emitter-transistor amplifier with feedback from collector to base. This is positive voltage feedback. Criteria for oscillation are strictly analogous to the vacuum-tube case. Such oscillators are sensitive to bias adjustments, although frequency stability may be obtained by operating so that electrode currents respond proportionately to fluctuations in supply voltage. In addition, various

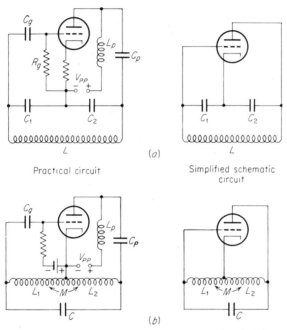

FIG. 14.15. Simple direct-coupled oscillator circuits: (a) The Colpitts oscillator. (b) The Hartley oscillator.

transistor characteristics, such as base input resistance, may become negative for certain bias conditions, for which oscillations will stop. Transistor oscillators are, as a result, easily pulsed.

14.4. Direct-coupled Oscillators. All direct-coupled oscillators have in common a direct connection between the output and input terminals of a tube or transistor. This is a single direct connection that applies to the input circuit a voltage 180° out of phase with that at the output terminal. Shown in Fig. 14.15 are two simple types of triode oscillator. Each of these has one common circuit element connecting the grid and plate circuits. Each also has one or more tuned circuits.

The Colpitts oscillator is the simplest of these. It has a tuned circuit consisting of an inductance L in series with capacities C_1 and C_2. A direct connection between plate and grid is provided through L. The tuned circuit is commonly connected to the plate and grid through capacitors C_p and C_g. These isolate the tuned circuit from the direct voltages but do not greatly change the alternating impedances because their reactances are generally small. It is then necessary to provide d-c connections between the cathode and the grid and also between the cathode and the plate. This is done through the resistance R_g in the grid circuit and the radio-frequency choke L_p in the plate circuit. The choke L_p has a high reactance to alternating current and is in series with the direct plate-supply voltage. The grid has a d-c path to the cathode through R_g. In small-signal oscillators, bias is generally provided by a cathode resistor. This ensures proper operating conditions for the tube. At the same time, if the alternating voltages developed should drive the grid positive, the grid current flowing through the resistor R_g will provide an additional bias, which will tend to limit the alternating voltage to barely positive values. The same circuit may be used in large-signal oscillators without the cathode resistor but including a bias generator. The magnitude of the resulting oscillations will then depend upon the value of R_g, which will determine the bias, and upon the relative values of C_1 and C_2. This combination will usually drive the grid strongly positive. The simplified schematic circuit shows the connections which apply for the a-c components only.

The Hartley oscillator of Fig. 14.15b has a direct connection between grid and plate through the capacity C. Coupling is also provided through the mutual inductance M between the inductances L_1 and L_2. Other features of the circuit are essentially the same as those of the Colpitts oscillator. The Hartley oscillator has the advantage that the frequency of oscillation may be controlled by the single capacity C.

The general method of analyzing direct-coupled oscillators is to set up the equivalent circuit and then determine relations between circuit and tube parameters corresponding to a condition of oscillation. *The general condition for oscillation, expressed in circuit terms, is that the determinant of the circuit equations shall be zero.* When this is true, infinitesimal voltages applied will give rise to infinite currents admitting the building up of oscillations. Even with zero impressed voltages the currents will have a value $0/0$, which is indeterminate in general but potentially finite in the majority of cases. There exists then the possibility of finite currents with zero impressed voltages, which corresponds to initiation of oscillation.

The above principles are readily illustrated in the case of the Colpitts oscillator. Shown in Fig. 14.16 is the equivalent circuit of such an oscillator. Here it is assumed for simplicity that the tube dynamic resistances r_{kg} and r_{gp} are infinite; i.e., small-signal Class A conditions prevail. The tube interelectrode capacities C_{kg}, C_{gp}, and C_{kp}, if large enough, may be included in Z_1, Z_3, and Z_2, respectively. The triode equivalent circuit with constant-voltage generator in the cathode-plate branch is assumed.

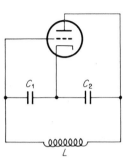

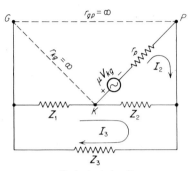

| Schematic tube circuit | Equivalent circuit |

FIG. 14.16. Equivalent circuit of the Colpitts oscillator: $V_{kg} = I_3 Z_1$; $Z_1 = 1/j\omega C_1 = jX_1$; $Z_2 = 1/j\omega C_2 = jX_2$; $Z_3 = j\omega L = jX_3$; $Z_0 = Z_1 + Z_2 + Z_3$.

For zero impressed voltages, the circuit equations for the assumed mesh currents I_2 and I_3 are

$$0 = I_2(r_p + Z_2) - I_3 Z_2 + \mu V_{kg} = I_2(r_p + Z_2) - I_3(Z_2 - \mu Z_1) \quad (14.11)$$
$$0 = I_2 Z_2 - I_3 Z_0 \quad (14.12)$$

where $Z_0 = Z_1 + Z_2 + Z_3$. From this, the determinant of the circuit equations is

$$\Delta = \begin{vmatrix} r_p + Z_2 & -(Z_2 - \mu Z_1) \\ Z_2 & -Z_0 \end{vmatrix} = 0 \quad (14.13)$$

or
$$0 = -Z_0(r_p + Z_2) + Z_2(Z_2 - \mu Z_1) \quad (14.14)$$

Both the real and the imaginary part of this expression must be equal to zero. The imaginary part is

$$jX_0 r_p = 0 \quad \text{or} \quad X_0 = 0 \quad (14.15)$$

since r_p cannot be zero. This indicates that the circuit composed of C_1, C_2, and L in series must be resonant for oscillation. The real part of the circuit determinant is

$$X_0 X_2 - X_2^2 + \mu X_1 X_2 = 0 \quad (14.16)$$

or since $X_0 = 0$,

$$\mu = \frac{X_2}{X_1} = \frac{C_1}{C_2} \quad (14.17)$$

This indicates that the ratio of X_2 to X_1 must be equal to the tube amplification factor for oscillations to exist.

Let us examine what happens if μ is smaller or larger than the value indicated by (14.17). Assume an impressed voltage V_3 in series with the inductance L. Then

$$Y_3 = \frac{I_3}{V_3} = -\frac{r_p + jX_2}{\Delta} \quad (14.18)$$

If μ is less than the value indicated in (14.17), then the real part of Y_3 will be positive, indicating that energy is absorbed from the voltage source.   Under these conditions, if V_3 is a pulse, the resulting transient will die down.   On the other hand, if μ is larger than the value indicated in (14.17), then the real part of Y_3 will be negative.   This means that the vacuum-tube circuit can deliver energy to the voltage source.   Under these conditions, the transient resulting from a pulse excitation will

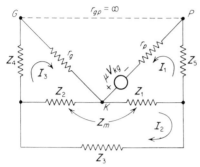

build up until the tube parameters change to the point where (14.17) again holds under conditions of steady oscillation.   In actual oscillator circuits, the oscillations will build up from some infinitesimal pulse disturbance within the circuit, such as from circuit or tube noise.

Fig.   14.17.   Equivalent   circuit   of the general vacuum-triode oscillator: $V_{kg} = I_3 r_g$; $Z_0 = Z_1 + Z_2 + Z_3 + 2Z_m$.

Other oscillator circuits may be analyzed in the same manner as above.   A general equivalent circuit, which includes most of the direct-coupled-oscillator circuits, is shown in Fig. 14.17 [Llt].   This is similar to the circuit just considered but includes the dynamic grid resistance r_g, coupling between Z_1 and Z_2, Z_m, and compensating impedances Z_4 and Z_5. The circuit equations here are

$$V_{kg} = I_1(r_p + Z_1 + Z_5) + I_2(Z_1 + Z_m) - I_3 Z_m$$
$$0 = I_1(Z_1 + Z_m) + I_2 Z_0 - I_3(Z_2 + Z_m) \qquad (14.19)$$
$$0 = -I_1 Z_m - I_2(Z_2 + Z_m) + I_3(r_g + Z_2 + Z_4)$$

where $V_{kg} = I_3 r_g$
$$Z_0 = Z_1 + Z_2 + Z_3 + 2Z_m$$

As before, the condition for oscillation is that the circuit determinant shall be zero.   This yields two expressions, one for the real part and the other for the imaginary part, each equal to zero.   One of these expressions will give the frequency of oscillation; and the other, a relation between reactances and tube constants necessary to start and sustain oscillations.   In addition, it is found that certain reactive values of Z_4 and Z_5 are possible which make the oscillation frequency equal to the resonant frequency of the isolated I_2 mesh and independent of tube constants.   Use of such reactive values is known as reactance stabilization. In addition, certain resistive values of Z_4 and Z_5 make the operation relatively insensitive to variation of tube constants.   This is known as resistance stabilization [Ter].

A direct-coupled transistor oscillator is shown in Fig. 14.18 [OsB, Ryb]. This is a grounded-base-transistor amplifier with positive current feedback between collector and emitter. The feedback circuit is a series-resonant circuit that permits maximum current feedback at the series resonance. Such an oscillator is easily pulsed either at the emitter or at the base.

There are also a number of transistor oscillator circuits which have no vacuum-tube analogy. They are more closely related to direct-coupled oscillators than are any other forms yet are not strictly in this class. They will be discussed in Sec. 14.6.

14.5. Negative-conductance Oscillators. There are many types of negative-conductance oscillator, and this section cannot do more than mention some of the most useful ones and give a qualitative description of their operation [Hep]. Basically, the negative-conductance oscillator is an electron device or electron device plus cir-cuit that exhibits a negative conductance to alternating currents at a pair of terminals. If

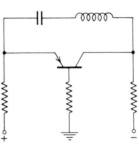

FIG. 14.18. Grounded-base transistor-triode oscillator.

there is connected to this pair of terminals a parallel-resonant circuit whose conductance at resonance is less in magnitude than that of the negative conductance, then the parallel combination of the two is still a negative conductance and the ensemble will oscillate at the resonant frequency of the external circuit. The operation of such oscillators thus depends upon the availability of stable negative conductances.

A first simple form of negative-conductance oscillator makes use of the negative conductance exhibited over part of the plate-current–plate-voltage characteristic of an ordinary screen-grid tube, or tetrode (beam power tubes do not exhibit this characteristic). The negative conduct-ance is evidenced by the negative slope of the curves of plate current in Fig. 10.17 for plate voltages equal to about half the screen voltages. The value of negative conductance is greatest in magnitude at the inflec-tion point of the $I_P V_P$ characteristic. It is then only necessary to insert a parallel-resonant circuit with a sufficiently high shunt resistance at resonance to produce an oscillator as shown in Fig. 14.19. Oscillations will build up until the average value of the negative resistance, as given by the dotted line between the limits of excursion a and b, is equal in magnitude to the external resistance. Such a device is simple of adjust-ment but relatively unstable because the negative resistance depends upon secondary emission from the plate, and such emission changes greatly with operating conditions and with the life of the tube. This circuit is known as the Dynatron and was originally proposed by Hull (1919).

Another simple negative-conductance oscillator is known as the Transitron. It makes use of a normal pentode but with an unconventional circuit connection [Hep, Brl]. This is shown in Fig. 14.20 along with the associated current-voltage characteristic. As seen here the plate is operated at a relatively low positive potential. The suppressor grid is operated at a slightly negative potential through a large resistance R and coupled to the screen grid through a large capacity C. As a result of this connection and because the suppressor grid draws virtually no current on account of its negative bias, the suppressor grid will follow alternating variations of the screen grid; i.e., there will tend to be a constant difference of potential between grids 2 and 3. The dynamic

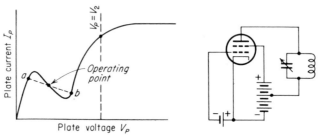

FIG. 14.19. Vacuum-tube-oscillator circuit based upon the negative output conductance of a screen-grid tetrode.

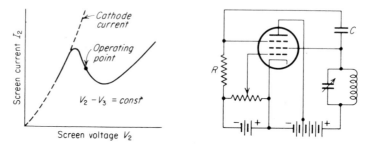

FIG. 14.20. Negative-conductance characteristic and circuit of the transitron oscillator.

conductance of the screen grid is positive under normal conditions when all other electrode potentials are constant. With the connection shown, there must also be considered the screen-suppressor transconductance dI_2/dV_3. This will be negative because an *increase* in the suppressor voltage reduces the number of electrons reflected back to the screen and hence *reduces* the screen current. The latter effect will usually dominate over the former, resulting in a negative equivalent conductance for the connection given. This circuit is quite stable since its operation depends upon space-charge and current-division effects within the tube rather than upon secondary emission.

Another negative-conductance circuit makes use of a pair of triodes with a cross connection between grids and plates [Reg]. The current-voltage characteristic resulting from this connection is shown in Fig. 14.21. The current flowing through the input terminals consists of two components, the first produced by the applied voltage, which is in one direction, and the second produced by the tubes, which will be in the opposite direction because of the cross connection of the grids. The latter component of current can be made much larger than the former by tapping across the entire plate resistor of the other tube. Analysis of

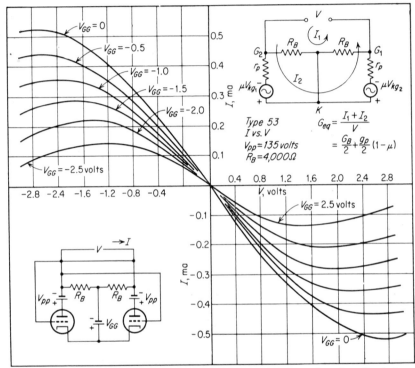

FIG. 14.21. Current-voltage characteristics of cross-connected push-pull triodes.

the equivalent circuit in the same figure shows the equivalent small-signal conductance at the plate terminals to be

$$G_{eq} = \frac{G_B}{2} + \frac{g_p}{2}(1 - \mu) \tag{14.20}$$

Here it is seen that, if μ is large enough, the input conductance is negative. This circuit will be recognized as a form of feedback circuit.

A final form of two-terminal negative-conductance circuit results from the application of positive feedback to conventional amplifiers [Gif]. Shown in Fig. 14.22 are two circuits that yield two-terminal negative conductances or negative admittances. Here, for purposes of study, the output circuit is replaced by the impedance seen looking back into the amplifier in series with an open-circuit output voltage. It is seen that, if the amplification A is made high enough, the input impedance is negative. Furthermore, the input impedance will be of the same character as the feedback impedance Z_f since the effects of resistances R_1 and R_2 can be made to cancel.

All negative conductances tend to be nonlinear, with the magnitude of the conductance decreasing as the signal amplitude increases. This serves as a mechanism for limiting oscillations when used with a tuned circuit. In spite of the attractiveness of the idea of negative-conductance oscillators, other forms appear to present over-all advantages and are preferred except in special applications.

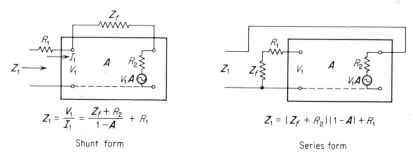

$$Z_1 = \frac{V_1}{I_1} = \frac{Z_f + R_2}{1 - A} + R_1$$

$$Z_1 = (Z_f + R_2)(1 - A) + R_1$$

Shunt form   Series form

Fig. 14.22. Circuits for developing negative admittances from positive-feedback-amplifier circuits.

14.6. Special Forms of Oscillators. An important problem with oscillators is that of frequency stability. Ordinary oscillators will be subject to variations with time of the order of several hundred parts per million. These variations are due to variations in supply voltage, changes in temperature affecting electric circuit constants, changes in load from various causes, and changes in tube constants with time. For commercial radio work, frequency is required to be constant to the order of several parts per million, and for many measurement purposes, it is required to be even more constant. With the reactive- or resistive-stabilization methods mentioned, it is possible to reduce the variations to the order of 10 to 20 ppm, which is sufficient for only certain types of measurements.

The Electron-coupled Oscillator. One form of stable oscillator which is particularly good from the standpoint of constancy of frequency with variations in load is the so-called electron-coupled oscillator [Dot]. The diagram of such an oscillator is shown in Fig. 14.23. The oscillator tube is a pentode. The cathode, control grid, and screen grid of this tube are connected to form a Hartley oscillator that will oscillate at the frequency determined by the circuit $L_0 C_0$. The oscillation of the first three elements modulates the electron stream to the plate, with the result that the current arriving there is amplitude modulated at the frequency of oscillation. The modulated plate current on flowing through the circuit $L_1 C_1$, which is tuned to the same frequency, causes a large voltage and circulating current to be developed there, which may be used for useful output. The operation of the plate circuit, however, has virtually no influence on the oscillating action of the first three elements. This is because of the electrostatic screening action of the suppressor grid. Also no current returns from the plate to the other grids, and in this sense the output is electron coupled to the oscillating portion of the tube. Such a circuit permits of rapid adjustments in frequency with large output and frequency independent of load conditions. With such an oscillator, stability of the order of a few parts per million may be obtained.

Crystal-stabilized Oscillators. Present-day transmitters require stability of 20 ppm or fewer; and even though such stability is obtainable with some of the above-mentioned circuits, it is difficult to maintain. Oscillators are, however, easily stabilized to a greater degree by the use of

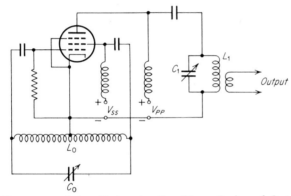

FIG. 14.23. Electron-coupled-oscillator circuit. The cathode and first two grids act as a triode oscillator. The output is taken from the plate circuit, which is coupled to the oscillator by the electron stream while shielded electrically by the suppressor grid.

certain mechanically resonant circuits electrically coupled to the circuit. The most effective of such resonators for radio frequencies is the quartz-crystal resonator, which makes use of the *piezoelectric effect*.

The piezoelectric effect is an effect encountered in certain crystals. If such crystals are deformed mechanically, a distribution of charges appears on their surface. Conversely, if the crystals are subjected to electric fields producing surface charges, mechanical deformation of the crystal results. Accordingly, the piezoelectric effect can be used to provide electromechanical coupling between a mechanical resonator, consisting of a block of the crystal, and a vacuum-tube circuit capable of oscillating. Quartz, rochelle salt, and tourmaline exhibit the piezo-electric effect. Rochelle salt is used in phonograph-pickup elements for audio work but does not have characteristics suitable for high frequencies.

The quartz-crystal mechanical resonator consists of a small block of crystal. A typical crystal will be about 1 cm square and 1 mm thick.

Such a crystal will have many resonant frequencies, including one of about 1.66 Mc.   This desired resonant frequency is called the fundamental of thickness shear and corresponds to a mode of vibration in which the top of the crystal wafer is displaced in one direction in shear while the bottom is displaced in the opposite direction.   This displacement results from an electric field applied across the thin dimension of the crystal.   Quartz wafers may be cut from the crystal at many different angles.   The cuts differ in frequency values and in temperature characteristics.   Some cuts give resonant frequencies with zero temperature coefficients over considerable ranges.

The coupling between a quartz-crystal wafer and an electric circuit is usually provided by putting the wafer between capacitor plates.   Often conductive coatings are plated on the crystal to form such plates.   The

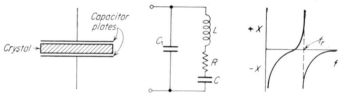

Fig. 14.24. Equivalent circuit of a quartz crystal mounted between capacitor plates.

crystal must be supported mechanically in such a way that the mechanical vibrations are not highly damped.

The equivalent circuit of such a crystal between two capacitor plates is shown in Fig. 14.24.   The equivalent circuit consists of a series-resonant circuit shunted by a capacitor C_1.   The latter represents a capacitive effect within the crystal itself.   The series-resonant effect is associated with one of the crystal resonances.   The equivalent inductance is quite high compared to the series equivalent capacity.   Typical values are given below:

$$L_1 = 0.57 \text{ henry} \qquad Q = 50{,}000$$
$$C_1 = 0.16 \ \mu\mu\text{f} \qquad R = 100 \text{ ohms}$$
$$C_0 = 40 \ \mu\mu\text{f} \qquad f_r = 1{,}660 \text{ kc}$$

Here f_r is the frequency of parallel resonance shown in the figure.   There is a series-resonant frequency just below this.   The high Q is the result of low damping.   Because of the relative equivalent values, the frequency of resonance is relatively little affected by additional shunt capacity across the crystal.   Since the equivalent circuit at the frequency of interest is essentially that of a parallel-resonant circuit, the crystal can be used in many standard oscillator circuits.   Two such are shown in Fig. 14.25.   In part (a) is shown a crystal used as part of a tuned-plate tuned-grid oscillator.   Pentodes are commonly used because of the small driving voltage required.   An auxiliary capacitor between grid and plate is often required because the tube interelectrode capacity is so low. The crystal takes the place of the tuned-grid circuit. The plate resonant circuit is adjusted for maximum output. The circuit of part (b) is known as the Pierce oscillator and requires no tuned circuit other than that provided by the crystal. This may be recognized as a modified Hartley oscillator with the resonant circuit replaced by the crystal. Electrode capacities to ground are an essential part of the circuit.

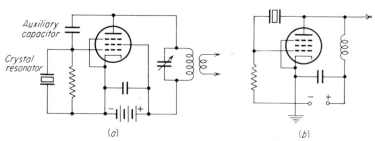

FIG. 14.25. Crystal-oscillator circuits: (a) Tuned-plate tuned-grid oscillator. (b) The Pierce oscillator (modified Hartley).

Crystal oscillators are easily stabilized to the order of several parts per million over long periods of time. This requires crystals with low temperature coefficients placed in a special holder whose temperature is automatically regulated. Special laboratory installations have stabilities of the order of 0.1 ppm.

Beat-frequency Oscillators. The beat-frequency oscillator is really a combination of two oscillators, one fixed and one variable, whose difference frequency is used to give an output adjustable over a wide range of fre-

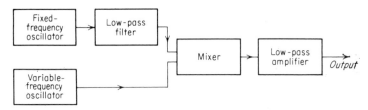

FIG. 14.26. Schematic diagram of a beat-frequency oscillator.

quency [TeB]. Such oscillators are particularly useful as signal generators in the radio-frequency range.

The schematic diagram of a beat-frequency oscillator is shown in Fig. 14.26. The two oscillators are low-level oscillators. The mixer is a detector that has a square-law action. As such, it produces the sum and difference of the frequencies introduced into it. The difference frequency is called the beat frequency and is the one selected for useful output.

The fixed-frequency oscillator is usually operated at several times the maximum output frequency desired. Thus if it is desired to make a radio-frequency-signal generator operating from 0.5 to 5 Mc, the fixed-frequency oscillator may operate at 20 Mc and the variable-frequency oscillator from 20.5 to 25 Mc. Thus a 25 per cent variation in frequency of the variable-frequency oscillator is sufficient to give a 10:1 frequency variation in the output. A filter is used to prevent harmonics of the fixed-frequency oscillator from beating with harmonics of the variable-frequency oscillator to produce spurious frequency components in the use-

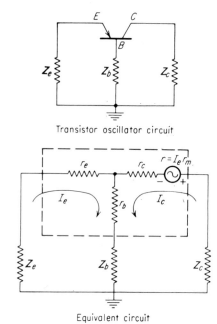

Transistor oscillator circuit

Equivalent circuit

Fig. 14.27. Circuit of a grounded-base transistor-triode oscillator and equivalent circuit.

ful output range. Thus if the two oscillator frequencies were 20 and 21 Mc producing a 1-Mc output, their second harmonics, 40 and 42 Mc, would produce a 2-Mc output. This consideration is more important for audio- than for radio-frequency operation. With the filter, the lowest spurious frequency would be produced by the combination of 20 and 42 Mc, giving a beat note of 22 Mc, which is above the range of interest.

The two oscillators are made as identical as possible so that they will be affected in the same way by such factors as line voltage and temperature variation. A zero-beat indicator or equivalent is included for calibration. It is easy to incorporate an absolute-frequency-increment adjustment by means of a trimmer capacitor, on the fixed-frequency oscillator. Output tends to be quite constant with frequency because the variable-frequency oscillator is tuned over only a small range of frequencies.

Transistor Oscillators. This section will be concerned with a class of transistor oscillators that has no vacuum-tube analogy [OsB]. The class considered is covered by the equivalent circuit of Fig. 14.27. From Fig. 13.13, the circuit determinant for this case is

$$\Delta = [(\mathbf{Z}_e + r_e) + (\mathbf{Z}_b + r_b)] [(\mathbf{Z}_b + r_b) + (\mathbf{Z}_c + r_c)]$$
$$- (\mathbf{Z}_b + r_b)[(r_b + \mathbf{Z}_b) + r_m] \quad (14.21)$$

For a condition of stability, this must be greater than zero, as was the case with the direct-coupled vacuum-tube oscillator. The above relation may be rewritten as follows to show the relation between the elements, for oscillation,

$$\frac{\mathbf{Z}_e + r_e}{\mathbf{Z}_b + r_b} < \frac{r_m - \mathbf{Z}_e - r_e}{\mathbf{Z}_c + r_c} - 1 \quad (14.22)$$

In this expression, the resistances are internal to the transistor and the impedances are external. It is seen that the oscillation condition may be obtained in four ways:

Case 1, increase $\mathbf{Z}_b$
Case 2, decrease $\mathbf{Z}_c$
Case 3, decrease $\mathbf{Z}_e$
Case 4, any combination of the above

For sine-wave oscillation, the appropriate values of impedance listed in the tabulation above must be frequency selective.

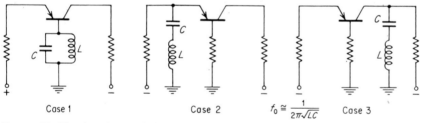

Case 1   Case 2 $f_0 \cong \dfrac{1}{2\pi\sqrt{LC}}$ Case 3

FIG. 14.28. Circuits of grounded-base transistor oscillators operating on the enhanced-instability principle.

Examples of transistor oscillators for the above cases are shown in Fig. 14.28. In case 1 the requirement of a high impedance in the base lead is provided by a parallel-resonant circuit. In cases 2 and 3 the requirement of a low impedance in the emitter and collector circuit is provided by a series-resonant circuit. Oscillation frequency is that of the resonant circuit. Biases must in some cases be different from usual because of large resistive drops in the base circuit.

CHAPTER 15

SMALL-SIGNAL NONLINEAR EFFECTS
IN ELECTRON DEVICES

15.1. Classification of Nonlinear Effects. All electron devices are inherently nonlinear. However, the degree of nonlinearity varies over a wide range. In Chaps. 12 and 13 we have treated electron devices as though they were linear. This is an obvious approximation to the true situation for small signals.

The degree of nonlinearity of an electron device is a relative matter. Where the signals are small compared to the extent of the device characteristics, the device may be treated as linear. As the signal grows, nonlinearities due to curvature of the device characteristics begin to appear, but the device can still be handled by linear circuit approximations with some corrections thrown in. As the signal excursions increase still further, this approach becomes cumbersome, and it is more convenient to approximate the device characteristics by a combination of straight-line segments. This is essentially what is done in large-signal applications, which will be treated in the next chapter.

For convenience, we classify the various degrees of nonlinearity as follows [Ryb]:

1. *Linear Operations.* These include low-level Class A amplifiers or questions relating to the initiation of oscillations. Equivalent circuits with a single internal generator are used, and problems are solved by linear circuit analysis, as indicated in Chap. 12. Voltage and current excursions on the device characteristics are so small that they may be considered to occur along the tangent to the operating point.

2. *Slightly Nonlinear Operations.* These include Class A *power* amplifiers. Here the voltage and current excursions about the operating point are large enough to introduce harmonics because of curvature of the device characteristics. Harmonic and intermodulation components may be treated by adding certain distortion generators to the circuit or by making small corrections to the linear equations. Performance is in terms of linear operation with harmonic corrections added.

3. *Highly Nonlinear Operations.* These include Class B and C amplifiers and oscillators, frequency multipliers, and various pulse and switching circuits. Here the voltage and current excursions are so large that the

small-signal theory does not apply. Device characteristics are most conveniently approximated by joined segments of straight lines. Graphical methods are used along with analytical methods that apply to the various straight-line segments.

4. *Combination Operations.* These include applications not covered in the previous items. They may include operations in which a small signal is superimposed upon a large signal so that the operation is linear in a region but the character of the operation may be changed by a change in value of the large signal. Applications in this category generally require special methods different for each application.

It should be pointed out that there is a large field of analysis related to the operation of nonlinear devices in general [Mid2]. In this field a number of general and special methods have been worked out. However, for most elementary applications of electron devices as treated in this book, the simple methods indicated above suffice.

15.2. Small Nonlinear Effects Due to Curvature of Device Characteristics. When the curvature of the device characteristics is sufficient, so that the characteristics are not linear, the output waveforms will still be somewhat different from the input characteristics. The difference will usually be slight but can be detected with sensitive instruments. If the harmonics are greater than about 5 per cent of the fundamental, they can frequently be detected in audio devices by the ear. If harmonics are greater than 10 per cent of the fundamental, they can be observed visually on a cathode-ray oscilloscope.

The above action is called *harmonic distortion.* This must be distinguished from *frequency distortion,* which refers to the fact that the amplification of a device is not constant with frequency. It must also be distinguished from *phase distortion,* which refers to the fact that the phase shift through a device is not linear with frequency. Frequency distortion may be detected by the ear. Phase distortion is not detectable by the ear except at high sound levels. Phase distortion does, however, alter wave shapes and is important in applications where waveforms must be preserved. Phase and frequency distortion can be reduced by various compensation or equalizing circuits.

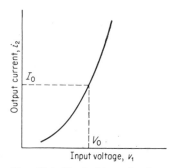

FIG. 15.1. Typical transfer characteristic of an electron device.

However, harmonic distortion, once present, cannot be eliminated. Hence a considerable interest exists in keeping it low.

For a given operating point and a given resistive load impedance, every electron device will have a *transfer characteristic* relating output current and input voltage, as shown in Fig. 15.1. Let I_0 and V_0 represent constant, or no-signal, values of output current and input voltage. Actual signals are superimposed upon these values. The characteristic of Fig. 15.1 can be represented by

$$i_2 = f(v_1) \tag{15.1}$$

if the device and circuit are predominantly resistive. Otherwise the characteristic may be a loop instead of a curve. In the vicinity of the

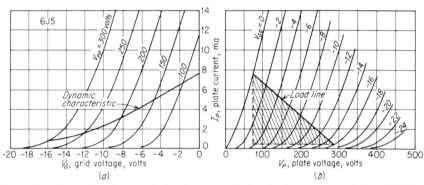

Fig. 15.2. Transfer characteristic of a grounded-cathode vacuum triode: (a) The plate-current–grid-voltage transfer characteristic. (b) The associated plate-current–plate-voltage characteristic and load line.

operating point V_0, this function may be expressed as a Taylor's-series expansion

$$i_2 = I_0 + a_1(v_1 - V_0) + a_2(v_1 - V_0)^2 + a_3(v_1 - V_0)^3 + \cdots \tag{15.2}$$

The coefficients in this equation are seen to be

$$a_1 = \left(\frac{di_2}{dv_1}\right)_0 \tag{15.3}$$

$$a_2 = \left(\frac{d^2 i_2}{dv^2}\right)_0 \tag{15.4}$$

$$a_n = \left(\frac{d^n i_2}{dv^n}\right)_0 \tag{15.5}$$

where the subscript 0 indicates that the derivative is evaluated at the point ($i_2 = I_0$, $v_1 = V_0$).[1]

If the input voltage has the form

$$v - V_0 = V_1 \cos \omega t \tag{15.6}$$

then (15.2) assumes the form

$$i_2 = I_0 + a_1 V_1 \cos \omega t + a_2 V_1^2 \cos^2 \omega t + a_3 V_1^3 \cos^3 \omega t + \cdots \tag{15.7}$$

A typical transfer characteristic of a vacuum triode is shown in Fig. 15.2a, where it is shown superimposed upon the static $I_P V_G$ characteristics.

[1] Coefficients for particular cases, such as vacuum-tube amplifiers, have been evaluated in terms of tube constants and load impedance. See [Ted].

In Fig. 15.2b this is shown in relation to a load line superimposed on the plate characteristic. The load line is simply the Ohm's-law excursion in the output-current-voltage representation. It will be discussed in the

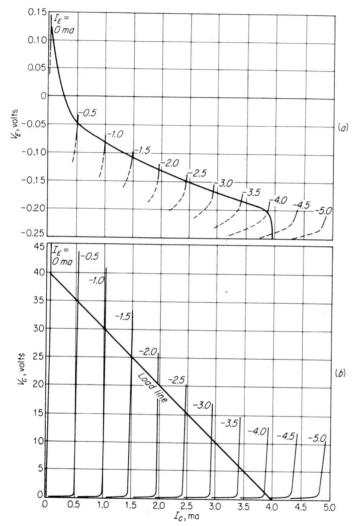

Fig. 15.3. Transfer characteristic of a grounded-base junction-transistor triode: (a) The collector-voltage–emitter-current transfer characteristic. (b) The associated collector-voltage–collector-current characteristic and load line.

next section. The transfer characteristic is readily obtained from the load line. The triode transfer characteristic is seen to have slight curvature.

A typical transfer characteristic of a junction transistor is shown in Fig. 15.3a superimposed upon the $V_E I_C$ characteristic. Shown in Fig. 15.3b is the load line superimposed on the collector characteristic. The transistor transfer characteristic also has a slight curvature. Both transfer characteristics would acquire large curvature at their extremities if extended.

The first term of (15.7), I_0, is the direct current in the output for no signal, corresponding to the operating point. The second term, $a_1 V_1 \cos \omega t$, is the desired linear output term, a replica of the input.

The third term of (15.7), $a_2 V_1^2 \cos^2 \omega t$, is the first distortion term, which appears as the input signal V_1 increases. It expands to give

$$a_2 V_1^2 \cos^2 \omega t = \frac{a_2 V_1^2}{2} (\cos 2\omega t + 1) \tag{15.8}$$

This is seen to include a second harmonic of the input frequency and an equally large d-c term. The latter is a rectification component due to the curvature of the characteristics. The former is a harmonic-distortion term.

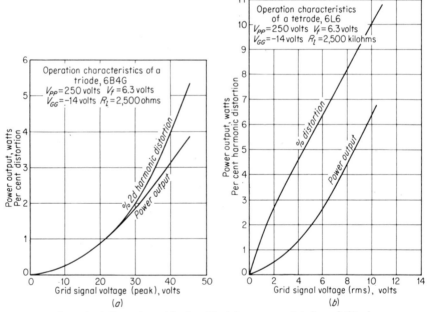

Fig. 15.4. Growth of distortion with signal in (a) a vacuum triode and (b) a beam power tetrode.

In a similar manner the fourth term of (15.7) introduces a third harmonic of the input signal and an additional increment of signal frequency.

The harmonic terms introduced above, when the signals are pure tones, are hard to detect by ear. However, the signal is seldom one of pure tones but rather a combination of many frequencies at once. When this is the case, the same action as above gives rise to sum and difference frequencies from the square-law action and more complex relations for higher-order effects. This is known as intermodulation distortion [Hie]. There exist special electronic instruments that measure harmonic distortion on this principle. A 400- and a 1,000-cycle sec^{-1} note, for instance, are introduced simultaneously into the input of an audio amplifier. If there is over-all square-law curvature in the amplifier, there will appear sum and difference frequencies, namely, 600 and 1,400 cycles sec^{-1}, in the output. The strength of these relative to the input components gives a measure of the amplifier harmonic distortion. Needless to say, the strength of the harmonic-distortion components grows rapidly with signal. The nature of this growth is complex, depending as it does upon the nature of the characteristics. Total harmonic distortion is measured

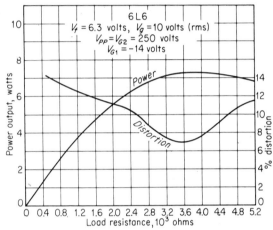

FIG. 15.5. Power output and distortion in a beam power tube as a function of load resistance.

by taking the rms value of all the harmonic terms in the output as a percentage of the fundamental term.

Harmonic distortion in triodes tends to increase at a moderate rate more or less uniformly with signal amplitude. Harmonic distortion in pentodes and beam power tubes is larger than in triodes and may increase more rapidly with signals. This action is shown in Figure 15.4. In addition, harmonic distortion in pentodes and beam power tubes increases rapidly from a minimum value with changes in load impedance, as shown in Figure 15.5. For these reasons, high-fidelity addicts prefer triode output stages.

15.3. Output Power as Determined by a Load Line. Load lines have previously been shown in Figs. 15.2b and 15.3b. A load line is simply a curve showing the relation between output current and voltage in an amplifier as a result of variations of control-electrode voltage or current. The load line is *always* a straight line regardless of the nature of the device characteristics, as may be seen from the equation relating voltage and current

$$v_p = V_P - i_p R_l \qquad (15.9)$$

which applies to a vacuum-tube amplifier with a resistance load in series with the plate lead. Here v_p is instantaneous plate voltage, V_P is the plate-supply voltage, i_p is instantaneous plate current, and R_l is the load resistance. Since V_P and R_l are constants, it is seen that the relation between v_p and i_p must be linear. The slope of this line will be

$$\frac{i_p}{v_p} = -\frac{1}{R_l} \qquad (15.10)$$

which is seen to be the negative reciprocal of the load resistance. A load line can thus be constructed by drawing a straight line with a slope of $-1/R_l$ through the point $(0, V_P)$ corresponding to zero current and plate-supply voltage. Although the load line is always a straight line, excursions from the no-signal point are not necessarily linear with signal voltage because of nonuniformities in the device characteristics. If the device characteristics were a set of parallel uniformly spaced lines, then the output waveform would be similar to the input waveform. In the absence of such ideal characteristics, harmonic distortion exists.

Output waveforms are readily constructed from Figs. 15.2 and 15.3. The degree of harmonic distortion will be influenced by both the amount of the voltage swing and the size of the load resistance. If the voltage swing in Fig. 15.2 is too great, the waveforms will be flattened out on both the top and bottom. The flattening on the bottom is due to the increased curvature of the characteristics. Flattening on the top occurs when the grid swings positive because the characteristics bend over in that region. If the plate resistance is too high, the slope of the load line will be too low and the output waveforms will first flatten on the top. If the resistance is too low, the slope of the load line will be too high and the output waveforms will first flatten on the bottom as signal is increased. From the harmonic-distortion viewpoint, then, there is an optimum load resistance.

For a *vacuum-triode* used as a Class A₁ power amplifier, a consideration of the above effects shows that the maximum undistorted power output occurs when the load resistance is equal to twice the plate resistance [Ted]. The demonstration of this property is a problem in maximization like that of carrying a ladder around a hall corner. Under the condition of load impedance equal to twice the plate resistance, the associated ideal Class A₁ triode-amplifier efficiency is 25 per cent, and practical efficiencies are less. All this is, of course, different from linear circuit theory, which would give maximum power output for a load impedance equal to the generator impedance with an efficiency of 50 per cent. When distortion limitations are considered, the current-voltage excursions are bounded and the linear circuit theory, of course, does not apply.

For the Class A_1 vacuum-pentode power amplifier, the situation is different due to the shoulder of the static characteristic. In general, for all types of devices, it may be said that the power output is maximum when the area is a maximum under the triangle formed by the load line, a vertical line through the uppermost point of the load line, and a horizontal line through the lowermost point of the load line. This comes about because the power output is approximately

$$P_{out} = \frac{(V_{max} - V_{min})(I_{max} - I_{min})}{8} \tag{15.11}$$

which is seen to be one-fourth of the area of the triangle described above. Such triangles are shown in Figs. 15.2b and 15.3b. With pentodes, a load line that gives maximum triangle area under the shoulder of the static characteristic (without swinging into the positive control-grid region or into the high-curvature region at low plate currents) calls for a load resistance about one-tenth of the plate resistance but permitting efficiencies close to 50 per cent, which is the ideal maximum for Class A_1 pentode operation.

The above comments have all been with respect to grounded-cathode circuits. These appear best suited for linear operation where a moderate power output is required and where a negligible driving power is wanted; i.e., a high power gain is desired. Other connections are, of course, not forbidden but have various limitations. Thus the grounded-grid circuit may be used. It has a relatively low input impedance and requires appreciable driving power. Accordingly, it has a moderate power gain. The grounded-plate, or cathode-follower, circuit may also be used. It has a high input impedance, a very low output impedance, and unity voltage gain. Accordingly, it is used only in special circumstances. Distortion considerations are about the same for all circuits.

With transistors, considerations are only slightly different [ShB2]. Here we again talk about Class A operation as that for which output current flows over the entire cycle. A certain amount of driving power will be required for each of the three circuit connections. Remarks will be confined to junction-transistor triodes. The grounded-base circuit has a low input impedance, a very high output impedance, and a good power gain. The grounded-emitter circuit has a higher input impedance, a lower output impedance, and a much higher gain, although with some attendant stability problems. The grounded-collector circuit has a very high input impedance, a very low output impedance, and a power loss rather than a gain. From these considerations alone, the grounded-collector circuit is eliminated and the grounded-base circuit is preferred.

Examination of the output-current-voltage relations for the three

transistor circuit connections shows characteristics as in Fig. 15.6.   From
these, considering that linearity, or low distortion, is of prime importance,

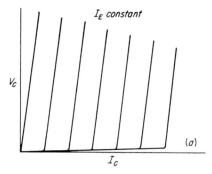

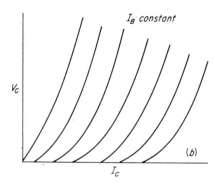

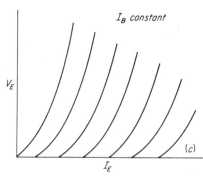

FIG. 15.6. Output characteristics of the
junction-transistor triode for various connections: (a) Grounded base.   (b)
Grounded emitter.   (c) Grounded collector.

the grounded-base circuit is preferred since it has nearly the characteristics of an ideal device.

A limitation of the grounded-base
connection is the low input impedance, which is approximately an
inverse function of emitter current.
This dependence is strong enough
to require that the source impedance be high to give an equivalent
circuit with values fairly constant.
Failure to provide this introduces
considerable harmonic distortion
from this source alone.   This is
roughly the dual consideration of
requiring a low impedance in the
control-grid circuit of a vacuum-
tube amplifier to reduce distortion
due to grid-current flow.

Considering   then   that   the
grounded-base circuit is most suitable for Class A power amplification, let us examine the limitations
on the load line.   These are shown
in Fig. 15.7.   A first limitation is
that there is a maximum power
dissipation, which must not be exceeded.   The contour of maximum
allowable power dissipation is a
hyperbola.   The operating point
must lie below this hyperbola.
Another limitation is the maximum
peak inverse voltage.   This must
not be exceeded or else nonlinearity
of current with voltage is encountered.   A third limitation is that
there is a maximum collector current, which must not be exceeded

or the value of the current-amplification factor α will fall off.   There is
also a limitation on the minimum voltage to avoid curvature of characteristics.   This, however, is not serious in the case of the grounded-base
amplifier because the voltage can fall to nearly zero before the character-

istics depart from linearity. The load line must then be fitted between these various limiting contours in such a way as to give maximum power or maximum area under the triangle formed by the load line itself and vertical and horizontal lines through the minimum current and the minimum voltage, respectively.

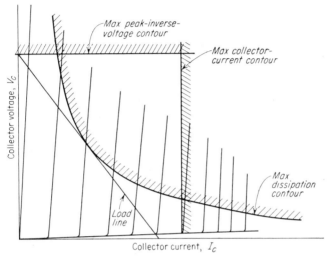

FIG. 15.7. Load-line limitations of the grounded-base-transistor amplifier.

15.4. Determination of Harmonic Distortion from a Load Line.

To determine the harmonic distortion in an amplifier, it is first necessary to know the waveform of the output current or voltage. This is easily obtained either numerically or graphically from taking points off the load line corresponding to various parts of the signal-voltage curve. When the waveform is known, there can then be made a Fourier-series analysis. Since the waveform is not known analytically, the work must be done numerically, taking values every 10 or 20°. Such a procedure will give a high accuracy for the first half dozen or so harmonics.

Since the output waveforms of the Class A amplifier are only slightly nonsinusoidal, expressions for them can be approximated using only the first few terms of a Fourier's series. Thus if only the second harmonic is of interest, we may write, in the case of a grounded-cathode-triode amplifier,

$$i_p = A_0 + A_1 \cos \omega t + A_2 \cos 2\omega t \qquad (15.12)$$

This polynomial, having three unknown coefficients, requires three values of i_p for its determination. These are supplied by taking values of ωt every 90° as follows:

$$\omega t = 0°: \qquad I_{max} = A_0 + A_1 + A_2 \qquad (15.13)$$
$$\omega t = 90°: \qquad I_0 = A_0 + 0 - A_2 \qquad (15.14)$$
$$\omega t = 180°: \qquad I_{min} = A_0 - A_1 + A_2 \qquad (15.15)$$

These are readily solved to give the various components:

Fundamental: $\qquad A_1 = \frac{1}{2}(I_{max} - I_{min})$ $\qquad\qquad\qquad$ (15.16)

Second harmonic: $\qquad A_2 = \frac{1}{4}(I_{max} + I_{min} - 2I_0)$ $\qquad\qquad$ (15.17)

Direct current: $\qquad A_0 = \frac{1}{4}(I_{max} + I_{min} + 2I_0)$ $\qquad\qquad$ (15.18)

The first result above, that of (15.16), is more or less obvious but is actually strictly true only in the absence of odd harmonics. The second result, that of (15.17), is new useful information obtained from maximum, minimum, and zero signal values. The third result, that of (15.18), shows that the d-c component with signal is slightly different from the no-signal value; i.e., a rectified component is introduced. If the zero signal component I_0 is subtracted out, the rectified component $A_0 - I_0$ is found to be the same in magnitude as the second harmonic component. This is a conclusion previously reached in (15.8) in connection with second-order distortion effects.

A more accurate determination of harmonics requires introducing values from more points. If there are introduced, in addition to the above, values of output current for 45 and 135° of the cycle and these be called I_2 and I_3, respectively, then approximate values of harmonics up to the fourth are as follows:

Fundamental: $A_1 = \frac{1}{4}[1.414(I_2 - I_3) + I_{max} - I_{min}]$ $\qquad\qquad$ (15.19)

Second Harmonic:

$$A_2 = \frac{1}{4}(I_{max} + I_{min} - 2I_0) \qquad\qquad (15.20)$$

Third Harmonic:

$$A_3 = \frac{1}{2}(I_{max} - I_{min} - 2A_1) \qquad\qquad (15.21)$$

Fourth Harmonic:

$$A_4 = \frac{1}{2}(2A_0 - I_2 - I_3) \qquad\qquad (15.22)$$

Direct current:

$$A_0 = \frac{1}{4}[\frac{1}{2}(I_{max} + I_{min}) + I_2 + I_3 + I_0] \qquad\qquad (15.23)$$

Thus by taking only five values of current it is possible to approximate the current waveform by the first five terms of a Fourier's series. The direct, fundamental, and second harmonic components are more accurately given than before but will not be greatly different numerically. The third and fourth harmonics are easily determined. In deciding which equations to use, one should compare the third harmonic [(15.21)] with the fundamental as given by (15.16). If it is small enough, Eqs. (15.16) to (15.18) may be used. If not, then Eqs. (15.19) to (15.23) should be used. Frequently the first set may be supplemented with (15.21) and (15.22) with sufficient accuracy.

15.5. Small-signal Detection and Modulation Circuits. Another use to which the slight nonlinearity of control-type electron devices may be put is that of effecting detection or modulation. Here discussion will be restricted to small-signal operation. Actually, large-signal types of detectors and modulators are more common.

It has already been pointed out in Sec. 9.5 that detection of this type is possible with diodes. For control-type devices, the same function is achieved by the slightly nonlinear transfer characteristic. Here the equation corresponding to (9.13) is

$$i_2(v_1) = a_1 v_1 + a_2 v_1^2 + \cdots + a_n v_1^n + \cdots \qquad (15.24)$$

which would apply between the output current and input voltage of any kind of vacuum tube or transistor. The analysis of the effect of this characteristic upon an amplitude-modulated wave is then the same as for a diode. Basically, the amplitude-modulated signal consists of a carrier and upper and lower sidebands equally spaced in frequency. The first term of (15.24) merely reproduces the input signal and is not of interest. The second, or square-law, term of (15.24) produces sums and differences of all the input frequencies. These include the desired audio signal and an undesired second harmonic of the audio signal. There are also produced some radio-frequency components, which are not of interest and are filtered out. This type of detection has the disadvantage of containing an inherent amount of distortion; and as a result, it is seldom used. It does, however, illustrate in principle the action of a slightly nonlinear characteristic.

Modulation is the inverse process of detection, or demodulation. It is the process whereby some aspect of a radio-frequency carrier is caused to vary in accordance with variations in an audio signal. The commonest type of modulation is amplitude modulation, in which the amplitude of the carrier is caused to vary in accordance with an audio signal. The expression for an amplitude-modulated signal has already been given as

$$v(t) = V_r(1 + m \cos \omega_a t) \cos \omega_r t \qquad (15.25)$$

where the subscript r denotes radio and the subscript a denotes audio. This expression expands to give

$$v(t) = \tfrac{1}{2} m V_r \cos (\omega_r + \omega_a)t + V_r \cos \omega_r t + \tfrac{1}{2} m V_r \cos (\omega_r - \omega_a)t \qquad (15.26)$$

showing that an amplitude-modulated wave is equivalent to the sum of three sine waves related as in (15.26). Conceptually, it is important to recognize that the modulated-wave representations of Fig. 15.8a and 15.8b are equivalent. That of Fig. 15.8a is most easily related to (15.25) and shows what one would see if an amplitude-modulated wave were applied to an oscilloscope. That of Fig. 15.8b is most easily related to

(15.26) and shows what would be measured by a frequency meter or wave analyzer.

The important properties of amplitude-modulated waves should be borne in mind. Maximum value of the modulation index m is unity. Sideband components are $m/2$ times as big as the carrier, being half as big for 100% modulation. At maximum modulation the power in each sideband is only 25 per cent of that of the carrier, giving total sideband power as a maximum of 50 per cent of the carrier. For lower degrees of modulation the power varies as $m^2/4$ times the carrier power in each sideband. Thus the majority of the power is in the carrier, which carries no

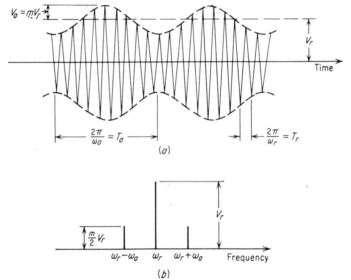

Fig. 15.8. Aspects of an amplitude-modulated wave: (a) The time aspect. (b) The frequency aspect.

intelligence. This makes amplitude modulation an inefficient form of modulation. It is, however, extensively used because of its simplicity.

An amplitude-modulated wave can be created by combining three sine waves, as indicated in (15.26). However, it is not sufficient for the three waves to have the proper relative amplitudes and frequencies; they must also have the proper relative *phase*, or a frequency-modulated wave will result. The phase requirement for an amplitude-modulated wave is that the time vectors for the three waves should add to the sum of the absolute magnitudes once each audio cycle. The phases of (15.25) are correct for this. If the carrier were a cosine wave and the sidebands were sine waves, the phases would not be correct and a frequency-modulated wave would result.

If now the transfer characteristic of an electron device is slightly nonlinear, amplitude modulation may be achieved simply by injecting radio and audio components into various parts of the circuit. The linear term reproduces the carrier. The square-law term gives sum and difference frequencies corresponding to the sidebands, and amplitude modulation results, accompanied by some distortion terms. The modulation efficiency is very low, but fortunately the desired frequency and phase requirements are met to produce an amplitude-modulated wave.

There is always a transfer characteristic which can be expanded into a Taylor's series of a composite variable. For the grounded-cathode vacuum tube, this is

$$i_p = f\left(v_g + \frac{v_p}{\mu}\right) = a_0\left(V_G + \frac{V_P}{\mu}\right) + a_1\left(v_g + \frac{v_p}{\mu}\right)$$
$$+ a_2\left(v_g + \frac{v_p}{\mu}\right)^2 + \cdots \quad (15.27)$$

For the grounded-base transistor, it is

$$v_c = f(\alpha i_e + i_c) = b_0(\alpha I_E + I_C) + b_1(\alpha i_e + i_c)$$
$$+ b_2(\alpha i_e + i_c)^2 + \cdots \quad (15.28)$$

where the subscripts g, p, e, c stand for grid, plate, emitter, and collector, respectively, μ is voltage-amplification factor, and α is current-amplification factor.

Both audio- and radio-frequency components may be introduced in series into the input circuit or into the output circuit. In addition, one may be introduced into the input and the other into the output. There are thus four arrangements possible. The action in each case is much the same, namely, that described above. The reader can easily verify that any of the four combinations will yield output components adding up to form an amplitude-modulated wave.

CHAPTER 16

LARGE-SIGNAL APPLICATIONS
OF ELECTRON DEVICES

16.1. Introduction. In previous chapters there have been discussed methods of analyzing electron-device operation for small- and medium-signal levels. For still larger levels different methods must be applied.

It will be recalled that for small signals the device characteristics were approximated by a single linear function. For larger signals the curvature of the characteristics was introduced, usually through a power-series approximation. For very large signals it is rarely possible to represent the characteristics by a single function. Instead the characteristics are usually best approximated by segments of simple functions, which are joined to make a continuous function. Frequently the characteristics can be closely approximated by straight-line segments, which are joined. An example is the approximation of a rectifier characteristic by two joined straight-line segments. However, in some cases the characteristics are approximated by segments of other functions. These other functions are usually simple but nonlinear.

It is not always apparent that there is a common denominator to all the various approaches to this topic. However, one common feature has already been mentioned, namely, that the characteristics are approximated by joining segments of simple functions. The other common feature is that standard methods of analysis are then applied piecewise to the approximate representations. These standard methods are usually the Fourier-series analysis for some steady-state situations and methods such as the operational calculus or the Laplace transform for others. The former usually applies where circuit elements are resistive; the latter, where reactive elements are included. If the reader will look for these common features of the large-signal methods of analysis, they will be readily apparent even though the approaches used in different cases at first seem unrelated.

16.2. Class B Amplifier Operation. This has previously been defined as operation in which output current flows in approximately half-sine-wave pulses when the input is a full sine wave. In the case of vacuum-tube amplifiers this requires that the tube be biased approximately to plate-current cutoff. Attention in this discussion will first be centered on vacuum-tube amplifiers.

Since in this type of operation each tube passes only a half sine wave, the output of two tubes must be combined for audio amplification. This requires connection of the two tubes with a common output transformer in what is known as a push-pull circuit. This is shown in Fig. 16.1 along with current waveforms in various parts of the circuit. A feature of this connection is that even-ordered harmonics are canceled in the output if

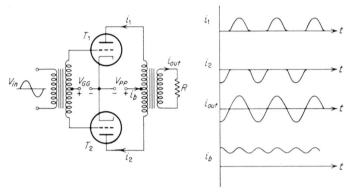

FIG. 16.1. Push-pull Class B audio-amplifier circuit and waveforms.

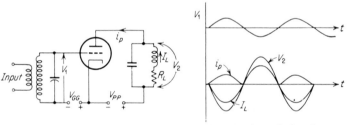

FIG. 16.2. Class B radio-frequency-amplifier circuit and waveforms.

the tubes are identical. Fundamental and odd-ordered harmonics combine in the output. Since the second harmonic is usually the largest distortion component, the push-pull circuit tends to be a low-distortion circuit.

Class B *radio-frequency* amplification is possible with a single tube if the output circuit contains a high-Q parallel-resonant circuit, which will maintain a sine wave of voltage even though excited with half-sine-wave pulses. Such an amplifier has a linearity between input and output but is restricted to a narrow band of frequencies as determined by the resonant response of the output circuit. The circuit of a Class B radio-frequency amplifier is shown in Fig. 16.2.

In either case, the tube characteristic can be approximated by, for $(v_g + v_p/\mu) \geqq 0$,

$$i_p = g_m \left(v_g + \frac{v_p}{\mu} \right)$$

(16.1)

or

$$i_p = 0$$

for $(v_g + v_p/\mu) \leqq 0$ [Evn]. A typical actual characteristic and the idealized characteristic, consisting of two straight-line segments, is shown in Fig. 16.3. The above approximation can usually be made sufficiently good for Class B application by proper selection of a bias voltage. Although the characteristic is concave upward at low equivalent voltages, it will usually be concave downward at high equivalent voltages owing to a combination of current saturation and diversion of plate current to a positive grid. For best linear operation the bias should be selected so as to give the best fit of the curves in Fig. 16.3. This will result in some current still flowing when the input signal is zero but in negligible effect for large signals.

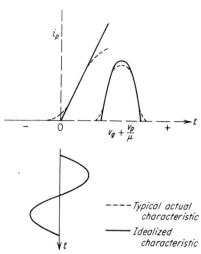

---- Typical actual characteristic

——— Idealized characteristic

Fig. 16.3. Actual and idealized vacuum-tube characteristics and resultant waveforms in Class B operation.

For either audio or radio signals, current, voltage, or power components can be computed by applying the Fourier-series analysis to the ideal characteristic of Fig. 16.3. Thus the fundamental component of plate current is given by considering

$$i_p = i_{p,\text{max}} \cos \theta \qquad \text{for } -\frac{\pi}{2} \leqq \theta \leqq \frac{\pi}{2}$$

$$= 0 \qquad \text{for } \frac{\pi}{2} \leqq \theta \leqq \frac{3}{2}\pi$$

(16.2)

where $i_{p,\text{max}}$ is the maximum instantaneous value of plate current. Accordingly, the maximum value of the fundamental component of plate current is given by

$$I_2 = \frac{i_{p,\text{max}}}{\pi} \int_{-\pi/2}^{\pi/2} \cos^2 \theta \, d\theta = \frac{i_{p,\text{max}}}{2}$$

(16.3)

and the direct component of plate current is given by

$$I_P = \frac{i_{p,\text{max}}}{2} \int_{-\pi/2}^{\pi/2} \cos \theta \, d\theta = \frac{i_{p,\text{max}}}{\pi}$$

(16.4)

To find the magnitude of the plate-current components in terms of the excitation and load resistance, it is necessary to refer to the approximate characteristic of (16.1). From this the maximum value of plate current is given by

$$i_{p,\text{max}} = g_m \left(v_{g,\text{max}} + \frac{v_{p,\text{min}}}{\mu} \right) \tag{16.5}$$

since the maximum of plate current coincides with the maximum of grid voltage and with the minimum of plate voltage for a resistive load, as

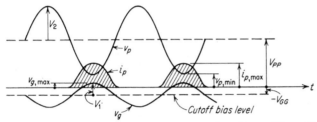

FIG. 16.4. Relative phase of voltages and current in a Class B amplifier with a resistive load.

shown in Fig. 16.4. The voltage components in turn are given by

$$v_{g,\text{max}} = V_{GG} + V_1 \tag{16.6}$$

where V_{GG} = bias voltage
  V_1 = max value of fundamental component of grid voltage
Likewise,

$$v_{p,\text{min}} = V_{PP} - \frac{i_{p,\text{max}}}{2} R_l \tag{16.7}$$

by virtue of (16.3), where V_{PP} is direct plate potential and R_l is the shunt resistance of the tuned plate circuit. Substituting these last two equations into (16.5), there results

$$i_{p,\text{max}} = g_m \left(V_1 - \frac{i_{p,\text{max}} R_l}{2\mu} \right) \tag{16.8}$$

since

$$V_{GG} + \frac{V_{PP}}{\mu} = 0 \tag{16.9}$$

which corresponds to the tube being biased to cutoff as required for Class B operation. Solving (16.8) for $i_{p,\text{max}}$ yields

$$i_{p,\text{max}} = \frac{\mu V_1}{R_l + 2r_p} \tag{16.10}$$

This equation shows the linearity of the Class B amplifier and applies to either the two-tube push-pull audio amplifier or to the single-tube radio amplifier. In the push-pull audio case the total fundamental component in the primary of the audio transformer is twice the fundamental component of either tube alone, that is,

$$I_{2,tot} = 2I_2 = i_{p,\max} \tag{16.11}$$

For the single-tube radio-frequency amplifier (16.3) applies.

Another observation that can be made from (16.10) is that the equivalent output impedance, per tube, of a Class B amplifier is $2r_p$. This is a consequence of the output waveform. In general, the output impedance increases as the angle of flow of plate current decreases [Evn].

The linear relation between $i_{p,\max}$ and V_1 seen in (16.10) also results in a linearity of I_2 and I_P with V_1, where I_P is the d-c component of plate current. This, of course, results from the linearity of the assumed characteristic. However, the variation of I_2 and I_P with V_1 in an actual case will be more linear than the actual characteristic because there is an integration process involved in the determination of these two components. It is well known in numerical approximation that the area under one curve approximating another will be closer to the actual area than the approximate curve is to the actual curve.

The efficiency of either audio- or radio-frequency Class B amplifiers can be estimated by taking the ratio of output a-c power to input d-c power.

$$P_{out} = \frac{V_2 I_2}{2} = \frac{(V_{PP} - V_{p,\min})i_{p,\max}}{4} \tag{16.12}$$

$$P_{in} = V_{PP}I_P = \frac{V_{PP}i_{p,\max}}{\pi} \tag{16.13}$$

The ratio of the above two expressions yields

$$\text{Efficiency} = \frac{\pi}{4}\left(1 - \frac{V_{p,\min}}{V_{PP}}\right) \tag{16.14}$$

Since the lowest value which $V_{p,\min}$ can assume is zero, the maximum theoretical efficiency is $\pi/4$ or 78.5 per cent. Actual practical maximum efficiency is somewhat less than this. If the minimum instantaneous plate voltage becomes less than the maximum instantaneous grid voltage, the grid begins to draw an excessive amount of current and a dip appears in the crest of the plate-current pulse. This condition usually corresponds to maximum output with minimum instantaneous plate voltage at about one-tenth of direct plate voltage. Under this condition efficiency is about 70 per cent.

The above remarks, made with respect to vacuum tubes, will also apply completely to transistors. The principal difference will be that the vacuum-tube circuits have relatively high-impedance inputs and low-impedance outputs. With transistors the reverse is the case, although even the high-impedance transistor levels are lower than the low-impedance tube levels. Accordingly, more attention must be paid to driving power in the case of the transistor.

With the development of complementary *n-p-n* and *p-n-p* junction transistors, some new transistor-circuit possibilities have been opened up [SzD]. By complementary transistors are meant types with voltage-current characteristics differing only in the algebraic sign of the currents and voltages. With such transistors it is possible to devise Class B audio-amplifier circuits that do not require a center-tapped output trans-former. Such single-ended circuits are not possible with vacuum tubes. Shown in Fig. 16.5 are two such circuits. These circuits have output impedances low enough to permit direct connection to moving-coil loud-speaker elements.

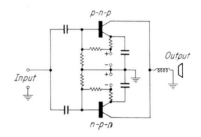

The first of these circuits uses *parallel* (rather than push-pull) connected *n-p-n* and *p-n-p* grounded-emitter-transistor stages. When the input voltage swings positive, the *n-p-n* transistor conducts, the current being through the load into the transistor. When the input voltage swings negative, the *p-n-p* transistor conducts, the current being out of the transistor through the load into ground. Bias is secured through resistive potential dividers across the supply for each transistor. The supply voltage is in

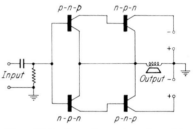

Fig. 16.5. Complementary-transistor Class B audio-amplifier circuits not requiring a center-tapped output transformer.

the emitter lead of each transistor and is opposite in polarity for the two types.

The second of the circuits in Fig. 16.5 uses parallel direct-coupled amplifiers. Each half uses one of the two types of transistor in tandem. The two parallel halves have complementary symmetry.

16.3. Class C Amplifiers. The Class C amplifier is one in which the input is biased so that output current flows for less than half a cycle. Such amplifiers generally use a single tube with a large driving voltage. They are nonlinear in their relation between input and output voltage and require tuned circuits to sustain sinusoidal voltages in their input and output. The relation between fundamental *output* current and direct *output* voltage for a fixed-signal input tends to be linear, which makes the circuit useful as a modulator. They are invariably used at a single radio frequency. A consequence of the mode of operation is very high efficiency—up to 80 per cent—and power gains of the order of 10 to 20.

Class C amplifier design and analysis is discussed in detail in other sources and so will be discussed only briefly here [Evn, GrD, Ted].

A simplified Class C amplifier circuit is shown in Fig. 16.6.   Here are

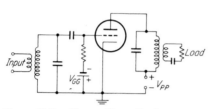

shown the tuned input and output circuits with coupling for excitation and load.   Grid bias is usually obtained from a combination of fixed potential and resistive drop resulting from grid current flowing during the positive peaks of grid voltage. The latter component is easiest to provide, but the former is necessary to ensure that bias is not lost if

FIG. 16.6. Class C radio-frequency-amplifier circuit.

excitation should fail.   Were bias to be lost, the grid would assume zero potential, which would result in a large continuous current drawn by the plate with possible attendant damage.

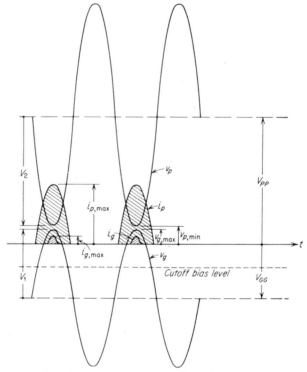

FIG. 16.7. Current and voltage waveforms in a Class C amplifier with a resistive load.

Current-voltage relations are similar to those encountered in the Class B amplifier except that plate current flows for less than half a cycle and grid-current pulses for positive grid swings are big enough to require consideration. These relations are shown in Fig. 16.7. It is observed that both grid and plate current flow in short pulses. Grid and plate voltage are, however, sustained in sinusoidal form by tuned resonant circuits.

Power into the plate circuit and load is supplied from a direct source. This direct power is partly converted into radio-frequency output power and partly dissipated as heat on the plate of the tube itself. Thus

$$I_P V_{PP} = \frac{I_2 V_2}{2} + W_p \tag{16.15}$$

where $I_P V_{PP}$ = direct input power

$I_2 V_2/2$ = alternating output power

W_p = plate dissipation

In contrast, the power into the grid circuit is supplied from the driving source in alternating form. This input power is partly converted into direct power, which heats the grid resistor or charges the bias battery. The rest heats the grid. Thus

$$\frac{I_1 V_1}{2} = I_G V_{GG} + W_g \tag{16.16}$$

where $I_1 V_1/2$ = alternating driving power

$I_G V_{GG}$ = rectified direct power into bias source

W_g = power dissipated on the grid

It is helpful in discussing Class C operation to have an over-all picture of the dynamic characteristics of a Class C amplifier. By dynamic

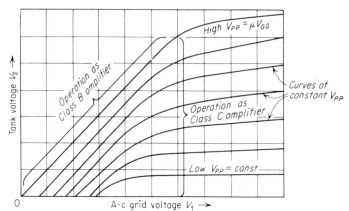

FIG. 16.8. Dynamic characteristics of a Class C radio-frequency amplifier: alternating output voltage as a function of alternating grid voltage and of direct plate voltage for combination bias.

characteristics are meant the relations between the various alternating and direct currents and voltages for conditions of steady alternating excitation. Such dynamic characteristics show the effect of four independently adjustable parameters. These are alternating grid voltage or signal excitation, grid bias, direct plate voltage and load resistance. The dependent variables are direct and alternating grid current, which in turn determine driving power, bias power required, and grid dissipation

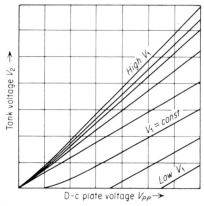

High V_1

$V_1 = const$

Low V_1

D-c plate voltage $V_{PP} \rightarrow$

Tank voltage $V_2 \rightarrow$

FIG. 16.9. Dynamic characteristics of a Class C radio-frequency amplifier: alternative representation of Fig. 16.8.

in the grid circuit, and direct and alternating components of plate current, which combined with other quantities determine power output and plate loss. These account for the 10 quantities in (16.15) and (16.16), of which 4 are independent and 6 are dependent.

It is a little difficult to represent graphically, let alone analytically, the relation between all the quantities mentioned above. A partial representation is given in Figs. 16.8 and 16.9. In the first of these figures is shown the alternating output voltage as a function of the alternating input voltage for various direct plate voltages [Evn]. It is seen that for the topmost curve, corresponding to Class B operation, the relation between output and input alternating voltages is linear up to a condition of saturation, which occurs when the minimum plate voltage drops below the maximum grid voltage. For fixed bias and load resistance lower values of direct plate voltage give Class C operation, which is progressively less linear as the direct plate voltage is reduced. In Fig. 16.9 is shown the variation of output alternating voltage as a function of direct plate voltage for various values of input signal alternating voltage. In this alternative representation of Fig. 16.8 it is seen that, for large enough signal excitation, the output voltage is linear with direct plate voltage. This action occurs only for the saturation region of Fig. 16.8. It is this feature of Class C amplifier operation which makes it suitable for amplitude modulation.

The operation of Class C amplifiers may be explained by reference to constant-current curves such as are shown in Fig. 10.9. Such curves are shown again in Fig. 16.10 with some additional features added to explain Class C operation. These include the cutoff line and lines corresponding to two and three times cutoff bias (Class C amplifiers are usually biased to two or three times cutoff). Of particular interest here is a *voltage-excursion line*. Since both grid and plate voltages are sinusoidal and 180° out of phase, the locus of instantaneous plate and grid voltage is a straight line, which will be known as the voltage-excursion line. A scale of electrical degrees can be marked off on this line as shown. Plate- and grid-current pulses can be constructed from intersections of the voltage-excursion line with the constant-current contours. The plate current flows for points on the voltage-excursion line above the cutoff line, that is,

$$i_p > 0 \qquad \text{for} \left(v_g + \frac{v_p}{\mu} \right) > 0 \qquad\qquad (16.17)$$

so that

$$\cos \theta_p = \frac{V_{GG} + V_{PP}/\mu}{V_2/\mu - V_1} \qquad\qquad (16.18)$$

since $v_g = V_{GG} + V_1 \cos \theta$ and $v_p = V_{PP} - V_2 \cos \theta$, where θ_p is the half

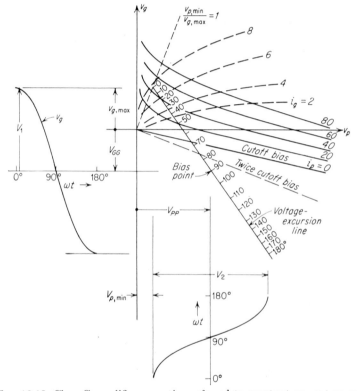

FIG. 16.10. Class C amplifier operation referred to constant-current curves.

angle of plate-current flow.   Similarly, grid current flows only for positive grid voltages, that is,

$$i_g > 0 \qquad \text{for } v_g > 0 \qquad\qquad (16.19)$$

so that

$$\cos \theta_g = - \frac{V_{GG}}{V_1} \qquad\qquad (16.20)$$

where θ_g is the half angle of grid-current flow.   Note that V_{GG} is usually a negative number.

Having in mind the representation of Fig. 16.10, we must now consider the problem of design.   This generally takes the form of determining the operating conditions that will give the greatest output and power amplification without exceeding the operating limitations of the tube.   These operating limitations include, in order of importance for *this* type of service, plate dissipation, grid dissipation, breakdown voltage, and peak emission.   Many design procedures are available to treat this complex problem.   These will be discussed briefly.

One such design procedure is based upon a linearization of the tube characteristics as used for Class B amplifiers and as shown in Fig. 16.3 [Evn].   By this method it is possible to analyze the problem and establish design curves to indicate the operating conditions for maximum output. This means that, given the plate dissipation and plate voltage, the procedure indicates the grid bias, the grid driving voltage, and the load resistance required to give maximum output.   This is quite an achievement for one set of design curves.   However, the method has some limitations.   The curves of some tubes have sufficient curvature so that the linear approximation is not good.   Also the design method sometimes calls for large grid driving voltages and grid dissipation.   Attempts to include grid dissipation as another limiting factor in the design are moderately successful but involve additional complications [Evm].

One means of taking into account the curvature of the tube characteristics provides curves from numerical integration based upon a tube characteristic of the form

$$i_s = i_p + i_g = K\left(v_g + \frac{v_p}{\mu}\right)^n \tag{16.21}$$

where K and n are constants for a particular tube, which are easily measured [Ted].   This constitutes a second important method.   Assumptions are made as to values of peak grid voltage, grid bias, plate-supply voltage, and minimum plate voltage.   These values determine the angles of grid- and plate-current flow according to (16.18) and (16.20).   Peak values of space current are determined from (16.21), using maximum grid voltage and minimum plate voltage.   From one set of simple curves the ratio of fundamental and direct components of current to maximum value may be determined.   These values enable the determination of the other quantities desired.

It is necessary in this second method to determine the division of the space current between grid and plate since Class C operation invariably involves swings to positive grid voltage.   This is readily done for peak current by means of (10.6), the current-division constant k_1 being a quantity easily measured.   When the maximum grid current is known, the fundamental and direct components of grid current can be determined from the fact that grid-current pulses commonly have a cosine-squared form over the angle of flow.

This second method is fairly accurate and rapid.   However, a number of trial-and-error computations are required to determine optimum operating conditions.

A third method, which is the most accurate of all, makes use of Fig. 16.10 to determine the shape of the grid- and plate-current pulses. It is usually necessary to use this method in cases where the grid exhibits appreciable secondary emission because no good approximations for grid current are available in this case. The fundamental and direct components of grid and plate current are determined by summations approximating the integrals used in the Fourier-series evaluation. It is usually sufficient to determine values of grid and plate current for every 10° of the voltage cycle. Performance is quite critical in peak current and associated voltages, i.e., the location of the upper end of the voltage-excursion line in Fig. 16.10. Although this method is the most laborious, it is most universally applicable [Crd, GrD].

Good operating conditions of Class C amplifiers with triodes will generally involve power gains of 10:1 and plate efficiencies of 70 to 80 per cent. With tetrodes and pentodes only the third method of analysis can be used, and even this requires constant-current curves. Power gains of as high as 50 may be obtained with such tubes.

16.4. Multivibrators. Another large-signal circuit is the multivibrator. The term multivibrator indicates a free-running circuit which generates a succession of uniformly spaced square (or rectangular) waves. It is specifically the astable form, which is the square-wave oscillator, as distinct from forms that require external excitation.

From one point of view, the astable multivibrator is simply an oscillator without resonant circuits that limits its own current and voltage waveforms by device saturation. Shown in Fig. 16.11 is such a circuit. It consists of a two-stage RC amplifier in which part of the output is fed back to the input. Such a circuit is capable of giving either sine-wave or square-wave oscillations, depending upon the adjustment of the feedback potentiometer. If this is set too low, no

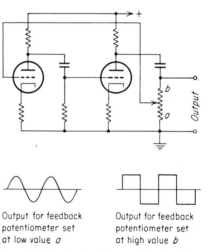

Output for feedback potentiometer set at low value a

Output for feedback potentiometer set at high value b

Fig. 16.11. A circuit capable of giving sine-wave or square-wave oscillations.

oscillations will occur at all. When the β factor (scalar for resistive potentiometer) becomes equal to the reciprocal of the amplification factor, oscillations can begin, in accordance with the principle of Sec. 14.3, which requires that $A\beta = 1$, where A is the amplification and β is the feedback factor.

Under the condition that the fraction of the output voltage fed back to the input is equal to, or slightly greater than, the reciprocal of the amplification, nearly pure sine waves will result. This circuit is, however, a poor oscillator circuit in that both amplitude and frequency have poor stability. The amplitude stability is poor because in the vicinity of this adjustment the amplification does not drop off much with increasing signal level. The frequency stability is poor because this RC circuit will have a slow variation of phase with frequency and will have a hard time deciding at which frequency to oscillate.

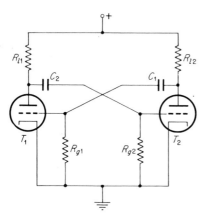

FIG. 16.12. Conventional vacuum-tube multivibrator circuit.

As the feedback-potentiometer setting is increased, the β factor is increased and the A factor must decrease in magnitude for their product to remain unity. This occurs as a result of increase in the signal level and attendant distortion of waveform. This distortion takes the form of flattening the tops and bottoms of the waves and results in a reduced amplification since for a given peak value the fundamental component of the waves decreases as the distortion increases, as discussed in connection with Fig. 14.7. The limit occurs when the feedback factor is unity and the waveforms are practically square.

The free-running, or astable, multivibrator circuit uses a unity feedback factor and is commonly drawn as shown in Fig. 16.12 [Ted, Reg, Sea2]. The action of this circuit can be explained in terms of amplifier operation. Assume that both tubes are conducting and that the voltage on the grid of T_1 is increasing. This causes the current in T_1 to increase and the voltage on the grid of T_2 to decrease, which in turn decreases the current in T_2 and causes the voltage on the grid of T_1 to be increased further. This action goes on very rapidly until the grid of T_2 is driven to cutoff and the current in T_1 assumes its maximum value. Beyond these conditions the circuit cannot go. These conditions will not last, however, because the charges on C_1 and C_2 will gradually leak off. This will gradually bring up the voltage on the grid of T_2 until T_2 begins to conduct. This then begins a similar chain of events, which results in T_2 being conducting and T_1 nonconducting.

As will be seen later, this action can also be explained by showing that the circuit is self-triggering between two stable states. The time required for a change from one state to another will depend upon the change of potential between states and the distributed capacity across the plates.

The time the circuit spends in one limiting condition will depend upon the time constant of the C_1R_{g1} and the C_2R_{g2} combination. The period of the square-wave oscillations is approximately twice the sum of the time constants of the two above-named combinations. In general, the rise time will depend upon the same factors that would determine the high-frequency performance of the circuit operated as an amplifier, whereas the period will depend upon the factors that would determine the low-frequency performance of the circuit operated as an amplifier.

Multivibrator circuits can, of course, also be made using transistors [SuC, SaD]. Since a two-stage RC-coupled amplifier can be made with various combinations of grounded-emitter, grounded-base, and grounded-collector stages, a number of multivibrator circuits are possible. A few of these are shown in Fig. 16.13. All these circuits produce square waves by alternate cutoff action in the two transistors involved. The period of oscillation is again determined by low-frequency-amplifier considerations, and the steepness of the output voltage in changing from conduction in one transistor to conduction in the other is determined

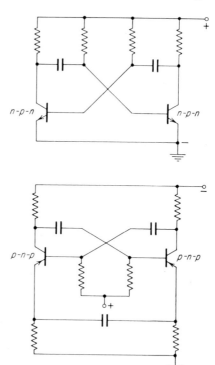

FIG. 16.13. Some transistor multivibrator circuits.

by high-frequency-amplifier considerations. In contrast to tube multivibrators, transistor multivibrators will have their "change times" governed more by equivalent circuit elements within the transistor than by distributed capacities outside, as is the case with tube circuits.

16.5. Trigger Circuits. Another large-signal special ability that electron devices have is to serve as trigger circuits [Reg, Chb, Sea2]. A trigger circuit is a circuit exhibiting two stable states and in which a small voltage, properly applied, is sufficient to cause the circuit to change from one state to another. Such circuits are also called flip-flop circuits. They are used in pulse generation, storage of information, counting, and in similar applications.

Trigger circuits generally owe their operation to an S- or N-shaped current-voltage characteristic as seen from a pair of terminals. Such a characteristic exhibits a negative resistance over part of its extent. When used with an external positive resistance, two stable states are available at the extremities of the negative-resistance region.

The operation of the above action is shown in Fig. 16.14. Here is shown a positive resistance R in series with a device whose characteristic has a negative-resistance region as evidenced by the negative slope between c and e. The relation between the current and the voltage across the device is given by

$$V = V_0 - IR \tag{16.22}$$

This relation leads to a load line, as in Sec. 15.3, which passes through the value of V_0 on the V axis and has a slope of $-1/R$. Permissible values of current are those corresponding to intersections of the load line and the device characteristic. Such intersections are at b, d, and f for the solid

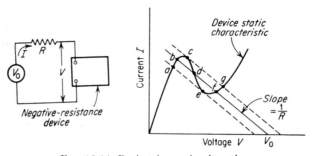

FIG. 16.14. Basic trigger-circuit action.

load line. Only the intersections at b and f, where the device characteristic exhibits a positive resistance, are stable. The intersection at d is unstable. This occurs since variations in voltage and current must follow the device characteristic because of reactances outside the device. Thus at point d a decrease in device voltage causes an increase in device current, which in turn decreases the device voltage further because of an increased voltage drop between the generator and the device. This action will carry the operating point over the top of the curve to the point b, where stable operation is had. Operation can now be stable between a and c as the generator voltage is varied between values corresponding to the upper and lower dashed load lines. If the generator voltage is raised slightly beyond the value for c, the operating point will jump to g. Operation will be stable above g and between g and e. If the generator voltage is dropped slightly below that corresponding to e, the operating point will jump to a, where operation is again stable. It is seen then that a relatively small voltage change can cause the device current to jump from one value to another.

Many vacuum-tube- and transistor-circuit characteristics exhibit the required S or N shape. A few of these will now be mentioned. The oldest of these still extensively used is the Eccles-Jordan trigger circuit, shown in Fig. 16.15. This is a two-tube bistable multivibrator circuit. It is similar to the free-running, or astable, multivibrator circuit of the previous section but uses direct instead of capacitive coupling. The N-shaped IV characteristic is shown in the same figure. This N-shaped characteristic results from an ohmic component I_1 into the terminals ab and a tube component I_2. The ohmic component is positive when the voltage is positive. The tube component is negative for small positive voltages. A positive voltage at b is applied to the grid of T_1 and causes a large electron current to flow out of the tube or a conventional current to flow *into* the tube T_1 and out of the tube T_2. The tube component dominates and thus gives a negative resistance until tube T_1 saturates and T_2 is cut off. Beyond this condition the tube component is constant and the ohmic component ultimately dominates, giving a positive resistance and later a positive current for a positive voltage. For the value of V_0 shown in the figure, stable currents correspond to points 1 and 3, point 2 being unstable. To change from a positive to a negative stable current, it is necessary for V_0 to swing through a value ΔV_0 and for the associated load lines to swing between the dashed limits shown.

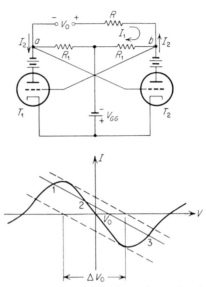

Fig. 16.15. Eccles-Jordan trigger circuit and characteristic.

A practical circuit is shown in Fig. 16.16. The tubes are alternately triggered into a conducting state by negative pulses passed through diodes T_3 and T_4. The diodes serve to render the circuit insensitive to positive pulses. Output may be taken from almost any point in the circuit but is conveniently taken from one of the tube anodes. The capacitors C_1 and C_2 are "speeding-up" elements, which initially apply the pulse voltages to the tube grids because of their instantaneous effective short-circuit action.

In addition to serving as a free-running, or astable, multivibrator and as a bistable multivibrator, or trigger, circuit, the two-tube cross-coupled circuit can also be used in some other ways. The first of these is as a monostable multivibrator, or single pulse-generating, circuit, as shown in Fig. 16.17. This circuit has direct coupling between the grid of T_1 and the plate of T_2 and capacitive coupling between the grid of T_2 and the plate of T_1. Because of this and the resistance connections, T_2 will become conducting and T_1 nonconducting when the capacitors have discharged to an equilibrium state. It is seen that the grid of T_2 goes positive but that the grid of T_1 is held negative. However, a negative input pulse can render the grid of T_2 instantaneously negative and the grid of T_1 instantaneously positive. As soon as C_1 discharges through R_1 and C_2 discharges through R_2, the circuit will return to its original state. Thus a negative input trigger pulse of extremely short duration will generate a rectangular output pulse of a prescribed time duration.

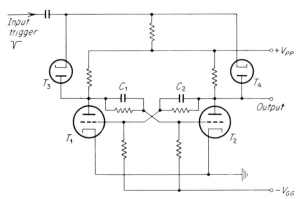

FIG. 16.16. Practical bistable multivibrator circuit.

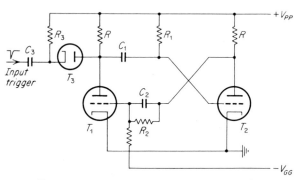

FIG. 16.17. Monostable multivibrator circuit.

It should also be mentioned that the circuit of Fig. 16.15 can be made to yield sine-wave oscillations by simply connecting a parallel-resonant circuit between the points a and b. If the resistance at resonance of the parallel LC circuit is greater than the magnitude of the small-signal negative resistance exhibited at the terminals, oscillations at the resonant frequency will build up until the latter resistance equals the former in magnitude. This is not a trigger circuit but is mentioned here to show an additional function that can be performed by this circuit. In general, circuits having an N- or S-shaped characteristic can be connected to serve as (1) astable multivibrators, (2) monostable multivibrators, (3) bistable multivibrators, or (4) negative-resistance sine-wave oscillators.

In addition to double-tube trigger circuits, there is a whole class of single-tube trigger circuits using variations of the Miller sweep action, including circuits known as the Phantastron, the Sanatron, and the Sanaphant [Chb]. These are circuits using pentodes whose action depends upon different interconnections between the various tube electrodes. The action of this class of circuit depends more upon the charging action of various RC connections than upon an N- or S-shaped current-voltage characteristic. A single-tube circuit yielding an N-shaped current-voltage characteristic may be obtained in the screen circuit of a pentode if the screen is suitably coupled to the suppressor grid [Reg].

In contrast to the situation with tubes, transistors admit of many single-transistor circuits yielding an S- or N-shaped characteristic [Web,

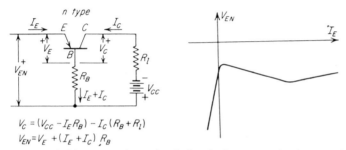

$$V_C = (V_{CC} - I_E R_B) - I_C(R_B + R_l)$$
$$V_{EN} = V_E + (I_E + I_C)R_B$$

FIG. 16.18. Grounded-base-transistor circuit developing a negative input resistance in the emitter circuit.

ScA, LoB, AnB, SuC]. In Secs. 13.4 to 13.6 it was seen that various transistor connections admitted of negative input and output resistances. The resistances are usually not negative over the entire range of voltages and currents but limited to a small negative-resistance region between larger positive-resistance regions.

A first example is the grounded-base connection of Fig. 16.18, having an additional resistance in series with the base lead. This circuit develops the N-shaped characteristic shown in the same figure. This characteristic may be obtained from static characteristics, such as those of Fig. 11.2, by application of the Kirchhoff-law equations for the input and output mesh currents. These are

$$V_C = (V_{CC} - I_E R_B) - I_C(R_B + R_l) \tag{16.23}$$
$$\text{and} \qquad V_{EN} = V_E + (I_E + I_C)R_B \tag{16.24}$$

The first of these shows that a load line with a slope of $-1/(R_B + R_l)$ can be drawn in the $V_C I_C$ plane for any particular value of I_E. Values of I_C can thus be determined which serve to locate points in the $V_E I_E$ characteristic from which values of $(I_E + I_C)R_B$ can be added to give the desired characteristic.

In a similar fashion, an N-shaped current-voltage characteristic can be developed about the collector circuit of a transistor. The required circuit and the associated characteristic are shown in Fig. 16.19. Likewise, an S-shaped current-voltage characteristic can be developed in the

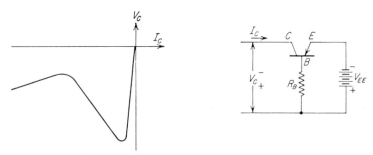

FIG. 16.19. Grounded-base-transistor circuit developing a negative resistance in the collector circuit.

base circuit of a transistor. Such a characteristic and the required circuit are shown in Fig. 16.20. All the above circuits require additional resistance in the base lead to emphasize the negative-resistance portion of the characteristic.

All the three single-transistor circuits mentioned above will give bistable operation when used with a proper bias and a suitably sized

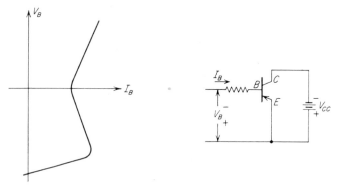

FIG. 16.20. Grounded-emitter-transistor circuit developing a negative resistance in the base circuit.

input resistance. These must be such that a load line will intersect the S- or N-shaped curve at three points. As before, the conditions corresponding to intersections of the load line with a portion of the circuit characteristic (with a slope of the opposite sign) are stable. The conditions corresponding to an intersection of the load line with a portion of the circuit characteristic (of the same sign) are unstable. In contrast to the two-tube bistable multivibrator circuit described earlier, pulses alternately positive and negative are required to change the circuit from one stable state to the other.

With a two-tube or two-transistor bistable circuit, a change from one stable state to the other is accomplished by successive pulses of the same

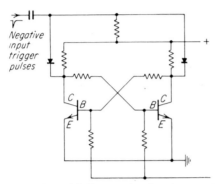

Fig. 16.21. Bistable multivibrator circuit using two transistors.

polarity.   A bistable multivibrator circuit using two identical transistors is shown in Fig. 16.21.   The correspondence between this circuit and the tube circuit of Fig. 16.17 will be apparent.   This circuit can be built in a compact and rugged form.   It requires very little input power and will trigger on a few tenths of a volt.

CHAPTER 17

PHOTOELECTRIC DEVICES

17.1. Photoeffects. There are three clearly recognized photoeffects. These are (1) the photoemissive effect, (2) the photoconductive effect, and (3) the photovoltaic effect. Each of these has a long and interesting history and has given rise to a different group of photoelectric devices.

The photoemissive effect refers to emission of electrons in a vacuum from metal and semiconductor surfaces, caused by absorption of electromagnetic energy from visible and near-visible radiation. It was discovered early and has given rise to a whole group of phototubes.

The photoconductive effect refers to the increase in conductivity observed in certain elements and compounds exposed to electromagnetic radiation. The selenium photoconductive cell is probably the oldest and most common device using this effect.

The photovoltaic effect refers to the voltage generated at metal-semiconductor and semiconductor junctions upon excitation by light rays. Most photographic exposure meters make use of this effect. They generally use either a copper–copper-oxide junction or a selenium-barrier junction connected directly to a sensitive current meter. The silicon solar battery (so-called) uses this effect.

Although the three above effects are closely related, they are sufficiently different to require separate discussion.

17.2. History of the Photoemissive Effect. The photoemissive effect has been known for a long time. In 1887 Hertz observed that the behavior of a spark gap was influenced by illumination. In 1888 Hallwachs investigated this effect and showed that it was caused by the emission of negative particles of electricity. In 1900 Lenard, Elster, and Geitel showed that the effect was due to the emission of electrons. They found that, for a given frequency of excitation, the photoemission current was proportional to the intensity of the illumination but that the velocity of emission was independent of the intensity of the illumination. In addition, they found that there was a long-wave excitation limit for each emitter beyond which no amount of illumination would produce photoemission. This last effect could not be explained by the classical physics of the time.

In 1905 Einstein applied Planck's quantum theory to explain theoretically the observed features of the photoelectric effect. In 1912 Hughes verified the theory of Einstein, and in 1916 Millikan checked the value of Planck's constant by photoemissive measurements [Zwb, EnC, Spc].

17.3. Observed Photoemission Characteristics. The principal effects of photoemission can be observed with the circuit of Fig. 17.1. The phototube used here consists of a large light-sensitive cathode and a small anode in an evacuated glass tube. If the current-voltage characteristic is measured as the intensity of illumination is varied, the curves of Fig. 17.2 are obtained. For accelerating voltages from cathode to anode, the current is constant for a given illumination but increasing linearly with the illumination. For a retarding voltage from cathode to anode, the current drops to extinction at a given voltage, showing a maximum velocity of emission of the photoelectrons independent of the illumination. If now the intensity of the illumination is held constant but the frequency or color of the light is changed, the characteristics of Fig. 17.3 are obtained.

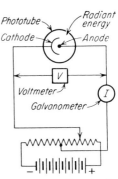

Fig. 17.1. Circuit for observing the photoemissive effect.

These show a progressively lower velocity of emission as the frequency of the incident radiation is decreased. If now the maximum emission energy of electrons or the extinction voltage is plotted against the frequency of

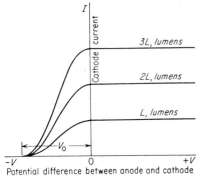

FIG. 17.2. Photoemission current vs. retarding voltage for various intensities of illumination.

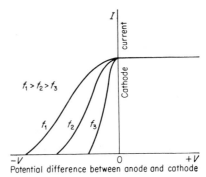

FIG. 17.3. Photoemission current vs. retarding voltage for various frequencies of illumination.

incident radiation, as shown in Fig. 17.4, a straight-line relation is obtained. This shows that the maximum emission energy is related to frequency of excitation by

$$\tfrac{1}{2}mv_m^2 = k_1 f - k_2 \tag{17.1}$$

The constants k_1 and k_2 have a definite significance given by the Einstein theory, as explained in Sec. 17.4.   Here m is electron mass, v_m is maximum emission velocity, and f is frequency.

17.4. Theory of Photoemission.   The wave theory of light meets with considerable difficulty in explaining the various aspects of the photoelectric effect.   The proportionality between the photoelectric current and the intensity of illumination is consistent with the wave theory,

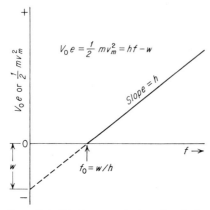

but the fact that the maximum velocity of emission is independent of the intensity of the illumination cannot be explained on the basis of the wave theory.

Einstein applied the quantum theory to explain photoelectric emission.   He suggested that radiant energy was transmitted by *photons*, which are hypothetical particles of zero mass, each with an energy hf and localized in space so that each is capable of reacting with an electron.   The photons are capable of transferring their entire energy to electrons, after which

FIG. 17.4. Maximum velocity of emission of photoelectrons as a function of frequency of exciting radiation.

they disappear.   Of the energy hf transferred from the photon to an electron, a certain amount w may be used up overcoming the potential barrier at the surface of the material.   This amount, w, will be recognized as the work function of the material, $w = hf$.   The maximum kinetic energy that any electron may have after emission is then

$$V_0 e = \tfrac{1}{2}mv_m^2 = hf - w \qquad (17.2)$$

which is known as the Einstein photoelectric equation.   With the help of this equation, it is seen that the curve of Fig. 17.4 is indeed a straight line.   Furthermore, the x intercept will be w/f; the y intercept, $-w$; and the slope of the line, h.

The work function is also seen to be proportional to the threshold (minimum) frequency and inversely proportional to the threshold (maximum) wavelength.

$$w = hf_0 = hc/\lambda_0 \qquad (17.3)$$

where w = work function

h = Planck's constant

f = frequency

c = velocity of light

λ = wavelength

The subscript zero refers to the threshold value.   This relation offers an experimental means of determining the work function.   The work function so determined is known as the photoelectric work function to distinguish it from the thermionic work function, which is determined by observations on thermionic emission. Values of the photoelectric and thermionic work functions are in good agreement for pure metals. For semiconductors the photoelectric work function tends to be slightly higher than the thermionic work function, as will be shown.

Another means of finding the photoelectric work function is from observations of the variation of photoelectric-emission current with temperature. Let it be assumed that with no illumination the distribution of electron energies (normal to surface) in a photocathode is as shown in Fig. 17.5a. The solid contour shows the appropriate energy distribution at room temperature, the dashed at absolute zero. For the conditions

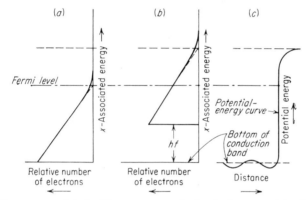

FIG. 17.5. Energy associated with a component of velocity normal to the surface of free electrons within a photocathode, with and without surface illumination.

shown, there is no emission at room temperature in the absence of illumination. If now the surface is illuminated with light of frequency f, the distribution is elevated an amount hf, as shown in Fig. 17.5b, on the assumption that each electron can absorb an energy hf. Under these conditions, the higher-energy electrons will be emitted. Fowler examined this effect theoretically [Fot] and found that the emitter current varied with temperature as

$$\ln \frac{I_{ph}}{T^2} = B + \ln f(x) \tag{17.4}$$

where B is a constant independent of f and T and

$$x = \frac{hf - w}{kT} \tag{17.5}$$

and $f(x)$ is a function of x given as a series expansion. The above is a universal function applicable to all metals. If now curves of emission as a function of temperature and frequency are plotted as shown in Fig.

17.6, curves of emission vs. frequency at different temperatures are all of the same shape but are merely displaced horizontally. The vertical displacement B is the same for all curves of the same material and has no particular significance. The work function may be determined from the horizontal displacement, and values so obtained agree well with values obtained from the long-wavelength limit.

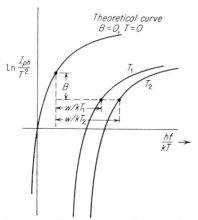

FIG. 17.6. Fowler curves showing the influence of temperature and work function upon photoemission.

17.5. Spectral Responses of Photoemissive Surfaces. All photoemissive surfaces exhibit a variation in sensitivity with wavelength. Shown in Fig. 17.7 are the spectral-response curves of the metals from the first column of the periodic table [Sez]. These curves show single-peaked responses with successive maxima that are lower, broader, and at longer wavelength as atomic number increases. Such curves actually have a second maximum at shorter wavelengths (not shown). The in-

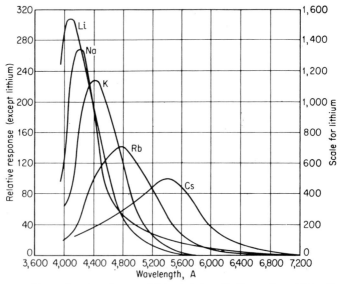

FIG. 17.7. Photoelectric color sensitivity of the alkali metals.   (*After Seiler.*)

crease in response for a given metal from the long-wave limit results from the increased number of electrons at successively lower energy levels. These electrons are presumed to lie in the conduction band.

As wavelength is decreased, a maximum occurs and then the response decreases. The decrease is due to a combination of factors, which include increased reflection of light from the surface, increased absorption of radiation with depth and frequency, and decreased interaction between photons and electrons. It will be noted that the area under the various curves tends to remain constant, indicating a kind of peak-bandwidth constant due to the equivalence of available electrons. The long-wave limit and the wavelength of maximum response correlate with the work function, which in turn correlates with the lattice constant (atomic spacing), as shown in Fig. 17.8.

For semiconductors and composite surfaces, the situation is much more complicated than for metals. Such materials commonly have pronounced double-peaked responses. These result from electrons being

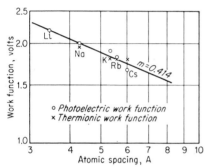

FIG. 17.8. Work function of the alkali metals as a function of atomic spacing.

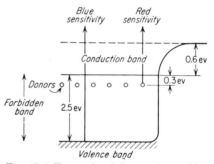

FIG. 17.9. Energy levels in a cesium oxide–silver–cesium photoemissive surface, showing the electron responses to long and short wavelengths.

drawn from different energy levels as the excitation radiation frequency changes. This is illustrated in Fig. 17.9, which shows the energy-level diagram for a cesium oxide–silver–cesium surface, one of the most sensitive surfaces available. This composite surface exhibits the properties of an n-type semiconductor. There are relatively few electrons in the conduction band at room temperature because of the relatively large donor-level–conduction-band spacing (0.3 ev). As a result, the first electrons liberated as radiation frequency is increased are from the donors themselves and account for the red response peak. The threshold wavelength depends upon the depth of the donor level below an outside zero potential energy. This will be greater than the work function encountered in thermionic emission, where the electrons are drawn on the average from a level halfway between the donor level and the bottom of the conduction band. As frequency is still further increased, electrons are drawn from the valence band, giving rise to a second response maximum in the blue region.

17.6. Vacuum-phototube Characteristics. *Current-Voltage Character-istics.* Vacuum phototubes exhibit characteristics that depend primarily upon the nature of the emissive surface and upon the transmission characteristics of the vacuum envelope. A typical set of vacuum-phototube characteristics is shown in Fig. 17.10. For a fixed illumination, the current-voltage characteristics are similar to those of a vacuum pentode. Like the pentode, the vacuum photocell acts as a constant-current generator. Space-charge limitation of emission is virtually absent because of the low current-emission densities. Load lines for various load resistances may be constructed as shown in the figure. The resultant

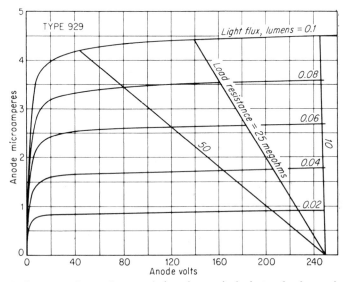

Fig. 17.10. Current-voltage characteristics of a typical phototube for various levels of illumination. Load lines for two values of load resistance are shown.

linearity between illumination and anode current is shown in Fig. 17.11. The characteristics are quite linear and almost independent of load resistance, provided only that the latter is not too large. The voltage output of a vacuum photocell obviously increases as the load resistance increases. The load resistance must not be made too large or the output voltage variation ceases to be linear, introducing distortion. Also the load resistance must be kept appreciably lower than the leakage resistance of the tube, for otherwise the leakage current tends to obscure the photo-emission current.

Experiments show that photoelectrons are emitted less than 3 mμsec after illumination. The photoelectric current ceases in less than 10 mμsec after the illumination is cut off. These times are so short that the transit time must be considered. In a phototube with a cathode radius of

0.5 mm, an anode radius of 10 mm, and a potential difference of 200 volts, the transit time for an electron is about 5 mμsec. Accordingly, the vacuum phototube can handle virtually any known type of light modulation without distortion due to time lag.

Spectral Characteristics. Phototubes are available with spectral sensitivities that cover the visible portion of the spectrum and carry well into the infrared and ultraviolet. In general, the response curves will be different from that of the eye, which is shaped something like a resonance curve with a peak at 5,550 A (1 A = 10^{-10} m) and dropping to virtually

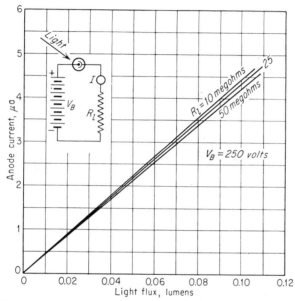

Fig. 17.11. Current as a function of illumination for various load resistances in a typical vacuum phototube.

zero at 4,000 and 7,000 A. Some typical spectral response curves of commercial phototubes are shown in Fig. 17.12. It is seen that there are tubes available which cover the visible spectrum, the short infrared rays, and the long ultraviolet rays. The majority of phototube applications depend upon a tungsten filament as a source of illumination. The tungsten filament has its spectral characteristic centered in the infrared range, with appreciable radiation in the visible portion of the spectrum. Light filters may be used with phototubes where selective response with respect to color is desired. Where high sensitivity in the ultraviolet is desired, special envelopes must be used with the tube, for the ordinary glass does not transmit ultraviolet rays well. Such special envelopes usually take the form either of a glass envelope with an extremely thin window in front of the cathode or of a quartz envelope.

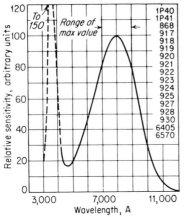

SPECTRAL SENSITIVITY CHARACTERISTIC
OF PHOTOTUBE HAVING S-1 RESPONSE
For equal values of radiant flux at all wavelengths

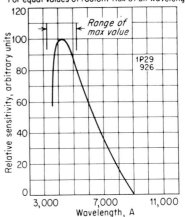

SPECTRAL SENSITIVITY CHARACTERISTIC
OF PHOTOTUBE HAVING S-3 RESPONSE
For equal values of radiant flux at all wavelengths

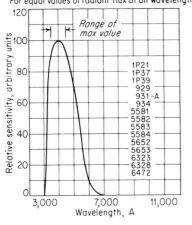

SPECTRAL SENSITIVITY CHARACTERISTIC
OF PHOTOTUBE HAVING S-4 RESPONSE
For equal values of radiant flux at all wavelengths

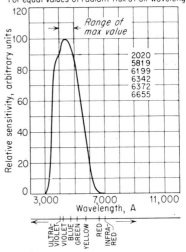

SPECTRAL SENSITIVITY CHARACTERISTIC
OF PHOTOTUBE HAVING S-11 RESPONSE
For equal values of radiant flux at all wavelengths

FIG. 17.12. Spectral response curves of some typical photoemissive surfaces.   (RCA.)

The spectral sensitivities of vacuum phototubes range from about 20 to 50 μa lumen^{-1} (1 lumen = 0.0016 watt for green light). The number of lumens L of light flux falling upon an area A of a surface a distance d from a point source of light of candle-power strength C is

$$L = \frac{CA}{d^2} \quad \text{lumens} \tag{17.6}$$

where any units of length may be used, provided only that they are the same for A and d^2.

17.7. Gas-phototube Characteristics.   The sensitivity of a phototube can be increased by utilizing what is known as the *gas amplification* of the photoemission current.   If a small amount of gas of the right kind and pressure is admitted into the phototube, then the photoelectrons in their travel from cathode to anode will strike some of the gas molecules, causing ionization.   This ionization splits the gas molecule into a free electron and a negative ion.   The free electron is now available to join the photoelectron in its travel toward the anode and may itself ionize other gas molecules, giving rise to more electrons, which can add to the effective current of the phototube.   The positive gas ions formed will move toward the cathode and, in doing so, will constitute a current that is nearly equal to the electron current.   In addition, the positive ions on

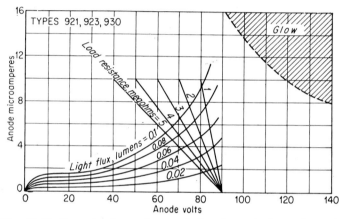

Fig. 17.13. Current-voltage characteristics of a typical gas phototube.

impact with the cathode will create some secondary electrons, which will further increase the total current.   As a result of the cumulative action of all the above effects, the net current to the anode of the phototube can be made as much as *ten times* the photoemission current.

The current-voltage characteristics of a typical gas phototube are shown in Fig. 17.13.   For low anode voltages, the characteristics are about the same as for the vacuum phototube, for at low voltages there is inappreciable ionization owing to the low energies of the photoelectrons. At higher anode voltages, ionization occurs, and the current increases rather rapidly with voltage.   At sufficiently high voltages, a glow discharge will be sustained between electrodes, as shown in Fig. 17.13, and the tube operation is impaired.   Some appreciable departures from current linearity with light intensity are expected in the gas phototube and are indeed present, as shown in Fig. 17.14.   The distortion resulting from this nonlinearity of the characteristics is, however, no greater than that encountered in ordinary vacuum tubes and does not prevent gas phototubes from being used to reproduce the sound recorded on film.

Factors in the Design of Gas Phototubes. There are a number of rather critical factors that must be properly adjusted in the gas photocell to obtain a good tube. These may be listed as follows: (1) chemical properties of the gas, (2) atomic weight of the gas, (3) pressure, (4) maximum allowable voltage.

The principal consideration involved in the choice of a gas is that it must not react with the photoemissive surface. The only gases that can be depended upon not to react with cesium surfaces are the inert gases helium, neon, argon, krypton, and xenon.

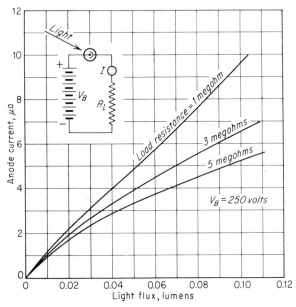

Fig. 17.14. Current as a function of illumination for various load resistances in a typical gas phototube.

The atomic weight of the gas used is a factor, for if the gas is too heavy, the transit time of the positive ions formed will be too great and the high-frequency response of the phototube will be poor. Correspondingly, the ionization potential, or potential of a striking electron that will free an electron from the gas molecule, must be low; otherwise the potential across the tube will be so high that the cathode emission may be impaired by the bombardment of high-energy positive ions.

The critical physical characteristics of the inert gases are listed in Table 17.1. From this tabulation it is seen that, as the atomic weight decreases, the ionization potential increases. A compromise must therefore be effected in realizing the requirements of low atomic weight and low ionization potential. The properties of argon represent a reasonable

TABLE 17.1

Gas	Atomic weight	Ionization potential, volts	Molecular diameter, cm × 10⁻⁸
Helium.............	4.002	24.46	1.9
Neon...............	20.183	21.47	2.35
Argon.............	39.944	15.68	2.9
Krypton...........	82.9	13.96	3.2
Xenon.............	130.2	12.08	3.5

compromise, and this gas is the one most commonly used, although other gases may be and sometimes are used in special applications.

The gas amplification that can be realized in a gas phototube depends upon the gas pressure and the voltage involved. These factors determine the number of ionizing collisions of a photoelectron. The greater the pressure, the less the average distance between molecules but, correspondingly, the less energy the electron has at each collision. The average distance between collisions of molecules or electrons in a gas is known as the "mean free path." The mean free path of an electron moving among gas molecules is in turn related to the pressure, or number of molecules per cubic centimeter, and to the molecular diameter of the gas molecules by the relation

$$\text{Mean free path} = \frac{4}{\pi d_m^2 n} \quad \text{cm} \qquad (17.7)$$

where d_m = molecular diameter, cm

n = no. of molecules, cm⁻³

The number of molecules per cubic centimeter of a gas depends only upon the pressure and the temperature and is independent of the gas involved,

$$n = 7.244 \times 10^{15} \frac{P}{T} \qquad (17.8)$$

where P = pressure, bars or dynes cm⁻² (1 atm = 10⁶ bars = 760 mm Hg)

T = temperature, °K (273 + °C)

Combining Eqs. (17.7) and (17.8) for argon and assuming room temperature to be 290°K,

$$\text{Mean free path of electron among argon molecules} = \frac{60.7}{P} \quad \text{cm} \quad (17.9)$$

where P is in dynes per square centimeter or bars.

A pressure of 0.2 mm Hg is commonly used in gas phototubes. This corresponds to a pressure of 263 bars and a mean free path of 0.23 cm. At every ionizing collision a new free electron is created that can itself produce more electrons by collision. Thus if the original photoelectron in traveling from cathode to anode experiences n collisions, each of which produces a single free electron, then 2^n free electrons reach the anode for each photoelectron emitted.   The potential distribution must be such that each electron acquires enough energy to ionize another molecule in a distance equal to, or slightly less than, the mean free path.   From the above figures it is seen that with a linear potential field it would be necessary to have a cathode-anode spacing of about only 0.8 cm and a total potential of about only 64 volts to ensure a gas amplification of at least fifteen times (since for every electron formed a positive ion is also formed that contributes to the current).

Frequency Distortion in Gas Phototubes.   Owing to the presence of the high-mass positive ions in the current flow of a gas phototube, there is appreciable frequency distortion in such tubes.   This arises from the

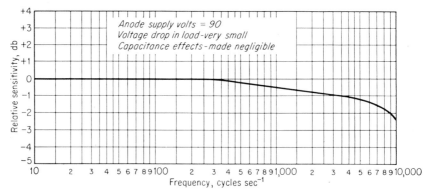

Fig. 17.15. Response of a gas tube as a function of illumination frequency.

time involved in the formation of the ions and in their large transit time. A typical response curve to a light ray that is sine wave modulated at a variable frequency is given in Fig. 17.15.   Distortion is small enough so that it is tolerable in the audio-frequency range.   It may be equalized by using an amplifier with a characteristic that rises with frequency in such a way as to offset the distortion introduced by the gas tube.   A little harmonic distortion is involved in the response of a gas phototube too, but it is generally small enough so that it is not serious.   If the light source is square wave modulated, the current output of the gas phototube will not be a perfect square wave but will have the form of the wave shown in Fig. 17.16.   The current does not build up instantaneously to its maximum value.   The principal cause of this time lag is the time required for the positive ions formed to reach the cathode.   When the light source is cut off, the current does not immediately drop to zero, for there are still positive ions floating about between electrodes.   The time lag here is primarily due to the time required for the positive ions to diffuse to the electrodes or to disappear by combination with free electrons.

17.8. Phototube Operation. Phototubes are extensively used for numerous functions. Among these are door openers, light switches, and sorting and grading operations. The output current of phototubes is so low that they generally require at least one stage of d-c amplification in order to operate a Thyratron, which in turn operates a relay. Some

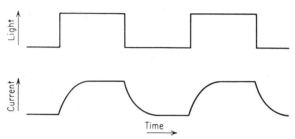

FIG. 17.16. Response of a gas phototube to a square-wave-modulated light signal at high frequencies.

small screen-grid Thyratrons, such as the RCA 2051, are now available that have a sufficiently high control ratio and a sufficiently low control-grid current to be operated from either a vacuum or a gas phototube directly. Circuits of these kinds are common and easy to build.

Another device of interest is a phototube with a built-in photomultiplier. Such tubes are called photomultipliers and often have the form shown in Fig. 17.17. The vacuum envelope contains a photocathode and a series of anodes, called dynodes, each at successively higher potentials. Photoelectrons are emitted from the cathode and attracted to the first dynode. Here the secondary electrons created are attracted to the second dynode. The secondary electrons created at the second dynode are attracted to the third dynode, and so on. If the secondary/primary current ratio is greater than 1, then large current gains are obtained. The secondary-emission current multiplication is commonly

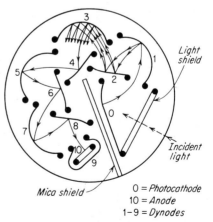

FIG. 17.17. Structure of a circular photomultiplier tube.

about 3.4 at 100 volts per stage. With ten dynodes a total current multiplication of about 60,000 (3.4^9) with a total potential of 1,000 volts is obtained. The sensitivity of such tubes is quite high (from 0.6 to 80 amp lumen^{-1}) but is limited by appreciable dark current and by noise. The signal/noise ratio of photomultiplier tubes is superior to that of phototube-amplifier combinations at low light levels and equal at high. Special photomultiplier tubes have also been used as scintillation counters.

17.9. Photoconductivity. In 1873 Willoughby Smith observed the decrease in resistance of selenium upon illumination. This observation occurred in some work with high resistances of selenium that were being developed for use in submarine telegraphy.

The general features of the photoconductive effect are that the conductivity of a material increases with illumination. The effect is moderately constant at short wavelengths, but at long wavelengths there is a photoconductive threshold beyond which the effect drops off exponentially. The effect is somewhat nonlinear with the level of illumination. It is sensitive to temperature. In addition, it is not instantaneous but exhibits both short- and long-term time reactions.

Virtually all insulators and semiconductors exhibit photoconductivity. A number of the chemical elements, especially those in the fourth, fifth, and sixth columns of the periodic table, as shown in Fig. 17.18, are included [MoB2, ScE]. The most useful of these are selenium, germanium, and silicon. Numerous intermetallic compounds exhibit the photoconductive effect [FrE, BuE]. These include compounds with the zinc blende structure, ZnS, made up of element pairs from opposite sides of the periodic table: III and V, II and VI, and I and VII compounds. Examples are aluminum antimonide, AlSb, cadmium sulfide, CdS, and copper bromide, CuBr. Many other types with different crystal structures are possible.

III	IV	V	VI	VII
B 1.1	C 0.23			
	Si 1.08	P 0.5 and 0.85	S 0.5	
	Ge 1.7	As 1.03	Se 0.5 and 0.8	
	Sn	Sb	Te 3.3	I 0.52 and 0.96

FIG. 17.18. Elements exhibiting photoconductivity. The numbers are the long-wave limit in microns. (*From T. S. Moss, "Photoconductivity in the Elements," Academic Press, Inc., New York, 1952.*)

The wavelength dependence of photoconductive sensitivity, current per volt, is theoretically of the form [MoB2]

$$S(\mathcal{E}) = \frac{1}{1 + \epsilon^{\beta(\mathcal{E}_0 - \mathcal{E})}} \qquad (17.10)$$

where S = relative response
   β = const
   $\mathcal{E} = hf$ = photon energy
   $\mathcal{E}_0$ = threshold energy

This function is constant at short wavelengths and drops off exponentially at long wavelengths. Measured results show a maximum before the long wave drop-off, as in Fig. 17.19. These are ideal rather than typical spectral characteristics. Trace impurities can radically alter the spectral characteristics.

It is an interesting property of polycrystalline deposits of the photoconductive lead compounds that the long-wave limit increases as temperature decreases [SmF]. This is partly because of a masking of photoionization by thermal ionization over small energy levels at ordinary temperature. As a result, cooled photoconductive cells are now the most sensitive infrared detectors. Whereas photoemissive cells can be used to only about 1 μ, photoconductive cells are available to 8 μ. The performance of some infrared detectors is given in the Table 17.2. The response curves of the above materials are similar to those of germanium and silicon shown in Fig. 17.19.

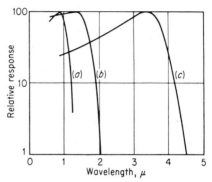

Fig. 17.19. Spectral response curves of the photoconductive effect in various semiconductors: (a) Intrinsic germanium. (b) Intrinsic silicon. (c) Indium arsenide.

Photoconductive cells at room temperatures have slightly nonlinear response to illumination. The current for a fixed applied voltage will generally lie between the 0.5 and 1.0 power of illumination. The usual response is linear at low levels and follows the half-power law at high levels of illumination. Occasionally responses with a power law greater than 1 are found. This is known as superlinearity.

TABLE 17.2

Material	Temp, °K	Wavelength of max sensitivity, μ	Long-wave limit (1% max response), μ
Lead sulfide.................	290	2.9	3.3
Lead sulfide.................	90	3.3	4.3
Lead telluride..............	90	4.0	5.7
Lead selenide..............	90	6.5	8.8

17.10. Theory of Photoconductivity. Photoconduction occurs by virtue of carriers produced in a semiconductor when electrons and holes are created by photoexcitation. Photoexcitation means that a photon imparts energy to an electron that enables it to move to a higher energy level. The excitation of current carriers, either electrons or holes, occurs from levels at which the carriers are bound at low temperatures to bands where they are free to move in an electric field. A few simple electron transitions are shown in Fig. 17.20.

Intrinsic excitation raises an electron from the valence band to the conduction band. It creates a mobile electron and a mobile hole. Excitation of an electron from a donor level to the conduction band creates a mobile electron and a bound hole at the donor site. An excitation of an electron from the valence band to an acceptor level produces a mobile hole and a bound electron at the acceptor site. The first type of excitation described is known as intrinsic excitation. The other two types are known as impurity excitation.

After carriers are produced by photoexcitation, they must be impelled by applied fields to reach an electrode before they can constitute a useful

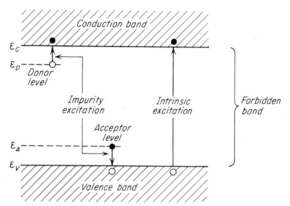

Fig. 17.20. Energy-level diagram showing the production of carriers by photoexcitation in the photoconductive effect.

current. This implies that they must be swept out of the photoconductor before they are lost by recombination. As a result, the useful photocurrent at the electrodes is

$$i = eF \frac{\tau_0}{T_r} \tag{17.11}$$

where i = electrode current
e = electron charge
F = total no. of excitations, sec^{-1}
τ_0 = mean lifetime of carriers in free states
T_r = average transit time

This means that the photocurrent can be greater or less than the number of carriers generated per second. For currents to be greater than the number of carriers generated per second, it is necessary that the electrodes be able to supply carriers to the photoconductor as they are needed. This requires ohmic contacts. The above relation is fundamental to an understanding of photoconductivity and can even be applied to vacuum photocells [RoA, RoC, RoE2].

The above relation can be better understood by a brief reference to its origin. In a given material the density of carriers is equal to the product of their rate of production and their mean lifetime after equilibrium has been attained, that is,

$$n = F\tau_0 \tag{17.12}$$

where n = carrier density
$\quad F$ = rate of production
$\quad \tau_0$ = mean lifetime
The photocurrent will now be given by

$$i = \frac{en}{T_r} \tag{17.13}$$

which assumes that new carriers are supplied as others are taken out of circulation. Upon substitution of the value of n from (17.12) the relation of (17.11) is obtained.

It is interesting in the above situation to define a current gain as

$$G_I = \frac{I}{eF} = \frac{\tau_0}{T_r} \tag{17.14}$$

which may be either greater or less than unity. The current gain can, in fact, be changed by simply changing the direct voltage across the cell. Likewise it is possible to define a voltage gain as

$$G_V = \frac{eV}{hf} \tag{17.15}$$

where V is the direct voltage applied to the cell. The voltage gain is seen to be equal to the ratio of the energy consumed per electron transit of the cell to the energy supplied per photon. A power gain will now be the product of the voltage and current gain and will be

$$G_p = G_I G_V = \frac{\tau_0}{T_r} \frac{eV}{hf} \tag{17.16}$$

Power gains of 10^8 are easily obtained in photoconductive cells by this definition.

In all the above considerations, the mean lifetime plays a significant role. Carriers are removed from the cell either at the electrodes or by recombination. Recombination may occur directly, at the surface or at recombination centers distributed throughout the volume. Direct recombination of electrons and holes is relatively rare. Surface recombination will depend upon the physical and chemical state of the surface. Surface-cleaning methods are known that reduce this factor to a low level. Volume recombination occurs at vacant deep-lying energy levels in the forbidden band. Such levels will commonly capture an electron (or hole), which is then neutralized by the subsequent capture of a hole (or electron). In the absence of trapping, the mean recombination time will be given by

$$\tau_0 = \frac{1}{v\sigma_c n} \tag{17.17}$$

where v = mean velocity

σ_c = mean capture cross section

n = carrier density

Mean recombination times are of the order of milliseconds.

The trapping action mentioned above refers to the probability that electrons, for instance, will drop from the conduction band to a vacant

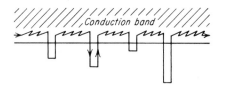

energy level to be held or trapped there for a while before being released to the conduction band for further travel. This action is indicated schematically in Fig. 17.21. This shows the path of an electron through the conduction band with normal lattice collisions, occasionally interrupted by being trapped in an empty energy level in the

forbidden band. The time spent

Fig. 17.21. Schematic diagram showing reduction of drift mobility by trapping action.

in the trapped condition is much more than the time spent in conduction for most photoconductors. As a result, the effective mobility is much less than the normal mobility and the effective velocity is much less than the velocity between traps. Trapping thus lowers the speed and increases the space charge. Reduction factors of the order of 10^5 are common. As a result, transit time will be given by

$$T_r = \frac{L}{\mu_e E} = \frac{L^2}{\mu_e V} \tag{17.18}$$

where T_r = transit time across cell of length L

μ_e = effective mobility, including trapping

E = electric field

V = potential difference across cell

Dimensions of photoconductive cells tend to be large compared to transistors so that the internal fields are small and currents tend to be limited by space charge. Under these conditions, the maximum current that can be drawn is [Moc, p. 172]

$$j_s = 10^{-13} \frac{V^2 \mu_e k}{L^3} \qquad \text{amp cm}^{-2} \tag{17.19}$$

where j_s = space-charge-limited current density
   V = potential difference across photoconductive cell
   μ_e = effective mobility
   k = relative dielectric constant
   L = length of cell[1]

This current seems low compared to that in a vacuum diode, where it has the form

$$j_v = 2.3 \times 10^{-6} \frac{V^{\frac{3}{2}}}{L^2} \qquad \text{amp cm}^{-2} \qquad (17.20)$$

which is the same as (9.1). These currents are actually nearly in the inverse ratio of velocities. For the photoconductive cell,

$$\frac{j_s}{v_e} = 10^{-13} \frac{Vk}{L^2} \qquad \text{(semiconductor)} \qquad (17.21)$$

since $v_e = \mu_e V/L$. For the vacuum diode,

$$\frac{j_v}{v_{av}} \cong 10^{-13} \frac{V}{L^2} \qquad \text{(vacuum)} \qquad (17.22)$$

since $v_{av} \cong \frac{3}{4} v_{max} = 4 \times 10^7 V^{\frac{1}{2}}$. Photoconductive-cell currents can of course be increased by raising the voltage until the dark currents become appreciable. Voltages as high as 150 volts may be used.

17.11. Operating Characteristics of Photoconductive Cells. Sensitivities of photoconductive cells run higher than those of simple photoemissive cells but are lower than those of photomultiplier tubes. Typical simple photoemissive cells have sensitivities of 20 to 50 μa lumen^{-1} for vacuum cells and of 40 to 150 μa lumen^{-1} for gas cells. Photoconductive cells have sensitivities of about 1.0 amp lumen^{-1}. Photomultiplier tubes have sensitivities of from 1.0 to 80 amp lumen^{-1}.

Commonest of the early photoconductive cells were the selenium cells. These had a fairly uniform response over the visible spectrum. Modern cadmium sulfide cells are sharply peaked in the blue-green at 5,000 A. Cadmium selenide cells have a broader peak at 7,000 A with response dropping through the visible spectrum at shorter wavelengths. Such cells give excellent response to light from incandescent bulbs with tungsten filaments [JaD].

Dark resistances of cadmium sulfide and cadmium selenide cells are above 5,000 megohms. When illuminated with light of 100 ft-intensity, the resistance of the cadmium sulfide cell drops by a factor of 10^4, while the resistance of the cadmium selenide cell drops by a factor of 10^6. Thus even with illumination of only millilumens, such cells give a good signal/noise ratio.

---

[1] In mks units this relation has the form $j_s = 9\mu_e k \varepsilon_0 V^2/8L^3$ amps m^{-2}.

Response times of photoconductive cells are of the order of milliseconds in contrast to times of the order of millimicroseconds in vacuum photocells and hundreds of microseconds in gas photocells.   As a result, photoconductive cells can be used only for light variations up to 1,000 cycles sec^{-1} in frequency.

The chief advantages of the photoconductive cells are that they operate on low voltages and have high enough output to operate relays directly without amplification.   In normal use they are expected to have a life up to 10,000 hr.   They are relatively inexpensive, do not require voltage regulation, and have good red response.   Their operation is, however, temporarily impaired by exposure to strong light; and they may be damaged by overheating.   They are otherwise very rugged and will withstand heavy shock and vibration.

17.12. The Photovoltaic Effect.   The photovoltaic effect refers to the generation by illumination of a voltage (more properly, a current). Like the other photoeffects, it has a long and interesting history [Zwb]. In 1839 A. E. Becquerel observed that the illumination of electrodes in an electrolyte changed the effective battery voltage.   In 1876 Adams and Day observed a photovoltaic effect at selenium junctions.   Practical selenium junctions were made as early as 1884 by Fritts.   They were rediscovered and refined by Lange in 1930 and Bergmann in 1931.   In 1922 Grondahl and Geiger observed a photovoltaic effect at the junction of copper-oxide rectifiers.   Later work by Lange and Schottky in 1930 put this effect on a scientific basis and developed it to a practical point.   Many means of obtaining power from sunlight have since been tested [TeD].

The photovoltaic effect is well known today.   There are thousands of selenium-junction photocells in use as photographic exposure meters. The photovoltaic effect has been highlighted recently by the development of the so-called silicon solar battery.   This effect may occur in any rectifying junction.   Electromagnetic radiation penetrates the material of the junction and if the photon energy is sufficient, creates an electron-hole pair across the forbidden band by photoexcitation.   The electric field within the junction sends the electron in one direction and the hole in the other.   This charges up the two sides of the junction with different polarities and thus creates a potential difference.   Actually, it is more correct to consider that the photoexcitation may be represented as a constant-current generator at the junction than to consider the effect in terms of an equivalent voltage.

The photovoltaic effect is most simply described with reference to a p-n junction as shown in Fig. 7.19 and redrawn in Fig. 17.22, although it could just as well be discussed with reference to metal-semiconductor junctions as in Fig. 7.16c.   In the electron-energy diagram of the p-n junction of Fig. 17.22, a photon is shown as creating an electron-hole pair in the transition region.   In such a diagram, electrons run downhill and holes float uphill. As a consequence, the electron is impelled by the junction field into the n region and the hole is impelled into the p region. This is the direction of flow for *reverse* bias with no illumination. The photocell must be designed so that these carriers created by photo-excitation are removed before they are lost by recombination. The electrode connections to the p and n sections must be ohmic to avoid complications from other rectifying junctions. Such a cell may be used not only for visible and near-visible radiations but also for α, β, and γ rays. They may also be used for high-energy-electron or -proton detection, although the energy of such

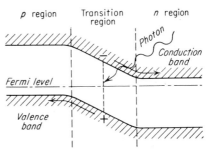

FIG. 17.22. Separation by the field of the junction of the electron-hole pair created by photoexcitation in a p-n junction.

particles must not exceed 0.3 Mev for silicon or 0.63 Mev for germanium if the cell is not to be damaged.

The photocurrents generated internally in a photovoltaic cell are linear with the excitation. The resultant external characteristics will, however, be dependent upon the rectifying characteristics, the external and internal resistances of the device. The frequency of excitation and the energy levels will, of course, be involved. The operating characteristics of a photovoltaic cell are best understood after examining an equivalent circuit and theory of operation, as is done in Sec. 17.13.

17.13. Theory of the Photovoltaic Effect. The theory of the photovoltaic effect is by now fairly well understood [PfD, PrE]. It is readily developed relative to a fairly simple equivalent circuit,[1] which is shown in Fig. 17.23. Part (a) of this figure shows schematically a p-n junction. Actually, these will usually consist of large, flat, and thin layers for photo applications. Part (b) of the figure shows a fairly good and complete equivalent circuit. The currents generated by photoexcitation and internal field are represented by a constant-current generator, indicated by the square box. The current strength of this generator I_g is a linear function of the illumination and will otherwise depend only upon such things as area, depth of junction, and forbidden-band energy gap but not upon temperature, materials, or circuit conditions. Across the junction is a capacity C. Also across the junction is a shunt resistance R_{sh}, representing surface leakage. In series with the junction are series resistances R_{s1} and R_{s2}, representing the ohmic resistance of the semiconductor and the electrode connections. The junction is presumed to

---

[1] The treatment presented here follows the approach of Pfann and van Roosbroeck [Pfd] though this same approach had been suggested earlier [Zwb].

obey the *p-n* junction law.   The external load resistance is represented by R.

A good idea of the behavior of a photovoltaic cell can be obtained from the circuit of Fig. 17.23*c*.   This is similar to part (*b*) but assumes that the series resistance is zero and the shunt resistance is infinite. Neither of these relations is true, but their assumption is adequate for a first approximation. The photocarriers moving in the reverse direction charge up the portions of the cell by making the *p* section positive and the *n* section negative. Reference to Fig. 17.20 shows that this is the forward bias, and hence a forward current I_f is shown flowing through the diode branch of the equivalent circuit.   The following three equations then determine completely the operation of the circuit:

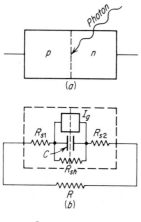

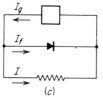

$$I_g = I_f + I \qquad (17.23)$$

$$I_f = \frac{kT}{eR_0}(\epsilon^{eV/kT} - 1) \qquad (17.24)$$

$$V = IR \qquad (17.25)$$

where the symbols have the significance of Fig. 17.23*c* and R_0 is the dynamic resistance of the equivalent diode for zero voltage.

To get an idea of the external characteristics of the photovoltaic cell it is necessary to manipulate the above three equations to get expressions for the voltage and current developed and for the power output and efficiency. First, let I_f and I be eliminated by substitutions of (17.23) and (17.25) into (17.24).   This yields

FIG. 17.23. Equivalent circuits for the photovoltaic effect in a *p-n* junction: (*a*) Junction diode. (*b*) A fairly exact equivalent circuit about a rectifying layer. (*c*) A simplified equivalent circuit for low frequencies, neglecting internal-resistance effects.

$$\frac{kT}{e}\frac{R}{R_0}(\epsilon^{eV/kT} - 1) + V = I_g R \qquad (17.26)$$

which relates the voltage developed V and the load resistance R.   The power developed is given by

$$W = I^2 R = IV \qquad (17.27)$$

Maximum power output occurs for $dW/dR = 0$, for which

$$\frac{1}{R} = \frac{\epsilon^{eV/kT}}{R_0} \qquad (17.28)$$

which is seen to equate the load and the dynamic resistance of the diode.

Under conditions of maximum output, then,

$$I_g = \frac{kT}{eR} \ln \frac{R_0}{R} + \frac{kT}{e}\left(\frac{1}{R} - \frac{1}{R_0}\right) \qquad (17.29)$$

which relates the photoexcitation current I_g to the dynamic diode resistance R_0 for maximum W.

The above and subsequent relations can be simplified by introducing dimensionless variables

$$G = \frac{eI_gR_0}{kT} \qquad (17.30)$$

which is the ratio of I_g to the reverse saturation current, and

$$z = \frac{R_0}{R} \qquad (17.31)$$

With these substitutions, (17.29) becomes

$$G = z \ln z + z - 1 \qquad (17.32)$$

The quantity z, which is a normalized load conductance, is plotted as a function of the normalized photoexcitation current G in Fig. 17.24. As the excitation current G is increased, a progressively higher load conductance z or lower load resistance R is required.

Current and voltage for maximum power are, from (17.25), (17.28), and (17.31),

$$I = \frac{kT}{eR_0} z \ln z \qquad (17.33)$$

$$V = \frac{kT}{e} \ln z \qquad (17.34)$$

Accordingly, the maximum power output W_m is

$$W_m = W_0 z (\ln z)^2 \qquad (17.35)$$

where $W_0 = (kT/e)^2/R_0$. The normalized maximum power output W_m/W_0 is also plotted against normalized excitation current in Fig. 17.24. The maximum power output increases as the square of the excitation current at low levels and as the first power of the excitation current at high levels.

The open-circuit voltage V_0 of the photovoltaic cell is obtained from (17.26) by setting R infinite,

$$V_0 = \frac{kT}{e} \ln\left(1 + \frac{eI_gR_0}{kT}\right) \qquad (17.36)$$

which shows that the open-circuit voltage at first increases linearly then logarithmically with the excitation current. This is the normal diode relation. Short-circuit current will of course be equal to the excitation current

$$I_0 = I_g \qquad (17.37)$$

An ideal efficiency may be obtained on the assumption that none of the carriers produced by photoexcitation is lost by recombination. If an energy $\varepsilon = hf$ of the radiation produces one electron-hole pair, then since each pair results in the equivalent of a charge e flowing through a potential V and since a fraction I/I_g of the carriers so produced flows through the load, the ideal efficiency is

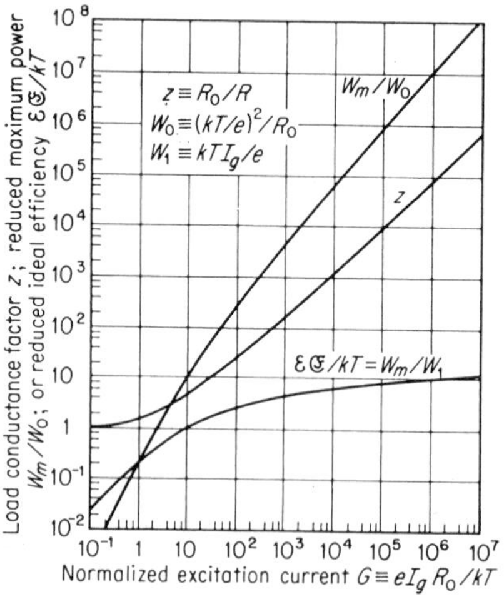

$$\mathfrak{E} = \frac{eV}{\varepsilon}\frac{I}{I_g} = \frac{eV^2}{\varepsilon I_g} \qquad (17.38)$$

in general, and for maximum power output, using (17.30) and (17.33),

$$\mathfrak{E} = \frac{kT}{\varepsilon}\frac{z(\ln z)^2}{G} \qquad (17.39)$$

A normalized ideal efficiency for maximum power then is

$$\frac{\varepsilon\mathfrak{E}}{kT} = \frac{z(\ln z)^2}{G} = \frac{W_m}{W_1} \qquad (17.40)$$

where $\quad W_1 = \dfrac{kTI_g}{e} = GW_0 \quad (17.41)$

By these equivalents, both the normalized ideal efficiency and the maximum power itself may be obtained from the curves of Fig. 17.24.

FIG. 17.24. Normalized load conductance z, normalized maximum power output W/W_0, and normalized ideal efficiency $\mathfrak{E}/kT$ as functions of normalized photoexcitation G of a photovoltaic cell operated as a solar battery. (*After Pfann and van Roosbroeck.*)

There have been developed then a set of relations and a group of universal curves for an idealized photovoltaic cell. It should be recalled that the case was idealized by assuming that the series resistance and shunt resistance of the cell were zero and infinity, respectively. Inclusion of finite values complicates the results slightly but does not change the basic picture [PrE]. Likewise, although the above relations were worked out for a *p-n* junction, they are perfectly general and apply equally well to metal-semiconductor junctions.

17.14. Construction of Photovoltaic Cells. The copper-oxide photovoltaic cell has much the same construction as the copper-oxide rectifier (see Fig. 9.12). A sheet of copper is oxidized to form the red cuprous oxide, Cu_2O. A layer of black cupric oxide usually forms on top of this, which needs to be removed chemically. A conducting layer of gold is then either sputtered or evaporated on top of the cuprous oxide as shown in Fig. 17.25. The rectifying junction is between the copper and the cuprous oxide, which acts like a p-type semiconductor. The energy-level diagram is like that of Fig. 7.16c. The top gold layer is made thin enough to be transparent and yet dense enough to serve as a conducting electrode. This arrangement of the electrodes forms what is known as a back-wall cell. The order of the electrodes can be reversed, forming what is known as a front-wall cell. The latter is somewhat more sensitive because the light does not have to penetrate so much material to get to the barrier layer. The front-wall cell also has a

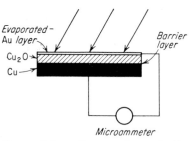

FIG. 17.25. Construction of the cuprous oxide photovoltaic cell, back-wall type. Compare with the copper-oxide rectifier of Fig. 9.12.

spectral response more like that of the eye, with a peak at 5,200 A. The back-wall cell has a major peak at 6,300 A and a shoulder at 8,000 A.

The selenium photovoltaic cell has a construction similar to that of the selenium rectifier of Fig. 9.15. Selenium is first deposited on an iron plate and then annealed to produce a crystalline structure. A low-melting-temperature alloy is then sprayed in a fine layer over the surface of the selenium to make a transparent but conducting counterelectrode as shown in Fig. 17.26.

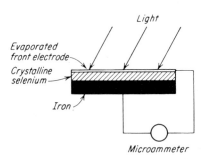

FIG. 17.26. Construction of the selenium photovoltaic cell. Compare with the selenium rectifier of Fig. 9.15.

Germanium p-n junction photocells have been made in various ways. Two forms are shown in Fig. 17.27. In part (a) of the figure is shown an early form, which is essentially a grown p-n junction rectifier with provision for illumination of the junction [ShB3]. Figure 17.26b shows a form in which a very thin wafer of germanium has the junction produced by alloying indium from the side opposite to that which is irradiated [RoD].

The silicon p-n junction photovoltaic cell, or solar battery, is made by depositing an n-type layer on a p-type block by diffusing donors from a vapor of the element in question at high temperatures [ChD2]. Boron is commonly diffused into silicon at temperatures above 1000°C. Layers as thin as 0.0001 in. may be thus deposited with good control. The form of the device may be that of Fig. 17.28, which shows a rectangular form, although some of the first solar batteries were of pillbox shape.

The top surface is illuminated while contact is made to the inner portion through the center part of the bottom, which was masked to diffusion.

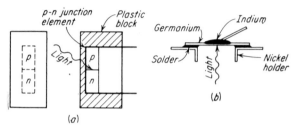

FIG. 17.27. Construction of germanium *p-n* junction photocells: (*a*) Grown-junction form illuminated at the edge of the junction. (*b*) An alloy-junction form illuminated through the thin germanium layer.

17.15. Operating Characteristics of Photovoltaic Cells. The operating characteristics of copper-oxide cells have already been mentioned. The front-wall cell is more sensitive than the back-wall cell. The back-wall cell has a sharp peak in its response at 5,300 A but covers the visible range well. The back-wall cell has a peak at 6,300 A and a shoulder at about half the peak response, at 8,000 A. Copper-oxide cells are temperature sensitive, fatigue easily, and cannot stand too high a temperature.

Selenium cells have a fairly broad peak in their response curve at 5,700 A and cover the visible spectrum well. The sensitivity is only about 100 μa lumen^{-1}. Efficiency under optimum conditions is about 2.5 per cent as a maximum. Reaction times are of the order of milliseconds and permit reproduction of variations to only a few thousand cycles per second.

A number of germanium photovoltaic cells are now available. They are known as phototransistors. A typical germanium photocell is the Bell Laboratories type 1N85 [ShE]. This cell has the general construction of Fig. 17.27*a*. Shown in Fig. 17.29 are the current-voltage characteristics of this cell for various levels of illumination. The cell is

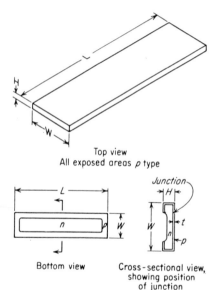

Top view
All exposed areas *p* type

Bottom view   Cross-sectional view, showing position of junction

FIG. 17.28. Rectangular form of silicon solar-battery units. Boron is diffused from vapor at high temperature into a block of *p*-type silicon. This forms an extremely thin layer of *n*-type silicon over the surface and a *p-n* junction about 10^{-4} in. beneath the surface. A portion of the bottom is masked for connection to the *p*-type material.

tion of Fig. 17.27*a*. Shown in Fig. 17.29 are the current-voltage characteristics of this cell for various levels of illumination. The cell is

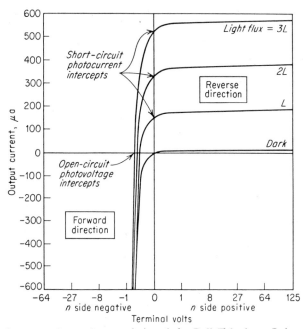

Fig. 17.29. Current-voltage characteristics of the Bell Telephone Laboratories 1N85 germanium phototransistor. (*From J. N. Shive and P. Zuk, Junction Phototransistors, Bell Lab. Record, December,* 1955.)

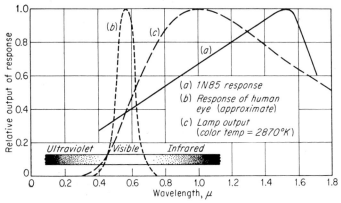

Fig. 17.30. Spectral response of the Bell Telephone Laboratories 1N85 germanium phototransistor. (*From J. N. Shive and P. Zuk, Junction Phototransistors, Bell Lab. Record,* December, 1955.)

used with reverse bias to give operation in the first quadrant, where the light sensitivity is greatest. The curves will be recognized as a family of displaced rectifier characteristics. Operation as a photocell differs from solar-battery operation. For the former, operation is in the first quadrant and the cell receives power from an external battery. For solar-battery operation, operation is in the second quadrant, where the cell is a source of power to an external circuit.

The spectral response curve of the germanium photocell is shown in Fig. 17.30. The cell has a peak in the far infrared at about 1.53 A. For comparison there are shown the response of the eye and the energy-distribution curve of a tungsten filament at 2870°K. The germanium, phototransistor matches fairly well the energy-distribution curve of a tungsten filament.

The phototransistor is usually masked to allow illumination of only the junction. This is because the response falls off away from the junction, giving rise to a resonance-shaped curve of response vs. position of excitation by an extremely small spot of light. The width of this resonance curve is only about 0.01 in. The speed of response also falls off away from the junction. For illumination on the junction the response time is of the order of 0.5 μsec. This makes the cell useful for sound on film installations, as does also the extremely small size. In this application the germanium cells have ten to twenty times the sensitivity of a vacuum phototube.

Information on silicon photocells is as yet fragmentary. Their outstanding characteristic is their high efficiency. Energy-conversion efficiency from sunlight of 10 per cent has been obtained. Voltage developed per cell is about 0.25 volt and the power output is about 20 mw. By arranging a suitable combination of elements in series, powers of 100 watts m^{-2} can be obtained. Experimental installations for telephone service have been made [RaE].

CHAPTER 18

NOISE IN ELECTRON DEVICES

18.1. Noise as a Limiting Factor in the Ultimate Sensitivity of Electron Devices. Vacuum-tube and transistor amplifiers are capable of giving extremely high amplification of power and voltage. In fact, amplification of any desired magnitude may be obtained with a combination of such amplifiers. This would, at first glance, seem to imply that arbitrarily small signals could be detected. However, this is not the case. There is always a limit determined by the noise generated by the random motion of electrons at the input of the amplifier. Any signal smaller than this electron noise will be masked by it. Accordingly, the sensitivity of amplifiers and receivers depends upon how noisy the input circuit is rather than upon how much amplification it has.

Electron noise is found in both circuits and devices. Even in a passive resistor, the electronic agitation resulting from Brownian motion produces an observable noise. In tubes and transistors the random passage of groups of carriers across their respective barriers produces a noise. Depending upon the relative circuit and device characteristics, either the circuit noise or the device noise may predominate.

Although the equations for various types of circuit and device noise are quite simple, their derivation is somewhat subtle. For this reason results and interpretations will be emphasized in the text; derivations will be given in appendixes. For further information the reader is referred to other sources [Mom, Tha, Pic, Vac, VaD1].

A figure of merit for specifying the noise characteristics of amplifiers, receivers, and electron devices in general is the so-called *noise figure* [Frg]. This tells how noisy the equipment or device is compared to an ideal device, expressed as a power ratio. Even ideal electronic equipment may have noise in its output due to amplified thermal-resistance noise from its input circuit. The common definition of the noise figure is that it is the ratio of the signal/noise power ratio of an ideal equipment to the actual signal/noise power ratio (adjustment for maximum available signal and noise power is always assumed).[1] This factor is always greater

---

[1] A more exact definition of the noise figure of a circuit is the ratio of the available signal/noise ratio at the signal-generator (input) terminals to the available signal/noise ratio at the output terminals. The term "available" signifies maximum available from perfect impedance matching.

than unity and applies properly only for small signals because of the non-linear nature of electron devices. A simpler but equivalent definition, which will be understood by reference to following sections, is

$$\text{Noise figure} = \frac{\text{noise power out}}{(\text{power gain}) \times (\text{input circuit noise})} \qquad (18.1)$$

If there is no internally generated noise, the noise power out will equal the input circuit noise times the power gain and the noise figure will be unity. This is the limiting minimum reference value for a device with gain. It will be shown that the input-circuit-noise power depends only on the frequency bandwidth (assuming constant temperature). A noise figure between 1 and 2 is very good. Noise figures may go as high as 10 to 20, which is very poor. Noise figures are also expressed in decibels.

The noise figure of electronic circuits tends to be a function of frequency, deteriorating very rapidly above 20 Mc. At frequencies below 10 Mc tube-receiver noise figures may be as low as 1.05. At 30 Mc a noise figure of 1.35 is very good. Microwave and ultrahigh-frequency devices have inherently poorer noise figures. The noise figures of radar receivers for 1, 3, and 9 kMc are about 10, 13, and 25, respectively.

The noise figure of amplifiers and other four-terminal vacuum-tube circuits may be measured in many ways. It is necessary for the circuit to have enough gain so that the noise in the output is measurable. It is then possible to introduce a known amount of noise or sine-wave power to give a comparison in output power with a new input condition [TeB]. Various noise sources include simple resistances, special vacuum diodes, and special gas-filled tubes (fluorescent light bulbs).

18.2. Noise in Resistors. Noise in resistors is due to the random motion of electrons within them resulting from molecular agitation. It shows itself as a noise voltage across the resistor proportional to the absolute temperature, to the resistance value, and (up to the highest measurable frequencies) to the width of the frequency band over which the observation is made. This thermal-agitation noise is independent of the material of which the resistance is made. There may, however, be additional noise due to variable contact between particles of resistive material.

The mean-square thermal-agitation noise voltage $\bar{v}^2$ across the terminals of a resistor R at an absolute temperature T, associated with a frequency bandwidth B, is

$$\bar{v}^2 = 4kTRB \qquad (18.2)$$

where $\bar{v}$ = rms value of noise voltage, volts
k = Boltzmann's constant, 1.3805×10^{-23} watt-sec °K^{-1}
T = resistor temperature, °K ($273 + °C$)
B = bandwidth, cycles sec^{-1}

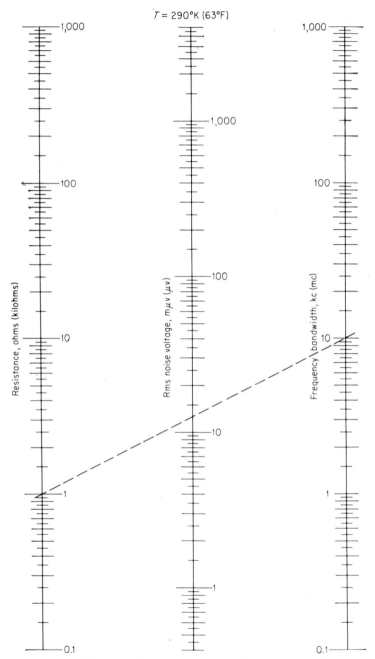

FIG. 18.1. Nomographic chart of noise voltage across a resistor.

If resistor temperature is room temperature, taken as 290°K (63°F), the expression for the rms noise voltage becomes

$$v_{\rm rms} = 126.0 \sqrt{RB} \qquad \text{volts} \qquad (18.3)$$

A nomograph of this equation is shown in Fig. 18.1.   For the sample construction line shown, the rms value of the noise voltage across a 1,000-ohm resistor in a frequency band of 10 Mc is 12.6 μv.   This is the voltage that would be measured across the resistor by a fictitious infinite-impedance noiseless voltmeter responding to effective value.

The effect of the noise in a resistor may be expressed by one of two equivalent circuits.   It may be given either by a voltage generator in series with a noise-free resistor of the same resistance as the actual noisy resistor or by a constant-current generator in parallel with the same-sized

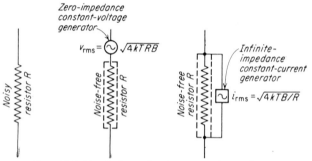

Fig. 18.2. Equivalent circuits of a noisy resistor.

noise-free resistor as shown in Fig. 18.2.   The strength of the current generator for the latter equivalent is given by

$$\bar{i}^2 = \frac{4kTB}{R} \qquad (18.4)$$

where $\bar{i}^2$ is the mean-square noise current.   Both equivalent circuits give the same answers.   The use of one or the other is a matter of convenience.

The noise voltage is capable of transferring power from one resistor to another.   The maximum power transferred will be that into another resistor of the same size and will have a value

$$N_a = \frac{\bar{v}^2}{4R} = kTB \qquad (18.5)$$

which is independent of the value of the resistance.   Since this is the maximum power, it is designated as the *available* noise power.   Theoretically this is the power that would be transferred from a resistance R at temperature T to a resistance R at a temperature of absolute zero. More commonly, the two resistances are at the same temperature, in which case each transfers this amount of power to the other.   For a derivation of (18.2), (18.4), and (18.5) see Appendix 12.   *It is convenient to remember that at room temperature the available noise power for a 1-Mc bandwidth is 144 db below 1 watt.*

The above independence of noise voltage, current, and power from frequency is an approximation since obviously a circuit with an infinite bandwidth cannot receive an infinite power from a resistor. The approximation holds well up to the highest measurable frequencies. The noise levels for ordinary situations are, however, so low that resistance noise is usually of importance only in the input circuits of high-gain amplifiers or sensitive receivers. Even here the resistance noise may be much smaller than the tube noise from the first tube of the amplifier or receiver. It must be emphasized that the noise values quoted above are only for perfect resistors and as such are the minimum values encountered. Resistors having defects or faulty contacts will be much noisier than indicated above.

18.3. Noise in Vacuum Tubes. Noise can occur in vacuum tubes from a large number of causes. These include *inherent* noise as follows:

1. Emission noise
   (*a*) Shot effect (emission temperature limited)
   (*b*) Reduced shot effect (emission space charge limited, space charge smoothing)
2. Partition noise (random division of current between electrodes)
3. Ionization noise (from ionization by collision)
4. Induced noise (from electron stream to control grid at ultrahigh frequencies)

Other *excess* noise will appear in *imperfect* tubes as follows:

5. Flicker effect (emission fluctuations of oxide cathodes)
6. Faulty tube construction
   (*a*) Hum
   (*b*) Poor insulation
   (*c*) Vibration
   (*d*) Varying wall charges

The most important of these are items 1 and 2 and, at the ultrahigh frequencies, item 4.

Shot noise derives its name from the resemblance that the noise bears to that of fine shot falling upon a diaphragm (also known as Schrot and Schottky noise). Shot noise results from random emission and arrival of electrons at the plate of a tube. It is due to grouping of electrons rather than to individual electrons alone. If the electrons were emitted at a uniform rate, the lowest-frequency component would be greater than the highest measurable radio frequency.

In a diode with temperature-limited emission the true shot noise depends only on the direct value of diode current and the bandwidth of observation. It is convenient to represent the noise diode by an equivalent constant-current generator having an output of

$$\bar{i}^2_{\text{rms}} = 2eI_0B \tag{18.6}$$

where I_0 = direct diode current
$\quad \bar{i}^2_{\text{rms}}$ = mean-square noise current
$\quad\ B$ = bandwidth, cycles sec^{-1}
$\quad\ e$ = electron charge, 1.602×10^{-19} coulomb
(See Appendix 13.) This value is independent of cathode temperature and of the resistance through which the noise current flows. It is also nearly independent of the type of emitter but holds most exactly for metal emitters. If the current from a diode with a temperature-limited emission is put through a resistor R, the diode effectively puts a noise power of value $\bar{i}^2_{\text{rms}}R$ into the resistor. A temperature-limited emission of 10 ma in a diode produces an rms noise current of 5.65 μa over a frequency band of 1 Mc. An equivalent circuit is shown in Fig. 18.3.

When the emission of a diode is space charge limited, there is a considerable reduction of the shot noise. This effect is referred to as *reduced shot noise*. The reduction in noise occurs as a result of an action at the virtual cathode in front of the actual cathode. This acts as a cushion in smoothing out the variations in emitted current, thus reducing the noise. The same equation as for shot noise applies but with a reduction factor Γ^2,

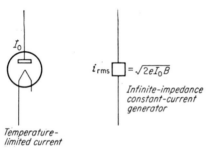

$i_{\text{rms}} \boxed{} = \sqrt{2eI_0B}$

Infinite-impedance constant-current generator

Temperature-limited current

FIG. 18.3. Constant-current-noise-generator equivalent of a diode with temperature-limited emission.

$$\bar{i}^2_{\text{rms}} = 2\Gamma^2eI_0B \tag{18.7}$$

The factor Γ^2 is known as the "space-charge noise-reduction factor" and generally has a value between 0.01 and 0.1. An approximate value for Γ^2 is $1.5 \times 10^{-4}T_c/V_p$, where T_c is cathode temperature in degrees Kelvin and V_p is cathode-plate potential difference in volts. According to this formula, a diode with an oxide cathode emitter at $1000°$K and with a cathode-plate potential of 10 volts has a value of Γ^2 of about 0.015. The above approximate value holds down to a few volts. Another approximate relation of use in diodes with emission space charge limited is that the approximate noise power from such a diode is approximately the same as that from a resistor equal in value to the a-c diode resistance and at the cathode temperature.

Usually diode noise is not a problem in electronic circuits; but because of the simple relations governing their behavior, diodes are often used as standards of noise value.

Triodes also have noise due to the reduced shot effect. It is convenient to represent triode noise by an equivalent circuit, using a noise-free tube and putting in its grid circuit a resistor which will produce the same noise in the plate circuit as is observed in the actual tube. The approximate value of the resistor in the grid circuit is

$$R_{eq} = \frac{2.5}{g_m} \quad \text{ohms} \quad (18.8)$$

where g_m is mutual conductance in mhos for typical operating conditions. Thus a tube with a mutual conductance of 2,000 μmhos produces the same plate-circuit noise as would an ideal noise-free tube with the same g_m and a resistance of 1,250 ohms in the grid circuit. Depending upon the relative values, the noise from the tube itself may be greater or less than that from the actual circuit resistance. Triodes are the least noisy of all forms of electron devices capable of amplification.

Pentodes are much noisier than triodes. This is because, in addition to triode effects, there is a random division of current between the screen grid and plate. Because the electron noise bursts are localized in spots smaller than screen-wire diameter, the screen current has associated with it a noise nearly equal to the full shot noise for that current even though the cathode emission is space charge limited. Plate-current noise is increased to nearly the same value. The equivalent noise resistor that would produce the same plate-current noise in a noise-free pentode is given by

$$R_{eq} = \frac{2.5}{g_m} \frac{I_P}{I_S} \left(1 + 8\frac{I_2}{g_m}\right) \quad \text{ohms} \quad (18.9)$$

where g_m = mutual conductance, mhos
I_P = plate current, amp
I_2 = screen current, amp
I_S = space or cathode current, amp[1]

The first term above is the normal triode component. The second results from partition noise. A pentode will generally have an equivalent resistance three to five times higher than that for the same tube, triode connected. Equivalent noise resistance and mutual conductance of

[1] The general expression for noise current in the nth electrode is

$$\overline{i_n^2} = 2eI_N B\left[1 - (1 - \Gamma^2)\frac{I_N}{I_S}\right]$$

where I_N is the direct current to the nth electrode, I_S is the total direct current in the tube, and Γ^2 is the space-charge-reduction factor of the virtual cathode [ThK]. It is seen that if Γ^2 is zero, the noise in the nth electrode is the full shot noise. If I_N/I_S is unity, the noise has the minimum value.

the commonest triodes and pentodes are shown in Fig. 18.4.   It is seen that the relation of (18.8) is closely observed for triodes.   Pentodes show a higher noise resistance and scatter about a median line because the screen current is not a constant portion of space current for all tubes.

The other important tube-noise relation is encountered in operation at very high frequencies.   Here it is found that there is a component of grid input conductance which varies as the square of frequency owing to the transit time of electrons between cathode and grid plate.   This

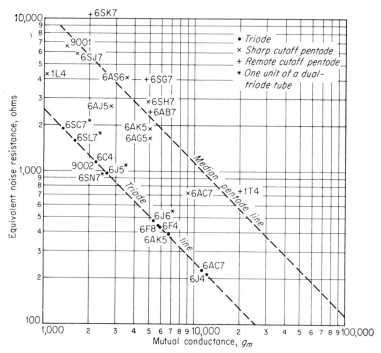

Fig. 18.4. Equivalent noise resistance of representative triodes and pentodes, showing inverse dependence on mutual conductance.

conductance corresponds to a consumption of energy that occurs even though none of the electrons hits the grid.   There is an additional component of noise associated with this effect.   The electrons in motion experience a bunching action which increases the noise as finally observed on the plate.   An empirical relation holding well for usual operating conditions has been found: There is an additional noise equal to that generated by a conductance in parallel with the grid input circuit and equal in magnitude to the input conductance of the tube but at five times room temperature (room temperature is assumed to be 300°K and cathode temperature 1000°K).   The equivalent circuit for this case is shown in Fig. 18.5.

Noise is also developed by ionization and imperfections in the tubes. The former is usually a small contributor. The latter may be large by a factor of several times over the values given by the formulas above.

Noise is also a factor in mixer operation. Here it is usually larger than in normal amplifier operation [Spc].

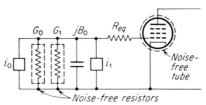

The noises listed above set a limit to the minimum detectable signals. Ordinarily, an amplifier will not be able to detect signals whose rms value is lower than the corresponding noise voltage referred to the input of the first tube. Some typical tube-noise values are given in Table 18.1.

FIG. 18.5. Equivalent circuit of a normal pentode in terms of a noise generator, a noisy resistor, and a noise-free pentode: i_0 = noise from antenna or input circuit; G_0 = input-circuit conductance; B_0 = input-circuit susceptance; R_{eq} = normal tube noise-equivalent resistor given by (18.9); $i_1{}^2 = 4 \times 5 T_r k B G_1$ = ultrahigh-frequency noise generator; G_1 = very-high-frequency tube input conductance.

18.4. Noise in Crystal Rectifiers. Crystal rectifiers of the point-contact type are relatively noisier than tubes except at superhigh frequencies. As yet, the theory of crystal noise is not completely understood, and few simple theoretical relations are available for their determination.

Crystal performance has, however, been extensively measured [Toc]. Crystals are described by a *noise temperature*, which is the ratio of their noise power output to that of an equivalent resistance at the same temperature. If the crystal is not excited by passage of current, its noise temperature will be nearly unity since its carriers will be in thermal equilibrium. If, however, the crystal has a bias current or voltage, the noise temperature goes up very rapidly. The noise temperature under these conditions is found to be an inverse function of frequency. The noise at 1,000 cycles sec^{-1} is often as high as 10,000 times that of an equivalent resistor for normal bias of a point-contact resistor. This noise decreases to nearly the resistive value at about 10 to 50 Mc, after which it increases slowly. Noise temperatures for microwave frequencies are of the order of 2 to 4, increasing slowly with frequency. Noise from junction rectifiers exhibits similar characteristics but is much lower in value.

The large values of noise observed in point-contact crystals may be due to a variation of the work function and contact resistance over the contact area. It may also be due to movement of impurity atoms over the junction. Even in filaments of pure crystal, the inverse-frequency noise variation is found. Here it is believed to be due to the movement of electrons and holes in and out of trapping centers distributed throughout the material.

TABLE 18.1. TUBE-NOISE VALUES[1]

| Type | Application | Voltages, volts | | Bias | Currents, ma | | | Trans-conductance, μmhos | Noise-equivalent resistances, ohms | | Noise-equivalent input voltage,[2] μv |
		Plate	Screen		Plate	Screen	Cathode		Calculated	Measured	
6SK7	Pentode amplifier	250	100	-3	9.2	2.4	11.6	2,000	10,500	9,400–11,500	0.94
6SJ7	Pentode amplifier	250	100	-3	3	0.8	3.8	1,650	5,800	5,800	0.70
6SG7	Pentode amplifier	250	125	-1	11.8	4.4	16.2	4,700	3,300	....	0.53
6AC7/1852	Pentode amplifier	300	150	-2	10	2.5	12.5	9,000	720	600–760	0.25
956	Pentode amplifier	250	100	-3	5.5	1.8	7.3	1,800	9,400	....	0.90
1T4	Pentode amplifier	90	45	0	2.0	0.65	2.65	750	20,000	....	1.3
6SA7	Frequency converter	250	100	0	3.4	8.0	11.9	450[3]	240,000	210,000	4.5
6K8	Frequency converter	250	100	-3	2.5	6.0	8.5[4]	350[3]	290,000	....	4.9
1R5	Frequency converter	90	45	0	0.8	1.8	2.75	250[3]	170,000	....	3.8
6L7	Pentagrid mixer	250	100	-3	2.4	7.1	9.5	375[3]	255,000	210,000	4.6
6J5	Triode amplifier	250	...	-8	9.0	...	...	2,600	960	1,250	0.28
955	Triode amplifier	180	...	-5	4.5	...	...	2,000	1,250	....	0.32
6AC7/1852	Triode amplifier	150	150	-2	...	...	12.5	11,200	220	200	0.14
6AC7/1852	Pentode mixer	300	150	-1[5]	5.2	1.3	6.5	3,400[3]	2,750	3,000	0.48
6SG7	Pentode mixer	250	125	-1[5]	3.0	1.1	4.1	1,180[3]	13,000	....	1.0
956	Pentode mixer	250	100	-1[5]	2.3	0.8	3.1	650[3]	33,000	....	1.7
6J5	Triode mixer	100	...	-1[5]	2.1	...	...	620[3]	6,500	....	0.74
6AC7/1852	Triode mixer	150	150	-1[5]	...	...	6.5	4,200[3]	950	....	0.28
955	Triode mixer	150	...	-1[5]	2.8	...	...	660[3]	6,100	....	0.72

[1] After W. A. Harris, RCA.
[2] For effective bandwidth of 5,000 cycles sec^{-1}.
[3] Conversion transconductance value.
[4] Hexode section only. Triode section takes its current from a separate part of the cathode.
[5] At peak of oscillator cycle.

Silicon-crystal point-contact diodes are often used as mixers in microwave receivers without previous radio-frequency amplification. This is because the noise of such an arrangement is generally lower than that of a tube mixer or tube radio-frequency amplifier. The noise figure of such a crystal-mixer receiver is

$$F = L_x(t_x - 1 + F_a) \tag{18.10}$$

where L_x = conversion loss of crystal mixer, i.e., (signal out)/(radio-frequency signal in)

t_x = noise temperature of crystal

F_a = noise figure of intermediate-frequency amplifier, which follows crystal mixer

The noise figures of the best intermediate-frequency amplifiers run from 1 to 6 db, depending upon frequency in the range of 6 to 180 Mc [Toc]. Crystal conversion losses are from 4.5 to 7 db at 10 cm and from 6 to 9 db at 3 cm. Crystal noise temperatures are of the order of 2 as commonly operated. Accordingly, receiver noise figures are as previously quoted in Sec. 18.1.

Characteristics of some typical microwave silicon converter crystals are given in Table 18.2.

TABLE 18.2. SILICON-CRYSTAL CONVERTERS

Type No.	Design frequency, Mc	Conversion loss, db	Noise temp
1N25	1,000	8.5	2.5
1N21B	3,000	6.5	2.0
1N23B[1]	10,000	6.5	2.7
1N26	25,000	8.5	2.5

[1] Recently reported results on a germanium point-contact crystal detector for 10,000 Mc have given a conversion loss at 5.25 db and noise temperature of 1.14 [McE].

18.5. Noise in Transistors.   Transistors, like all other electron devices, are also limited by noise. Interestingly enough, the noise effects in transistors are phenomena for the most part similar to those in tubes. Transistors are somewhat noisier than tubes but still low enough to be competitive. Early transistor pocket radios had sensitivities of about 40 μv m^{-1} [BaD]. This compares favorably with small tube receivers, which are often less sensitive, and with good tube receivers, which have sensitivities of about 4 μv m^{-1}.

Some ideas of the character of transistor noise may be had by studying the noise characteristics of simple semiconductor filaments treated as resistors [MoB1]. Such studies show noise power proportional to the first power of current and resistivity. They show an irregular dependence upon temperature, which is clearly not a first-power dependence but rather a constancy with temperature. Characteristic of semiconductors is an inverse first-power dependence upon frequency at low frequencies. Normal resistance noise is independent of frequency. The above characteristics suggest that the noise is due to fluctuations of the conductivity of the material. Such fluctuations could result from variations in the concentration of minority carriers.

With junction transistors many of the above characteristics are apparent. Low-frequency noise exhibits an inverse-frequency characteristic. This $1/f$ dependence will predominate up to 1 to 50 kc. There is a middle range in which the noise output is approximately constant. The upper limit of this range varies from 100 to 500 kc. Above this limit the noise power increases with frequency though no simple frequency law is apparent. The general picture is somewhat as shown in Fig. 18.6. The frequency limits quoted refer to performance in 1955. Future developments will undoubtedly lower and broaden the constant low-noise region.

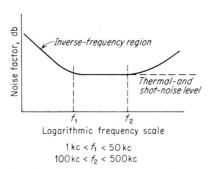

Fig. 18.6. Frequency spectrum of transistor noise.

An equivalent circuit of a transistor, including noise sources, is shown in Fig. 18.7. Five separate noise sources are shown [MoC, VaD2]. Each of these may be identified with an effect or characteristic of transistor noise. Thus

$$(v_e^2)_{\text{av}} = 2kTr_e \, df \tag{18.11}$$

where k = Boltzmann's constant
T = absolute temperature
$r_e = kT/eI_E$ = equivalent emitter resistance
df = bandwidth

This is a constant-voltage generator associated with shot noise of emission across the emitter junction. The mean-square noise current of such emission is presumed to be $(i_e^2)_{\text{av}} = 2eI_E \, df$, the same as for thermionic emission. Combination of this with the value of emitter resistance yields the above mean-square emitter-noise voltage. A second constant-voltage generator represents the thermal noise associated with the base resistance

$$(v_b^2)_{\text{av}} = 4kTr_b \, df \tag{18.12}$$

where r_b is the base resistance. A third generator corresponds to the shot emission of the collector saturation current across the base-collector junction

$$(i_s^2)_{\text{av}} = 2eI_{CO} \, df \tag{18.13}$$

where I_{CO} is the collector reverse saturation current. This current component, instead of the entire collector current, is used because the bulk of the collector current has already been accounted for, in terms of the emitter current, by (18.11). A fourth generator has its origin in the noise of partition of emitter current between base and collector

$$(i_p^2)_{av} = 2e\alpha I_E(1 - \beta) \, df \qquad (18.14)$$

where I_E = direct emitter current
    α = current-amplification factor
    β = transport factor, i.e., fraction of emitter majority-carrier current injected into base that succeeds in getting to collector

A fifth noise generator corresponds to semiconductor noise and will have a voltage given by

$$(v_{sc})_{av}^2 = \frac{K}{f} \qquad (18.15)$$

where the constant depends upon the particular transistor, the collector current, and the collector dynamic resistance. In general, the constant must be evaluated experimentally. This generator accounts for the inverse-frequency component of noise. The inverse-frequency spectrum can be explained by a collection of noise sources of different time constants [RoE2]. In a semiconductor and particularly on a semiconductor surface, there are imperfections capable of trapping electrons for times ranging from 10^{-12} to 10^4 sec. A pulse of current is induced every time

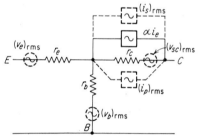

FIG. 18.7. Equivalent circuit of a transistor triode, showing internal noise sources.

an electron goes in and out of a trap. A collection of pulse pairs with random time spacing exhibits the inverse-frequency spectra of noise observed. The inverse-frequency noise in semiconductors has been shown to be a strongly surface-dependent phenomenon that can be entirely eliminated in some cases by proper surface treatment [PeF].

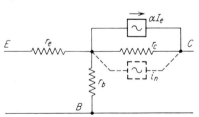

FIG. 18.8. Simplified equivalent circuit of a transistor triode with a single noise source.

The noise circuit of Fig. 18.7 is instructive in that every generator has a physical significance. However, an equivalent circuit with five generators is a bit cumbersome for ordinary use. Accordingly, it is convenient to use an equivalent circuit with a single current generator in parallel with the equivalent collector resistance. Such a generator will have a current strength that is a function of frequency. If an equivalent diode current I_{eq} is defined by the relation

$$(i_n^2)_{av} = 2eI_{eq}\, df \tag{18.16}$$

then the equivalent current of some typical transistors has the form shown in Fig. 18.8 [VaE, HaE]. As before, the noise current has random phase

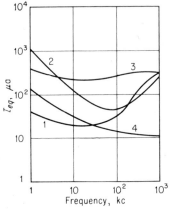

Fig. 18.9. Equivalent noise current of typical transistor triodes as a function of frequency in accordance with the equivalent circuit of Fig 18.8. 1, Raytheon CK727. 2, RCA TA 153. 3, Inverted RCA TA 153. 4, Philco surface-barrier transistor. (*From G. H. Hanson, Shot Noise in p-n-p Transistors, J. Appl. Phys., vol. 26, pp. 1388, 1389, November, 1955.*)

so that the sum of the effects of the current generators is the square root of the sum of the squares of the individual generators.

The equivalent-current curves of Fig. 18.9 exhibit the general trend of noise rising at low and high frequency. The high-frequency limit of the low-noise region correlates with the α cutoff frequency so that the higher this is, the larger the low-frequency region. Over-all noise figures of junction transistors currently run from 9 to 30 db at 1 kc, dropping to between 3 and 5 db at the frequency of lowest noise. Although transistors are still inferior to vacuum tubes in noise characteristics, the gap is closing fast.

APPENDIX 1

RELATIVITY EFFECTS
WITH HIGH-VELOCITY ELECTRONS

THE TERM "relativity" has a mysterious and forbidding sound. Actually, it is not too mysterious. The basic results of interest for this book that are new are the following:

1. Electrons never have velocities greater than that of light.

2. The mass of the electron increases with the velocity or voltage through which it has been accelerated.

Furthermore, the above results are easily obtained from two principles. The *first* of these is a consequence of the theory of relativity. It states that mass is a manifestation of energy and vice versa. This is the only idea we have to take for granted. The *second* is the general form of Newton's reaction equation, which states that force is proportional to the time rate of change of momentum. Momentum is the product of mass and velocity, and this general relation allows for change of mass on acceleration. The only mathematics needed is the calculus.

The general relation between energy and mass given by relativity theory is

$$\mathcal{E} = mc^2 = m_0c^2 + \tfrac{1}{2}mv^2 \tag{A1.1}$$

where $\mathcal{E}$ = total energy

m = mass

c = velocity of light

It is seen that the square of the velocity of light is the proportionality constant between mass and total energy. At zero velocity the rest mass m_0 corresponds to the energy stored in the electrostatic field of the electron. As the acceleration is increased, the electron acquires kinetic energy corresponding to the energy stored in the magnetic field of the current created by the electron in motion.

From (A1.1),

$$d\mathcal{E} = c^2\, dm = F\, ds \tag{A1.2}$$

where F = force

s = distance

But

$$F\, ds = \frac{d(mv)}{dt}\, ds = v\, d(mv) \tag{A1.3}$$

Let $d(mv) = v\,dm + m\,dv$, and separate variables.   Substituting (A1.3) into (A1.2) yields

$$\frac{dm}{m} = \frac{v\,dv}{c^2 - v^2} \qquad (A1.4)$$

This integrates to give

$$\frac{m}{m_0} = \frac{1}{\sqrt{1 - (v/c)^2}} \qquad (A1.5)$$

by using $m = m_0$ when $v = 0$.   This equation is the same as (4.42) and tells how the mass increases as a function of velocity.   It is independent of how the velocity is acquired.

If the kinetic energy is acquired by acceleration through a potential V, then

$$Ve = v\,d(mv) \qquad (A1.6)$$

from (A1.3).   Using the general expression for m from (A1.5) and integrating between limits of 0 and v yield

$$eV = m_0c^2 \left[\frac{1}{\sqrt{1 - (v/c)^2}} - 1 \right] \qquad (A1.7)$$

Solving for v/c,

$$\frac{v}{c} = \sqrt{1 - \frac{1}{(1 + eV/m_0c^2)^2}} \qquad (A1.8)$$

This is the same as (4.41) in the text.   It tells the velocity acquired by an electron on being accelerated through V volts.   Rearranging (A1.7) and substituting from (A1.5),

$$\frac{m}{m_0} = \frac{1}{1 - (v/c)^2} = 1 + \frac{eV}{m_0c^2} \qquad (A1.9)$$

which is the same as (4.43).   It tells how the mass of an electron increases on being accelerated through V volts.   A factor of approximately 2 in mass is added for every 1 million volts.

APPENDIX 2

ELECTRON ARRANGEMENTS OF THE ATOMS[1]

Atomic no. and element	Principal and secondary quantum numbers									
n	1	2		3			4			
l	0	0	1	0	1	2	0	1	2	3
1 H	1									
2 He	2									
3 Li	2	1								
4 Be	2	2								
5 B	2	2	1							
6 C	2	2	2							
7 N	2	2	3							
8 O	2	2	4							
9 F	2	2	5							
10 Ne	2	2	6							
11 Na	2	2	6	1						
12 Mg	2	2	6	2						
13 Al	2	2	6	2	1					
14 Si	2	2	6	2	2					
15 P	2	2	6	2	3					
16 S	2	2	6	2	4					
17 Cl	2	2	6	2	5					
18 A	2	2	6	2	6					
19 K	2	2	6	2	6		1			
20 Ca	2	2	6	2	6		2			
21 Sc	2	2	6	2	6	1	2			
22 Ti	2	2	6	2	6	2	2			
23 V	2	2	6	2	6	3	2			

[1] After Wm. Hume-Rothery, "Atomic Theory for Students of Metallurgy," The Institute of Metals, London, 1947.

Atomic no. and element	Principal and secondary quantum numbers									
n	1	2		3			4			
l	0	0	1	0	1	2	0	1	2	3
24 Cr	2	2	6	2	6	5	1			
25 Mn	2	2	6	2	6	5	2			
26 Fe	2	2	6	2	6	6	2			
27 Co	2	2	6	2	6	7	2			
28 Ni	2	2	6	2	6	8	2			
29 Cu	2	2	6	2	6	10	1			
30 Zn	2	2	6	2	6	10	2			
31 Ga	2	2	6	2	6	10	2	1		
32 Ge	2	2	6	2	6	10	2	2		
33 As	2	2	6	2	6	10	2	3		
34 Se	2	2	6	2	6	10	2	4		
35 Br	2	2	6	2	6	10	2	5		
36 Kr	2	2	6	2	6	10	2	6		

n	1	2	3	4				5			6
l	...	...	...	0	1	2	3	0	1	2	0
37 Rb	2	8	18	2	6			1			
38 Sr	2	8	18	2	6			2			
39 Y	2	8	18	2	6	1		2			
40 Zr	2	8	18	2	6	2		2			
41 Nb	2	8	18	2	6	4		1			
42 Mo	2	8	18	2	6	5		1			
43 Tc	2	8	18	2	6	6		1			
44 Ru	2	8	18	2	6	7		1			
45 Rh	2	8	18	2	6	8		1			
46 Pd	2	8	18	2	6	10		...			
47 Ag	2	8	18	2	6	10		1			
48 Cd	2	8	18	2	6	10		2			
49 In	2	8	18	2	6	10		2	1		
50 Sn	2	8	18	2	6	10		2	2		
51 Sb	2	8	18	2	6	10		2	3		
52 Te	2	8	18	2	6	10		2	4		
53 I	2	8	18	2	6	10		2	5		
54 Xe	2	8	18	2	6	10		2	6		
55 Cs	2	8	18	2	6	10		2	6		1
56 Ba	2	8	18	2	6	10		2	6		2
57 La	2	8	18	2	6	10		2	6	1	2
58 Ce	2	8	18	2	6	10	2	2	6		2
59 Pr	2	8	18	2	6	10	3	2	6		2
60 Nd	2	8	18	2	6	10	4	2	6		2
61 Pm	2	8	18	2	6	10	5	2	6		2
62 Sm	2	8	18	2	6	10	6	2	6		2

Atomic no. and element	Principal and secondary quantum numbers										
n	1	2	3	4				5			6
l	...	...	...	0	1	2	3	0	1	2	0
63 Eu	2	8	18	2	6	10	7	2	6		2
64 Gd	2	8	18	2	6	10	7	2	6	1	2
65 Tb	2	8	18	2	6	10	8	2	6	1	2
66 Dy	2	8	18	2	6	10	10	2	6		2
67 Ho	2	8	18	2	6	10	11	2	6		2
68 Er	2	8	18	2	6	10	12	2	6		2
69 Tm	2	8	18	2	6	10	13	2	6		2
70 Yb	2	8	18	2	6	10	14	2	6		2
71 Lu	2	8	18	2	6	10	14	2	6	1	2
72 Hf	2	8	18	2	6	10	14	2	6	2	2

	n	1	2	3	4	5				6			7
	l	...				0	1	2	3	0	1	2	0
73 Ta		2	8	18	32	2	6	3		2			
74 W		2	8	18	32	2	6	4		2			
75 Re		2	8	18	32	2	6	5		2			
76 Os		2	8	18	32	2	6	6		2			
77 Ir		2	8	18	32	2	6	7		2			
78 Pt		2	8	18	32	2	6	8		2			
79 Au		2	8	18	32	2	6	10		1			
80 Hg		2	8	18	32	2	6	10		2			
81 Tl		2	8	18	32	2	6	10		2	1		
82 Pb		2	8	18	32	2	6	10		2	2		
83 Bi		2	8	18	32	2	6	10		2	3		
84 Po		2	8	18	32	2	6	10		2	4		
85 At		2	8	32	32	2	6	10		2	5		
86 Rn		2	8	18	32	2	6	10		2	6		
87 Fr		2	8	18	32	2	6	10		2	6		1
88 Ra		2	8	18	32	2	6	10		2	6		2
89 Ac		2	8	18	32	2	6	10		2	6	1	2

The exact electronic configuration of the later elements is uncertain; but according to Glenn T. Seaborg, University of California at Berkeley (private communication), the most probable arrangements of the outer electrons are:

90 Th	$5f^1, 6d^1, 7s^2$
91 Pa	$5f^2, 6d^1, 7s^2$
92 U	$5f^3, 6d^1, 7s^2$
93 Np	$5f^5, 7s^2$ or $5f^4, 6d^1, 7s^2$
94 Pu	$5f^6, 7s^2$
95 Am	$5f^7, 7s^2$
96 Cm	$5f^7, 6d^1, 7s^2$
97 Bk	$5f^8, 6d^1, 7s^2$ or $5f^9, 7s^2$
98 Cf	$5f^{10}, 7s^2$
99 E	$5f^{11}, 7s^2$
100 Fm	$5f^{12}, 7s^2$
101 Mv	$5f^{13}, 7s^2$

APPENDIX 3

THE DIFFUSION EQUATION

This appendix is concerned with the development of the diffusion equation (6.19). This will be developed for holes as minority carriers in n-type material.

In (6.13) it was shown that the net rate of appearance of holes was equal to the generation rate minus the recombination rate minus the divergence of hole current. Considering only the generation and recombination rate and recalling that recombination rate is proportional to the product of electron and hole densities, then at equilibrium

$$g - r_1 = g - knp = g - kn_i^2 = 0 \tag{A3.1}$$

Now let hole and electron densities be given by

$$\begin{aligned} p &= p_n + \delta p \\ n &= n_n + \delta n \end{aligned} \tag{A3.2}$$

where the subscript n denotes the equilibrium value.

With these relations, the time rate of change of hole density is

$$\frac{d(\delta p)}{dt} = kn_i^2 - k(n_n + \delta n)(p_n + \delta p) \tag{A3.3}$$

Since $n_i^2 = np$ and $p_n \ll n_n$, this reduces to

$$\frac{d(\delta p)}{dt} \cong -kn_n\, \delta p \tag{A3.4}$$

This says that the rate of change in density is proportional to the departure from equilibrium and is in the direction to restore equilibrium. The reciprocal of the coefficient of δp has the dimensions of time, and it is convenient to define this as a mean recombination time, that is, $kn_n = \tau_p$. With this notation δp varies as ϵ^{-t/τ_p}, and τ_p is the time it takes the incremental density to decay to 36.8 per cent of the initial value. With this notation (A3.4) becomes

$$\frac{d(\delta p)}{dt} = -\frac{\delta p}{\tau_p} = \frac{p_n - p}{\tau_p} \tag{A3.5}$$

Substituting the above for $g - r$ in (6.13) yields

$$\frac{\partial p}{\partial t} = \frac{p_n - p}{\tau_p} - \frac{1}{e}\frac{dJ_p}{dx} \tag{A3.6}$$

If we now say that the hole current density J_p is due only to diffusion effects and is itself equal to $-eD_p\, dp/dx$, then (A3.6) can be written as

$$\frac{\partial p}{\partial t} = \frac{p_n - p}{\tau_p} + D_p\frac{\partial^2 p}{\partial x^2} \tag{A3.7}$$

This is obviously equivalent to (6.19) since the derivative of p_n is zero.

APPENDIX 4

DISTRIBUTION OF ENERGY
AMONG FREE ELECTRONS IN A METAL

$\mathrm{E}_{\mathrm{QUATION}}$ (7.3) shows that the distribution of energy states among the free electrons in a metal is given by

$$dS = \frac{4\pi(2m)^{\frac{3}{2}}}{h^3} \mathcal{E}^{\frac{1}{2}} d\mathcal{E} \qquad (7.3)$$

where m = electron mass

$\quad h$ = Planck's constant

$\quad \mathcal{E}$ = total energy

$\quad dS$ = no. of quantum states in energy range $d\mathcal{E}$

This comes about from the assumption that the outermost electron in a metal atom is free to move from atom to atom as though it were in a region of constant potential, arbitrarily taken as of value zero, corresponding to zero potential energy. In addition, the phenomenon viewed from the quantum-mechanical point of view requires restrictions on the electron velocity imposed by the *Heisenberg uncertainty principle* and the *Pauli exclusion principle*.

The energy of each electron will be kinetic and will be determined by components of velocity v_x, v_y, and v_z. These velocity components are replaced for convenience by components of momentum $p_x = mv_x$, $p_y = mv_y$, and $p_z = mv_z$. In classical theory the condition of each electron can be specified exactly by giving its coordinates of position x, y, and z and its coordinates of momentum p_x, p_y, and p_z. However, from the quantum-mechanical point of view an uncertainty in position dx is related by the de Broglie relation to a corresponding uncertainty in momentum dp by

$$\delta p \cong \frac{h}{\delta x} \qquad (5.24)$$

where h is Planck's constant.

Let it be supposed that there are N electrons, under the conditions assumed above, in a cubical piece of metal of side L and volume $V = L^3$. There is now an uncertainty about each coordinate of position of value L and a corresponding uncertainty about each component of momentum of value h/L.

It is convenient in discussing particle momentum to make use of a momentum diagram as shown in Fig. A4.1. This shows a three-dimensional space with axes giving components of momentum. In the classical theory the momentum of each particle is represented by a definite point, as for the point P_1. The total momentum is given by the vector from the origin. In a classical assembly of particles, as for molecules of a gas, there is then a dust of points corresponding to the distribution of momenta. At absolute zero for such a system, the velocities become zero, and there is then a concentration of points at the origin with infinite density.

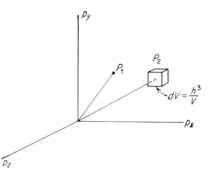

FIG. A4.1. Quantum element of volume in momentum space.

In a quantum-statistical assembly of particles, as with free electrons in a metal, the momentum is known only within an interval $dp_x = h/L$, or a point P_2 is known only within a momentum cell of volume

$$dV = \frac{h^3}{V} = \frac{h^3}{L^3}$$

This element of volume is independent of the shape of the metal. Each such element of volume, or momentum cell, *represents a quantum state* specified by momenta p_x, p_y, and p_z in lieu of other quantum numbers. For an electron gas (assembly of free electrons in a metal) each quantum state, by Pauli's exclusion principle, can be occupied by only two electrons, one for each of two values of spin.

At absolute zero the electrons will assume the minimum energy distribution. They cannot all have zero momentum because of Pauli's exclusion principle, which sets a limit of two electrons per cell. They will, however, group themselves as close to the origin as this restriction permits and for a large number of electrons will assume a spherical distribution about the origin. N electrons must occupy at least $N/2$ cells and hence a total volume of $(N/2)(h^3/V)$ in the momentum diagram. The volume of such a spherical distribution will be

$$\left(\frac{4\pi p^3}{3}\right)_{\max} = \frac{Nh^3}{2V} \tag{A4.1}$$

Total energy of any particle will be kinetic, of value $\frac{1}{2}mv^2$ and equal to $p^2/2m$. Accordingly, the maximum electron energy at zero temperature will be

$$\varepsilon_{\max} = \left(\frac{p^2}{2m}\right)_{\max} = \frac{h^2}{2m}\left(\frac{3N}{8\pi V}\right)^{\frac{2}{3}} \tag{A4.2}$$

The above relation shows that electrons in a metal have energies spread over a range of values even at absolute zero. As the volume of the metal becomes larger, the volume of a cell h^3/V in the momentum diagram becomes smaller so that the difference between the various electron energies becomes so small as to be almost continuous. However, the maximum energy ε_{max} depends upon N/V and so is independent of the volume of the metal.

If the number of energy states is determined by introducing electrons into a metal of volume V at absolute zero, then from (A4.2) the number of states S completely filled with electrons increases as

$$S(\varepsilon) = \frac{8\pi V}{3} \left(\frac{2m\varepsilon}{h^2} \right)^{\frac{3}{2}} \tag{A4.3}$$

which shows that the number of states occupied will vary as the three-halves power of the maximum energy. The distribution of the states with energy is given simply by differentiating the above with respect to ε to give (7.3), the relation first cited. The relation between dS and ε is seen to be parabolic, as shown in Fig. 7.2 for 0°K. These states will be filled up to a level of the maximum energy given by (A4.2).

The above relations may also be derived directly from Schrödinger's equation. See [KiC, p. 224].

APPENDIX 5

THE FERMI-DIRAC DISTRIBUTION FUNCTION

CONSIDER a group of electrons in a region of constant potential. The quantum numbers are n_x, n_y, n_z (and n_s for spin). It was shown in Appendix 4 that the number of quantum states is $S = 2V/h^3$.

Suppose there are s_i states at an energy level $\mathcal{E}_i$.

Suppose there are n_i electrons ($n_i \leqq s_i$) for states s_i.

The *Pauli exclusion principle* permits only one or zero electrons per state. If there are s_i states and n_i electrons, the number of ways n_i electrons can be thus distributed among s_i states is given by the formula for the number of combinations of s_i things taken n_i at a time.

$$_sC_n = \frac{s_i!}{n_i!(s_i - n_i)!} \qquad (A5.1)$$

Here the exclamation point indicates the factorial function. Combinations rather than permutations are used because of the indistinguishability of electrons.

Example. How many ways can two electrons be arranged in four states? The figure at the left shows this number to be six. From (A5.1),

$$_sS_n = {}_4C_2 = \frac{4!}{2!(4-2)!} = 6$$

For a Maxwellian distribution it would be possible to have both electrons in one state; so there would be four additional, or ten total, arrangements possible.

It is convenient to use the logarithm of the number of combinations

$$\ln {}_sC_n = \ln s_i! - \ln n_i! - \ln (s_i - n_i)! \qquad (A5.2)$$

Then the total number of combinations or arrangements for all levels is

$$\ln C = \Sigma \ln {}_sC_n = \Sigma[\ln s_i! - \ln n_i! - \ln (s_i - n_i)!] \qquad (A5.3)$$

The above can be simplified by the use of Stirling's approximation for the factorial function, which is good for large values of n,

$$\ln n! \cong n \ln n - n \tag{A5.4}$$

to give

$$\ln {}_sC_n = \Sigma[s_i \ln s_i - n_i \ln n_i - (s_i - n_i) \ln (s_i - n_i)] \tag{A5.5}$$

According to thermodynamical theory from the statistical point of view, the electrons will be in equilibrium when the entropy, or disorder, is a maximum. This corresponds to a maximum number of combinations or distinguishable arrangements

$$\frac{\partial(\ln {}_sC_n)}{\partial n_i} = 0 \tag{A5.6}$$

as the number of electrons in each energy level fluctuates because of random variations.

The maximization of (A5.6) is subject to the conditions that (1) the total number of electrons remains constant:

$$n = \Sigma n_i \tag{A5.7}$$

and (2) the total energy of the electrons remains constant:

$$\mathcal{E} = \Sigma \mathcal{E}_i n_i \tag{A5.8}$$

The above three equations are most conveniently written as

$$\delta(\ln {}_sC_n) = \sum \ln \frac{s_i - n_i}{n_i} \, \delta n_i \tag{A5.9}$$

$$\delta n = \sum \delta n_i = 0 \tag{A5.10}$$

$$\delta \mathcal{E} = \sum \mathcal{E}_i \delta n_i = 0 \tag{A5.11}$$

${}_sC_n$ may now be maximized subject to conditions (1) and (2) by combining the last three equations with undetermined multipliers α and β (Lagrange's method of undetermined multipliers) to give

$$\sum \left(\ln \frac{s_i - n_i}{n_i} - \alpha - \beta \mathcal{E}_i \right) \delta n_i = 0 \tag{A5.12}$$

from which

$$\ln \frac{s_i - n_i}{n_i} - \alpha - \beta \mathcal{E}_i = 0 \tag{A5.13}$$

This gives

$$\frac{s_i - n_i}{n_i} = \mathcal{E}^{\alpha + \beta \mathcal{E}_i} \tag{A5.14}$$

or

$$\frac{n_i}{s_i} = (\mathcal{E}^{\alpha + \beta \mathcal{E}_i} + 1)^{-1} \tag{A5.15}$$

For a sufficient number of energy levels the energy may be considered continuous, and the above becomes

$$\frac{n_i}{s_i} = f(\mathcal{E}) = (\mathcal{E}^{\alpha + \beta \mathcal{E}} + 1)^{-1} \tag{A5.16}$$

The distribution of electrons among the states at very high temperatures should be the same as for gases. Since here ε is high and $n/s \ll 1$, the probability of more than one molecule per state is small. The results of the kinetic theory of gases then establish the value

$$\beta = \frac{1}{kT} \tag{A5.17}$$

where k = Boltzmann's constant
T = absolute temperature

The quantity α is defined as a reference energy level ε_f/kt so that

$$f(\varepsilon) = \frac{1}{\varepsilon^{(\varepsilon-\varepsilon_f)/kT} + 1} \tag{A5.18}$$

which is the relation sought. The reference energy level ε_f is the level at which the distribution function has a value of one-half. It is also the level at which the states are completely filled at zero temperature.

APPENDIX 6

FERMI DISTRIBUTION FUNCTION
FOR A SINGLE COMPONENT OF VELOCITY

THE NUMBER of electrons per unit volume per cell in a momentum space as discussed in Appendixes 4 and 5 is

$$d^3n = \frac{2}{h^3} \frac{1}{\epsilon^{(\mathcal{E}-\mathcal{E}_f)/kT} + 1} \, dp_x \, dp_y \, dp_z \tag{A6.1}$$

from (7.1) and (7.4). There are h^3 such cells in the entire volume, and two electrons are allowed per cell. As before, $p_x = mv_x, \cdots$.

To find the distribution in any one component of velocity, integrate (A6.1) over all values of the other two components

$$dn_x = \frac{2}{h^3} \left(\int_{-\infty}^{\infty} \int_{-\infty}^{\infty} \frac{1}{\epsilon^{(\mathcal{E}-\mathcal{E}_f)/kT} + 1} \, dp_y \, dp_z \right) dp_x \tag{A6.2}$$

where

$$\mathcal{E} = \frac{1}{2m} (p_x^2 + p_y^2 + p_z^2)$$

Let $p_y^2 + p_z^2 = r^2$ and change to polar coordinates in the $p_y p_z$ plane. Then $dp_x \, dp_y = r \, dr \, d\theta$ and

$$dn_x = \frac{2}{h^3} \left(\int_{r=0}^{\infty} \int_{\theta=0}^{2\pi} \frac{r \, dr \, d\theta}{\exp \dfrac{(r^2 + p_x^2)/2m - \mathcal{E}_f}{kT} + 1} \right) dp_x \tag{A6.3}$$

Let $r^2/2mkT = s$. Then $r \, dr = mkT \, ds$. Also let

$$\exp \frac{(p_x^2/2m - \mathcal{E}_f)}{kT} = a$$

Then

$$dn_x = \frac{4\pi mkT}{h^3} \left(\int_0^{\infty} \frac{ds}{a\epsilon^s + 1} \right) dp_x \tag{A6.4}$$

$$dn_x = \frac{4\pi mkT}{h^3} [- \ln (a + \epsilon^{-s})]_{\infty}^0 \, dp_x \tag{A6.5}$$

$$dn_x = \frac{4\pi mkT}{h^3} \ln \left(1 + \frac{1}{a} \right) dp_x \tag{A6.6}$$

450

or finally

$$dn_x = \frac{4\pi m^2 kT}{h^3} \ln\left(1 + \exp\frac{\mathcal{E}_f - \frac{1}{2}mv_x^2}{kT}\right) dv_x \qquad (8.1)$$

This equation is also shown in the center section of Fig. 8.1. It gives the relative number of electrons in an increment of the x component of velocity as a function of the x-associated energy $\frac{1}{2}mv_x^2$. It is the relation used in deriving the emission equation.

APPENDIX 7

DERIVATION OF THE
THERMIONIC-EMISSION EQUATION

T HE EQUATION for the distribution of electrons with a single component of velocity given in (8.1) and derived in Appendix 6 is easily applied to obtain the Richardson-Dushman emission equation (8.2). Here we are concerned with summing the high-energy electrons of Fig. 8.1 that are able to surmount the potential-energy barrier. Equation (8.1) gives the distribution of the x component of velocity of the conduction electrons as a function of temperature, Fermi level, and x-associated energy, that is,

$$dn_x = \frac{4\pi m^2 kT}{h^3} \ln \left(1 + \exp \frac{\mathcal{E}_f - \frac{1}{2}mv_x^2}{kT} \right) dv_x \qquad (8.1)$$

Let $\frac{1}{2}mv_x^2$ of (8.1) be designated by $\mathcal{E}_x$ and consider $\mathcal{E}_x \gg \mathcal{E}_f$ for the electrons with enough energy to escape, where $\mathcal{E}_f$ is the Fermi level. Then the expression

$$\ln (1 + \epsilon^{(\mathcal{E}_f - \mathcal{E}_x)/kT}) \cong \epsilon^{(\mathcal{E}_f - \mathcal{E}_x)/kT} \qquad (A7.1)$$

The number of electrons per second hitting 1 cm^2 of metal boundary normal to the boundary from among the conduction electrons is

$$n_x \sec^{-1} \text{cm}^{-2} = \int_{v_1}^{\infty} v_x \, dn_x$$

where v_1 is the velocity corresponding to $\mathcal{E}_1 = \frac{1}{2}mv_1^2$, the height of the potential-energy barrier above the bottom of the conduction band, and dn_x is given by (8.1). Current density of emitted electrons will be simply e times this. Thus

$$J_e = \frac{4\pi m^2 kTe}{h^3} \int_{v_1}^{\infty} \exp \frac{\mathcal{E}_f - \frac{1}{2}mv_x^2}{kT} v_x \, dv_x \qquad (A7.2)$$

or putting in terms of $\mathcal{E}$,

$$J_e = \frac{4\pi mkTe}{h^3} \int_{\mathcal{E}_1}^{\infty} \epsilon^{(\mathcal{E}_f - \mathcal{E}_x)/kT} \, d\mathcal{E}_x \qquad (A7.3)$$

452

This integrates to

$$J_e = \frac{4\pi m k^2 T^2}{h^3} \epsilon^{(\mathcal{E}_f - \mathcal{E}_1)/kT} \tag{A7.4}$$

which has the desired form of

$$J_e = A_e T^2 \epsilon^{-e\phi/kT} \tag{8.2}$$

where

$$A_e = \frac{4\pi m k^2 T^2}{h^3} = 120 \text{ amp cm}^{-2} \text{ °K}^{-2} \tag{A7.5}$$

is a universal constant and

$$e\phi = \mathcal{E}_1 - \mathcal{E}_f \tag{A7.6}$$

is the height of the potential-energy barrier above the Fermi level.

APPENDIX 8

DERIVATION OF THE CHILD-LANGMUIR LAW

THE CHILD-LANGMUIR law [(9.1)] gives the relation between current and voltage as encountered in a plane-electrode diode as a result of space-charge limitation of current flow.

$$J = \frac{2.335 \times 10^{-6} V^{\frac{3}{2}}}{x^2} \qquad \text{amp (unit area)}^{-1} \qquad (9.1)$$

where J = current density

V = potential above cathode at distance x from cathode

This is a good approximation to what actually occurs. The current density is independent of cathode material and temperature, provided only that the emission current density is appreciably greater than that required by (9.1).

Equation (9.1) may be derived by invoking the energy relation, Poisson's equation, and the relation between current density, charge, and velocity. These are

$$\tfrac{1}{2}mv^2 = Ve \qquad (A8.1)$$

$$\frac{d^2V}{dx^2} = -\frac{\rho}{\varepsilon_0} \qquad (A8.2)$$

$$J = \rho v \qquad (A8.3)$$

where e = electron charge

m = electron mass

V = potential relative to cathode

ρ = space-charge density

v = electron velocity

x = distance from cathode

ε_0 = dielectric constant of free space

If now ρ is expressed in terms of J and v from the first and third equation and substituted into the second, there results

$$\frac{d^2V}{dx^2} = \frac{J}{\varepsilon_0}\sqrt{\frac{m}{2e}}\,V^{-\frac{1}{2}} \qquad (A8.4)$$

where J is now taken as the magnitude of current density; actually, electron flow in the positive x direction corresponds to negative current. A

454

first integration is achieved by multiplying both sides of (A8.4) by $2\,dV/dx$ and integrating

$$\left(\frac{dV}{dx}\right)^2 = \frac{4J}{\varepsilon_0}\sqrt{\frac{m}{2e}}\,V^{\frac{1}{2}} + c_1 \tag{A8.5}$$

The constant of integration is taken as zero because the space charge has been assumed to decrease the potential gradient to zero at the cathode, where the potential is zero.

A second integration gives

$$\frac{4V^{\frac{3}{4}}}{3} = \sqrt{\frac{4J}{\varepsilon_0}}\sqrt{\frac{m}{2e}}\,x + c_2 \tag{A8.6}$$

where the constant of integration is again zero because the potential at the cathode is zero, where the distance x is zero. Solving for current density,

$$J = \frac{4\varepsilon_0}{9\sqrt{\frac{m}{2e}}}\frac{V^{\frac{3}{2}}}{x^2} \tag{A8.7}$$

When numerical values of the constants are substituted, (9.1) results.

APPENDIX 9

DESIGN FORMULAS
FOR THE PLANE-ELECTRODE TRIODE

IT IS convenient at times to know the tube constants as a function of interelectrode geometry. Various engineering design formulas are available for this purpose. In general, there are no exact equations but only various approximations that, as they become more accurate, become also more complex in form. The formulas presented here represent a compromise between simplicity and accuracy.

Formulas for amplification factor are derived from electrostatic field considerations. This is done by finding the relative effectiveness of grid and plate in controlling the gradient of potential in front of the cathode [BeC, DoB, Spc]. A cold-tube determination can be used because the gradient of potential at the cathode will determine the current flow in actual operation.

One of the most extensively used formulas for amplification factor is that proposed by Vodges and Elder [Spc]

$$\mu = \frac{2\pi d_{gp}/a - \ln \cosh \pi S}{\ln \coth \pi S} \tag{A9.1}$$

where d_{gp} = grid-plate spacing
  a = spacing between parallel grid wires
  $S = 2r_g/a$, the so-called screening fraction, wherein
  r_g = radius of grid wires

This formula is accurate to within a few per cent out to screening fractions of one-fifth. For larger screening fractions, more accurate formulas must be used. Note that amplification factor is independent of cathode-grid spacing. In general, this is true only if the cathode-grid spacing exceeds the spacing between grid wires. A graphical representation of amplification factor for screening fractions out to 0.4 is given in Fig. 10.5.

Mutual conductance is calculated by finding a diode equivalent to the triode and then calculating current by the Child-Langmuir law. A diode equivalent to the triode may be found by assuming that the equivalent diode-plate voltage is $V_g + V_p/\mu$ and then calculating the equivalent diode spacing that will give the same field and current density at the cathode. Alternatively, the grid may be replaced by the diode plate and the equivalent voltage of this plate calculated. The latter process appears to give answers which best fit all aspects of operation.

The equivalent voltage of a diode plate in the grid plane is

$$V_{eq} = \frac{V_g + V_p/\mu}{1 + 1/\mu + (4/3\mu)(d_{gp}/d_{cg})} \tag{A9.2}$$

This is seen to be slightly less than the value of $V_g + V_p/\mu$.

Using the above equivalent voltage, current will then be given by

$$J = \frac{2.335 \times 10^{-6} V_{eq}^{\frac{3}{2}}}{d_{cg}^2} \tag{A9.3}$$

in accordance with (9.1).

To find mutual conductance, we now merely take the partial derivative of (A9.3) with respect to V_g. To find the dynamic plate resistance, we take the partial derivative of (A9.3) with respect to V_p and then take the reciprocal. An interesting and useful property of mutual conductance is that it varies as the cube root of the anode current.

APPENDIX 10

THEOREMS OF THÉVENIN AND NORTON

Thévenin's Theorem. This states that at a single frequency any complex generator consisting of actual physical generators and linear bilateral impedances and having two output terminals may be replaced by a single generator in series with a single impedance. The single generator is a constant-voltage generator whose voltage is equal to the voltage observed at the output terminals when the actual generator is open-circuited. The single impedance is an impedance equal to that measured looking into the actual generator terminals when the voltage and current sources are inactive, i.e., replaced by their internal impedances [EvF]. This is easily demonstrated by reference to Fig. A10.1, in which there is shown a

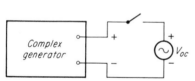

Fig. A10.1. Complex generator with un-connected opposing voltage in output.

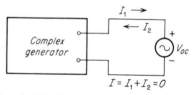

Fig. A10.2. Complex generator with connected opposing voltage in output circuit.

complex generator represented by a box with two terminals. Let there be connected in the output circuit of this generator a switch and a voltage generator of zero impedance whose output voltage is at all times equal and opposite to that appearing at the terminals of the complex generator when the switch is open, as in Fig. A10.2. Then, clearly, when the switch is closed, no current will flow. By the principle of superposition, the zero current can be considered to be the sum of equal and opposite currents I_1 due to the actual generator acting alone and I_2 due to the external generator acting alone. Since I_2 is equal to the open-circuit voltage divided by the impedance looking into the actual generator producing the current, I_1 can be considered due to a simple equivalent generator consisting of a zero-impedance voltage generator of strength V_{oc}, the open-circuit voltage, in series with an impedance Z_{in}, the impedance looking into the actual generator terminals with all sources inactive. This equivalent generator is shown in Fig. A10.3. Although the equivalence was worked out for a particular load condition, it will be equally valid for all loads because of the linear properties of the network assumed.

Norton's Theorem. This states that any complex generator consisting of actual physical generators and linear bilateral impedances and having two output terminals may be replaced at a single frequency by a simple generator consisting of a constant-current generator in parallel with the impedance seen looking into the actual generator terminals when the voltage and current sources are inactive, i.e., replaced by their internal impedances. This may be demonstrated by an argument similar to that used in the previous case. Let the actual generator be short-circuited. A current I_{sc} will flow through the external short. Let now an external

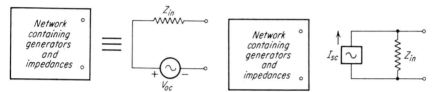

FIG. A10.3. Equivalent of a complex generator by Thévenin's theorem.

FIG. A10.4. Equivalent of a complex generator by Norton's theorem.

constant-current generator with a strength I_{sc} be connected across the shorted output terminals with such a polarity that the current through the short is made zero. If now the actual generator is rendered inactive but not disconnected, the current through the short will be the same as originally, except for direction. Looking back from the short, there is seen a constant-current generator of strength I_{sc} in parallel with the impedance looking into the actual generator with the sources inactive, i.e., replaced by their internal impedances. Accordingly, the actual generator can be replaced by an infinite-impedance constant-current generator of strength I_{sc} in parallel with the impedance Z_{in} seen looking into the actual generator terminals with the sources inactive, i.e., replaced by their internal impedances, as shown in Fig. A10.4. It is also easily shown that the equivalent generator of Fig. A10.4 will give the same current through any load as the generator of Fig. A10.3.

APPENDIX 11

FUNDAMENTAL RELATIONS
IN FOUR-TERMINAL NETWORKS

GIVEN the five basic equation pairs below:

$$V_1 = z_{11}I_1 + z_{12}I_2$$
$$V_2 = z_{21}I_1 + z_{22}I_2 \qquad (A11.1)$$

$$I_1 = y_{11}V_1 + y_{12}V_2$$
$$I_2 = y_{21}V_1 + y_{22}V_2 \qquad (A11.2)$$

$$V_1 = h_{11}I_1 + h_{12}V_2$$
$$I_2 = h_{21}I_1 + h_{22}V_2 \qquad (A11.3)$$

$$I_1 = g_{11}V_1 + g_{12}I_2$$
$$V_2 = g_{21}V_1 + g_{22}I_2 \qquad (A11.4)$$

$$V_1 = \mathfrak{A}V_2 - \mathfrak{B}I_2$$
$$I_1 = \mathfrak{C}V_2 - \mathfrak{D}I_2 \qquad (A11.5)$$

And letting the determinants of the five equation pairs be

$$|z| = \begin{vmatrix} z_{11} & z_{12} \\ z_{21} & z_{22} \end{vmatrix} = z_{11}z_{22} - z_{12}z_{21} \qquad (A11.6)$$

$$|y| = \begin{vmatrix} y_{11} & y_{12} \\ y_{21} & y_{22} \end{vmatrix} = y_{11}y_{22} - y_{12}y_{21} \qquad (A11.7)$$

$$|h| = \begin{vmatrix} h_{11} & h_{12} \\ h_{21} & h_{22} \end{vmatrix} = h_{11}h_{22} - h_{12}h_{21} \qquad (A11.8)$$

$$|g| = \begin{vmatrix} g_{11} & g_{12} \\ g_{21} & g_{22} \end{vmatrix} = g_{11}g_{22} - g_{12}g_{21} \qquad (A11.9)$$

$$|\mathfrak{M}| = \begin{vmatrix} \mathfrak{A} & \mathfrak{B} \\ \mathfrak{C} & \mathfrak{D} \end{vmatrix} = \mathfrak{A}\mathfrak{D} - \mathfrak{C}\mathfrak{B} \qquad (A11.10)$$

then the following relationships exist between the coefficients:

$$y_{11} = \frac{z_{22}}{|z|} = \frac{|g|}{g_{22}} = \frac{1}{h_{11}} = \frac{\mathfrak{D}}{\mathfrak{B}}$$

$$y_{12} = -\frac{z_{12}}{|z|} = \frac{g_{12}}{g_{22}} = -\frac{h_{12}}{h_{11}} = -\frac{|\mathfrak{M}|}{\mathfrak{B}}$$

$$y_{22} = \frac{z_{11}}{|z|} = \frac{1}{g_{22}} = \frac{|h|}{h_{11}} = \frac{\mathfrak{A}}{\mathfrak{B}} \qquad (A11.11)$$

$$y_{21} = -\frac{z_{21}}{|z|} = -\frac{g_{21}}{g_{22}} = \frac{h_{21}}{h_{11}} = -\frac{1}{\mathfrak{B}}$$

$$z_{11} = \frac{y_{22}}{|y|} = \frac{1}{g_{11}} = \frac{|h|}{h_{22}} = \frac{\mathcal{A}}{\mathcal{C}}$$

$$z_{12} = -\frac{y_{12}}{|y|} = -\frac{g_{12}}{g_{11}} = \frac{h_{12}}{h_{22}} = \frac{|\mathfrak{M}|}{\mathcal{C}}$$

$$z_{22} = \frac{y_{11}}{|y|} = \frac{|g|}{g_{11}} = \frac{1}{h_{22}} = \frac{\mathcal{D}}{\mathcal{C}}$$ (A11.12)

$$z_{21} = -\frac{y_{21}}{|y|} = \frac{g_{21}}{g_{11}} = -\frac{h_{21}}{h_{22}} = \frac{1}{\mathcal{C}}$$

$$g_{11} = \frac{|y|}{y_{22}} = \frac{1}{z_{11}} = \frac{h_{22}}{|h|} = \frac{\mathcal{C}}{\mathcal{A}}$$

$$g_{12} = \frac{y_{12}}{y_{22}} = -\frac{z_{12}}{z_{11}} = -\frac{h_{12}}{|h|} = -\frac{|\mathfrak{M}|}{\mathcal{A}}$$

$$g_{22} = \frac{1}{y_{22}} = \frac{|z|}{z_{11}} = \frac{h_{11}}{|h|} = \frac{\mathcal{B}}{\mathcal{A}}$$ (A11.13)

$$g_{21} = -\frac{y_{21}}{y_{22}} = \frac{z_{21}}{z_{11}} = -\frac{h_{21}}{|h|} = \frac{1}{\mathcal{A}}$$

$$h_{11} = \frac{1}{y_{11}} = \frac{|z|}{z_{22}} = \frac{g_{22}}{|g|} = \frac{\mathcal{B}}{\mathcal{D}}$$

$$h_{12} = -\frac{y_{12}}{y_{11}} = \frac{z_{12}}{z_{22}} = -\frac{g_{12}}{|g|} = \frac{|\mathfrak{M}|}{\mathcal{D}}$$

$$h_{22} = \frac{|y|}{y_{11}} = \frac{1}{z_{22}} = \frac{g_{11}}{|g|} = \frac{\mathcal{C}}{\mathcal{D}}$$ (A11.14)

$$h_{21} = \frac{y_{21}}{y_{11}} = -\frac{z_{21}}{z_{22}} = -\frac{g_{21}}{|g|} = -\frac{1}{\mathcal{D}}$$

$$\mathcal{A} = -\frac{y_{22}}{y_{21}} = \frac{z_{11}}{z_{21}} = +\frac{1}{y_{21}} = -\frac{|h|}{h_{21}}$$

$$\mathcal{B} = -\frac{1}{y_{21}} = \frac{|z|}{z_{21}} = +\frac{g_{22}}{g_{21}} = -\frac{h_{11}}{h_{21}}$$

$$\mathcal{C} = -\frac{|y|}{y_{21}} = \frac{1}{z_{21}} = +\frac{g_{11}}{g_{21}} = -\frac{h_{22}}{h_{21}}$$ (A11.15)

$$\mathcal{D} = -\frac{y_{11}}{y_{21}} = \frac{z_{22}}{z_{21}} = +\frac{|g|}{g_{21}} = -\frac{1}{h_{21}}$$

Notice that

$$|y| = |z|^{-1}$$ (A11.16)

and

$$|g| = |h|^{-1}$$ (A11.17)

Note also that these equations are quite general. They apply to active as well as passive networks.

APPENDIX 12

NOISE IN RESISTANCES

Noise in resistances is due to thermal agitation of the electrons, akin to Brownian motion. It is often referred to as Johnson noise [Jow]. An idea of how this noise is distributed in frequency may be had by considering a section of ideal (lossless) transmission line terminated at each end in its characteristic resistance R [Nyw]. If the system is in thermal equilibrium, i.e., all at the same temperature, then each resistor will feed noise power into the line directed at the other resistor and absorbed by it. The arrangement is that shown in Fig. A12.1.

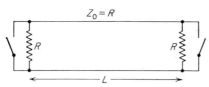

FIG. A12.1. Resistances terminating a lossless transmission line act as generators of thermal noise power, each feeding power into the other.

Let the line suddenly be shorted at each end after equilibrium is established. The shorted line then becomes a resonator with an infinite number of modes of resonance. The first of these will be that for which the line is one-half wavelength long, the second will be that for which the line is three-halves wavelengths long, the third that for which the line is five-halves wavelengths long, and so on. The associated resonant frequencies will be $c/2L$, $3c/2L$, $5c/2L$, . . . , where c is the velocity of light and L is the length of the line. It is seen that the resonant frequencies are spaced by a frequency Δf, where

$$\Delta f = \frac{c}{2L} \tag{A12.1}$$

According to the equipartition theorem of statistical mechanics, there is an energy of $kT/2$ associated with each degree of freedom or each of the means whereby energy may be stored, where k is Boltzmann's constant and T is absolute temperature [Goc]. In each resonant mode energy is stored equally in the electric and magnetic fields. Hence the energy stored is kT per resonant mode. The energy per unit bandwidth is then given by

$$w = \frac{kT}{\Delta f} = \frac{kT}{c/2L} \tag{A12.2}$$

462

Here w represents the energy per unit bandwidth that flowed into the line from *both* resistances in a period L/c since it takes a wave a time of L/c to pass from one end of the line to the other. If p is the power *per unit bandwidth* from *one resistance*, then

$$w = 2p\frac{L}{c} = \frac{kT}{c/2L} \tag{A12.3}$$

or

$$p = kT \tag{A12.4}$$

Accordingly, the power flow from one resistance into a matched load, the available noise power, for a bandwidth B is

$$N_a = kTB \tag{A12.5}$$

which is the same as (18.5). From this, by Ohm's law,

$$\bar{v}^2 = 4kTRB \tag{A12.6}$$

which is the same as (18.2), and

$$\bar{i}^2 = \frac{4kTB}{R} \tag{A12.7}$$

which is the same as (18.4).

APPENDIX 13

SHOT NOISE

THE EXPRESSION for shot noise, (18.6), may be made to seem reasonable by considering a special vacuum diode with two cathodes aligned face to face and shorted externally [Pic]. If the cathodes have the same work function, if they are of identical materials at the same temperature, and if the emitted currents are small enough to avoid a space-charge depression of potential, then all the electrons emitted from cathode 1 will reach cathode 2 and vice versa, as shown in Fig. A13.1.

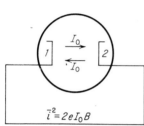

FIG. A13.1. Special vacuum diode, containing two identical cathodes at the same temperature, for the analysis of shot effect.

The Maxwellian distribution of velocity of electrons on emission results in a current I_r capable of overcoming a retarding potential V_r given by

$$I_r = I_e \epsilon^{(eV_r/kT)} \tag{A13.1}$$

where I_e = emitted current
e = electron charge
k = Boltzmann's constant
T = absolute temperature

This is the same as (8.3). The conductance of a single diode for $V_r = 0$ is given by $\partial I_r / \partial V_r$, which has the value

$$G = \frac{e}{kT} I_0 \tag{A13.2}$$

This is the conductance of one cathode for retarding voltages. The conductance for accelerating voltages is zero. Hence the special diode of Fig. A13.1 has a composite conductance for voltages in either direction given by (A13.2).

Application of (18.4) gives a mean-square-noise current of

$$\overline{i^2_{\text{rms}}} = 4kTGB = 4kT\frac{eI_0}{kT} = 4eI_0B \tag{A13.3}$$

This is the noise due to two independent noise sources, and hence that due to a single cathode is

$$\overline{i^2_{rms}} = 2eI_0B \tag{A13.4}$$

which is the same as (18.6). The above demonstration is not really a derivation but rather a rationalization. It assumes that the phenomenon giving rise to resistance noise is the same as that giving rise to emission noise. It will at least make the formula seem reasonable and dimensionally correct.

PROBLEMS

CHAPTER 1

1.1. Obtain data, and plot a curve of the growth of the installed electrical power-generating capacity in the United States over the last 25 years. Compare with the curve of the growth of population. Comment on the significance of these.

1.2. Obtain and tabulate data on the installed electrical power-generating capacity per capita of the ten leading industrial nations of the world. Comment on the significance of this factor relative to the industrial strength of these countries.

1.3. Obtain data on the size of the American Physical Society, the American Institute of Electrical Engineers and the Institute of Radio Engineers. Estimate, by sampling members among your own acquaintances, what are the numbers of members common to each two of the three societies.

1.4. Develop arguments for and against the designation of a separate group of electronic engineers. Develop arguments for and against the establishment of separate curricula of electronics and electrical engineering. Discuss the relative merits of having a program of electronics as part of a program of physics rather than of electrical engineering.

1.5. Examine the extent of the "Positions Open" section in the *Proceedings of the IRE* for the past decade or two. Comment on the variation.

1.6. Analyze recent position openings in terms of topical interests.

CHAPTER 2

2.1. A current in a gas discharge is composed of electrons moving to higher potentials and singly charged positive mercury ions moving in the other direction. If the number of electrons passing a given plane per second is greater than the number of mercury ions passing the plane per second in the opposite direction by the inverse square root of the mass ratio of the two carriers, how many electrons will pass the plane per second to give a current of 1 amp?

2.2. In a sample of p-type germanium there are 10^{15} holes per cubic centimeter and one-tenth this number of free electrons. Assuming that these move in opposite directions with the same velocity, determine the carrier velocity to give a current density of 1 ma cm^{-2}.

2.3. What is the absolute mass of a proton? Of a neutron?

2.4. What is the equivalent wavelength of 30,000-volt electrons?

2.5. Justify the dimensions of ε_0.

2.6. Justify the dimensions of μ_0.

CHAPTER 3

3.1. Two particles are suspended by weightless strings of the same length L from the same point. Each has a mass m and a charge q. As a result of forces arising from the mutual repulsion of like charges, the particles will separate. Show that the angle θ that each string makes with the vertical in the equilibrium position is given by

$$4mgL^2 \sin^3 \theta = 4\pi\varepsilon_0 q^2 \cos\theta$$

3.2. Two *point* charges are located as follows: $+2.0$ coulombs at $(0,0,0)$ m; -1.0 coulomb at $(1,0,0)$ m. What is the force, in magnitude and direction, on a charge of -0.5 coulomb at (a) $(0,1,0)$; (b) $(1,1,0)$; (c) $(2,0,0)$; (d) $(-2,0,0)$; (e) $(2,2,2)$?

3.3. Two *point* charges are located as follows: $+10$ coulombs at $(1,0,0)$ m; -0.5 coulomb at $(-1,0,0)$ m.

(a) Calculate and plot a curve potential along the x axis.

(b) At what points on the x axis is the potential zero?

(c) At what points on the x axis is the electric field zero?

(d) Where else is the electric potential zero?

(e) Where else is the electric field zero?

3.4. Two point charges are located as follows: -3.0 coulombs at $(1,0,0)$ m; $+2.0$ coulombs at $(0,0,0)$ m. Give for this disposition of charges the five answers requested in Prob. 3.3.

3.5. Find the electric field at a distance r from the center of an electric dipole—an assembly of two equal positive and negative charges spaced a distance s. Find the field along the line through the charges.

Solution (in Part). Referring to Fig. P3.5, the field due to the positive charge q given in magnitude by (3.5) is

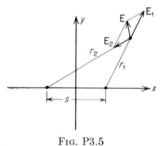

$$E_1 = \frac{q}{4\pi\varepsilon_0 r_1^2}$$

This is represented by the vector $\mathbf{E}_1$ in the diagram and is directed away from the positive charge.

The field due to the negative charge $-q$ is given in magnitude by

$$E_2 = \frac{q}{4\pi\varepsilon_0 r_2^2}$$

Fig. P3.5

and is directed toward the negative charge.

The resultant electric field is the vector sum of these two vectors, as shown by $\mathbf{E}$. An analytic expression for the vector summation in terms of either rectangular or polar coordinates is quite involved.

Along the line of the charges the expression for electric field is

$$E_x = \frac{q}{4\pi\varepsilon_0(x - s/2)^2} - \frac{q}{4\pi\varepsilon_0(x + s/2)^2}$$

This simplifies to

$$E_x = \frac{q}{4\pi\varepsilon_0} \frac{2xs}{(x^2 - s^2/4)^2}$$

For distance x much greater than spacing s, this simplifies to

$$E_x \cong \frac{q}{4\pi\varepsilon_0} \frac{2s}{x^3}$$

This last equation shows that the field of a dipole drops off inversely with the cube of distance rather than inversely with distance squared, as is the case for point charges.

3.6. Find the potential of a dipole along the line of the charges. Obtain the electric field along the line of the charges from the expression for potential.

Solution.   Referring to Fig. P3.5 and using (3.7),

$$V = \frac{q}{4\pi\varepsilon_0}\left(\frac{1}{x - s/2} - \frac{1}{x + s/2}\right)$$

which reduces to

$$V = \frac{q}{4\pi\varepsilon_0}\frac{s}{x^2 - s^2/4}$$

This shows that at large distances potential of a dipole varies as inverse distance squared instead of as inverse distance, as is the case with point charges.

Taking the derivative of the first expression above in accordance with (3.4),

$$E_x = -\frac{\partial V}{\partial x} = \frac{q}{4\pi\varepsilon_0}\frac{2xs}{(x^2 - s^2/4)^2}$$

This is approximately the same expression that was obtained in Prob. 3.5.

3.7. Two *line* charges have a uniform charge distribution and are parallel to the z axis. The first has a linear charge density of $+2.0$ coulombs m^{-1} and passes through the point $(0,0,0)$. The second has a linear charge density of -1.0 coulomb m^{-1} and passes through $(1,0,0)$. If the potential at the point $(2,0,0)$ is 100 volts, (*a*) calculate and plot a curve of potential along the x axis; (*b*) determine where the potential has zero and maximum or minimum values; (*c*) determine where the electric field is zero or maximum.

3.8. The same as Prob. 3.7 but with linear charge densities of -0.5 coulomb m^{-1} through $(1,0,0)$ and $+1.0$ coulomb m^{-1} at $(-1,0,0)$.

3.9. Show that the electric intensity inside an infinitely long straight cylindrical section of radius a that has a charge of λ per unit length uniformly distributed throughout its cross section, as shown in Fig. P3.9, is

$$E_r = \frac{\lambda r_1}{2\pi\varepsilon_0 a^2}$$

whereas outside it is

$$E_r = \frac{\lambda}{2\pi\varepsilon_0 r_2}$$

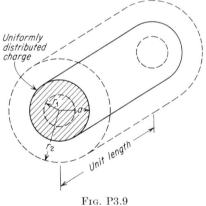

Uniformly distributed charge

FIG. P3.9

Solution.   To find the field within the cylinder of charge at a radius r_1, consider a unit length of the section and an imaginary circular cylinder of radius r_1 concentric with the axis of the charge distribution. From considerations of symmetry the flux from any element of charge will have an outward radial direction, none will have an inward direction, and the flux density will vary only with radius, not with angle. To find the radial electric field, it is then only necessary to apply Gauss's law to the charge within the cylinder of radius r_1. By Gauss's law, the net outward flux must equal the charge enclosed. These quantities may be equated as

$$2\pi r_1\varepsilon_0 E_r = \frac{r_1^2\lambda}{a^2}$$

The left side is the product of the area $2\pi r_1$ and the radial flux density $D_r = \varepsilon_0 E_r$, assuming the free-space value of the dielectric constant. The right side gives the fraction of the total charge per unit length λ within a cylinder of radius r_1. Solving for E_r gives the indicated answer. The radial electric field is seen to increase linearly *within* the charge distribution.

To find the radial electric field outside the charge, the same process is applied to a cylinder of radius r_2. In this case Gauss's law yields

$$2\pi r_2 \varepsilon_0 E_r = \lambda$$

The left side is again the net outward flux. There is no flux through the end surfaces of the cylinder because the flux is all radial. The right side is in this case the total charge per unit length. The electric field is seen to vary inversely with radius *outside* the charge.

3.10. A 100-ma 1,000-volt electron beam is 1 mm in diameter and is directed along the axis of a copper tube 2 mm in inner diameter. Determine the relative electric potential as a function of radius.

3.11. A total charge Q is uniformly distributed throughout a sphere of radius a. Show that the electric field is radial and varies as $E_r = Qr/3a^3\varepsilon_0$ inside the sphere and as $E_r = Q/4\pi\varepsilon_0 r^2$ outside the sphere.

3.12. Write expressions for the field and potential within a concentric cylindrical capacitor whose outer and inner radii are r_2 and r_1 and whose inner and outer potentials are V_1 and V_2.

3.13. Write expressions for the field and potential within a concentric spherical capacitor whose inner and outer radii are r_1 and r_2 and whose inner and outer potentials are V_1 V_2.

3.14. A concentric line has a square outer conductor 8 cm on edge and a circular inner conductor 2 cm in diameter. Make a sketch of flux and potential lines over the cross section, using curvilinear squares.

Estimate the capacity per unit length from the relation $C = \varepsilon_0(\text{No. of flux tubes})/$ (No. of potential intervals). Estimate the characteristic impedance as a radio-frequency line from the relation $Z_0 = 377(\text{No. of potential intervals})/(\text{No. of flux tubes})$. Estimate the accuracy of your answer. Compare with results by available formulas. Verify the relations given.

3.15. Explain how you would use a current-flow model to measure equipotential lines in a cylindrical triode having a cylindrical cathode and plate and a helical grid.

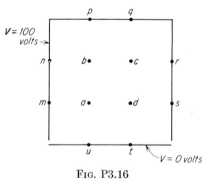

Fig. P3.16

3.16. The potential on three sides of a long box of square cross section, as shown in Fig. P3.16, is 100 volts and on the remaining side 0 volts. Find, by net-point computations, the variation of potential within the box.

To illustrate the method, a very coarse network will be set up as shown. In practice, networks of points must be finer. The potential at m, n, p, q, r, and s is 100 volts, that at u and t is 0 volts. The potential at a, b, c, and d is unknown.

By symmetry, $V_b = V_c$ and $V_a = V_d$.

Hence only V_a and V_b must be found.

Assume that $V_{a1} = 80$ volts and $V_{b1} = 50$ volts. Then

$$V_{a2} = \tfrac{1}{4}(V_u + V_m + V_{b1} - V_{a1})$$
$$= \tfrac{1}{4}(0 + 100 + 80 + 50) = 57.5 \text{ volts}$$

since $V_{d1} = V_{a1}$.

$$V_{b2} = \tfrac{1}{4}(V_n + V_p + V_{b1} + V_{a2})$$
$$= \tfrac{1}{4}(100 + 100 + 80 + 57.5) = 84.4 \text{ volts}$$

Repetition of this process yields

$$V_{a3} = 60.5 \text{ volts} \qquad V_{b3} = 86.1 \text{ volts}$$

Final values of these voltages from simultaneous equations are $V_a = 62.5$ volts and $V_b = 87.5$ volts *for the network of points assumed.* It is thus seen that the process indicated above converges rapidly upon the correct values. If a finer network with more points is used, the final result is a better one.

3.17. Using the method of net-point computations and the relation (3.26), obtain by successive approximations a field plot for a section of a plane-electrode triode with the following dimensions: cathode-grid spacing = 50 mils; grid-plate spacing = 100 mils; intergrid spacing = 50 mils; grid-wire diameter = 5 mils. Do this for grid at −10 volts and plate at +100 volts relative to cathode.

3.18. Derive (3.29), giving the magnetic flux density at a radius r from a long straight wire.

3.19. Derive (3.32) for the magnetic flux density on the axis of a circular loop of wire.

CHAPTER 4

4.1. Through what potential must an electron be accelerated from rest to attain a velocity equal to the velocity of sound, 700 mph?

4.2. What gradient of potential gives to an electron an acceleration of $100g$?

4.3. At a velocity resulting from acceleration through 1,000 volts, how long would it take an electron to travel around the world, 24,000 miles?

4.4. The deflecting plates of an oscilloscope are 2 cm long and are spaced 0.5 cm apart. If the screen is 30 cm from the center of the deflecting plates and the electron stream has been accelerated through 800 volts, what deflecting voltage is required to give a deflection of 2.5 cm at the screen?

4.5. An electron is shot through a hole in a conducting plate into a retarding potential between two conducting parallel plates. If the potential difference between the plates is 100 volts and the plate spacing 10 cm and if the electron initially makes an angle of 30° with the normal to the plates, through what potential must the electron have been accelerated in order just to graze the more negative plate?

Solution. For an angle of 30° with the normal, the component of velocity toward the negative plate will be cos 30° = 0.866 times the original velocity, and the component of velocity parallel to the plates will be sin 30° = 0.500 times the original velocity. The energy *associated* with the normal component of velocity will be cos² 30° = 0.75 times the original energy, and the energy associated with the parallel component of velocity will be sin² 30° = 0.25 times the original energy. The energy associated with the normal component of velocity in electron volts must be equal to the retarding potential in volts. Since this is three-quarters of the total energy, the total energy must be 133.3 ev and the electron must have been accelerated through 133.3 volts.

4.6. Two parallel conducting plates are spaced at a distance of 2 cm and have a potential difference of 50 volts. Electrons that have been accelerated through 100 volts are shot through a hole in the positive plate toward the negative plate at angles of 0, 30, 45, and 60° with the normal to the plates. Calculate and tabulate the following data for each angle: (*a*) sidewise displacement from the hole at which the electrons strike a conducting plate; (b) energy associated with transverse and normal components of velocity at impact.

4.7. When electrons are shot into a retarding field, at what angle with the normal to the initial plane will they experience the greatest translation parallel to the plane for a given initial energy? It is assumed that electrons are shot through a hole in a plane and that the field is perpendicular to the plane, as in the previous problem. It is also assumed that the electrons are free to rise and return to the original plane.

4.8. At certain points on the globe the magnetic field of the earth is about 0.5 gauss. What is the maximum deflection this magnetic field can give to a 1,000-volt electron over 30 cm of travel (typical cathode-ray tube)?

Solution. Using (4.23), the radius of curvature of the electron path for a normal field is

$$r_1 = \frac{3.37 \sqrt{1,000}}{0.5} = 213 \text{ cm}$$

Use now the equation of a circle of radius 213 cm with center at $x = 0$ and $y = 213$ cm to find the value of y for $x = 30$ cm. This turns out to be $y = 2.16$ cm deflection.

4.9. Electrons are shot through a hole in the center of a face of a cubical box 10 cm on an edge. Inside the box they encounter a uniform magnetic field parallel to an edge. On the side of the box toward which the electrons are deflected are a series of holes spaced at 2-cm intervals from the edges and along the center line of the face normal to the magnetic field. With what energy must electrons enter the box to emerge through each hole? What is the transit time in microseconds in each case?

4.10. Show that, when electrons are shot into a magnetic field with an initial angle between the electron velocity and magnetic field other than 90°, the resultant path is a helix.

4.11. Show that there is a focusing effect when electrons of the same velocity are shot through a hole into a region of uniform magnetic field, all electrons being at different small angles with the field. What is the focal length?

4.12. Justify the membrane-model analogy for electron paths. Do this with suitable assumptions on the basis of equivalence-of-energy relations.

4.13. Describe qualitatively the path of an electron shot through a coil of wire carrying a current. Let the electron be initially parallel to the axis of the coil but displaced slightly from it. Show that such an arrangement is capable of focusing a stream of parallel electrons to a point.

4.14. Show that the path of an electron injected at right angles to a uniform magnetic field is a circle by solving the differential equations of motion in rectangular coordinates.

4.15. Discuss the considerations in obtaining wide-angle linear deflection in television cathode-ray tubes with either electric or magnetic deflection.

CHAPTER 5

5.1. A point source emits radiant energy at the rate of 1 watt, the intensity being uniform in all directions. At what distance from the source will the photon density be 1 cm^{-3} if the wavelength of radiation is (a) 10 cm, (b) 5,000 A, (c) 0.5 A?

5.2. At what distance from the source of Prob. 5.1 will the photons be passing through an aperture of area 1 cm^2 at the rate of 1 μsec^{-1} for the same three wavelengths?

5.3. What is the longest wavelength at which photoemission will occur, using an anode of a pure element? Work functions of certain special oxide surfaces are better going to 1 ev or slightly below. What work function is required to detect long infrared rays?

5.4. Newtonian mechanics breaks down when the de Broglie wavelength is of the order of the physical dimensions of the problem. How does the orbit of Mercury stand on this criterion? How about an electron in the lowest Bohr orbit of hydrogen?

5.5. Apply the uncertainty principle to the Bohr orbits. How certain are we that an electron is in a given orbit rather than in an adjacent one?

5.6. Assume that a photon transmits *all* its energy to a hydrogen electron and thus ionizes the atom. (This rarely happens because of the Compton effect; usually only a few per cent of the energy is thus transmitted.) What is the longest wavelength at which a photon can ionize a hydrogen atom and also give the electron a velocity greater than the escape velocity from the earth's gravitation? How does the ionization energy compare with the escape energy? Assuming that the photon transmits only 1 per cent of its energy, answer the same questions.

5.7. Explain Moseley's observations in more detail than is given in the text.

5.8. Discuss solutions of Schrödinger's equation for a potential-energy well in one dimension in which potential energy U is zero for $-d < x < d$ and equals W outside this range. Total energy ε is less than W. Show that solutions are parts of sinusoids inside the well and parts of exponentials outside the well.

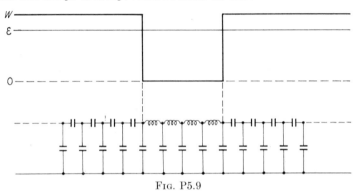

Fig. P5.9

5.9. Show that the differential equation of current as a function of distance of the special transmission line shown in Fig. P5.9 is the analogue of Schrödinger's equation in Prob. 5.8.

CHAPTER 6

6.1. Tabulate the electron structures of tin, boron, tellurium, and selenium.

6.2. How many grams of phosphorus must be added to 100 g of pure germanium to yield a resistivity of 10 ohm-cm? Assume that the phosphorus is uniformly distributed throughout the germanium, that all the excess electrons introduced by the phosphorus are excited, and that the mobility of these electrons is 3,600 cm^2 sec^{-1} volt^{-1}.

6.3. What is the density of the phosphorus atoms in Prob. 6.2?

6.4. How many grams of indium must be added to 100 g of silicon to yield a resistivity of 1 ohm-cm? Assume that the indium is uniformly distributed and that each acceptor atom is excited to produce a hole with a mobility of 250 cm^2 sec^{-1} volt^{-1}.

6.5. What is the Hall coefficient for the material of Prob. 6.4?

6.6. A sample of *n*-type semiconductor has a resistivity of 0.1 ohm-cm and a Hall coefficient of 100 cm^{-3} coulomb^{-1}. Assuming only electrons as carriers, determine the electron density and mobility.

6.7. Explain qualitatively why the valence of germanium is 4, given the electron structure.

6.8. Calculate and plot the theoretical electron density in intrinsic germanium as a function of temperature, given the width of the forbidden band as 0.75 ev.

6.9. Plot a family of curves for (6.1) showing the variation of electron density in an intrinsic semiconductor as a function of temperature and forbidden-energy gap. Let temperature range from 200 to 400°K and let the forbidden gap range from 0.2 to 1.2 ev.

6.10. Find an expression similar to (6.18) but derived from (6.16), of the form $x_1 = kD_nt$, that gives the distance from the plane of injection of carriers to a plane at which the carrier density is $1/\epsilon$ times the density at $x = 0$.

6.11. Derive or verify (6.16).

6.12. Justify the assumption that conduction currents are small compared to diffusion currents in transistor materials. Consider holes in n-type germanium with a resistivity of 10 ohm-cm at room temperature. The diffusion constant is 93 cm² sec⁻¹, and the mean lifetime of holes is 100 μsec.

6.13. Consider electrons in p-type germanium with a resistivity of 1 ohm-cm. If the electron density at one side of a slab 0.1 mm thick is 10^{13} cm⁻³ and on the other side is 10^{12} cm⁻³, what is the density in the intervening space? The intrinsic density is 1.73×10^{13} cm⁻³, and the equilibrium density is 1.25×10^{11} cm⁻³. Use $D_n = 93$ cm² sec⁻¹ and $\tau_n = 100$ μsec.

6.14. For the same material as in the previous problem but with a slab large compared to the diffusion length, what will be the electron density as a function of position for electron density of 10^{12} cm⁻³ on the left-hand boundary? The electron density is presumed to go to the equilibrium value at the right-hand boundary.

6.15. Calculate the electron current due to diffusion in Prob. 6.13.

6.16. Calculate the electron current due to diffusion in Prob. 6.14. What must the corresponding hole current be in order to keep total current constant through the slab? Is the hole current a drift or diffusion current?

CHAPTER 7

7.1. Show by integration of (7.3) that the height of the Fermi level in metals above the bottom of the conduction band is given by

$$W = \frac{h^2}{2m} \left(\frac{3N}{8\pi} \right)^{\frac{2}{3}}$$

where N is the number of free electrons per unit volume. Show that, for $N = 10^{21}$, $W = 0.38$ ev; for $N = 10^{23}$, $W = 8.2$ ev.

7.2. Given that the Fermi levels of copper, gold, and silver above the bottom of the conduction band are, respectively, 7.10, 5.56, and 5.52 ev and using the results of Prob. 7.1, determine the number of free electrons per unit volume.

7.3. Show that the Fermi-Dirac electron-density–energy distribution function for metals of (7.5) reduces to the Maxwellian distribution function of (7.6) in cases in which $\varepsilon \gg \varepsilon_f$. Do this by integrating (7.5) to find N in terms of $\epsilon^{\varepsilon_f/kT}$ and then by eliminating the latter in the former expression.

7.4. Sketch a series of curves showing the expected variation across a p-n junction of potential, density of acceptors, density of donors, density of free electrons, density of holes, and net space-charge density.

7.5. Assuming a diode rectifier to be made of a junction of pieces of p-type and n-type semiconductor, what are the requirements on the choices of metals for leads to the diode in terms of the possibilities shown in Fig. 7.16?

7.6. Derive the Fermi distribution function (by the method outlined in the last paragraph of Appendix 5).

7.7. Show that, in an n-type semiconductor, the donors are almost completely ionized except for extremely high impurity concentrations. This is equivalent to saying, " . . . except for Fermi levels close to the conduction band."

7.8. Show that, in an impurity-type semiconductor, the product of electron and hole densities is the same as in intrinsic material at the same temperature except for extremely high impurity concentrations.

7.9. Show that, in an impurity-type semiconductor with equal amounts of n- and p-type impurities, the conductivity is nearly the same as in the intrinsic value at the same temperature.

7.10. Show that, in an n-type semiconductor, the conductivity decreases instead of increases when small amounts of p-type impurities are added.

CHAPTER 8

8.1. Explain why the curve of the center section of Fig. 8.1, given by (8.1) for high T, has the form it does.

8.2. Given a metal for which $A = 40$ amp cm^{-2} °K^{-2} and $\phi = 4.0$ volts operating at a temperature of 2000°K, what is the percentage change in thermionic emission resulting from a 1 per cent change in temperature? What is the percentage change in emission resulting from a 1 per cent change in work function?

8.3. A thermionic cathode is operating at 1000°K. What fraction of the emitted electrons can overcome a retarding potential of 1.0, of 0.1, of 0.01 volt? What is the average velocity of emission?

8.4. What are the characteristics of an ideal tungsten filament 2 cm long, which is to give an emission of 200 ma and have a life of 1,000 hr?

8.5. What are the considerations for a thoriated-tungsten filament with the same requirements as the tungsten filament of Prob. 8.4?

8.6. What is the relative increase in emission due to the Schottky effect for a cathode operating at 1000°K and with a surface potential gradient of 100 volts cm^{-1}?

8.7. At what potentials do the following materials have unity secondary/primary emission ratios: copper, nickel, molybdenum, cesium-silver, quartz, glass? Use Fig. 8.20 and the maximum values in Table 8.2.

8.8. What are the relative emission densities of a pure-tungsten and a thoriated-tungsten filament at 2500°K? For the case of a filament 2 cm in length and 0.1 mm in diameter, what are the relative emission efficiencies in milliamperes per watt?

8.9. Explain how you could measure the contact-potential difference in a vacuum diode between cathode and plate, i.e., the difference in potential between plate and cathode seen by electrons when cathode and plate are externally shorted.

CHAPTER 9

9.1. What must the cathode-anode spacing of a vacuum diode with a cathode area of 1 cm^2 be in order that the current density be 100 ma cm^{-2} when the cathode-anode potential difference is 100 volts? Assume space-charge-limited emission.

9.2. Under the conditions of Prob. 9.1, what is the voltage gradient in the mid-plane and at the anode?

9.3. In a vacuum diode with space-charge-limited emission, show by curves how the electron velocity, potential, gradient of potential, and space-charge density vary from cathode to anode. Normalize your curves so that the values at the anode correspond to 100 per cent.

9.4. What are the dynamic and d-c plate resistances of the diode of Prob. 9.1?

9.5. What would be the active area and number of junctions required for a dry rectifier stack that is to handle a current of 5 amp and a back voltage of 500 volts for each of the four types of junctions available for such service?

9.6. A germanium detector-type diode has a current-voltage characteristic [(9.8)] for which $I_0 = 10$ ma and $a = 10$ volt^{-1}. If an rms voltage of 1.0 volt is applied, what is the resulting rectified current?

9.7. Verify Eq. (9.14).

9.8. Consider that the rectifier circuits of Fig. 9.32 have an applied voltage of 115 volts rms. The transformers are 1:1 in turns ratio. The diodes are considered to have ideal characteristics with an infinite backward resistance and a zero forward resistance. The load resistance is 100 ohms. Calculate the magnitude of the rectified current for the three circuits shown.

9.9. For the conditions of Prob. 9.8, design a two-section filter of both the LC and the RC type for each of the three rectifying circuits to give a maximum ripple current that is 1 per cent of the direct current.

9.10. Referring to the choke-input full-wave filter characteristics of Fig. 9.40, suggest operating conditions and circuit values to give 200 ma at 400 volts.

9.11. Referring to the full-wave capacitor-input rectifier characteristics of Fig. 9.42, suggest operating conditions and circuit values to give 200 ma at 400 volts.

9.12. Describe the filtering action necessary in Fig. 9.46a to obtain the simple amplitude-modulated wave as shown in Fig. 9.27.

9.13. Discuss the factors governing the output-voltage regulation of the rectifier and filter circuit of Fig. 9.41.

9.14. For the 6H6 peak-detector characteristics of Fig. 9.30, plot a curve of ratio of direct output voltage to peak signal voltage as a function of load resistance for a given signal input.

CHAPTER 10

10.1. Using the relations (10.3) to (10.7), plot the curves of constant space, plate, and grid current of a hypothetical vacuum triode for which $\mu = 50$, $k_1 = 8$, $G = 0.01$ amp volt$^{-\frac{3}{2}}$.

10.2. Using the design formulas of Appendix 9, calculate the plate current of a plane-electrode vacuum triode operating with a plate voltage of 150 volts and a grid voltage of -5 volts relative to the cathode. The tube dimensions are plate and cathode area = 0.5 in.^{2}, $d_{cg} = 20$ mils, $a = 20$ mils, $r_g = 1$ mil, $d_{gp} = 40$ mils.

10.3. For the tube and conditions of Prob. 10.2, calculate the mutual conductance and plate resistance.

10.4. Suggest some methods for calculating the amplification factor and mutual conductance of a screen-grid tetrode.

10.5. Explain how you can estimate the tube constants of a pentode.

10.6. Discuss the pros and cons of viewing the beam power tube as a pentode in which the beam-forming plates constitute a very-low-pitch suppressor grid.

10.7. Discuss factors contributing to the sharpness of the shoulder of the plate-current vs. plate-voltage characteristics of the pentode and the beam power tube. Which would you expect to be the sharpest?

10.8. The suppressor grid of power pentodes is sometimes operated at a low positive potential. Why is this done?

10.9. Sketch curves showing what the current-voltage characteristics of a screen-grid tetrode would be in the absence of secondary emission. Compare with pentode characteristics.

10.10. Indicate how the important characteristics of a pentode change as all electrode potentials are changed proportionately.

10.11. In a triode with a μ of 35, the plate current is 6.0 ma for a plate voltage of

200 volts and a grid voltage of -5 volts. What is the mutual conductance of the tube for these operating conditions? What will the mutual conductance be if the plate voltage is raised to 250 volts and the grid voltage is kept constant?

10.12. A triode has a μ of 20 and a g_m of 5,000 μmhos. What is the plate current when the plate voltage is 150 volts and the grid voltage is -3 volts?

10.13. Suggest methods of construction for a pentode whose mutual conductance will be a strong function of grid bias.

10.14. Discuss how triode grid-current characteristics are modified by secondary emission from grid and plate. Explain under what conditions grid currents can be negative.

CHAPTER 11

11.1. Describe the carrier action in a Haynes-Shockley experiment, as in Fig. 11.4, conducted with p-type semiconductor.

11.2. Verify (11.2).

11.3. How is (11.6) obtained from (7.11)? What approximation is involved?

11.4. Derive (11.9). Compare with the formula for the capacity of a sphere in free space.

11.5. Calculate and plot the carrier densities of Fig. 11.23a for a germanium triode with the conductivities shown. Let the emitter-base bias be -0.2 volt and the collector-base bias be 5 volts. Use Fig. 7.6 and equations (11.13) to (11.15) along with (6.20). Values of the mean recombination distance are $L_n = 0.15$ cm and $L_p = 0.10$ cm. Take base width as 1 mil $= 0.00254$ cm.

11.6. Given the charge densities of Prob. 11.5, calculate the current-density components as shown in Fig. 11.23c. Use (6.12).

11.7. Calculate and plot transistor-triode constant-voltage curves similar to those of Fig. 11.25. Do this for a p-n-p transistor for which $I_{C0} = -30$ μa, $I_{E0} = -10$ μa, $\alpha_n = 0.95$, $\alpha_I = 0.6$.

11.8. Show that the density of carriers in intrinsic germanium doubles about every $15°C$. Use (6.1).

11.9. Show that the density of carriers in intrinsic silicon increases by a factor of 10 every $42°C$. Use (6.1).

11.10. Make a chart showing the value of emitter resistance from (11.35) as a function of emitter current and temperature. Will this apply to both germanium and silicon?

11.11. Assuming that the value of a_{11} in (11.36) is given primarily by the first term, that $D_p = 44$ cm^2 sec^{-1} for germanium, and that $L_p = 0.10$ cm, calculate and plot a_{11} as a function of p_n.

11.12. The same as Prob. 11.11 but for n_p and assuming that the second term dominates. Use $D_n = 93.5$ cm^2 sec^{-1} and $L_n = 0.15$ cm.

11.13. Calculate and plot curves showing how β in (11.38) varies as a function of w and L. Let w range from 5 to 9.5 mils and L from 0.05 to 0.5 cm. Compare with approximate results from (11.39).

11.14. Calculate the ejection efficiency from (11.40) of a transistor for which $A_e = 1$ mm^2, $A_b = 2$ mm^2, $L_b = 0.2$ cm, $L_e = 0.1$ cm, $w = 1$ mil.

11.15. Sketch curves showing carrier densities in a diffused-base transistor. Assume that the donor density in the emitter region is 10^{18} cm^{-3}, that the acceptor density in the base region decreases exponentially from 10^{17} to 10^{16} cm^{-3}, and that the donor density in the collector region is 10^{15} cm^{-3}.

11.16. Show that it is possible to produce an n-p-n transistor by simultaneous diffusion of a group III acceptor and a group V donor into n-type material if the diffusion coefficient of the former is much larger than that of the latter. Assuming that the resultant concentration of each of the diffused materials is a negative exponential, sketch the resultant curve of $N_d - N_a$. See [TaF].

CHAPTER 12

12.1. Find the impedance coefficients of the transistor of Fig. 11.2 for $I_E = 0.6$ ma and $V_C = -25$ volts.

12.2. Find the admittance coefficients corresponding to the impedance coefficients of Prob. 12.1.

12.3. Find the admittance coefficients of the vacuum tube of Fig. 10.9 for $V_G = +50$ volts and $V_P = +1,000$ volts.

12.4. Find the impedance coefficients corresponding to the admittance coefficients of Prob. 12.3.

12.5. Find the elements of Figs. 12.12 and 12.13 corresponding to the conditions of Prob. 12.1.

12.6. Find the elements of Fig. 12.8 corresponding to the conditions of Prob. 12.3.

12.7. Find the elements of Fig. 12.4 corresponding to the conditions of Prob. 12.3.

12.8. Find the elements of Fig. 12.5 corresponding to the conditions of Prob. 12.1.

12.9. Find the h coefficients of the transistor of Fig. 11.24 for Class A operating conditions.

12.10. Justify the following approximate relations between resistance and h parameters:

$$r_e = h_{11} - \frac{h_{12}}{h_{22}} (1 + h_{21})$$

$$r_b = \frac{h_{12}}{h_{22}}$$

$$r_c = \frac{1}{h_{22}}$$

$$\alpha = -h_{21}$$

CHAPTER 13

13.1. Compare the operation of a grounded-cathode vacuum-tube pentode connected to operate as a pentode amplifier and as a triode amplifier. Which circuit gives the higher voltage amplification? the lower distortion?

13.2. In the grounded-emitter-transistor amplifier, how does the transducer gain compare with the maximum gain available? How does it compare with the insertion gain?

13.3. Demonstrate the approximations for voltage gain and current gain given for the grounded-emitter-transistor amplifier in Fig. 13.11.

13.4. In a low-frequency Class A grounded-grid vacuum-tube amplifier, where does the input power go?

13.5. Justify the approximations for input resistance and voltage amplification given for the grounded-base-transistor amplifier in Fig. 13.13.

13.6. Would you prefer a pentode or a triode for a cathode-follower circuit?

13.7. Discuss distortion in cathode-follower circuits. Examine graphical construction methods to assist your reasoning.

13.8. What is the lowest output impedance that can be obtained with ordinary receiving tubes? with available transistors?

13.9. Develop and tabulate, for the three transistor circuits, formulas for the insertion gain, maximum available gain, and the generator and load resistances for maximum available gain.

13.10. Develop and tabulate formulas for the current, voltage, and power gain of the three transistor circuits in terms of the h parameters.

13.11. Calculate and plot the response of the circuit of Fig. 13.16 for a tube with a g_m of 5,000 μa volt^{-1} and a plate resistance of 0.1 megohm when the plate circuit has a Q of 50 and is resonant at 10,000 cycles sec^{-1}. The coupling capacitor has a capacity of 0.01 μf, and R_{gl} has a value of 0.1 megohm. Neglect for the calculation the effect of the other circuit elements. Discuss the effect of the RC combination in the screen and cathode circuits. How must these values be chosen so as not to disturb the circuit response adversely?

13.12. Calculate and plot the response of the circuit of Fig. 13.21 for a circuit with the following values: $g_m = 8,000$ μa volt^{-1}, $r_p = 0.25$ megohm, $R_c = 100$ kilohms, $R_{gl} = 0.25$ megohm, distributed capacity is 20 $\mu\mu$f. Neglect the influence of the other circuit elements in the calculation. Discuss the effect of the other elements in the circuit.

13.13. Compare the operation of the circuit of Fig. 13.30 using pentodes with that using triodes.

13.14. Design a circuit like that of Fig. 13.28 to give audio amplification flat from 20 to 15,000 cycles sec^{-1}.

13.15. Develop formulas for the output impedance of an amplifier, using (a) voltage feedback and (b) current feedback.

13.16. Design a three-stage audio amplifier to have an output of 5 watts over the frequency range of 20 to 15,000 cycles sec^{-1}. Output shall be available to a 50-ohm load, and input is from a record crystal pickup unit.

13.17. Verify the relations of Fig. 13.37.

13.18. Calculate and plot the vector gain and input impedance of a single-stage 6AK5 amplifier, using the circuit of Fig. 13.39. Use the values from a tube manual for 120-volt operation. Consider operation into a simple 10,000-ohm load. Input conductance is 200 μmhos at 140 Mc. Make the calculation for 50 to 150 Mc.

13.19. An audio amplifier develops 5 per cent distortion in the absence of negative feedback. Indicate how much negative feedback is required to reduce this to 1 per cent and how much the input voltage must be increased for the same output.

13.20. A four-stage audio amplifier operates from a phonopickup unit to a power output transformer. It is a single-ended amplifier with RC coupling except for the output transformer. How is negative feedback best applied to give low distortion and good frequency response? Should it be from output to input, primarily around the last stage, around pairs of stages to avoid stability problems, or applied in some other fashion?

13.21. A common problem with negative-feedback amplifiers is their tendency to oscillate, or "motorboat," at low frequencies. Discuss means of overcoming this tendency.

13.22. Calculate the admittance coefficients of a transistor like the one in Sec. 13.10 but having a base thickness of 5 mils. Calculate the collector-junction capacity for an area of 0.01 in.^{2} and a voltage of 20 volts across the junction.

13.23. For Prob. 13.22, find the circuit elements for Fig. 13.45 if the shunt resistance across the collector junction is 0.1 megohm.

CHAPTER 14

14.1. An oscillator consists of a two-stage RC amplifier with unity positive voltage feedback from output to input through a series RLC circuit. If the half-power points of the amplifier fall at 500 and 5,000 cycles sec^{-1}, what will be the frequency of oscillation (a) when the RLC circuit is tuned to 1,500 cycles sec^{-1}, (b) when the RLC circuit is tuned to 5,000 cycles sec^{-1} and has a Q of 20?

14.2. Sketch a circuit for a low-frequency oscillator using a twin T in the feedback circuit. Suggest means for introducing nonlinearity into the circuit in order to stabilize the output.

14.3. A phase-shift oscillator uses the circuit of Fig. 14.9 except that the resistances and capacitances are interchanged. Obtain an expression for the resonant frequency. What is the minimum gain necessary for oscillation?

14.4. Obtain an expression for the oscillation frequency of the Hartley oscillator circuit of Fig. 14.15b.

14.5. Obtain an expression for the oscillation frequency of the direct-coupled transistor oscillator of Fig. 14.18, including internal and external resistance elements.

14.6. Discuss the problem of obtaining stable negative-resistance elements from transistors. Suggest some circuits.

14.7. Discuss the problem of limiting the amplitude of oscillation in transistor oscillators.

14.8. Discuss the problem of obtaining stable negative-inductance or negative-capacity elements with tube or transistor feedback circuits.

14.9. Does the Pierce-oscillator circuit of Fig. 14.25b oscillate on the series or parallel resonance of the crystal? Obtain an expression for the conditions that must hold to give oscillation.

14.10. Describe how the circuit of Fig. 14.9 may be stabilized by an automatic-volume-control action using a variable-μ tube.

14.11. Discuss the problems in designing a beat-frequency audio oscillator to cover as wide a range as possible on a single dial.

14.12. An oscillator consists of an amplifier with feedback through a Wien bridge in which one of the single resistance arms is replaced by a thermistor. Discuss the factors determining the frequency of oscillation, the stability, and the phase requirements in the oscillator.

CHAPTER 15

15.1. The notes in the major triad C E G—a musical chord—are in the approximate frequency ratio $4:5:6$. Discuss the harmonic distortion of such a chord upon amplification. Which of the second-order distortion terms are harmonious and which are discordant?

15.2. What is the resistance value for the load line of Fig. 15.2b? Construct a load line for the characteristics of Fig. 15.2 for operation with a 250-volt supply and a series resistance of 20,000 ohms. What is the optimum bias and maximum power output for this latter condition of operation?

15.3. The triode whose characteristics are given in Fig. 15.2 is to feed a 100-ohm load through an audio transformer. Specify the turns ratio, bias, and excitation for maximum power output with a 200-volt power supply.

15.4. For the conditions of Prob. 15.3, determine the percentage of second, third, and fourth harmonic distortion.

15.5. Prove that the maximum undistorted power output from a vacuum-triode amplifier occurs when the load resistance is approximately twice the plate resistance. Show that the plate efficiency is 25 per cent under these conditions.

15.6. Show that the maximum plate efficiency obtainable with a Class A pentode amplifier is about 10 per cent.

15.7. What is the maximum undistorted power that can be obtained from the pentode characteristics of Fig. 10.21 for a plate supply of 200 volts? Assume that a total harmonic distortion of 2 per cent is permissible.

15.8. Derive Eqs. (15.16) to (15.18).

15.9. Derive Eqs. (15.19) to (15.23).

15.10. Show that there is an inherent second harmonic distortion which accompanies square-law detection. What is the magnitude of this distortion as a percentage of the desired signal?

15.11. Show that amplitude modulation results from imposing a radio and audio signal in series in a square-law device.

15.12. What are the most serious distortion terms created as a result of obtaining amplitude modulation by putting radio and audio signals in series in a nonlinear device?

CHAPTER 16

16.1. A pair of triodes with the characteristics of Fig. 15.2 are biased for Class B with a plate-supply voltage of 200 volts. Assuming that the load is adjusted for maximum output and that the grids are driven to zero voltage, determine the following operating characteristics: grid bias, power output, and efficiency. Do this using approximate formulas.

16.2. Find the answers to Prob. 16.1 by plotting curves of output current and voltage and determining the fundamental and direct components by Fourier analysis.

16.3. Repeat Probs. 16.1 and 16.2, assuming that the grid is driven to the point where the maximum instantaneous grid voltage equals the minimum instantaneous plate voltage. Determine the direct and fundamental components of grid current for this condition. Determine the grid driving power and the power amplification. Assume that (10.6) and (10.7) hold with a value of $k_1 = 8.0$.

16.4. Explain in detail how the circuits of Fig. 16.5 work.

16.5. A Class C amplifier uses the tube characteristics of Fig. 10.9. The tube is biased at $V_1 = -200$ volts and $V_2 = +2000$ volts. The grid is driven to the point ($V_G = +100$ volts, $V_P = +250$ volts). Plot curves of grid and plate voltage and current as in Fig. 16.7.

16.6. Determine the load resistance corresponding to the condition of excitation of Prob. 16.5. Determine by numerical integration the components of grid and plate current and power. Determine the plate efficiency and the power amplification.

16.7. For the situation of Prob. 16.5 indicate what must be done to increase the plate efficiency and the power output.

16.8. Discuss factors governing the rise time and frequency of the multivibrator circuit of Fig. 16.16. Obtain an approximate formula for the frequency.

16.9. The transistor of Fig. 11.24 is operated with $R_b = 1,000$ ohms, $R_l = 20,000$ ohms, and $V_2 = 10$ volts. Construct the N curve for the grounded-base connection of Fig. 16.18.

16.10. Explain the stability consideration applying to each of the lettered points on the N curve of Fig. 16.14.

CHAPTER 17

17.1. What is the longest wavelength that can be observed with a cesium vacuum phototube? What retarding voltage is required to inhibit completely photoemission for radiation of 6,000 A wavelength?

17.2. Which of the surfaces of Fig. 17.12 would you use (a) to simulate the eye response, (b) for maximum response to a tungsten filament at 2870°K, (c) for a sodium lamp, (d) for a neon lamp, (e) for a mercury-vapor lamp?

17.3. A vacuum phototube has a sensitivity of 150 μa lumen^{-1} to light from a tungsten filament in a normal light bulb. If the light bulb has a mean horizontal candlepower of 120 and the photocell has a semicylindrical cathode 1 in. long and

0.5 in. in diameter, what will be the photocurrent when the cell is illuminated by the lamp at a distance of 10 ft?

17.4. A photoemissive surface as in Fig. 17.9 is illuminated first with red light and then with blue light. Would you expect the photocurrent for simultaneous illumination with both colors to be the sum of the currents for the individual colors or more or less? Explain your answer.

17.5. Explain how it is possible for photoconduction currents to be greater than the number of carriers generated per second times electron charge.

17.6. What energy-level structure is desired in a photoconductor to give a good response in the visible spectrum at room temperatures?

17.7. What energy-level structure is desired in a photoconductor to give a good response at long wavelengths at liquid-air temperature?

17.8. How would you expect the response of a photoconducting cell to vary as the temperature is raised above room temperature?

17.9. How would you expect the potential to vary throughout a photoconductor which is uniformly illuminated and in which the current flow is space charge limited?

17.10. What is the maximum power that can be obtained from the photocell of Fig. 17.29, under the conditions of maximum illumination shown, when operated as a solar battery?

17.11. A solar-battery unit has an internal resistance R_0 of 1,000 ohms and a photocurrent I_g of 1 ma. What will the voltage developed across the cell be when the cell is connected to an external load of 100 ohms? What will the external current be? Assume shunt resistance of the cell infinite and series resistance zero. Consider operation at room temperature.

17.12. Solve Prob. 17.11 if the series resistance of the cell is 100 ohms and the shunt resistance is 5,000 ohms.

17.13. Solve Prob. 17.11 if the cell is operated into the optimum value of load resistance. What is the normalized ideal efficiency?

17.14. Would you expect germanium or silicon to make the better solar battery?

17.15. What are the open-circuit voltage and short-circuit current of the solar battery of Prob. 17.12?

CHAPTER 18

18.1. Find the rms voltage and current associated with the thermal-agitation noise in a 20,000-ohm resistor over a bandwidth of 100,000 cycles sec^{-1}.

18.2. What is the available noise power from the resistor of Prob. 18.1?

18.3. A 10,000-ohm resistor at 0°C is connected to a 50,000-ohm resistor at 100°C. What are the direction and amount of the power flow over a bandwidth of 1 Mc?

18.4. What is the noise power available from the parallel combination of the resistors of Prob. 12.4?

18.5. Show that the mean-square noise voltage from a parallel combination of a resistance R and a capacity C over an infinite bandwidth is $v^2 = kT/C$.

18.6. What is the rms noise current in a diode whose emission is temperature limited when the current is 50 μa and the bandwidth is 10 Mc?

18.7. A diode whose emission is space charge limited has a current of 5 ma, a plate voltage of 50 volts, and a cathode temperature of 1000°K. What is the mean-square noise current over a bandwidth of 10 Mc? What is the value of Γ^2?

18.8. What resistance in series with the grid circuit of a triode will produce as much noise in the plate circuit as does the tube itself if the mutual conductance is 8,000 μmhos and the plate current is 3 ma?

18.9. What resistance in series with the grid of a pentode will produce as much noise as does the tube itself if the mutual conductance is 6,000 mhos, the plate current is 10 ma, and the screen current is 2 ma?

18.10. For a pentode with a value of Γ^2 of 0.01, a plate current of 11 ma, and a screen current of 1.5 ma, find the mean-square noise current in the plate, screen, and cathode circuits over a bandwidth of 0.5 Mc.

18.11. Show that the noise figure of two amplifiers in cascade is $F_{12} = F_1 + (F_2 - 1)/G_1$, where G_1 is the gain of the first amplifier.

18.12. What is the noise figure of a crystal receiver without preamplification for which the crystal conversion-loss factor is 0.6, the noise temperature is 3.5, and the noise figure of the intermediate frequency is 3 db?

18.13. For the receiver of Prob. 18.12, what is the minimum power that can be detected over a bandwidth of 10 Mc?

BIBLIOGRAPHY

Tʜɪs book uses a three-letter code to identify bibliographic items: The first two letters are the first two letters of the author's last name (or of the first author's name where there is joint authorship); the third letter symbolizes the year of publication by capital or lower-case letters as follows:

a	1950	A	1951
b	1949	B	1952
c	1948	C	1953
.	.	.	.
.	.	.	.
.	.	.	.

z 1925 and earlier

Thus a paper by Schultz in 1953 would be indicated by the triad [ScC]; by Einstein in 1905, by [Eiz]. Occasionally a duplication of three-letter combinations occurs; in this case the numbers 1, 2, 3, . . . are added for distinction. The principal advantage claimed for this system is that it enables the reader to determine at a glance the vintage of a given reference.

AnA   Anderson, Carl D.: A Revised Table of the Elementary Particles, *Am. Scientist*, vol. 39, pp. 260, 261, April, 1951.

AnB   Anderson, A. L.: Transistors in Switching Circuits, *Proc. IRE*, vol. 40, pp. 1541–1549, November, 1952.

AsA   Ashworth, F.: Field Emission Microscopy, in "Advances in Electronics," vol. III, pp. 1–42, Academic Press, Inc., New York, 1951.

Atb   Attwood, S. S.: "Electric and Magnetic Fields," 3d ed., John Wiley & Sons, Inc., New York, 1949.

Baa   Baroody, E. M.: A Theory of Secondary Electron Emission from Metals, *Phys. Rev.*, vol. 78, pp. 780–787, 1950.

Bab   Bardeen, J., and W. H. Brattain: Physical Principles Involved in Transistor Action, *Phys. Rev.*, vol. 75, pp. 1208–1225, 1949.

BaD   Barton, L. E.: An Experimental Transistor Personal Broadcast Receiver, *Proc. IRE*, vol. 42, pp. 1062–1066, July, 1954.

Beb   Becker, J. A., and J. N. Shive: The Transistor, A New Semi-conductor Amplifier, *Elec. Eng.*, vol. 68, pp. 215–221, March, 1949.

Bed   Becker, J. A., C. B. Green, and G. L. Pearson: Properties of Thermistors, *Bell System Tech. J.*, vol. 26, pp. 170–212, January, 1947.

BeC   Beck, A. H. W.: "Thermionic Values," Cambridge University Press, New York, 1953.

Ble   Blewett J. P.: Oxide Coated Cathode Literature, 1940–1945, *J. Appl. Phys.*, vol. 17, pp. 643–647, August, 1946.

Bll1   Blewett, J. P.: Properties of Oxide-coated Cathodes: I, *J. Appl. Phys.*, vol. 10, pp. 668–679, October, 1939.

Bll2   Blewett, J. P.: Properties of Oxide-coated Cathodes: II, *J. Appl. Phys.*, vol. 10, pp. 668–679, December, 1939.

Blq   Black, H. S.: Stabilized Feed-back Amplifiers, *Elec. Eng.*, vol. 53, p. 114, January, 1934.

Bof   Bode, H. W.: "Network Analysis and Feedback Amplifier Design," D. Van Nostrand Company, Inc., Princeton, N.J., 1945.

BoC   Boone, E. M.: "Circuit Theory of Electron Devices," John Wiley & Sons, Inc., New York, 1953.

Brl   Brunetti, C.: The Transitron Oscillator, *Proc. IRE*, vol. 27, pp. 88–94, February, 1939.

BrC   Bradley, W. E., et al.: The Surface-barrier Transistor, *Proc. IRE*, vol. 41, pp. 1702–1720, December, 1953.

BrD   Bruining, H.: Physics and Application of Secondary Electron Emission, McGraw-Hill Book Company, Inc., New York, 1954.

BuE   Bube, R. H.: Photoconductivity of the Sulfide, Selenide and Telluride of Zinc or Cadmium, *Proc. IRE*, vol. 43, pp. 1836–1850, December, 1955.

Cal   Caruthers, R. S.: Copper Oxide Modulators in Carrier Telephone Systems, *Bell System Tech. J.*, vol. 18, pp. 315–337, April, 1939.

CaF   Carroll, John M.: Diffusion Transistors Raise Frequency Limits, *Electronics*, vol. 29, pp. 137–139, February, 1956.

Chb   Chance, Britton, Vernon Hughes, Edward F. MacNichol, David Sayre, and F. C. Williams: "Waveforms," Massachusetts Institute of Technology Radiation Laboratory Series, vol. 19, McGraw-Hill Book Company, Inc., New York, 1949.

Che   Chadwick, E. W.: Selenium Rectifiers for Broadcast Receivers, *Elec. Commun.*, vol. 23, pp. 464–467, December, 1946.

ChD   Christensen, H.: Surface Conduction Channel Phenomena in Germanium, *Proc. IRE*, vol. 42, pp. 1371–1375, September, 1954.

ChD1   Cheng, C. C.: Transistor Equations Using h-Parameters, *Electronics*, vol. 27, pp. 191–194, April, 1954.

ChD2   Chapin, D. M., C. S. Fuller, and G. L. Pearson: A New Silicon p-n Junction Photocell for Converting Solar Radiation into Electrical Power, *J. Appl. Phys.*, vol. 25, pp. 676, 677, May, 1954.

Clj   Clarke, C. A.: Selenium Rectifier Characteristics, *Elec. Commun.*, vol. 20, pp. 47–66, 1941.

Cos   Cockruft, J. D., and E. D. Walton: Experiments with High Velocity Positive Ions, *Proc. Roy. Soc. (London)*, A, vol. 136, p. 619, 1932.

Cot   Compton, K. T., and I. Langmuir: Electrical Discharges in Gases: II, *Revs. Mod. Phys.*, vol. 3, pp. 191–257, April, 1931.

Cou   Compton, K. T., and I. Langmuir: Electrical Discharges in Gases: I, *Revs. Mod. Phys.*, vol. 2, pp. 124–242, April, 1930.

CoB   Conwell, E. M.: Properties of Silicon and Germanium, *Proc. IRE*, vol. 40, pp. 1327–1337, November, 1952.

CoC   Coblenz, A., and H. C. Owens: Transistors: Theory and Application: I, *Electronics*, vol. 26, p. 98, March, 1953; Energy Levels in Transistor Electronics: II, *Electronics*, vol. 26, p. 138, April, 1953; Physical Properties of Electrons in Solids: III, *Electronics*, vol. 26, p. 162, May, 1953; Transistor Action in Germanium and Silicon: IV, *Electronics*, vol. 26, p. 166, June, 1953; Point Contact Transistor Action: V, *Electronics*, vol. 26, p. 158, July, 1953; Operation of Junction Transistors: VI, *Electronics*, vol. 26, p. 156, August,

1953; Equivalent Transistor Circuits and Equations: VII, *Electronics*, vol. 26, p. 156, September, 1953; Small-signal Transistor Operation: VIII, *Electronics*, vol. 26, p. 158, October, 1953; Grounded Emitter and Collector Circuits: IX, *Electronics*, vol. 26, p. 166, November, 1953; Switching Circuits Using the Transistor: X, *Electronics*, vol. 26, p. 186, December, 1953; Cascading Transistor Amplifier Stages: XI, *Electronics*, vol. 27, p. 158, January, 1954.

CoD   Conwell, E. M.: Fundamental Properties of Semiconducting Materials, *Sylvania Technologist*, vol. 7, pp. 41–44, April, 1954.

Crd   Cruft Laboratory, War Training Staff: "Electronic Circuits and Tubes," chap. 14, McGraw-Hill Book Company, Inc., New York, 1947.

Cua   Cutler, C. C., and C. F. Quate: Experimental Verification of Space Charge and Transit Time Reduction of Noise in Electron Beams, *Phys. Rev.*, vol. 30, pp. 875–877, 1950.

Dab   Danforth, W. E.: Abstract of Summary of Bartol Cathode Work, *J. Franklin Inst.*, vol. 248, pp. 449–456, 1949.

Dac   Dailey, H. J.: Designing Thoriated Tungsten Filaments, *Electronics*, vol. 21, pp. 107–109, January, 1948.

Dav   Darrow, K. K.: Statistical Theories of Matter, Radiation, and Electricity, *Bell System Tech. J.*, vol. 8, pp. 672–748, October, 1929.

DaA   Danforth, W. E.: Elements of Thermionics, *Proc. IRE*, vol. 33, pp. 485–499, May, 1951.

DaD   Dawson, Maynard: The Problem of Transistor Action, 1954 *Transistor Short Course Proc.*, Pennsylvania State College, State College, 1954.

Dez   De Forest, L.: U.S. Patent No. 879,532, appl. Jan. 29, 1907, granted Feb. 18, 1908.

Dot   Dow, J. B.: A Recent Development in Vacuum Tube Oscillator Circuits, *Proc. IRE*, vol. 19, pp. 2095–2108, December, 1931.

DoB   Dow, W. G.: "Fundamentals of Engineering," John Wiley & Sons, Inc., New York, 1952.

Duu   Dushman, S.: Thermionic Emission, *Revs. Mod. Phys.*, vol. 2, pp. 381–476, October, 1930.

DuC   DuMond, J. W. M., and E. R. Cohen: Least-squares Adjustments of the Atomic Constants, *Revs. Mod. Phys.*, vol. 25, pp. 691–708, July, 1953.

DyC   Dyson, F. J.: Field Theory, *Sci. American*, vol. 188, pp. 57–65, April, 1953.

DyE   Dyke, W. P.: Progress in Electron Emission at High Fields, *Proc. IRE*, vol. 43, pp. 162–167, February, 1955.

EaB   Early, J. M.: Effects of Space-charge Layer Widening in Junction Transistors, *Proc. IRE*, vol. 40, pp. 1401–1406, November, 1952.

EaC   Early, J. M.: Design Theory of Junction Transistors, *Bell System Tech. J.*, vol. 32, pp. 1271–1312, November, 1953.

EaD   Early, J. M.: P-N-I-P and N-P-I-N Junction Transistor Triodes, *Bell System Tech. J.*, vol. 32, pp. 517–534, May, 1954.

EbB   Ebers, J. J.: Four Terminal P-N-P-N Transistors, *Proc. IRE*, vol. 40, pp. 1361–1364, November, 1952.

EbD   Ebers, J. J., and J. L. Moll: Large Signal Behavior of Junction Transistors, *Proc. IRE*, vol. 42, pp. 1761–1772, December, 1954.

Eic   Eisenstein, A. S.: Oxide Coated Cathodes, in "Advances in Electronics," vol. I, pp. 1–65, Academic Press, Inc., New York, 1948.

EnC   "Encyclopaedia Britannica," Encyclopaedia Britannica, Inc., Chicago, 1953.

Eso   Eshbach, O. W.: "Handbook of Engineering Fundamentals," 1st ed., John Wiley & Sons, Inc., New York, 1936.

EsB   Espersen, G. A.: The L-cathode Structure, *Proc. IRE*, vol. 40, pp. 284–289, 1952.

Evm   Everitt, W. L., and K. R. Spangenberg: Grid-current Flow as a Factor in the Design of Vacuum-tube Power Amplifiers, *Proc. IRE*, vol. 26, pp. 612–639, May, 1938.

Evn   Everitt, W. L.: "Communication Engineering," 2d ed., McGraw-Hill Book Company, Inc., New York, 1937.

EvB   Everitt, W. L.: Let Us Re-define Electronics, *Proc. IRE*, vol. 4, p. 899, August, 1952.

Feb   Federal Telephone and Radio Company: "Reference Data for Radio Engineers," 3d ed., New York, 1949.

FiB   Fitzgerald, A. E., and Charles Kingsley, Jr.: "Electric Machinery," McGraw-Hill Book Company, Inc., New York, 1952.

FlE   Fletcher, N. H.: Some Aspects of the Design of Power Transistors, *Proc. IRE*, vol. 43, pp. 551–559, May, 1955.

Foo   Fowler, R. H.: "Statistical Mechanics," Cambridge University Press, New York, 1936.

Foq   Fowle, F. E.: "Smithsonian Physical Tables," Smithsonian Institution, Washington, 1934.

Fot   Fowler, R. H.: The Analysis of Photoelectric Sensitivity Curves for Clear Metals at Various Temperatures, *Phys. Rev.*, vol. 38, pp. 45–56, 1931.

Frg   Friis, H. T.: Noise Figures of Radio Receivers, *Proc. IRE*, vol. 32, pp. 419–422, July, 1944.

FrE   Frederikse, H. P. R., and R. F. Blunt: Photoeffects in Intermetallic Compounds, *Proc. IRE*, vol. 43, pp. 1828–1835, December, 1955.

Gai   Gardner, M. F., and J. L. Barnes: "Transients in Linear Systems," John Wiley & Sons, Inc., New York, 1942.

Gea   Gebbie, H. A., P. C. Banbury, and C. A. Hogarth: Crystal Diode and Triode Action in Lead Sulfide, *Proc. Phys. Soc. (London), B*, vol. 63, p. 371, 1950.

GeD   Geyger, W. A.: "Magnetic Amplifier Circuits," McGraw-Hill Book Company, Inc., New York, 1954.

Gif   Ginzton, E. L.: Stabilized Negative Impedances, *Electronics*, vol. 18, pp. 140–144, September, 1945.

Gij   Ginzton, E. L., and L. M. Hollingsworth: Phase Shift Oscillators, *Proc. IRE*, vol. 29, pp. 43–49, February, 1941.

GiB   Giacoletto, L. J.: Junction Transistor Equivalent Circuits and Vacuum Tube Analogy, *Proc. IRE*, vol. 40, pp. 1490–1493, November, 1952.

GiC   Giacoletto, L. J.: Terminology and Equations for Linear Active Four-terminal Networks Including Transistors, *RCA Rev.*, vol. 14, pp. 28–46, March, 1953.

GiD1   Giacoletto, L. J.: Power Transistors for Audio Output Circuits, *Electronics*, vol. 27, pp. 144–148, January, 1954.

GiD2   Giacoletto, L. J.: Study of P-N-P Alloy Junction Transistors from D-C through Medium Frequencies, *RCA Rev.*, vol. 15, pp. 506–562, December, 1954.

Goc   Goldman, Stanford: "Frequency Analysis, Modulation, and Noise," McGraw-Hill Book Company, Inc., New York, 1948.

GrD   Gray, Truman S.: "Applied Electronics," 2d ed., John Wiley & Sons, Inc., New York, 1954.

Gup1   Guillemin, E. A.: "Communication Networks," vol. I, John Wiley & Sons, Inc., New York, 1935.

Gup2   Guillemin, E. A.: "Communication Networks," vol. II, John Wiley & Sons, Inc., New York, 1935.

GuC   Guillemin, E. A.: "Introductory Circuit Analysis," John Wiley & Sons, Inc., New York, 1953.

Hab1   Haynes, J. R., and W. Shockley: Investigation of Hole Injection in Transistor Action, *Phys. Rev.*, vol. 75, p. 691, 1949.

Hab2   Hannay, N. B., D. MacNair, and A. H. White: Semiconducting Properties in Oxide Cathodes, *J. Appl. Phys.*, vol. 20, pp. 669–681, July, 1949.

Hac1   Hanley, T. E.: Spectral Emissivity and Emission Constants of Thoria Cathodes, *J. Appl. Phys.*, vol. 19, pp. 583–589, June, 1948.

Hac2   Harris, Wm. A.: Some Notes on Noise Theory and Its Application to Input Circuit Design, *RCA Rev.*, vol. 9, pp. 406–418, September, 1948.

Hac3   Hamilton, Donald R., Julian K. Knipp, and J. B. Horner Kuper: "Klystrons and Microwave Triodes," Massachusetts Institute of Technology Radiation Laboratory Series, vol. 7, McGraw-Hill Book Company, Inc., New York, 1948.

HaB   Hall, R. N.: Power Rectifiers and Transistors, *Proc. IRE*, vol. 40, pp. 1512–1518, November, 1952.

HaD   Haneman, D.: Expression for the "α Cut-off" Frequency in Junction Transistors, *Proc. IRE*, vol. 42, pp. 1808, 1809, December, 1954.

HaE   Hanson, G. H.: Shot Noise in p-n-p Transistors, *J. Appl. Phys.*, vol. 26, pp. 1388, 1389, November, 1955.

Heb   Herring, C.: Thermionic Emission, *Revs. Mod. Phys.*, vol. 21, pp. 185–270, April, 1949.

Heh   Herold, E. W., and L. Malter: Some Aspects of Radio Reception at Ultrahigh Frequency, *Proc. IRE*, vol. 31, pp. 423–438, 491–510, 567–582, 1943.

Hep   Herold, E. W.: Negative Resistance and Devices for Obtaining It, *Proc. IRE*, vol. 23, pp. 1201–1223, October, 1935.

HeA1   Hermann, G., and S. Wagener: "The Oxide-coated Cathode: Manufacture," vol. I, Chapman & Hall, Ltd., London, 1951.

HeA2   Hermann, G., and S. Wagener: "The Oxide-coated Cathode: Physics," vol. II, Chapman & Hall, Ltd., London, 1951.

Hie   Hilliard, John K.: Intermodulation Testing, *Electronics*, vol. 19, pp. 123–127, July, 1946.

HoC   Holt, Arthur W.: An Experimental Rapid Access Memory Using Diodes and Computers, *Natl. Bur. Standards* Computer Laboratory Repts., pp. 133–141, 1953.

Hud   Hume-Rothery, Wm.: "Atomic Theory for Students of Metallurgy," The Institute of Metals, London, 1947.

HuB   Hughes, R. C., and P. P. Coppola: Bariated Tungsten Emitters, *J. Appl. Phys.*, vol. 23, pp. 1261, 1262, November, 1952.

HuD   Hunter, F. L., and B. N. Slade: High Frequency Operation of p-Type Point-contact Transistors, *RCA Rev.*, vol. 15, pp. 121–134, November, 1954.

Inc   Ingrahm, M. G.: Modern Mass Spectroscopy, in "Advances in Electronics," vol. I, pp. 219–268, Academic Press, Inc., New York, 1948.

InB   Institute of Radio Engineers: transistor issue, *Proc. IRE*, vol. 40, November, 1952.

IrF   IRE Standards on Letter Symbols for Semiconductor Devices, *Proc. IRE*, vol. 44, pp. 934–937, July, 1956.

JaD   Jacobs, J. E.: The Photoconductive Cell, *Gen. Elec. Rev.*, vol. 57, pp. 28–31, July, 1954.

Jez   Jeans, J. H.: "Electricity and Magnetism," Cambridge University Press, London, 1911.

Jof   Jonker, J. H. L.: The Current to a Positive Grid in Electron Tubes, *Philips Research Repts.*, pp. 13–32, October, 1945.

Joj   Jones, R. B., and A. M. Glover: Recent Developments in Phototubes, *RCA Rev.*, vol. 6, pp. 43–54, July, 1941.

Jow   Johnson, J. B.: Thermal Agitation of Electricity in Conductors, *Phys. Rev.*, vol. 32, pp. 97–109, July, 1928.

Jox   Jones, H. A., and I. Langmuir: The Characteristics of Tungsten Filaments, *Gen. Elec. Rev.*, vol. 30, pp. 310–319, 354–361, 408–412, 1927.

JoA   Jonker, J. H. L.: The Angular Distribution of the Secondary Electrons of Nickel, *Philips Research Repts.*, vol. 6, pp. 372–387, October, 1951.

JoB   Jonker, J. L. H.: On the Theory of Secondary Electron Emission, *Philips Research Repts.*, vol. 7, pp. 1–20, February, 1952.

KiC   Kittel, C.: "Introduction to Solid State Physics," John Wiley & Sons, Inc., New York, 1953.

KiF   Kingston, R. H.: Review of Germanium Surface Phenomena, *J. Appl. Phys.*, vol. 27, pp. 101–114, February, 1956.

Kln   Kleynen, P. H. J. A.: Motion of an Electron in Two Dimensional Fields, *Philips Tech. Rev.*, vol. 2, pp. 338–345, November, 1937.

LaB   Law, R. R., C. W. Mueller, J. I. Pankove, and L. D. Armstrong: A Developmental Germanium P-N-P Junction Transistor, *Proc. IRE*, vol. 40, pp. 1352–1357, November, 1952.

LaD   Law, J. T.: A Mechanism for Water Induced Excess Reverse Dark Current of Grown Germanium n-p Junctions, *Proc. IRE*, vol. 42, pp. 1367–1370, September, 1954.

LeB   LePage, Wilbur, and Samuel Seeley: "General Network Analysis," McGraw-Hill Book Company, Inc., New York, 1952.

LeC   Levi, R.: New Dispenser-type Thermionic Cathode, *J. Appl. Phys.*, vol. 24, pp. 233, 234, February, 1953.

LeF   Lee, C. A.: A High-frequency Diffused Base Germanium Transistor, *Bell System Tech. J.*, vol. 35, pp. 23–34, January, 1956.

Lia   Liebmann, G.: Field Plotting and Ray Tracing in Electron Optics—A Review of Numerical Methods, in "Advances in Electronics," vol. II, pp. 101–149, Academic Press, Inc., New York, 1950.

LiC   Linvill, J. G.: Transistor-negative Impedance Convertors, *Proc. IRE*, vol. 41, pp. 725–729, June, 1953.

Llg   Llewellyn, F. B., and L. C. Peterson: Vacuum Tube Networks, *Proc. IRE*, vol. 32, pp. 144–166, 1944.

Lll   Llewellyn, F. B.: "Electron Inertia Effects," The Macmillan Company, New York, 1939.

Llt   Llewellyn, F. B.: Constant Frequency Oscillators, *Proc. IRE*, vol. 19, pp. 2063–2094, December, 1931.

LoB   Lo, A. W.: Transistor Trigger Circuits, *Proc. IRE*, vol. 40, pp. 1531–1540, November, 1952.

Mal   Mayer, H. F.: Control of the Effective Internal Impedance of Amplifiers by Means of Feedback, *Proc. IRE*, vol. 27, pp. 213–217, March, 1939.

MaB   Marshak, Robert E.: The Multiplicity of Particles, *Sci. American*, vol. 186, pp. 23–27, January, 1952.

MaD   Mason, W. P., and R. F. Wick: Ferroelectrics and the Dielectric Amplifier, *Proc. IRE*, vol. 42, pp. 1606–1619, November, 1954.

Mcc   McKay, K. G.: Secondary Electron Emission, in "Advances in Electronics," vol. I, pp. 66–131, Academic Press, Inc., New York, 1948.

McD   McIntyre, H. N: Germanium Rectifiers—Big Low Cost Power, *Gen. Elec. Rev.*, vol. 57, pp. 11–14, November, 1954.

McE   McCoy, C. T.: The 1N2C3, A Low-noise Microwave Mixer Diode, *Electronics Components Conf. Proc.*, Los Angeles, pp. 56–60, May, 1955.

Mia   Michaelson, H. B.: Work Function of the Elements, *J. Appl. Phys.*, vol. 21, pp. 536–540, June, 1950.

Mid1   Millikan, R. A.: "Electrons (+ and −), Protons, Photons, Neutrons, Mesotrons, and Cosmic Rays," University of Chicago Press, Chicago, 1947.

Mid2 Minorsky, N.: "Introduction to Non-linear Mechanics," J. W. Edwards, Publisher, Inc., Ann Arbor, Mich., 1947.

MiE Middlebrook, R. D.: A Junction-transistor High-frequency Equivalent Circuit, *Stanford Univ. Tech. Rept.* 83, May 2, 1955.

Moc Mott, N. F., and R. W. Gurney: "Electronic Processes in Ionic Crystals," Oxford University Press, New York, 1948.

Mom Moullin, E. B.: "Spontaneous Fluctuations of Voltage," Oxford University Press, New York, 1938.

MoB1 Montgomery, H. C.: Electrical Noise in Semiconductors, *Bell System Tech. J.*, vol. 31, pp. 950–975, September, 1952.

MoB2 Moss, T. S.: "Photoconductivity in the Elements," Academic Press, Inc., New York, 1952.

MoC Montgomery, H. C., and M. A. Clark: Shot Noise in Junction Transistors, *J. Appl. Phys.*, vol. 24, pp. 1337, 1338, October, 1953.

MoD Moore, A. R., and J. I. Pankove: The Effect of Junction Shape and Surface Recombination on Transistor Current Gain, *Proc. IRE*, vol. 42, pp. 907–913, June, 1954.

MoE Moers, H. T.: Recent Developments in Power Transistors, *Trans. IRE*, vol. ED-2, pp. 63–73, January, 1955.

NaA U.S. Navy, Bureau of Ships: Magnetic Amplifiers, *NavShips Rept.* 900–172, Aug. 1, 1951.

NeB Nergaard, L. S.: Studies of the Oxide Cathode, *RCA Rev.*, vol. 13, pp. 464–545, December, 1952.

Nys Nyquist, H.: Regeneration Theory, *Bell System Tech. J.*, vol. 11, pp. 126–147, 1932.

Nyw Nyquist, H.: Thermal Agitation of Electric Charge in Conductors, *Phys. Rev.*, vol. 32, pp. 110–113, July, 1928.

OsB Oser, E. A., R. O. Enders, and R. P. Moore, Jr.: Transistor Oscillators, *RCA Rev.*, vol. 13, pp. 369–385, September, 1952.

Owg Owen-Harries, J. H.: Secondary Electron Radiation, *Electronics*, vol. 17, pp. 100–108, September, 1944.

Pec Peterson, L. C.: Equivalent Circuits of Linear Active Four-terminal Networks, *Bell System Tech. J.*, vol. 27, pp. 593–622, October, 1948.

Ped Peterson, L. C.: Space-charge and Transit Time Effects on Signal and Noise in Microwave Tetrodes, *Proc. IRE*, vol. 35, pp. 1264–1272, 1947.

PeB Pearson, G. L., and B. Sawyer: Silicon P-N Junction Alloy Diodes, *Proc. IRE*, vol. 40, pp. 1348–1351, November, 1952.

PeD Pearson, G. L., and C. S. Fuller: Silicon P-N Junction Power Rectifiers and Lightning Protectors, *Proc. IRE*, vol. 42, p. 760, April, 1954.

PeF Pearson, G. L., H. C. Montgomery, and W. L. Feldman: Noise in Silicon p-n Junction Photocells, *J. Appl. Phys.*, vol. 27, pp. 91, 92, January, 1956.

PfD Pfann, W. G., and W. van Roosbroeck: Radioactive and Photoelectric p-n Junction Power Sources, *J. Appl. Phys.*, vol. 25, pp. 1422–1434, November, 1954.

Pic Pierce, J. R.: Noise in Resistances and Electron Streams, *Bell System Tech. J.*, vol. 27, pp. 158–174, January, 1948.

Pie Pipes, Louis A.: "Applied Mathematics for Engineers and Physicists," McGraw-Hill Book Company, Inc., New York, 1946.

PoA Pomerantz, M. A., and J. F. Marshall: Fundamentals of Secondary Electron Emission, *Proc. IRE*, vol. 39, pp. 1367–1373, 1951.

PrB Pritchard, R. L.: Frequency Variations of Current-amplification Factor for Junction Transistors, *Proc. IRE*, vol. 40, pp. 1476–1481, November, 1952.

PrC Prince, M. B.: Drift Mobilities in Semiconductors: I. Germanium, *Phys. Rev.*, vol. 92, pp. 681–687, Nov. 1, 1953.

492   BIBLIOGRAPHY

PrD   Prince, M. B.: Drift Mobilities in Semiconductors: II.   Silicon, *Phys. Rev.*, Mar. 15, 1954.

PrE   Prince, M. B.: Silicon Solar Energy Converters, *J. Appl. Phys.*, vol. 26, pp. 534–540, May, 1955.

Raa   Radio Corporation of America: "Radiotron Tube Manual," tech. ser. RC16, Harrison, N.J., 1950.

RaE   Raisbeck, Gordon: The Solar Battery, *Sci. American*, vol. 193, pp. 102–110, December, 1955.

Reg   Reich, Herbert J.: "Theory and Application of Electron Tubes," 2d ed., McGraw-Hill Book Company, Inc., New York, 1944.

RiE   Richtmyer, F. K., and E. H. Kennard: "Introduction to Modern Physics," 5th ed., McGraw-Hill Book Company, Inc., New York, 1955.

RoA   Rose, A.: An Outline of Some Photoconductive Processes, *RCA Rev.*, vol. 12, pt. I, pp. 362–414, September, 1951.

RoB1   Rouault, C. L., and G. N. Hall: A High-voltage, Medium-power Rectifier, *Proc. IRE*, vol. 40, pp. 1519, 1520, November, 1952.

RoB2   Rose, G. M., and B. N. Slade: Transistors Operate at 300 Megacycles, *Electronics*, vol. 25, pp. 116–118, November, 1952.

RoC   Rose, A.: Photoconductivity, Semiconducting Materials, *Symposium Semiconductor Transistor Electronics*, University of Illinois Graduate School, Urbana, Ill., 1953.

RoD   Rothlein, J. J., and Alan B. Fowler: Germanium Photovoltaic Cells, *Trans. IRE*, vol. ED-1, pp. 67–71, April, 1954.

RoE1   Rockett, F.: Metallic Rectifiers Approach Infinite Life, *Electronics*, vol. 28, pp. 162–166, March, 1955.

RoE2   Rose, A.: Performance of Photoconductors, *Proc. IRE*, vol. 43, pp. 1850–1868, December, 1955.

Ryb   Ryder, R. M., and R. J. Kircher: Some Circuit Aspects of the Transistor, *Bell System Tech. J.*, vol. 28, pp. 367–401, July, 1949.

San   Salinger, H.: Tracing Electron Paths in Electric Fields, *Electronics*, vol. 10, pp. 50–54, October, 1937.

SaB   Saby, John S.: Fused Impurity P-N-P Junction Transistors, *Proc. IRE*, vol. 40, pp. 1358–1360, November, 1952.

SaD   Sard, E. W.: Junction Transistor Multivibrators, *Convention Record IRE*, pt. 2, p. 119, 1954.

Scd   Scaff, J. H., and R. S. Ohl: Development of Silicon Crystal Rectifiers for Microwave Radar Receivers, *Bell System Tech. J.*, vol. 26, pp. 1–30, January, 1947.

Sch   Schade, O. H.: Analysis of Rectifier Operation, *Proc. IRE*, vol. 31, pp. 341–361, July, 1943.

ScA   Schultheis, P. M., and H. J. Reich: Some Transistor Trigger Circuits, *Proc. IRE*, vol. 39, pp. 627–632, June, 1951.

ScE   Schultz, M. L., and G. A. Morton: Photoconduction in Germanium and Silicon, *Proc. IRE*, vol. 43, pp. 1819–1828, December, 1955.

Seal   Sears, F. W.: "Thermodynamics," Addison-Wesley Publishing Company, Cambridge, Mass., 1950.

Sea2   Seely, Samuel: "Electron-tube Circuits," McGraw-Hill Book Company, Inc., New York, 1950.

Sek   Seitz, Frederick: "The Modern Theory of Solids," McGraw-Hill Book Company, Inc., New York, 1940.

Sez   Seiler, E. F.: Color-sensitiveness of Photoelectric Cells, *Astrophys. J.*, vol. 52, pp. 129–153, October, 1920.

Sha   Shockley, Wm.: "Electrons and Holes in Semiconductors," D. Van Nostrand Company, Inc., Princeton, N.J., 1950.

Shb   Shockley, Wm.: The Theory of p-n Junctions in Semiconductors and p-n Junction Transistors, *Bell System Tech. J.*, vol. 28, pp. 435–489, July, 1949.

Shl   Shockley, W.: The Quantum Physics of Solids, *Bell System Tech. J.*, vol. 18, pp. 645–723, October, 1939.

Shm   Shortley, G. H., and R. Weller: The Numerical Solution of Laplace's Equation, *J. Appl. Phys.*, vol. 9, pp. 334–348, May, 1938.

ShA1   Shockley, W.: Hot Electrons in Germanium and Ohm's Law, *Bell System Tech. J.*, vol. 30, pp. 990–1034, October, 1951.

ShA2   Shockley, W., M. Sparks, and G. K. Teal: The p-n Junction Transistors, *Phys. Rev.*, vol. 83, pp. 151–162, July, 1951.

ShB1   Shockley, W.: Transistor Electronics, *Proc. IRE*, vol. 40, pp. 1289–1313, November, 1952.

ShB2   Shea, R. F., et al.: "Principles of Transistor Circuits," John Wiley & Sons, Inc., New York, 1952.

ShB3   Shive, John M.: Properties of the M-1740 P-N Junction Photocell, *Proc. IRE*, vol. 40, pp. 1410–1413, November, 1952.

ShE   Shive, J. N., and P. Zuk: Junction Phototransistors, *Bell Lab. Record*, pp. 445–449, December, 1955.

Slj   Slack, C. M., and L. F. Ehrke: Field Emission X-ray Tube, *J. Appl. Phys.*, vol. 12, p. 165, February, 1941.

Sll   Slater, J. C.: "Introduction to Chemical Physics," McGraw-Hill Book Company, Inc., New York, 1939.

SlA   Slater, J. C.: "Quantum Theory of Matter," McGraw-Hill Book Company, Inc., New York, 1951.

SlB   Slade, B. N.: The Control of Frequency Response and Stability of Point-contact Transistors, *Proc. IRE*, vol. 40, pp. 1382–1384, November, 1952.

SlC   Slade, B. N.: Factors in the Design of Point-contact Transistors, *RCA Rev.*, vol. 14, pp. 17–27, March, 1953.

SmF   Smith, R. A.: Recent Developments in the Detection and Measurement of Infrared Radiation, *Sci. Monthly*, vol. 82, pp. 3–19, January, 1956.

Sok   Southwell, R. V.: "Relaxation Methods in Engineering Science," Oxford University Press, New York, 1940.

Spc   Spangenberg, Karl R.: "Vacuum Tubes," McGraw-Hill Book Company, Inc., New York, 1948.

Ste   Stephens, W. E.: Crystal Rectifiers, *Electronics*, vol. 19, pp. 112–119, July, 1946.

StA   Stansel, F. R.: Characteristics and Applications of Varistors, *Proc. IRE*, vol. 39, pp. 342–358, April, 1951.

StB   Steele, E. L.: Theory of Alpha for P-N-P Diffused Junction Transistors, *Proc. IRE*, vol. 40, pp. 1424–1428, November, 1952.

StCl   Stansel, F. R.: Transistor Equations, *Electronics*, vol. 26, pp. 156–158, March, 1953.

StC2   Stansel, F. R.: The Common-collector Transistor Amplifier at Carrier Frequencies, *Proc. IRE*, vol. 41, pp. 1096–1102, September, 1953.

StD   Statz, H., E. A. Guillemin, and R. A. Pucel: Design Considerations of Junction Transistors at Higher Frequencies, *Proc. IRE*, vol. 42, pp. 1620–1627, November, 1954.

SuC   Sulzer, P. G.: Junction Transistor Circuit Applications, *Electronics*, vol. 26, pp. 170–173, August, 1953.

SzD Sziklai, G. C.: Symmetrical Properties of Transistors and Their Applications, *Proc. IRE*, vol. 41, pp. 717–724, June, 1954.

TaF Tanenbaum, M., and D. E. Thomas: Diffused Emitter and Base Silicon Transistors, *Bell System Tech. J.*, vol. 35, pp. 1–22, January, 1956.

Ted Terman, Frederick E.: "Radio Engineering," 3d ed., McGraw-Hill Book Company, Inc., New York, 1947.

Teh Terman, Frederick E.: "Radio Engineers' Handbook," McGraw-Hill Book Company, Inc., New York, 1943.

Tel Terman, F. E., R. R. Buss, W. R. Hewlett, and F. C. Cahill: Some Applications of Negative Feedback with Particular Reference to Laboratory Equipment, *Proc. IRE*, vol. 27, pp. 649–655, October, 1939.

Ten Terman, Frederick E.: "Radio Engineering," 2d ed., McGraw-Hill Book Company, Inc., New York, 1937.

Ter Terman, F. E.: Resistance Stabilization of Oscillators, *Electronics*, vol. 6, pp. 190–193, 1933.

TeB Terman, F. E., and J. M. Pettit: "Electronic Measurements," 2d ed., McGraw-Hill Book Company, Inc., New York, 1952.

TeD Telkes, M.: Solar Thermoelectric Generators, *J. Appl. Phys.*, vol. 25, pp. 765–777, June, 1954.

Tha Thompson, B. J., D. O. North, and W. A. Harris: Fluctuations in Space-charge-limited Currents at Moderately High Frequencies, *RCA Rev.*, vols. 4–6, January, 1940–July, 1941.

Thz Thomson, J. J.: Measurement of the Ratio of Electron Charge to Mass, *Phil. Mag.*, vol. 44, ser. 5, p. 298, October, 1897.

ThB Thomas, D. E.: Transistor Amplifier-cutoff Frequency, *Proc. IRE*, vol. 40, pp. 1481–1483, November, 1952.

ThD Thompson, R. W.: Revised Symbols for the New Unstable Particles, *Science*, vol. 120, pp. 585–587, Oct. 15, 1954.

Toc Torrey, Henry C., and Charles A. Whitmer: "Crystal Rectifiers," Massachusetts Institute of Technology Radiation Laboratory Series, vol. 15. McGraw-Hill Book Company, Inc., New York, 1948.

TuE Turner, R. P.: Survey of Power Transistors Currently Available, *Tele-Tech*, vol. 14, p. 112, June, 1955.

Vac Valley, George E., Jr., and H. Wallman: "Vacuum Tube Amplifiers," Massachusetts Institute of Technology Radiation Laboratory Series, vol. 18, McGraw-Hill Book Company, Inc., New York, 1948.

VaB Valdes, L. B.: Effect of Electrode Spacing on the Equivalent Base Resistance of Point Contact Transistors, *Proc. IRE*, vol. 40, pp. 1429–1434, November, 1952.

VaD1 Van der Ziel, A.: "Noise," Prentice-Hall, Inc., New York, 1954.

VaD2 Van der Ziel, A.: Note on Shot and Partition Noise in Junction Transistors, *J. Appl. Phys.*, vol. 25, pp. 815, 816, June, 1954.

VaE Van der Ziel, A.: Shot Noise in Junction Diodes and Transistors, *Proc. IRE*, vol. 43, pp. 1639–1646, November, 1955.

VaF Valdes, L. B.: The Frequency Response of Bipolar Transistors with Drift Fields, *Proc. IRE*, vol. 44, pp. 178–184, February, 1956.

WaA1 Wallace, R. L., Jr., and G. Raisbeck: Duality as a Guide in Transistor Circuit Design, *Bell System Tech. J.*, vol. 30, pp. 381–418, April, 1951.

WaA2 Wallace, R. L., Jr., and W. J. Peitenpol: Some Circuit Properties of n-p-n Transistors, *Proc. IRE*, vol. 39, pp. 753–767, July, 1951.

WaB Wallace, R. L., Jr., L. G. Schimpf and E. Dickten: A Junction Transistor Tetrode for High-frequency Use, *Proc. IRE*, vol. 40, pp. 1395–1400, November, 1952.

Wea Weber, Ernst: "Electromagnetic Fields: Theory and Application," John Wiley & Sons, Inc., New York, 1950.

Web Webster, W. M., E. Eberhard, and L. E. Barton: Some Novel Circuits for the Three-terminal Semiconductor Amplifier, *RCA Rev.*, vol. 10, pp. 5–15, March, 1949.

Wec Westinghouse Electric Corporation: "Industrial Electronics Reference Book," John Wiley & Sons, Inc., New York, 1948.

WeD Webster, W. M.: On the Variation of Junction-transistor Current-amplification Factor with Emitter Current, *Proc. IRE*, vol. 42, pp. 914–920, June, 1954.

Wil Wilson, A. H.: "Semi-conductors and Metals," Cambridge University Press, New York, 1939.

WrC Wright, D. A.: A Survey of Present Knowledge of Thermionic Emitters, *Proc. Inst. Elec. Engrs. (London)*, *Pt. III*, vol. 100, pp. 125–138, May, 1953.

Zwb Zworykin, V. K., and E. G. Ramberg: "Photoelectricity," John Wiley & Sons, Inc., New York, 1949.

INDEX